INNOVATIVEINDIA RISES

MEDIALAND
L O N D O N

INNOVATIVEINDIA RISES

Editor: L K Sharma

Managing Editor: Sima Sharma

Editorial support:
Nigel Pamphilion
Suguna Ramanathan
S R Madhu

Marketing: Sheila Taylor

Design: **CircleLine**
Production: **MOVINGWORDS**
Typeset: **Sanchauli Image Composers, New Delhi, India**
Printed: **Pragati Offset Pvt. Ltd., Hyderabad, India.**

Published by **MEDIALAND LONDON**

Registered in England No 3270515

E-mail: innovativein@gmail.com

ISBN 978-0-9534981-1-6

Acknowledgement

We are very grateful to the eminent
scientists, technologists, economists,
diplomats and decision-makers who
enriched this book through their
valuable contributions. We are
indebted to Prof M M Sharma and
Dr R A Mashelkar, for encouraging us
to undertake the project and to INSA
for permission to use the Heritage
section.

SPONSORS

Reliance
Industries Limited
Growth is Life

Four key elements of RIL's Innovation Agenda

☐ Build innovation leaders of today and tomorrow within RIL

☐ Deploy best and next transformational innovative practices that will impact the country and the business

☐ Develop new business based on emerging and disruptive technology

☐ Strategically deploy a corporate venture capital fund to maximize value

Confederation of Indian Industry

The private sector has taken a lead in putting Innovation into their business strategy. Indian Industry must Innovate or 'Perish'. CII launched the Manufacturing Innovation Mission two years ago under the leadership of Dr Surinder Kapur when Mr R Seshasayee was President CII. Some case studies reflecting innovation at the organization, product and process levels are presented in this volume. These are symbolic of the journey that many enterprises have started upon. CII considers Innovation as essential to India's present mode of economic growth and for inclusive and sustainable development.

Public Diplomacy Division

Ministry of External Affairs
Government of India
New Delhi

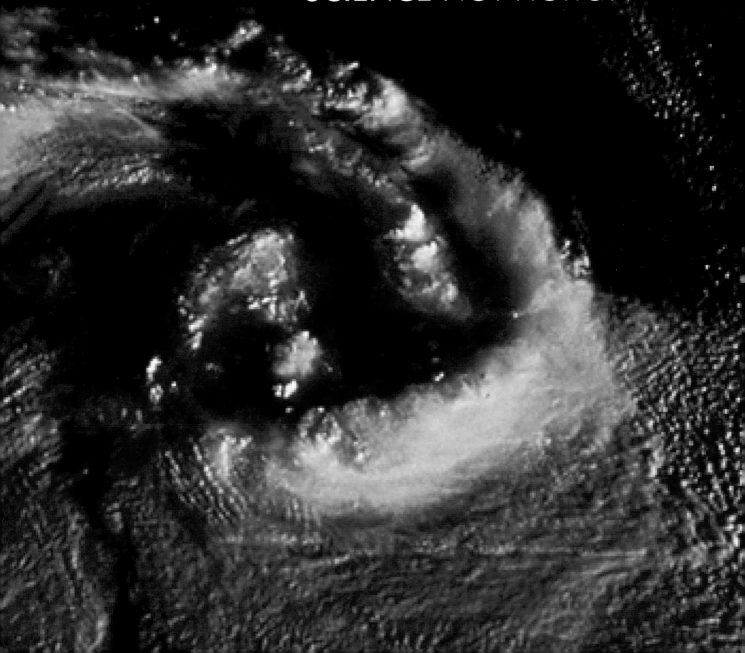

long long ago, in the country that knew infinity, science met nature. today in india science meets business.
in india the exploration of the unknown was carried on through illuminated centuries of knowledge and creativity. fifty years ago, the newly independent nation decided to pick up the threads. a chain of scientific institutions was established. today research and development in india has taken off. technology business has begun to boom. with a new entrepreneurial spirit, a large cluster of research laboratories, multidisciplinary resources, impressive scientific and technical manpower and supportive governments, the future is INDIA.

zero is not an old story

SCIENCE NOT FICTION

HEAVEN AND EARTH

▼IRS-1D image of part of Gujarat by WiFS sensor   IRS-1C LISS-3 image of Mayurakshi Reservoir in Bihar ▶

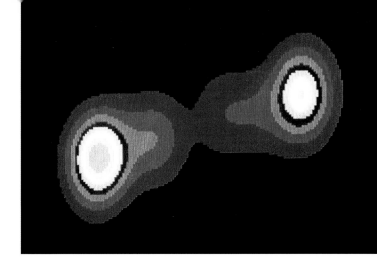

The first 'radio picture' of a distant galaxy made with India's giant metrewave radio telescope (GMRT)

The first radio image of a radio galaxy known as PKS 1331-09 made with eight antennas of the partially completed GMRT in June 1997. The radio galaxy is known to be at a distance of about 1600 million light years from us and the two 'lobes' of radio emission seen in the image are estimated to be separated by about 5 million light years. A massive 'black hole' in the nucleus of the galaxy near the mid-point of the lobes is believed to be responsible for ejecting energetic electrons and magnetic fields in the opposite directions that give rise to the radio emission.

The Writers

R A Mashelkar R Chidambaram
K Kasturirangan M G K Menon
M M Sharma Samir K Brahmachari
M S Swaminathan Anil Kakodkar
Kiran Mazumdar-Shaw C N R Rao
Ashok Jhunjhunwala S S Mehta Arun Maira
S Varadarajan Guri Marchuk Govind Swarup
M Natarajan Bikash Sinha P K Kaw
Sunil Mittal Kiran Karnik Surinder Kapur
V S Ramamurthy Ashok Parthasarathi
Bimal Jalan John Marburger
Anil K Gupta S Ramadorai Aditya Mittal
Ananda M Chakrabarty

INNOVATIVEINDIA

INNOVATIVEINDIA has articles
by eminent scientists, technologists, administrators, chairmen
of companies, scholars and
entrepreneurs. The volume
presents a comprehensive picture
of India's core competence in
different sectors. The insights
provided by Secretaries to the
Government of India are valuable
to business and industry

ATOMIC ENERGY ASTRONOMY
SPACE BIOTECHNOLOGY
LASERS NANOTECHNOLOGY
INFORMATION TECHNOLOGY
WEATHER FORECASTING
INDUSTRIAL R&D ENERGY
GRASSROOT INNOVATIONS
INTERNATIONAL COOPERATION
DEFENCE RESEARCH

an indispensable S&T Guide to India

C O N T E N T S

Reflections on the ascent of India

Because a book has a life of its own and emerges at a precise juncture of time, as if for a purpose, one tries to sense its wholeness. Even so, its patterns are very faint, and call for reflection.

When the first INNOVATIVEINDIA came out it was seen as an act of faith and the affirmation of a dream. It's a dream shared among many of us — the same that led Homi Bhabha, Vikram Sarabhai and other pioneers to put down the foundations of a science and technology enterprise on which to build a modern India. There was no looking back. Time and again, it is this domain that answered to the young nation's yearning for excellence. The pursuit continues and this volume follows.

Starting with a practically clean slate, the S&T community was given its mandate: to work, above all else and with speed, to deliver a better life to citizens of this country. The prime motivation for India's scientific enterprise was neither military ambition nor commercial gain but distinctly that of development and the greater good. The men and women who entered to take up the tasks in the early years of freedom, lacked no zeal. This volume is clearly the editor's tribute to this community, of whom so many have contributed papers here.

Alongside the ideas of authors coming from science, are those of contributors from various other walks of life, Indian and international. They come from: the corporate world and entrepreneurs, civil society, bureaucracy, diplomacy, academia, social advocacy and development NGOs and of course, journalism.

So diverse is the compilation, that it could well have produced a post-modernist collage of snapshots, but for the signature of time—the turn of the millennium and the 21st century. The patterns that weave through the text can be discerned against the grain of emergent realities. They are patterns of discontinuities, disruption, asymmetries and unforeseen abundance that confounds imagination. The S&T of the 21st century is unrecognizably different from that of the previous century. Read some of the accounts here from genomics research, space and nuclear technologies or new frontiers in molecular biology and astronomy.

We need no longer look for signposts for we have already arrived in a new and totally unknown territory. Innovation is not an option, but the very ground we walk on. It is no longer products or technology but a cultural process working out powerfully through younger people. Technology is paramount, but it is not all of innovation which is indeed a mindset that embraces all enterprise. It is a 'movement' as R A Mashelkar asserts, and urges that India must urgently propel this for itself — breaking the stranglehold of the past with its old values, old blinkers and the old carrot and stick. This man of science is a proponent of change, of risk, and also of the essential human potential.

There is excitement. Opportunity has exploded and nothing is impossible. Barriers are crumbling fast. Time and distance have conflated and the world is flat. Choice is unfettered but also extremely problematic, for it is not about goods on the shelf, but about ways of thinking and living. Paradox, always a part of life, makes its presence felt in labs, boardrooms, farms, factories, in schools and on the street.

Science has the habit of opening Faustian choices. Hiroshima happened. "Science can be misused" said the scientist, "what can we do about it? It is not our domain." No longer so. Even as she works in the lab, the scientist worries about the ethical dilemmas that crop up and around her work. This awareness is expressed by today's scientist, sometimes implicitly, or along with a brave assertion that Frankenstein shall be overcome.

There is something infinitely sad in reading M S Swaminathan describe how India's proud Green Revolution became its 'Greed' revolution. Why? Was it our mindset that lagged behind, not having innovated its ruling moral standards? The renowned scientist left the hurt behind, and has gone on to pursue an 'Evergreen' revolution.

Scientist Samir Brahmachari is immensely enthused by the marvellous new therapeutic possibilities that can open up through a genome mapping of the population. But he spends time to discuss the economics of the innovation, deeply aware of the minefield of ethical dilemmas in his discipline. The commonest one here comprises cost, affordability and selective exclusion. Which is also a concern for Kiran Mazumdar-Shaw viewing the scenario from her perch at the helm of her company. The asymmetries, rising out of the poor-rich divide, can range from distressful to horrific. The issue has to be confronted squarely—which is what Anil Gupta did while working with the village folk in Bangladesh who shared knowledge freely. Inclusive development makes sense—morally and in other ways.

The torchlight is turned upon the "Bottom of the Pyramid" in paper after paper from the corporate world. People like S S Mehta, Bharat Wakhlu, Arun Maira, Arjun Malhotra, among others, are looking at it with unclouded eyes. The poor may no longer be seen as the problem but as part of the innovation agenda—as a powerhouse of innovative ideas, as the next 250 million-people market segment, rightful owners of knowledge, producers of value, our human resource pool.

Concern, in it own way, is the thematic undercurrent running through this book on innovation. It is a different kind of concern—call it corporate social responsibility, developmental challenge, social conscience, fair practice or plain good sense. In fact, a couple of our authors have argued how adversity can indeed be an asset to innovation, providing the context for lateral thinking and invention—much more so than affluence.

The message coming in from diverse sectors of Indian enterprise is: Include or perish, innovate and win.

Sima Sharma

L K Sharma

Scientific India surges ahead

What an eventful decade it has been since INNOVATIVEINDIA was first brought out! Ten years ago, not many would have joined the two words. Between then and now, while India's grand Science Project continued, the forces that transformed the Indian economy infused a new life into the national research and development establishment. In these years, 'innovation' became a key word in Indian business strategies and the country grew into a centre of global research.

Scientific India has entered the 'bio-century' with remarkable self-confidence. It is tapping its substantial science and technology infrastructure, building innovative communities, enhancing its industrial competitiveness and using S&T to improve lives. A new phase in the journey has begun. Years of groundwork have gone in to prepare India's S&T enterprise. India will reap enhanced returns on investments as some major R&D projects mature simultaneously.

Much can be written on the lost opportunities and inefficiencies of the government's R&D apparatus, but despite shortcomings and constraints, the successes in the field of S&T and especially of the projects implemented in the mission mode, call for celebration. The core competence built up through years of dedication and determined effort has given India an instrument of economic and social development. India's technological advances in the sensitive fields have started to weaken the technology denial regimes. It is now being invited to hover in the proximity of the exclusive clubs of the nuclear haves.

The social and economic benefits from India's low-cost space programme have been substantial. The rate of returns will impress even the most hard-headed businessman. Such successes are seen and measured easily. However, it is not easy to assess the learning experience in a host of disciplines that results from the implementation of very complex and slow-moving. But unused or inconclusive R&D has its uses. It brings in returns just by being there and by compelling technology suppliers to drop prices or offer know-how that they would have otherwise held back. The dormant R&D work enhanced the country's expertise in assessing foreign technologies. The commercial benefits derived from this capacity-building are beyond audit.

It is India's growing scientific and technological prowess, coupled with its economic strength, that has forged an effective tool of diplomacy, fit to be used in India's relations with powerful nations. A relationship with the world's storehouse of creativity is bound to enhance India's technological empowerment. These ties and economic liberalisation have also facilitated the return of accomplished NRIs with zest for innovation and risk-taking and accumulated technical and business experience.

The new turn in America's relations with India was the result of not only a changed strategic scenario but also of India's growing economic and technological status. To a large extent, Indian scientists and technologists provided yet another reason for the US rethink. They had defeated the purpose of the denial regimes. The US Government concluded that it is not in its national interests to try and check India's capabilities. It is removing some of the export embargoes, imposed as a response to specific technological advances made by India in the sensitive sectors of atomic energy and space. This should help India since the US happens to be the biggest supplier of sophisticated technologies as also the prime mover of technology denial regimes.

India's experience has shown that there is nothing more potent than denial to bestir the scientific community. It was not amused by the denial of technologies for making tyres and detergents, not to talk of nuclear components or cryogenic engines for space launchers! Vikram Sarabhai used to say: "If imports are shut off, indigenous resources will materialise." They did.

Of course, the pursuit of self-reliance has not been easy. Competence building required grit and ingenuity. But the effort has paid off in many ways. The world has begun to see the Scientific India. The foreign media now takes note. In this, India's information technology business has played a major role even if its focus was on services rather than creative products. Once media and business began to see India in a new light, leaders of developed countries recognised India's capabilities in high-technology sectors.

More than ever before, cooperation in S&T now drives India's bilateral relations. It is India's 60-year-long endeavour that has secured the country participation on an equal basis in international scientific projects. Gone are the days when as a token of cooperation, a lone Indian scientist would be granted a fellowship to work in a prestigious project.

Why Moon

At times, India's aspirations in frontier S&T areas are still not understood. Many voices have questioned the need to map minerals on the Moon when much remains to be done in Bihar or any other backward region. Those who worry about a developing country barging into the high technology playground, ought to know that India lives and will continue to live simultaneously in several centuries. The satellite and the bullock cart can and do co-exist. India has also proved itself adept at leap-frogging. Furthermore, economic research has established that knowledge and skill spill-overs from high technology activities tend to be higher than from low technology.

Societal concerns do deserve the highest priority, but those engaged in scientific pursuits have not been forgetful of real life and its needs. The high-tech achievers boast as much about developmental spin-offs as about their core programme. The nuclear

establishment has delivered capabilities in diverse industrial fields with commercial and developmental implications for the nation. Space research is not just igniting rockets but also helping farmers. The lists of technology spin-offs available with the space or atomic energy organisations bear witness to this. In this context, it is worth remembering that developed countries derived no small part of their industrial and competitive advantage from their military technologies. It is a well-known fact that military programmes yield technological advantages for industry and society. India cannot afford to keep out of a high technology area at the bidding of others. In scientific exploration, like in love, one thing leads to another.

Government's commitment

The Government's support to science and technology is an old tradition in the political establishment whose formative years were shaped by Jawaharlal Nehru. Successive prime ministers made large investments in S&T, accorded a status of dignity to scientists and provided the fullest political backing to the mega projects. Official commitment was backed by increased funding of scientific institutions and programmes. The Government continues to expand the infrastructure for basic research as well as for technology development. It is taking fresh initiatives in the strategic sectors and the key areas of nano technology, space, biological and industrial research, renewable energy sources, microelectronics, new materials and ocean sciences.

A noteworthy policy shift of the decade is the government's encouragement of private participation in research and in some high-technology industries that were its exclusive domains. While the government is opening up the 'sensitive' sectors to the private sector, it is also venturing into new areas with great enthusiasm. Innovation is projected as a shared objective, and this word features in government policy papers and ministerial utterances almost as frequently as in the speeches of the CEOs.

Important policy changes are designed to promote innovation. The common goal has helped intensify interaction between the government R&D establishment and industry. This is such a welcome change from the era when the former had locked itself up in an ivory tower and the latter had convinced itself that an in-house laboratory was a white elephant, a beast one had to steer clear of order to make money.

Once exposed to economic liberalisation and global competition, a new generation of business leaders began to heed the warning: 'Innovate or perish'. It has led to a cultural change. They do not see the national laboratories as centres of esoteric activities. In fact, they want to keep in touch and if possible, collaborate. Having taken to research and development, industry happened to have enough money to afford in-house research. New money-spinning high-tech ventures have had an electrifying effect. They have seen an advance in molecular biology upsetting hundreds of well-laid business plans in the pharmaceutical industry. Overnight a new billion-dollar business becomes a possibility.

Industry as a whole, not just the sunrise units, changed its approach to science and technology. It has come out to take the lead in R&D. Venture capital is becoming more venturesome in appraising new ideas. Imagine a venture capitalist contacting a scientific worker in the area of Cold Fusion!

Indian talent

As the global innovations chase intensified, business leaders abroad were struck by India's advantage as a centre for business-driven research and development. Scouts of multinationals now wander around in India's scientific institutions, laboratories, and the IITs in search, not of skilled manpower, but of potential 'disruptive' technologies. The developed nations, with their fast aging population, look towards India as a potential source of innovations. The top multinationals have set up shop here. Many of these R&D facilities are involved not just in peripheral work but in vital pieces of major research projects under the direction of headquarters in the parent countries.

Of course, young Indian researchers are setting their sights higher. They want to get to the stage when Indian intellect is used for Indian IP.

The rise of the researcher entrepreneur is a very recent phenomenon. The Indian technology scene is strewn with their success stories. And some of these entrepreneurs came from government laboratories! Dynamic directors of the national laboratories demonstrated modes of partnership with industry that are both possible and mutually beneficial. The use of Indian laboratories by

the transnationals for commissioned research has enhanced their credibility in the eyes of domestic industry too.

One sees the overall atmosphere today becoming increasingly favourable to R&D. Scientific workers have a greater awareness of industry's requirements and of the need for interaction with potential users. They are less preoccupied with peer group recognition and far more keen to have feedback from entrepreneurs. They want to work within a national research agenda, conscious of performance targets and the need to earn one's keep. This has made laboratories more accountable and their critics less hostile.

Fortunately, pressures related to accountability are not so extreme as to disrupt the very culture of research and to turn a laboratory into a workshop. As R A Mashelkar has cautioned, the coupling of research institutions and industry should not be "too rigid", because that would prevent the national laboratories from looking ahead and tempt them to stay clear of projects lacking the prospects of immediate returns. That would be disastrous. In science, as Mashelkar puts it, the "right to fail" is as precious as success. While problem-solving research has its own place, it is new knowledge that contributes to long-term economic growth and innovation.

The right measure of flexibility in such linkages will put more funds at the disposal of scientists, to do work that may not be instantly useful. Science is full of surprises and free thinkers should be allowed to set their own questions and be left free to devise ways of finding answers.

New challenges

Economic liberalisation has given an impetus to the R&D sector in different ways. Awareness of quality standards, shorter product cycles and sharper marketing methods entered the hitherto sheltered economy. The issues of core competence, skill formation and technology development have come to the fore in the wake of liberalisation.

The heightened awareness of technology sweeps across the country through several state-level initiatives. Some states are establishing linkages among technology, enterprise, government and the people. They have deployed information technology to help citizens to transform their lives and the nature of their interaction with the government. The progressive leaders have no time for the specious satellite-vs-tubewell debate. They are promoting popular understanding of technology through a daily demonstration of electronic governance.

Creativity is now more critical than ever. Long-term, both strategic and basic research, has vital implications for the future. The S&T community, political leadership, bureaucracy, workers and entrepreneurs are aware of the frantic pace of change as in IT, biotechnology and nanotechnology. Developments in one area impact on another.

Indian policy makers see the waves of innovation that are transforming other national economies and keep reviewing the national research agenda. One committee surveyed the IIT system, another examined the vast defence research establishment. It must, of course, be ascertained why, despite the emergence of high-tech islands over the years, India still lags behind say, Taiwan or South Korea in the number of high-tech companies. Such success eludes India, which finds it easier to win acclaim for high quality work in mathematics, physics, chemistry, metallurgy, polymers and biotechnology. Individual achievements cause much excitement such as when Ashoke Sen of Allahabad electrifies the string theory groups with a contribution to the 'duality revolution'.

Fundamental research

The early post-Independence years saw much individual scientific talent, brilliant flashes of fundamental research work, and feats of institution building and groundwork by visionary pioneers. The take-off stage has come and India is ready to tap the potential of organised mega S&T projects. India's space programme is soaring towards a self-reliant operational capability. Ongoing projects in space, atomic energy, electronics, computers, defence research and biotechnology will place India in a different league amongst nations.

The State will have to continue to bear the main burden of scientific research and technology development. The nation has to innovate in a big way, but in this the market tends to fail. The US Government spends billions of dollars annually on research, and this in a country where 80 per cent of industrial R&D is done by corporations in their in-house facilities. Chinese leaders have called for 'technology to build the country'. China began commercialising the work of state laboratories some years ago and allowed private technology companies easier access to stock market listings.

New companies have been spun off from state laboratories. Science budgets in many countries are going up.

The US is worried about the impact of new hotspots of innovation emerging outside its own States. It has always understood that research is a cornerstone of continuing leadership. Research in the areas of physics, electrical engineering, computer sciences, material science and engineering benefited a great deal from the generosity of its own Department of Defense.

In India, the early reasons for funding scientific research were developmental, cultural and educational. Strategic considerations and the compulsions of technology denial came subsequently. Now the funding levels must be examined on economic and commercial grounds. Scientific research is an area in which India has a comparative advantage and it must seize the opportunity.

Space programme

The cost-effectiveness of science can be judged by what India's space programme and some other scientific programmes have delivered with limited resources. The kind of sum that India spends on its space programme, the US may allocate for building a space museum. CSIR, the largest public sector network of laboratories, spends less than a major multinational drug company's annual R&D budget. No Indian company has the astronomical turnover that would allow it to be an equal player in the global R&D field. India, like France, must groom selected technology-intensive public undertakings to be its global players of the future. Increased R&D spending, which is feasible in some cases, will bring disproportionately high returns. If India or an Indian company has global ambitions, increasing the R&D expenditure is a step that needs to be taken. In developed countries the returns from R&D enable them to further finance their research.

We are talking today of innovations-led growth. Without a zealous pursuit of self-reliance, India would have missed a set of achievements and fallen into the trap of dependence in strategic sectors. This pursuit was accompanied by a sense of national pride and was part of the nation-building venture. It enthused both the scientific community as well as other personnel working in scientific establishments. One remembers the heady days when the first Indian tractor, Swaraj, was greeted as if it were a cricket victory or when 'Suri Transmission' created excitement in the engineering community in India and abroad. In those days, Vikram Sarabhai could walk into the Prime Minister's office and persuade her to let the satellite earth station be built at home. Nor has that ethos quite vanished in the smoke of 'globalisation'. When the Tatas unveiled their Nano, what an ovation the new car got at home! And the new product coming out of India caught global attention.

Thanks partly to the denial regimes, the resistance to technological hegemony will not go out of fashion. The challenge is to make 'Swadeshi' a really effective strategy, not allowing it to be turned into an empty slogan. The way the self-reliance strategy was implemented created some islands of world-class expertise. However, India was unable to build a large components base to meet the high volumes of demand in critical sectors. It could not diversify sources of technology development or start a self-sustaining process in key industries.

Buy or Make

There is no shame in buying technology from abroad provided it is used to make things better and to compete in the world market. There are examples of some small countries that merrily allowed themselves to become assembly shops of the multinationals but later used their industrial sinews, market connections and brand image to fuel independent high quality research. These countries tailored their industrial policies to meet the demands of technology development. They pooled, not fragmented, industrial capacities. Low volumes of production are not conducive to high investments in R&D. Fragmented industrial capacities are injurious to a significant innovation effort. India must strengthen its large public sector enterprises on this ground alone. The experience of liberalisation, globalisation, technology development and external constraints has brought in valuable inputs for shaping a national innovations system.

Today, while the country's vast R&D establishment tries to overcome its old weaknesses, it is faced with new problems such as the migration of skills from the ongoing projects. In the sixties and seventies, bright young scientists returned from America and Britain, attracted by outstanding institutions and leaders in India. Since then, the disparity between the commercial sector and public service has grown. The R&D institutions, as with other public services, are finding it harder to attract and retain talent in a tough, competitive globalised market. They are under great pressure as a result of economic liberalisation and the rapidly changing value system could drain them of talent. Nor can the government bank on the 'irrational' sentiment of commitment on the part of the scientific personnel.

Global context

India must focus on some sectors with the kind of commitment with which Japan chose brain research or America picked the Advanced Technology Programme. Strategic planning in the global context means working out alliances and marketing mechanism. If the activity remains at sub-optimal levels, India will lag behind the late starters and less skilled countries. India remembers its earlier experience in the aeronautics sector. In spite of an early start in the design of military aircraft such as Marut and Kiran, three decades were gone before it could make meaningful investments and build capabilities.

There are compelling reasons to protect and strengthen India's science base. For India, merely to be able to meet the IT needs of foreign banks or airlines will not suffice. The investment climate is good for the next stage of development of creative IT products. The intellectual climate is also there. On the hardware side, the momentum gained by turning out the latest supercomputer is being kept up.

Governmental support and funding are essential for major scientific ventures. However, the roots of science and research are nurtured by the culture of a society itself. The capacity to absorb research funds is created organically over years and generations. S&T projects are never one-shot operations. Teachers, students and the appropriate value system, together create the intellectual disposition and enthusiasm. Government does not produce them, society does. Historically, India's intellectual base has weathered extreme changes in circumstances and thus it is an ethos that will endure. □

MILESTONES

CAPABILITIES IN Space Launchers, Nuclear Fuel Cycle, Heavy Water, Lasers, Remote-sensing

Supercomputers, Multilingual Software, Special Materials & Metals

Alloys Components, Photovoltaics, Blood Bags, Heart Valves, Artificial Limbs

Catalysts, Agrochemicals, Petrochemicals, Drugs

New Param Supercomputer, Nuclear tests, both fission and fusion

Fast Breeder synchronised, PSLV operational

First Polar Satellite Launch Vehicle flight

Tissue Culture, Supercomputer, Aviation & Tank technologies

India tests the Agni intermediate-range missile

Missiles, Telecom Switch C-Dot, White Revolution

Fast Breeder Test Reactor goes critical

INSAT system commissioned, Prithvi, short-range missile test fired

SLV-3's first experimental flight

Aryabhata satellite, Satellite Instructional Television Experiment

Pokhran underground nuclear explosion, zero fallout

Aarvi satellite communications project

Ooty radio telescope operational

Green Revolution

Apsara - India first in Asia to design and build a nuclear reactor

WIDE
ANGLE

जय विज्ञान   जय विज्ञान   जय विज्ञान   जय विज्ञान

It is science alone that can solve the problems of hunger and poverty, of insanitation and illiteracy, of superstition and deadening customs and traditions, of vast resources running to waste...Even more than the present, the future belongs to science and those who make friends with science.

Jawaharlal Nehru

Science, with its spectacular achievements, in increasing production and multiplying a thousand-fold the speed of man's movement and the range of his sight and sound, has aroused limitless expectation. What is more, it has the capacity to fulfil them.

Indira Gandhi

The 'blue-sky' research needed support but all scientific work could not be a pursuit of the esoteric and most of the research work had to be translated into action for national development.

Rajiv Gandhi

India is a nuclear weapon state. This is a reality that cannot be denied. It is not a conferment that we seek; nor is it a status for others to grant. It is an endowment to the nation by our scienists and engineers. It is India's due, the right of one-sixth of human-kind.

Atal Behari Vajpayee

Scientists are the creators of a new India; an India that is free from the shackles of ignorance. It is an India imbued with scientific temper and a liberal outlook. I am happy to recognize the very important role our scientists and technologists have played and will play in the ongoing task of Nation building.

Manmohan Singh

R Chidambaram
Principal Scientific Adviser to
the Government of India

Innovation in the Indian perspective

The development level in any societal field depends on the level of technology use. In India this level varies from field to field. Therefore, our immediate goals are threefold: we have to keep pace with the developed countries in some fields (e.g. nuclear and space), catch up in some (e.g. small and medium enterprises), and leapfrog in a few (e.g. rural development). Beyond that, India aims to become a major player in global innovation. India can indeed become a global innovation leader. However, for that to happen, there are three imperatives: use technology foresight to make the right technology choices in a national perspective; establish a robust innovation ecosystem; leverage international cooperation to reinforce our own innovation strategies.

In order to pursue our goals purposefully, we shall have to selectively promote some technology areas, with a long-term perspective. This should be done through 'directed basic research', particularly in cross-disciplinary sectors. This must be in addition to self-directed basic research and participation in international mega-science projects. What we need is to infuse 'Coherent Synergy' in our science & technology-related activities. Synergy, as the positive life-affirming principle, by enhancing the effort of one entity in the system, creates momentum for the whole. By pointing all efforts to the country's chosen goals, the forward movement gains a smooth coherence.

It is not easy to measure the progress of science and technology in a country. The measures are different for say, basic research (publications) and for industry-oriented research and development (patents and innovations which are converted into useful products and processes). The measures for achievements of mission–oriented agencies are obvious but not easily quantifiable.

How do we measure the success of the Department of Atomic Energy in building totally indigenous Pressurized Heavy Water Reactors or in designing the Advanced Heavy Water Reactor or the Prototype Fast Breeder Reactor? How do we measure the success of the Department of Space in launching advanced geosynchronous or polar orbit satellites for various applications? Measuring the progress of science and technology in rural development is even more difficult. We have, therefore, initiated projects for measuring the progress of science and technology in various fields.

Innovation is generally seen as the means to turn research results into commercially successful products and capturing economic value from an invention. While not all innovations are research-based, technology in today's world is the critical dimension of the innovation capacity of a country. Innovations can be *radical* like the discovery of the transistor or the building of the first nuclear power plant. They can also be *incremental improvements*, based on core innovations, or thirdly, they may be *new applications* of old inventions. Most of the patents worldwide belong to the second category and some futurologists believe that this trend will get stronger. Breakthrough inventions are not only rare but very expensive to introduce into the market. One current definition of invention is: 'something new which can be patented'. To be an important player in the strong and well-entrenched global Intellectual Property Rights (IPR) system—with its expensive patenting and patent dispute culture—is difficult but a vital necessity for India.

The Indian Science & Technology (S&T) platform is extensive, with mission-oriented laboratories (Nuclear, Space, Defence, Agriculture), the Council of Scientific and Industrial Research, Universities, the Indian Institute of Science and the Indian Institutes of Technology, etc. The corporate in-house research and development (R&D) structures are growing. Then there are industry-specific cooperative research associations, as in the textiles sector. The Indian government also encourages cooperation with trans-national corporates in industrial R&D. Several trans-national companies have placed their R&D projects in Indian academic institutions and national laboratories. More than 150 of the *Fortune 500* companies have their own R&D centres in India.

Technology is Power

India's pursuit of self-reliance has to be understood in its appropriate historical context. American futurologist Alvin Toffler said many years ago "Yesterday violence was power, today wealth is power and tomorrow knowledge will be power." I paraphrase Toffler to say "Technology is Power". Technology domination is, therefore, sought both by companies and by countries through the instruments of Intellectual Property Rights (IPR) and Technology Control Regimes (TCR). Self-reliance, therefore, should no longer be interpreted as self-sufficiency but as immunity against technology denial.

Self-reliance does not mean avoidance of international scientific and technological cooperation. India must take and must give in equal measure in international cooperation. India must engage in international cooperation, including in mega-science projects, on an equal-partner basis. India participates in projects like the Large Hadron Collider being built by CERN (Centre for European Nuclear Research) in Geneva and has also recently joined the ITER (International Thermonuclear Experimental Reactor) co-operative programme. We have recommended a multi-10 gigabits/sec network of high speed computing and communication system on an open platform and the establishment of this Integrated National Knowledge Network has been approved in principle by the Government. While this is intended to satisfy the needs of the Indian scientific and academic community, it will also be valuable for international scientific collaboration.

Cooperation is becoming a key word in the process that leads to innovation. Collaborative Innovation Networks (COINS), based on the idea of "swarm creativity", are cyber teams enabled by the web to share knowledge "directly and not through hierarchies". Overcoming the climate change threat offers a great opportunity for collaborative innovation. Co-innovation can also help companies and institutions, transcending international borders, to complement their R&D strengths, as well as for technology delivery capabilities, while taking credit for their individual Intellectual Property contributions.

Technology foresight

Again, national perspective comes into play in technology foresight analysis that has a forecasting component. But it also includes economic, social and security assessments. If you ask questions in this context, the answer may be different from India than, say, from USA.

An example of this is the fast breeder reactor: It is important for India to reprocess the spent fuel and close the nuclear fuel cycle, because we have limited uranium reserves and the world's largest thorium reserves. USA, with easy access to the world's relatively cheap uranium—though the price has risen sharply in the last couple of years—may put away the spent fuel as 'waste' for decades. Of course, plutonium, with its half-life of 24,000 years, is not running away anywhere. In fact, the later you reprocess, the easier it becomes because other shorter-lived radioactivity would have died down significantly. But India's needs and choices come from a different context. It is not surprising, therefore, that four of the six advanced reactor systems proposed under Gen. IV by the consortium led by USA would require reprocessing of spent fuel.

India's choice of fast breeder technology as part of the closed nuclear fuel cycle strategy, illustrates how technology foresight analysis helps in the selection of critical technologies for development at any point of time. The three-stage nuclear power programme is the fulcrum of our efforts in nuclear technology. We are now one of the leaders in the world in Pressurized Heavy Reactor Water (PHWR) technology. We have self-reliance in the entire fuel cycle in this technology. This is the first stage.

The second stage involves reprocessing the spent fuel from the PHWRs and using the resultant plutonium in fast breeder reactors (FBRs). A test reactor has operated successfully for more than two decades and the first 500 MWe prototype fast breeder reactor is under construction in Kalpakkam.

By closing the fuel cycle with plutonium, we can extract 50 times more power from our limited resources of uranium. But that is not all. By using our vast reserves of thorium, we would then enter the third stage of our nuclear programme. Thorium-232, used as blanket in the fast reactors, gets converted to Uranium-233, which is an excellent nuclear fuel. By going into the Thorium-Uranium-233 cycle which, of course, would require an enormous amount of R&D, we can effectively produce 600 times more power starting from a given resource of uranium. That is why it is so important for India to close the nuclear fuel cycle with thorium. Any emerging international nuclear cooperation could be an additional dimension of our own vigorously pursued three-stage programme.

India is one of the two countries (the other is China) where nuclear power is growing rapidly due to high energy demand. India has gathered rich experience in knowledge management in nuclear technology, unlike those countries where the nuclear power development has been stagnant. However, because of fresh concerns about the global climate change threat, some countries including the US are planning for a nuclear renaissance. India will thus have something to offer to other countries in nuclear science and technology.

Critical technologies

In a broader sense, what are the critical technologies for India today? India is a large country and its technology requirements also correspondingly span a wide range from nuclear to rural. It has to continue to develop strategic technologies—nuclear, space and defence-related. Technologies related to energy security, food and nutritional security, health and water security and environmental security, advanced manufacturing and processing, advanced materials, etc. are all important for us. So are the so-called 'knowledge-based' technologies (information technology, particularly hardware; nanotechnology, particularly nanoelectronics; biotechnology; and convergence of these technologies like nano-biotechnology for drug delivery). Success in the development of most of these critical technologies would be predicated on tackling basic research problems underlying these technologies. The support for basic research in nuclear and related sciences provided by the Bhabha Atomic Research Centre, along with nuclear technology development, is an excellent example.

The rural development-related technologies must also get a high priority. In spite of a great deal of technology effort related to rural development, its impact, particularly in the non-farm sector, has been not very significant. Several fresh initiatives are now on, to correct this deficiency. One of them is the Rural Technology Action Groups (RuTAGs) that we started. The RuTAG initiative is based on the realization that active scientists are not the best people for grassroots technological intervention in rural India. This is because they focus on their own areas of research and development. However, if some voluntary organization or a government agency has recognized a problem in a rural area and implemented a technological solution up to a point, the higher-level R&D institutions and universities can carry it further.

Rural technology delivery

RuTAGs are located either in a premier educational institution or a corporate body and have strong linkages with reputed science and technology-based voluntary organisations. A nationally acknowledged person is identified to be the adviser and a senior and retired scientist is nominated as the coordinator of RuTAG. So far, three such RuTAGs have been set up, one each in Chennai (Tamil Nadu), Dehradun (Uttarakhand) and Guwahati (Assam).

Some of the projects taken up in Uttarakhand through a voluntary organization (Himalayan Environmental Studies and Conservation Organisation) are: upgradation of water mills with assistance from the Indian Institute of Technology (IIT) Delhi; improved packaging and food processing technology with the help of Central Food Technology Research Institute, Mysore, and increased water recharge technology introduction through the Bhabha Atomic Research Centre, Mumbai, using the isotope hydrology technique. In Tamil Nadu, projects have been taken up in the areas of natural dyes (conversion from liquid to powder), improved and energy-efficient manufacturing process for ayurvedic medicines. Institutions such as IIT, Madras, Central Leather Research Institute, Anna University, National Institute of Ocean Technology are providing technology as well as R&D support.

The RuTAG Centres for these regions are located in the Oil and Natural Gas Commission, Dehradun, IIT Madras and IIT Guwahati.

Much of rural technology delivery can take place on the basis of known science, what Gerhard Sonnert calls 'Baconian Science'. However, we also need what he calls 'Jeffersonian Science'—securing a social need through new knowledge—for rural development. This can be part of what I call 'directed basic research'. The successful application of technology for rural economic growth is generally more a problem of technology delivery than of technology development. This is contrary to the situation vis-à-vis industry, where the problem is more of 'development' rather than 'research' and 'delivery'. The drive for 'delivery' in industry comes from the profit motive. By contrast, the drive for rural technology delivery has to come from government efforts or from a sense of social responsibility in others. While technology-based innovation and technology development interfaces are important for industrial development, innovative technology delivery systems are, I think, more important for rural development.

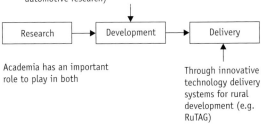

Through innovative interaction interfaces for industrial development (e.g. CAR: Core advisory group for automotive research)

Research → Development → Delivery

Academia has an important role to play in both

Through innovative technology delivery systems for rural development (e.g. RuTAG)

Fig. 1. Mechanisms for overcoming major weaknesses in Development and Delivery (Industrial Development vs. Rural Development)

Talking of creating 21st century capable innovation systems, Larry Quick talks of an 'open platform' strategy, which involves "a central strategy and a range of strategic modules that allow broader stakeholders to have a direct and practical involvement" and this goes beyond the Information Technology (IT) sector. RuTAG is an 'Open Platform Innovation' strategy.

Reverting to hi-tech industry, we have success stories in atomic energy, space, etc.—the outcomes of successful interactions between academia and industry. I am using the term 'academia' to include both the university system and the national laboratory system. However, the driving force for these interactions in the fields of atomic energy and space came from the mission-oriented agencies. Can we have a similarly strong academia-industry interaction with the driving force originating in the industry? The mindset problem affecting both scientists and industry leaders prevented this from happening in a significant measure in the past. The situation has changed in the current liberalized environment. Indian companies are also becoming globally competitive. If industry begins to interact actively with academia, it can also play a greater role in guiding academic activities in the direction of industry interests, be it human resource development, R&D prioritization, or the choice of areas of international co-operation.

Academia-industry interaction

The industry-academia interaction organized by us led to a suggestion for seeding 'directed' basic research. Very often engineering graduates don't go in for research and technology development, even though they may have a talent for it, but opt for jobs in Information Technology, management, or just go abroad. Now, if the industry were to send some of their fresh employees to do research with professors whom the industry respects it would lead to industry-oriented research. The student should be no different from any other student of the professor and his or her research should not be limited to problem-solving for the company, which is too restrictive. Although the employee-student might not be addressing the company's problems consciously, subconsciously the company's products would manifest in his or her thoughts and actions in all professional interactions. Over four to five years, the employee will evolve into someone very useful for the company's product or process development.

Kenan Sahin feels that "universities and labs, as innovation sources, are characterized as R&d (big research, small development) organizations. Most companies, with their marketing and production arms, would be d&D (small development, big delivery) enterprises. This lack of a strong connection between these groups is partly responsible for today's innovation backlog [in the US]. Therefore we need more rD&d organizations to bridge the gap. Their main activity is in developing innovations for the market". This has also been a weakness in the Indian S&T system, obviously even more than in the US.

Automotive sector

The academia-industry interaction led us to form, in 2003, a core group for R&D in the automotive sector, appropriately called CAR 2003. This group deals with all vehicles from two-wheelers to heavy vehicles. CAR is mandated to identifying frontier technologies, so as to promote development of vibrant, world-class automotive systems, sub-systems and parts industries. The group has drawn up a technology road-map for the Indian automotive sector and its recommended programme includes advanced materials and manufacturing, alternate propulsion and automotive infotronics, all of which involves basic research directed eventually to benefit the automotive sector.

We jointly funded these projects for pre-competitive applied research. A booming industry is likely to be interested in R&D in order to become globally competitive and, therefore, also likely to be keen to interact with academia. That is why we started with the booming automotive sector.

This initiative has had significant success. For example, an 'Engine Management System' for two or three wheelers (hitherto available only from global MNCs) has been developed by IIT Bombay in collaboration with IIT Madras and other partners from the industry. Initial results indicate improvement in fuel economy and also better emission performance apart from being much cheaper compared to models available in the market. We set up an R&D Advisory Group for the machine tool industry and a group is planned for the semiconductor industry.

SME sector

The Small and Medium Enterprises Sector is a very important sector for both job creation and wealth creation for India. Many SMEs in India can now manufacture products of six-sigma quality. But this is only in a few sectors such as auto components, and even here mostly to foreign designs. The majority of SMEs have little access to modern R&D facilities. There are, of course, exceptions and many innovation-driven companies are rapidly springing up in India. Tejas Networks in Bangalore, for example, produces state-of-the-art optical networking products, backed by strong R&D. Their approach is based on the fact that any R&D effort in an advanced field in India costs only one-quarter as

much as in a developed country. It means that "they will do twice the R&D at half the cost", compared to global leaders! Another example is Bilcare in Pune, which specialises in pharma packaging, backed by research as well as clinical services. Their model is a non-conflicting complementary R&D relationship with pharmaceutical market leaders in India and abroad.

The Government is keen on strengthening SMEs through technology infusion. Academia-industry interaction could be a very effective means for enabling SMEs to bridge the technology and knowledge gap. One approach could be through incubators in academic institutions, in particular those proximate to technologically homogenous SME clusters.

A triangular partnership between the government, an academic institution and industry is useful. Most of the industry partners are SMEs and the disciplines of relevance involved are focused and range from fireworks safety and environmental engineering to wireless technologies and pharmacogenomics. An assessment of technology needs by a knowledge partner, in co-operation with the SMEs, is now being done to design interventions for them making diverse products, ranging from sports goods and agricultural implements to surgical instruments and forgings.

Innovation Eco-system

A strong and vibrant innovation ecosystem is essential *inter alia* for increasing the velocity of R&D. It requires an education system which nurtures creativity; an R&D culture and value system which supports basic and applied research and technology development; an industry culture which is keen to absorb academic inputs; a bureaucracy which is supportive; a policy framework which encourages young people to enter scientific careers; and an ability to scan scientific developments in the world and to use technology foresight to select critical technologies in a national perspective.

The innovation ecosystem depends on the courage of the science establishment and industry to take risks and an S&T system that is supportive of risk-taking. The greater the innovation, the higher is the risk in converting it into a marketable product or process; consequently greater is the support required from the Government, as in the SBIR (Small

Business Innovative Research) Programme of USA. The US federal government provides between 20 and 25 per cent of all funds for early stage technology development. Thus the competitive government awards address segments of the innovation cycle that private investors find too risky. India must have similar programmes. The vital activity of development is the link between research (as in labs and academic institutions) and delivery (as carried out competently by the companies). We need more organizations to focus on development—developing innovations for the market. We are working towards nurturing strong connections among all groups in the country involved in innovation.

Careers in science

The biggest problem before the scientific community today in India—perhaps all over the world—is to attract talented young people to careers in science and to retain them there. I have postulated a theorem with which all the teachers to whom I have talked to are in general agreement: "Given a certain number of senior scientists, the research output from a laboratory is directly proportional to the number and quality of research students."

The Steering Committee for Science & Technology for the Eleventh Plan (2007–2012) recommended that, at the end of 10+2 years education, talented science students must be offered a 15-year career support programme. During the first five years, they get an attractive fellowship while they work towards their MSc (Master of Science) degree. During the next five years, they get a substantial fellowship matching the kind of salaries of the same age group in jobs while they do their PhD; and an assurance of a proper job in a university or any national laboratory for five years after PhD.

Many young people, after winning silver and gold medals in International Olympiads for Physics, Chemistry and Mathematics, give up scientific careers and take up professional courses because of better career prospects. These young people told me that, if they had this 15-year career support programme, they would have stayed in science. Unless this is done, leading institutions in India could get depleted of top class scientists in the future. The INSPIRE programme of the Department of Science & Technology is the beginning of an effort to identify and nurture talented young people in science.

India is too big a country to absent itself from any field of Science and Technology. But how much it invests in any field at any point of time is a "matter of wisdom" to quote Frederick Seitz. The 'exciting' areas of basic research are often, 'directed' by the interests of the industries in the developed countries or their strategic interests. This happens because their scientific research is at the frontiers of science and their industry, active at the cutting edge of technology, quickly absorbs the results of applied basic research based on current scientific knowledge.

In other words, there is a thermodynamic equilibrium between the knowledge in the academic system and the knowledge that has been transferred to industry. There is, of course, a time gap involved in the transfer of this knowledge. When a new phenomenon is discovered, like high-temperature superconductivity or novel carbon nano-structures, USA and other developed countries readily see the possible potential for their industry and direct their basic research to these areas. High impact journals publish the results of such research.

Directed basic research

What is 'directed basic research' for the developed countries then inevitably becomes a frontier area of undirected basic research for us, if we want to publish in front-line journals. We must be present in these areas because usually they also involve excellent science and perhaps will also help Indian technology in the longer term. What we should guard against and prevent, is such research becoming 'parasitic' research (excessive collaboration with developed countries in such areas, feeding exclusively into the latter's technology system; excessive value given to recognition and accolades from abroad), because it may distort our own national priorities.

Even Bell Labs has changed its paradigm for research in recent years. A Wall Street Journal report said in 2006: "Lucent Technologies Inc's Bell Labs, the birthplace of the transistor and the laser, has... set more of its scientific stars to work on breakthrough technologies that could quickly turn into businesses. ... Steven Chu, who won a Nobel in Physics... says: 'working on applied things doesn't destroy a kernel of genius... it focuses the mind'." India should do this today, for example, in 'Nanotechnology', using technology foresight analysis to make the right technology choices in this field. My own choices are nanoelectronics and nano-biotechnology for drug delivery.

We should thus select areas of 'directed basic research' with an Indian perspective. The approach could be from the side of societal interest. Examples are basic science behind Ayurveda (an Indian system of medicine); heath-related (for diseases endemic to India) macromolecular crystallography; megaprostheses implants for cancer affected patients etc. The approach could also be on behalf of industry or strategic interests. Examples are nanoelectronics, cyber security and automotive infotronics.

The culture gap that exists between the practitioners of basic research on the one hand, and applied research and product development, on the other, could be closed through 'directed basic research' and pre-competitive applied research. In its execution, and in the requirement of no other deliverables than knowledge generation, 'directed basic research' is no different from 'self-directed' basic research. So the university academics should be comfortable with this kind of research.

From a national perspective, scientists carrying out 'directed basic research' in any area would find it easier to interact with the related industry or related strategic mission or to participate in related societal development programmes. The Department of Atomic Energy, for example, has been very successful in directing basic research to areas of relevance to their mandate and has benefited greatly from it.

Though linkages among the various kinds of research and development efforts do exist, the borders between them are very fuzzy, particularly between 'directed basic research' and 'pre-competitive applied research'. The difference between 'self-directed basic research' and 'directed basic research' may often be only a problem choice in a proximate field of the scientist's own interest area. 'Directed basic research' could be particularly valuable for cross-disciplinary technology areas. Such areas recognized in the Steering Committee's report referred to above, range from desalination and water purification technologies and health care to advanced manufacturing, combustion research and advanced functional materials.

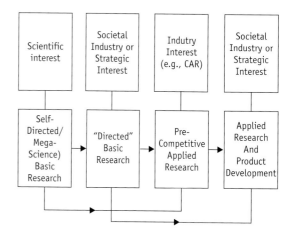

Fig. 2. The possible dominant linkages between needed research and development efforts

Coherent synergy

'Coherent Synergy' is a new phrase I have defined in the S&T context! The S&T system, in order to contribute maximally to national development, requires a variety of efforts—human resource development, R&D with prioritization, academia-industry interaction, international collaboration, etc. Every S&T effort requires synergy among the concerned parties and every such synergetic effort gives the country a momentum for development. And momentum is a vector. All the vectors must point in the same direction for rapid development of the country. This requires space-time synchronization and phase relationship among the efforts. This is coherence. That is, synergy in every effort and coherence among all the efforts! In R&D (industrial) globalization, this implies coherence between the motivation of the transnational corporates and national technology needs.

India is so large and diverse and change is necessary at such a rapid pace that it is impossible to talk about any single innovation policy. But India can become a global innovation leader. It will happen provided we make the right technology choices, have a robust innovation ecosystem, leverage international cooperation to reinforce our own innovation strategies, and introduce 'Coherent Synergy' in our S&T system-related activities. □

R A Mashelkar
Bhatnagar Fellow
National Chemical Laboratory

Resurgence of Innovative India

This is the Century of Knowledge. The nations that lead in knowledge—its production, its dissemination, its conversion into wealth and social good and its protection—are those that will assume leadership. Innovation is the process that creates new knowledge and then converts it into wealth and social good. This total knowledge is greater than the sum of its parts. India was such a leader in innovation several centuries ago. However, for historical and other reasons, the civilization went through a period of stagnation. This cloud started to lift towards the close of the 19th century and the upsurge that led to the Independence movement also brought forth an intellectual ferment and a spectacular array of thinkers, including a galaxy of renowned scientists.

Today we stand at a watershed of history again, one which brings us the opportunity to usher in the resurgence of an innovative India. The momentum that has built up makes it clear, through symbols, that the 'I' in 'India' stands for 'Innovation'. I believe that just as we had entered a movement which freed us from foreign dominion, we now stand at the threshold of an 'Indian Innovation Movement'. This is an imperative and it must happen, so that India can make its unique and critical contribution. The freedom movement gave the world a meaning and a content to the idea of freedom. The new movement will do the same for innovation. Revival of creativity and innovation will be propelled by the same spirit and on the same scale as that which moved our freedom movement.

We on our part have some unique assets with which to forge ahead in this new venture. One is the demographic advantage of our young population and another is the innovative potential of people, no matter what their disadvantages in terms of wealth and formal education, as I will soon illustrate.

To capitalize on this opportunity, the youth of India must imbibe the spirit of a true innovator. An innovator is one who does not know that it cannot be done, who sees what everyone else sees, but thinks what no one else does. Innovators refuse *status quo*, they convert inspirations into solutions and ideas into products. Raising such innovators will require an all-pervasive attitudinal change towards life and work—a shift from a culture of drift to a culture of dynamism, from a culture of idle prattle to a culture of thought and work, from diffidence to confidence, from despair to hope.

A vital ingredient of such a culture has been missing a long time from the Indian scene—our fundamental Right to Fail! A culture of innovation has no place for those who wish only to preserve systems. A friend of mine, the CEO of a company abroad, once said, "We do not shoot people, who make mistakes. We shoot people who do not take risks. What do you do?" I said, "In India, we shoot people who take risks!"

Years ago, as the Director of the National Chemical Laboratory, I created a 'Kite Flying Fund' to support ideas which aim to attain some unattainable goals and where the chance of success may be one in a thousand! The response was excellent. Later, when I moved to CSIR, I used the same concept to create a 'New Idea Fund' and happily, now even individual laboratories are setting up such funds.

At a national level, a New Millennium India Technology Leadership Initiative (NMITLI) has been set up as a vehicle for India to attain a global leadership position in niche areas. NMITLI looks beyond today's technologies and seeks to build, capture and retain for India a leadership position in the global technology arena by synergizing the best competencies of publicly funded R&D institutions, academia and private industry. It is based on the premise of consciously and deliberately identifying, selecting and supporting risky ideas, concepts, technologies, etc. which could be potential winners.

Over 200 R&D and academic institutions along with around 80 partners in industry have been catalyzed as a result of this initiative. This is the biggest Indian Knowledge Network so far, in which the private sector too has participated with great enthusiasm. The Government has invested around Rs 100 crores in NMITLI which is co-ordinated by CSIR. The projects evolved cover a wide spectrum of technologies. These include: defunctionalisation of carbohydrates as building blocks replacing petroleum-based hydrocarbons for the chemical industry of the future; stimuli-sensitive nano-particle based drug delivery systems for specific therapeutics; flat panel liquid crystal display systems, with switching speeds that are a hundred times faster than the state-of-the-art system. Most of these projects seek to usher in a complete new paradigm in technology perspective with support for risky ideas, daring and creativity.

We must also understand that the challenge is not only that of funding risky ideas, but also one of spotting and funding mavericks who have the potential to create breakthroughs. Such unusual innovators refuse to preserve the *status quo*. Whereas standard science management practices tend to avoid conflict, such people create conflicts. They bring unusual spontaneity and exceptional qualities to the table. Such individuals can make a difference. Such individuals are impatient with old ideas and set patterns.

A certain amount of irreverence is essential for creative pursuit in science. If we promote that subtle irreverence in Indian science, through a change of personal as well as social attitudes, change of funding patterns, and create that extra space for risk-taking, respecting the occasional mavericks and rewarding the risk-takers, then not only will the fun and joy of doing science increase, but also Indian science will make that 'much awaited' difference.

Let us look at what F C Kohli, a doyen of the Indian IT industry, has done. He has developed a Computer-based Fundamental Literacy (CBFL)

method which focuses on reading ability. Based on theories of cognition, language and communication, in this method, the scripted graphic patterns, icons and images are recognised through a combination of auditory and visual experiences through using computers. It starts with learning words rather than letters. While it focuses on reading, it acts as a trigger for people to learn to write on their own.

Based on this method, Kohli's team developed innovative methodologies using IT and computers to build reading capability within a short time. The experiment was first conducted in Medak village near Hyderabad. Without a single trained teacher, the group which was not literate started reading the newspaper in Telugu in 8 to 10 weeks! Thereafter, Kohli's team carried out more experiments at 80 centres, and with over 1000 adult participants. The results were spectacular.

Kohli is an engineer in deliverables. His team developed these lessons to run on Intel 486 and earlier versions of Pentium PCs modified to display multimedia. About 200 million such obsolete PCs in the world get discarded. By using such PCs, the cost of making one person literate comes to less than Rs 100. With CBFL, Kohli says he can raise the nation's literacy to 90 to 95 per cent within 3 to 5 years, instead of the 20 years now projected. It can be done. Provided we think positively. Provided, we believe it can be done.

Kohli's example is one of lateral thinking at the high end of the spectrum of education, training, and socio-economic status. Would you say that the quality of innovation is directly related to these factors? No, it is not. Innovation is something else. I referred earlier to the innovative potential of the people of this land, regardless of their wealth or formal education. Let me cite a stunning example of a largely illiterate network of people whose business model has been taken up as a classroom study in some management institutes.

In Mumbai city, more than a hundred thousand citizens in their offices or workplace sit down to eat lunch out of lunch boxes called *dabbas*, delivered by the humble *dabbawalla*. Some 3500 such *dabbawallas* deliver 1.6 lakh lunch boxes each working day, without fail and without error. The *dabbawallas* have the six sigma rating or an efficiency rating of 99.999999, which means one error in one million transactions. This rating has been given by *Forbes Global*, the American business weekly. The secret lies in a coding system devised over the years. Each *dabba* is marked in indelible ink with an alpha-numeric code of about 10 characters. In terms of price and the reliability of delivery, say compared to a Federal Express System, *dabbawallas* remain unbeatable.

Survival

By this one example, I am trying to illustrate the innovative potential of people who are illiterate or semi-literate. They have to innovate in order to survive and succeed.

To acknowledge the genius of the invisible sections, the National Innovation Foundation (NIF) was set up under my chairmanship. We were looking at ideas coming from grassroot innovators, be they farmers, slum dwellers, artisans, school drop-outs or whoever. We set up a national innovation competition. In the first year, there were less than a thousand entries, but the number shot up to 16,000 in the second year. One year, among the winners was an eighth standard drop-out who developed a complex robot. Other NIF winners include a farmer who developed a cardamom variety which has taken over a good 80 per cent share of the market in Kerala; an illiterate individual who developed a disease-resistant pigeon pea variety and so on. These

disadvantaged individuals have shown us what they can do by using their powers of observation, analysis and synthesis while working in the laboratory of life.

Technologies developed by local artisans, craftsmen, potters, farmers, and weavers are considered to be traditional and somehow they do not count. These technologies are never included in the fabric of modern technology. It is a mindset that creates appalling contradictions. There is a disconnect between the scientist in his lab and the same scientist at home or in his community. Let me give an example.

Millions of women, drawing water from wells, feel the need for a pause to catch their breath. But they have to keep holding on to the rope with a full bucket at the other end, not daring to loosen their grip lest the bucket falls back. Although communities have devised ways of retrieving a fallen bucket (for example, by using hooks tied to another rope), nothing apparently could prevent the bucket falling back into the well. This was the situation until an artisan felt challenged by the problem and resolved it by simply attaching a small lever to the pulley. The lever did not get in the way while the rope was on the pull but the moment it slackened, the lever pressed against it and arrested the downward movement, thus holding the full bucket suspended in the position. Now even an old or weak person can pause, rest, chat and then resume pulling. Thousands of such pulleys are now being installed all across Gujarat's villages.

Old concepts

Why did such a problem affecting millions of people every day never get solved through the use of the existing knowledge—traditional or modern? Remember, for ages navigators have used a concept similar to the lever on the pulley for the ropes that set the oars in boats, and the chain pulley system in the construction industry also uses a similar concept.

Thus, the knowledge was not new but its application in real life did not happen. It is possible that there was a problem with society and its values that it did not push for attention. It is equally possible that formal science and the way it is taught does not encourage one to apply science to everyday problems. The strange disconnect between classroom and field is a sad part of our legacy. The illiterate artisan, who developed this pulley system was acknowledged and rewarded by the National Innovation Foundation.

Yet given the same historical legacy, ours is a country that has been, and still is, contributing top-class scientists to the world.

Let us just take the example of the IT industry. The dominant position of the Indian diaspora in the American IT industry is legendary. *India and the Knowledge Economy*, the World Bank report, says that approximately 300,000 Indians now work in Silicon Valley. They account for more than 15 per cent start-ups. They have an average annual income of about 200,000 dollars, almost five times compared to the US average! And it is not in terms of income alone that they have done well. What the Indian diaspora has been able to accomplish is path breaking, whether it is Suhas Patil of Cirrus Logic, or Gururaj Deshpande of Sycamore Networks, or Vinod Khosla of Sun Microsystems, or Victor Menezes of Citibank, or Rajat Gupta of McKinsey, or Raghuram Rajan of IMF or Rakesh Gangwal of US Airways, or Arun Netravali of Bell Laboratories. The list goes on and they have all done us proud.

Returning NRIs

NASSCOM has studied a large number of returning Indian professionals. The CEO of a major venture capital company, which exclusively funds biotech start-up companies, told me that 60 per cent of the proposals they have cleared are from young techno-entrepreneurs who want to return to India from USA. GE's R&D Centre has more than 2400 professionals working there. Some 700 of them were young Indians who had returned to India in the last four years. The Intel chief told me that of the 2600 professionals in their Indian R&D Centre, 400 are those who have come back from USA over the last four years. Admittedly, this is a trickle and not a torrent. But it is heartening to see the change.

The Italian scientist Riccardo Giacconi, Nobel Laureate in Physics, summed it up beautifully when he said: "A scientist is like a painter. Michaelangelo became a great artist because he had been given a wall to paint. My wall was given to me by the US." Are such walls to paint now being given in India? In other words, can India be perceived as a land of opportunity? I am happy to find some winds of change.

Indian industry is beginning to realise that if they do not innovate, they will perish. The Indian drugs and pharmaceutical industry has survived so far by copying known molecules. Now, at least ten Indian companies have got into discovery research, working on new molecules. Some pharma industry leaders have told me that collectively, they are looking to employ hundreds of bright young PhDs. In fact, they are complaining about the shortage of suitably skilled PhDs in India!

In other sectors too magical changes are taking place. In the auto industry, the wheel has come full circle. Sixty years ago, it was the British Morris Oxford which was sold as the Indian Ambassador on Indian roads. Today, the Indian Indica is sold as City Rover on London roads! It happened because Indian talent was given an 'opportunity', thanks to the vision of a leader and thanks also to a conducive policy of the Government.

In March 1978, JRD Tata had said: "If Telco had been allowed to make a car; we would have been as good in it as we were in trucks." But he was not allowed to make the Tata car. India's closed economy killed competition.

Challenge

In 1991, when the economy was opened up, Ratan Tata was allowed to make cars. He had the courage to throw a challenge to 700 engineers who had never done an auto-design in their lives. He invested Rs 1760 crores, the highest ever in backing an indigenously designed, developed and manufactured product. The result was a world-class car, namely Indica. What is the lesson in this? The 'Indian Talent' of 700 engineers found an expression only when the Government policies allowed competition and a visionary leader trusted the 'Indian Talent'. The winner was India. And now the peoples' car Nano has created a paradigm shift in low-cost transport.

India's dream of finding the right place in the comity of nations will be fulfilled when two things happen. The first is the universal recognition of India's undoubted progress, the second is the infusion of the scientific temper in the intellectual, emotional, social and cultural life of our masses, not just of a select few. The first condition seems nearly realized. As for the second, it is up to us. If we can collaborate with the tide in the affairs of humanity, everybody will be a winner. Innovation is indeed a movement—and the surge is here. □

M S Swaminathan MP
Chairman, MSSRF

From Green to Ever-Green Revolution

Jointly with the World Food Programme, the M S Swaminathan Foundation worked on a very detailed analysis and mapping of food insecurity in India. A glance at the maps shows, interestingly enough, that the regions more food secure now, such as Punjab and other states in the north and south, might become food insecure by 2020 if sustainability of food security is considered. The reasons are that the soil is overexploited, the groundwater has gone down very deep, and there is extensive salinization. The crop rotation, which normally included at least one legume, has now given way to a sequence of rice-wheat because there is a ready market for both products and the government buys them at the support price. It is important therefore, to have a paradigm shift in production technology from Green Revolution to what I have been calling an 'Ever-Green Revolution', which involves the mainstreaming of ecological principles in technology development and dissemination.

Sustainable green revolution is an ecological and economic necessity in our country of small holdings and over a hundred million farm families. Therefore it will be better to coin another term to denote the unsustainable use of yield enhancing technologies, I would like to refer to it as the Greed Revolution. What we should strive in both agriculture and aquaculture is the promotion of an evergreen revolution or sustainable green revolution and the curbing of the Greed Revolution. The failure to make a distinction between the two will cause confusion in the public mind and will harm the public interest.

I define Ever-Green Revolution as a revolution that can lead to productivity improvement in perpetuity without associated ecological and social harm. The difference in approach is that the Green Revolution has been commodity-centered, whereas the Ever-Green Revolution must centre on integrated natural resources management. This notion is very aptly captured by Edward O Wilson (2002) in *The Future of Life*:

> The problem before us is how to feed billions of new mouths over the next several decades and save the rest of life at the same time without being trapped in a Faustian bargain that threatens freedom from security. The benefits must come from an evergreen revolution. The aim of this new thrust is to lift production well above the levels attained by the Green Revolution of the 1960s, using technology and regulatory policy more advanced and even safer than now in existence.

An Ever-Green Revolution will only be possible if there is synergy between technology and public policy. Without appropriate public policy, the technology will just lie without sprouting on the ground. It is important to underscore the interaction between technology and public policy, as an Ever-Green Revolution requires even better public policies involving management of groundwater to avoid overexploitation, conservation of prime farmland for agriculture, promotion of integrated pest management, and so on. It involves a suitable mix of education, social mobilization through Gram Sabhas and Panchayats, and regulation through appropriate legislation.

This broad view allows the reconciliation of approaches such as organic farming and biotechnology that have sometimes been presented as antagonistic when in fact they are not. 'Biotechnology' is a broad term. Productivity can be improved in perpetuity without associated ecological harm if an organic farming approach is adopted with

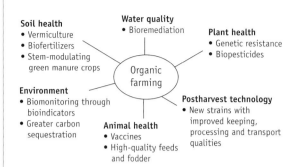

Fig. 1. The Ever-Green Revolution: Synergy between Organic Farming and Biotechnology
Source: M S Swaminathan

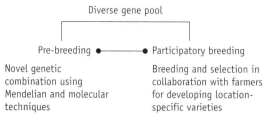

Fig. 2. Integrating genetic efficiency with genetic diversity
Source : M S Swaminathan

support from a number of approaches that fall under the umbrella of biotechnology, from vermiculture and biofertilizers to greater carbon sequestration. The adoption of organic farming, which ensures that high productivity is maintained in perpetuity, requires support from a whole series of biotechnologies, as shown in Fig. 1.

Sustainable food security

Sustainable food security involves, to begin with, defending the gains already made. This is where the biotic and abiotic stresses, as well as the probable effects of climate change, must be considered. First, a rise in sea level is a real possibility, according to the Intergovernmental Panel on Climate Change; an anticipatory programme must therefore be implemented to meet such an eventuality. Second, the gains achieved to date must be extended to rainfed and marginal environments; and third, new gains must be made for farming systems through diversification and value addition.

Let me cite an example with mangroves, which are wonderful plants found along estuaries in many countries. About a century ago most coastal areas, including the US coast, had numerous mangroves. Many of them have gone, but now people are starting to realize the great importance of mangroves for carbon sequestration, soil stabilization, prevention of coastal sea erosion, and sustainable fisheries.

The M S Swaminathan Foundation in Chennai has initiated a large programme on the conservation of mangrove forests along the east coast—significant amounts of carbon are sequestered from the atmosphere by the mangrove plant, apart from their biomass contribution. There is also a US group, the Seawater Forest Initiative, that has taken up a large programme in Eritrea to plant mangroves, along with shrimp farming. They plant trees

(mangroves, casuarinas, and other trees), and as a result, along the creeks one can harvest prawns, fish and so on. There are, clearly, extensive opportunities for seawater farming, involving integrated attention to culture and capture fisheries and to forestry and agroforestry.

Another important issue is integrating genetic diversity and genetic efficiency (Fig. 2). Most CGIAR centres, such as the International Rice Research Institute and the International Maize and Wheat Improvement Centre, function as pre-breeding centres. They try to generate novel genetic combinations.

A good example of pre-breeding comes from the M S Swaminathan Research Foundation, where we have taken genes from mangroves for seawater tolerance; put them in rice, some millets, and mustard. We plan to give them to the local farm families for breeding, using participatory breeding approaches. In this way, one attains genetic diversity without losing genetic efficiency. In other words, if there is a problem of genetic homogeneity, possibly leading to genetic vulnerability to diseases and pests, it can be overcome by having a series of varieties available through participatory breeding programmes carried out with the cooperation of farmers. Participatory research and knowledge management hold the key to sustainable agriculture.

Genetically modified crops

Perceptions vary greatly in governments and nongovernmental and civil society organizations with regard to the risks and benefits associated with genetically modified (GM) crops. Let me quote two statements from the World Food Summit Plus 5 of June 10–13, 2002, one from the official declaration, and the second from civil society organizations.

The government declaration stated, "We are committed to study, share, and facilitate the responsible use of biotechnology in addressing development needs" (FAO 2002, 86); while the civil society organizations said, "Genetically modified organisms represent a threat to family farmers, other food producers, the integrity of genetic resources, and human and environmental health. They will affect particularly the rural poor who cannot afford this costly alternative."

In my opinion the second statement has mixed up issues that raise certain questions. First, what is wrong with science? Second, who controls science? And third, who will have access to products of science? Unless these issues are disaggregated, it will be impossible to clarify the analysis and policy implications.

Regarding the first and looking at the scientific aspects, it is important to remember that about 54 years ago (on April 25, 1953) James D Watson and Francis H C Crick published their now famous paper in *Nature* in which they described the double helix structure of DNA. Thus molecular genetics has over 50 years of science behind it and a great deal of knowledge has accumulated on the scientific aspect of the problem. The second and third issues relate to the control of science and access to the new technology. The concern is that multinationals having control of the technology through IPR regimes, resource-poor farmers will be at a disadvantage. This is why the Department of Biotechnology has been dealing with biotechnology policy—to ensure beneficial

outcomes for all farmers and society. Unless the stakeholders disaggregate the issues involved in the GM organism debate and deal with them separately, acceptable solutions will not be found. And without regulatory mechanisms that are transparent, involve multiple stakeholders, and inspire confidence in the objectivity of the risk-benefit analysis mechanisms, this technology will not take off. This is why an autonomous and professionally led National Biotechnology Authority is urgently needed.

I am not surprised at the reactions against biotechnology, because even Mendel's Laws, published in 1865, were not accepted for 35 years. It was only in 1900 that Mendel's work was rediscovered. I do not think one should worry too much about many of these reactions, but it is important to look at all problems in a fair and objective way. This approach will involve greater investments of public funds for research in the public good.

Rural professions, particularly crop and animal husbandry, fisheries and forestry and agro-processing need technological upgrading. Young professionals can be attracted and retained in agriculture only if farming becomes intellectually stimulating and economically rewarding. Fortunately, modern science has opened up uncommon opportunities for achieving such a blend of brain and brawn. □

Bimal Jalan
Former Governor
Reserve Bank of India

Science, technology and development

History has shown that modern economic growth has been inspired by a rapid and persistent upgrading of technology and scientific know-how. One-third to one-half of the growth experienced by the industrially advanced countries is estimated to have come from technological progress. Thus, technology has emerged as the principal driving force for long-term economic growth. Economic growth results from slow and steady improvements in technology and knowledge embodied in physical and human capital as well as from the 'breakthrough' inventions. Breakthrough inventions are, however, unpredictable and these at times change the direction of the entire industrial structure. What is the relation between science and technology? How do they influence growth trajectories of the world economy and well-being of the people? What should be the relative roles of the state and market in ensuring the blooming of scientific knowledge and its culmination into technological know-how? What do the successful countries' experiences teach us in this regard?

As for the relation between science and technology, the Austrian economist Joseph Schumpeter made a fundamental distinction between invention, which is the discovery of new techniques, and innovation, which consists of the practical application of an invention to production for the market. Invention is performed by the inventor, while innovation is the task of the entrepreneur.

The classic example of this is the Industrial Revolution in Britain in the late 18th and early 19th centuries. The success of Britain then did not merely lie in the invention of scientific tools, which may be primitive by modern standards, but also in their commercial adoption. Thus James Watt is remembered not only as the inventor of the steam engine but also as one who put it to commercial use. It is this commercial adoption that Schumpeter referred to as innovation. Many developers of modern software too fall into this combined category of inventor and innovator rolled into one. Bill Gates is often portrayed as not only the pioneer of MS-DOS and Windows, but as the one who marketed it successfully. However, often the entities of innovator and inventor are distinct, and it is the intimate interlink between invention and innovation that marks the relationship between science and technology.

In Schumpeter's analytical structure, there is a third stage of the twin process of invention-innovation, namely, diffusion, which occurs only when the scientist and the entrepreneur join hands. The invention and initial innovation of any product or process may be the property or outcome of an individual or company effort. But how are they made popular? What ensures their cost-reduction and universal adoption? It is only through proper diffusion of the scientific knowledge embodied in the marketable form of a particular product or process that it gets universalised. Technological history is full of examples of such diffusion, or 'knowledge spill-over'.

The link between science and technology is the prime force behind economic progress, but what is the optimal mode of interplay between them? Often the question arises, what kind of research is more necessary, pure or applied? The issue becomes all the more important in the context of funding science programmes. However, like many of the fundamental choice problems of human life, there is no standard model that can be universally pursued. At a conceptual level, nevertheless, one can have a two-way classification of the agencies involved with scientific research: knowledge generation agencies and knowledge application/diffusion agencies. While the former include universities or technical schools, big science national networks like the CSIR or various corporations are examples of the latter. A related question would be what kind of research do we need more? Would the research paradigm of the scientific pursuit be dictated solely by utilitarian consideration and accordingly subjected to social controls?

All economies in the world faced this dilemma at some time or the other. In fact, the issue can be traced as far back as a public debate that took place in Great Britain during the 1930s between Michael Polanyi and J D Bernal. Polanyi stressed the need for autonomy and self-governance for the scientific community, while Bernal expressed his preference in favour of societal and government regulation over research agenda. Often one finds a tension between what is called an 'open science' and what is called an 'appropriable science'. Such dichotomy, in my opinion, arises from a confusion between private and social rate of return of scientific pursuit.

Social rate of return

The immediate social rate of return out of an otherwise esoteric research programme may be low, but over the long run it could have the potential of being appropriable. The contribution to science and technology comes from both these kinds of research and often their cohesion determines the extent of success in the field of technical capabilities. It may be noted that in many fields of today's world of scientific research, like modern biology, the distinction between basic and applied science is increasingly getting blurred. One is reminded of Louis Pasteur, who used to say, 'There is nothing like basic research and applied science. There is only science and its application'. The distinction developed by the European Commission is instructive in this respect. They have adopted a three-way classification of knowledge-based research: a) fundamental research, b) basic industrial research, and c) applied research and development (R&D). It is my firm belief that India as a nation needs all the three kinds of research and should endeavour to maintain a close relation between them.

Enhanced labour, capital and technical progress are the three principal sources of economic growth of nations. The distinction between capital and technical progress in economists' terminology is often a matter of degree. While increase in capital is interpreted as the quantitative change in the existing capital stock of any country, technical progress refers to qualitative changes in the production technique. However, the term 'capital' needs to be taken in a rather broad sense, so that it encompasses the three distinct kinds of capital, namely, physical, financial and human. The concept 'technical progress' extends to all three kinds of capital. This basic broad definition of capital is central to our understanding of the impact of science and technology on economic well-being. Moreover, the contribution of science and technology to economic growth comes in the form of both capital and technical progress.

What is the process through which these technological innovations get transmitted to a higher growth trajectory? Schumpeter describes this process as one of 'creative destruction'; in his own words, "The fundamental impulse that sets and keeps the capitalist engine in motion comes from the new goods, the new methods of production or transportation, the new markets, the new form of industrial organisation the capitalist enterprise create ... [These] illustrate the same process of industrial mutation that incessantly revolutionises the economic structure from within, incessantly destroying the old one, incessantly creating a new one. This process of Creative Destruction is the essential fact about capitalism."

Theories of growth

Recent theories of endogenous growth stress two facts about innovation. First, it is the engine of growth, and secondly, it is endogenously generated by competing profit-seeking firms. The key feature of the process is that knowledge acts as a public good and creates economy-wide increasing returns. The public stock of knowledge that has accumulated from the spill-over of the previous inventions is a crucial input in the technology to generate new ideas. Research has established that while the rate of knowledge obsolescence has risen dramatically, the rate of knowledge diffusion is even faster. A study in the USA found that 70 per cent of product innovations were known and understood by rivals within 12 months of the innovation, and only 17 per cent took longer than 18 months. There is also evidence of increasing patent-research input ratio (as measured by R&D expenditure) for a number of developed countries. However, the crucial impact that science and technology has on the economic growth of a nation is through a broad-based technical progress. The influence of technical progress in the growth process of any economy is referred to as total factor productivity growth (TFPG). There have been various studies on growth accounting in a number of countries. A report for the G-7 countries and the Netherlands, for the period 1947–73, found that the annual growth rates for TFP for these countries were substantial, ranging from 1.4 per cent in the USA to 4.0 per cent in Japan. TFPG accounts for over one-third of the overall growth rate in all these countries. Interestingly, the same study finds a rather low growth of TFP in the high growth nations of East Asia, where capital contributed the lion's share to the growth process. There is, however, no riddle in this finding; after all from the measurement standpoint a small variation from earlier technique may still be defined as one of change of capital. Much of the technological capabilities of the East Asian countries came either from technological licensing agreements or from foreign direct investment.

Productivity front

Let me now turn to the Indian performance on the productivity front. Because of inherent measurement problems of TFPG, estimates by different researchers differ quite substantially in the Indian context. For example, Prof B N Coldar of Delhi University estimated TFPG for 1960–80 to be 1.3 per cent per annum for India. On the contrary, Prof I J Ahluwalia of the Centre of Policy Research, New Delhi, found considerable inter-industry differences insofar as TFPG was concerned. In fact, her calculations indicated that TFPG for India was in the range of –0.6 to +0.3 per cent per annum during the sixties and the seventies. Nevertheless, researchers found a positive turnaround in Indian TFPG since the early eighties. Productivity performance may alternatively be measured by how much incremental output investment has generated in different time-periods. This, in the economists' tool-kit, is termed 'incremental capital output ratio' (ICOR). The ICOR that exhibited an ever-increasing path during the first three decades of the post-Independence period started reducing in the early '80s. During the post-

liberalisation period there has been a further decreasing trend, indicating productivity gains in the Indian economy.

An important issue governing the impact of science and technology on the well-being of a nation is the employment potential of any technology. An oft-expressed fear associated with the emergence of any technological innovation is that it is labour displacing. The crucial issue in this context is the employment elasticity of an innovation induced growth. Though per se the innovation of a new technology may be labour-saving, but the development of ancillaries or related products may give rise to newer employment opportunities; it is the net employment absorption that determines the employment-elasticity of growth.

There is strong evidence that so long as technology helps to widen the resource base of the production system of the economy, there is no a priori reason for technological innovation to be employment reducing in an aggregate sense. The East Asian example is a case worth considering in this context. It is now widely accepted that notwithstanding the proportions of factor-utilisation of any production process, there has to be ample emphasis on labour for ensuring the welfare of the working class. East Asian governments used many such policies—land reform in South Korea and Taiwan, housing subsidies in Hong Kong and Singapore, credit targeting for small business and investment in rural infrastructure in Indonesia and Malaysia. Accordingly, despite varied degree of tolerance of labour unions, wages increased as fast as Gross Domestic Product (GDP) and unemployment declined in all of the East Asian countries.

International experience is full of success stories with different kinds of innovation.

Technology transfer

There are four different forms of technology transfer: a) acquisition of a share of the equity of the technology producing firm; b) license agreement; c) outright purchase of equipment, know-how or blue-print and d) flow of human resources.

There are success stories in all these modes of upgrading technology. As for example, countries like Japan acquired patents from outside and then took recourse to their indigenous assimilation and further development, so as to finally export them. Similarly, many of the high-growth East Asian countries have little original technological inventions. The bulk of the technological capabilities came from licensing agreements or direct foreign investment.

Technological activity in developing countries, accordingly, tends to be almost of the 'incremental type' rather than of 'Schumpeterian-frontier-moving-type'. Numerous case studies of such experiments can be cited from the Indian experience. Some examples include adapting imported designs of power plant equipment to suit local quality of coal and changes in the designs of tractors, vehicles and a variety of consumer durables to suit local conditions of production of components.

It must, however, be recognised that success stories of 'in-country research' leading to output growth are exceptions rather than the rule. We have had our constraints. There is a large time lag between 'effort' and 'results' in any innovation activity. An economy has to 'afford' it. And an economy that is pursuing a pattern of investment (such as infrastructure development) where projects have long gestation periods, may not find it very easy to allocate large resources to innovative activities where gestation lags are even larger than these infrastructure projects. Besides, there are the risks associated with innovation effort.

Principal elements

The principal elements that should be taken into account in drawing up a framework of policies to facilitate science and technology development effort are: 1. the trade option in technology; 2. the time lag between 'efforts' and 'results' and the associated risks; 3. the areas/ industries to be given priority; and 4. the institutional framework, the role of the public sector, particularly the government, in facilitating innovation and the direct participation by the government in R&D effort.

Looking at science and technology in the context of its contribution to production of goods and provision of services to the people, the objective is maximisation of output. If the needs of the society are to be fulfilled at the lowest cost, the 'make' versus 'buy' issues become important, i.e., the trade option has to be kept in view. While the commodity markets may tend to be 'perfect', technology markets, even if they exist, are characterised by their 'imperfectness' marked by inadequate information and exclusive rights acquired through patents or otherwise. In the Indian situation, we are frequently compelled to

acquire technology through imports. Firms trade in 'technology' not as a commodity but as a 'perceived' economic advantage for a stream of returns in the future.

International political considerations also cannot be ruled out in technology trade. Licensing by governments of developed countries and export embargoes are common. However, when it comes to bargaining regarding technology transfer, the issue of indigenous availability often becomes extremely important. For example, it has been observed in India that the prices quoted by foreign firms for capital goods and equipment drop when a distinct alternative supply possibility emerges. This has been the experience in a number of industries like electric power equipment, telephone exchange equipment and machine tools. Hence, to appropriate the benefits of the trade option in technology, the nation needs some effort at technology development, which generates a supply alternative. Consequently, the efforts towards development of indigenous capabilities make immense commercial sense and are a way of getting the right kind of technology at a right price.

Fundamental issues

Two fundamental issues are central to any policy governing science and technology. First, what is the funding process of innovation activities? Secondly, if the diffusion of technological innovation is indeed fast what is the incentive of the innovator? Often there is a wedge between the commercial successes of a new innovation and the profits appropriated by the innovator—the problem becomes all the more important in view of the fact that in a number of cases innovative activity has a substantial fixed cost. A number of solutions are practised in different degrees in various countries. Use of subsidies or tax-concessions for R&D expenditure, adoption of co-operative R&D ventures and national champions, and detailed patent laws are the major policy instruments in this regard. As regards the funding of R&D expenditure, considerable differences exist even among the advanced economies. While Japan and the USA spent 2.8 per cent of their GDP on R&D in 1989, 20 per cent of Japanese R&D came from the government as against 50 per cent in the USA. Nevertheless, public expenditure on technology development for civilian industrial application accounts for a small share of public R&D

budgets in the industrial economies. A number of studies have found that the effect of direct government funding on the productivity performance of the recipient firms is smaller than in privately financed R&D investment.

The funding of innovative activities by the private sector is indeed problematic. Gone are the days of individual entrepreneurs, capable of financing risky but full of profitable potential technological innovations. On the other hand, stock markets also may not be forthcoming in financing these high-growth-but-risky ventures. To get rid of this finance constraint 'venture capital' comes in, which is essentially equity investment in companies that are not mature enough to get access to capital market but have high growth potentials to compensate for the uncertainties inherent in such ventures. There are a number of success stories of such venture capital financing in the developed world; successful corporations like Apple Computers or Genetech producing biomedical products would not have been born without active venture capital participation.

Nehru's vision

Nationalist leaders recognised the importance of science and technology for development as early as in 1939, when a National Planning Committee was constituted under the chairmanship of Jawaharlal Nehru. The Science and Technology Policy was greatly influenced by Nehru's vision, who from early days had an abiding interest in the application of science and technology to development. Nehru said:

> Though I have long been a slave driven in the chariot of Indian politics, with little leisure for other thoughts, my mind has often wandered to the days when as a student I haunted the laboratories of that home of science, Cambridge. And though circumstances made me part company with science, my thoughts turned to it with longing. In later years, through devious processes, I arrived again at science, when I realised that science was not only a pleasant diversion and abstraction, but was the very texture of life, without which modern world would vanish away. Politics led me to economics, and this led me inevitably to science and the scientific approach to all our problems and to life itself.

India was perhaps one of the first countries of the world in creating in 1951 a Ministry of Scientific Research and Natural Resources for organising and directing scientific research for national development. The Scientific Policy Resolution passed by Parliament in 1958 laid

down specific objectives, seeking to promote all aspects of scientific research, pure, applied and educational. Active pursuit of these policies bore fruits and educational institutions and scientific laboratories were established so as to reap the benefits of scientific progress. The next major landmark in the policy domain was announcement of the technology policy of the Government of India at the Indian Science Congress, Tirupati, held in January 1983. Apart from reinforcing the above objectives, this resolution specifically called for developing internationally competitive technologies with export potential, energy saving technologies and technologies which will recycle waste material. As for priorities, it called for special consideration to be given to employment, energy, efficiency of activities, and environment. In the field of acquisition of technology, though it called for a selective role for import of technology and foreign investment, it specifically stressed the need for absorption, adaptation and subsequent development of imported know-how through adequate investment in R&D to which importers of technology were expected to contribute. In the context of the efficiency of the invention-innovation process, the role of the CSIR is of paramount importance.

CSIR

Much has been written on the strengths and weaknesses of the CSIR. The CSIR Review Committee in 1986 found that the multiplicity of objectives, sub-optimal scale of operation, lack of sustained and meaningful interaction between the CSIR and its actual and potential users, and the lack of suitable incentive support had in the past limited the usefulness of the CSIR. Some of the factors were beyond the control of the scientific institutions which were also affected by industry's indifference and the regulatory regime. Often the reasons for lack of smooth functioning of institutions like the CSIR were interactive and consequently the responsibility became collective. What is required is a proper blend of situation-specific modes, like technology missions, technology programmes, sponsored research, basic research and societal science programmes.

In 1991, the government introduced a liberalised policy for technology transfers. Apart from giving a number of tax concessions for R&D purposes, the government has undertaken a number of policy measures with far reaching significance in the field of science and technology. A Technology Development Board has been established with a three-fold strategy: (a) facilitating development of new technologies, (b) assimilation and adaptation of imported technologies, and (c) providing catalytic support to industries and R&D institutions to work together. In the budget for 1994–95, the Fund for Technology Development and Application was created.

Legal framework

Innovative activities often turn out to be risky from the standpoint of the financier. An effective and speedy legal patent framework goes a long way to solve the incentive problem associated with any innovative venture. Though the Indian Patent Act, 1970, came as big break from the earlier archaic Indian Patent and Design Act, much still needs to be done.

The following example may illustrate the point. During 1994, whereas in India 4,000 patents were filed, China in the same year had 70,000 patents. A slow process of patenting not only hurts the interests of the innovator but also discourages the potential ones. Loose patent laws or their violation, like software piracy, cause concern. However, the global regime represented by trade-related intellectual property rights (TRIPS) tilted the balance of benefits of innovation in favour of the private innovator. As a signatory to the 1994 Uruguay Round of multilateral trade negotiations, India is bound by the WTO regulatory framework.

This may have consequences for the oft adopted modes of industrial research in India like imitative research or reverse engineering. We need to develop the intermediaries like patent agents and patent attorneys, who will bridge the gap between the market and the scientists.

What is the Government's role in the advancement of science and upgrading of technology in a liberalised market? In popular parlance, liberalisation is equated to the withdrawal of state from the economic domain. However, science and technology is a field where such a popular notion may turn out to be fallacious. It is widely argued that there are three sources of market failure, namely, indivisibility, uncertainty and externalities. R&D which seeks to generate knowledge suffers from all three types of market failure.

Moreover, when there is a wedge between private and social profitability, like that existent in pure research, private finance may not be forthcoming. Thus, even in a deregulated regime the state will have three specific and selective roles in fostering science and technology: financier of fundamental research, provider of infrastructure, and regulator of property rights. The government is required to co-ordinate and guide technology development since free markets might not suffice to create the technological dynamism that industrial growth needs.

India has come a long way in her quest for scientific pursuit, both in the material and intellectual spheres. Winds of change have been blowing in the field of science in India. Information Technology poses new challenges and has opened up newer opportunities. True, there is still much to be done in the policy and legal spheres. But the direction is right. In the liberal environment, let thousands of ideas bloom and be turned into innovative ventures by our entrepreneurs. India has the talent, the skills and the resources to be in the forefront of the technological revolution taking place in the new sectors of growth in the global economy. □

Kiran Mazumdar-Shaw
Chairman, Biocon Limited

India's mantra: Affordable innovation

Innovation in the life sciences has a new meaning today. More than at any time in the past, the value placed on innovation is being measured on its commercial and more importantly, its social impact. Innovation itself has no geographical boundaries, whatever the field of endeavour, nor is it the preserve of only affluent countries. One recent example is the enormous impact of the micro-credit banking model, pioneered by Bangladeshi economist Mohammed Yunus. It's no surprise that Prof Yunus and the bank he founded, Grameen Bank, should have been honoured with the Nobel Peace prize in 2006 for their "efforts to create economic and social development from below."

This prompts the question: Do we in the developing world need to blindly emulate the western model for innovation in the life sciences? The answer is a clear "No". The west is, no doubt, the global powerhouse of innovation in healthcare and medicine, but the existing approach needs radical change if it is to achieve greater social impact. The existing model has inherent limitations. A new drug for instance is accessible in the initial years to only a small, affluent section of the world's population. This reach is expanded through an effective system of public and private reimbursements that make these products more affordable to a larger user base. Subsequently, upon patent expiry, the drugs are made available as cheaper generic versions to patients across a broader economic spectrum only to be replaced by more expensive next generation drugs. The approach is plainly unsuited to developing countries like India, particularly in the absence of mechanisms for public and private reimbursements, and inadequate venture funding, so critical for R&D effort in frontier areas of the life sciences. Therefore there is an urgent need to put in place a practical, alternative model that spurs innovation in R&D and makes the products that emerge from it affordable to a much larger section of the populace.

Crux of the issue

Cost is the crux of the issue. Estimates of the costs of drug development vary, but one widely quoted figure is $1–2 billion per drug—staggering by Third World standards. Only one out of five drugs that start human clinical trials reaches the market. This high investment in R&D—and the risks associated with it—is one reason why the pharma industry has shown a noticeable lack of enthusiasm to invest in developing medicines and therapies for 'non-profitable' diseases that plague the poorer countries.

In recent times, frameworks that support and subsidize national healthcare structures are being forced to rethink their models. The UK's National Institute of Clinical Efficacy (NICE) as well as the German health authorities have withdrawn reimbursements to a number of new drugs like monoclonal antibodies for the treatment of a number of cancers, insulin analogs and other drugs, on the grounds that the cost benefit ratio simply does not justify such spends. NICE has evolved a metrics based on QALYs or Quality Adjusted Life Years to decide on its reimbursement plan for new drugs being introduced into the market. This is an approach that the US is evaluating for adoption.

Affordability is now the underlying mantra that is being chanted by national health systems and private insurance companies across the globe in their efforts to build sustainable models for healthcare against a challenging backdrop of aging populations and scientific progress. It is also well accepted that developing new therapeutics for Malaria, TB, AIDS and other neglected diseases will have to be done in the developing world if they are to reach the patients that need them. Affordable innovation that delivers affordable drugs to the market is the only way forward. India needs to leverage its affordable cost base to deliver high value innovation to global markets by building excellence across the innovation chain from discovery to product and clinical development.

A stocktaking of India's developing capabilities indicate the following:

- A large reservoir of scientific manpower, a wide network of research laboratories, a vibrant pharma industry, and fast-growing clinical capabilities
- The largest number of USFDA-approved pharma manufacturing facilities outside the US, and the largest number of annual generic drug filings with the USFDA for any country outside the U.S.
- Rising investment in Biotechnology—expected to increase five-fold by the end of the current decade, from US $2 billion to $10 billion, largely as a result of growing collaboration between multinational corporations and indigenous research efforts
- Drug development cost at one-tenth of what it is in the West. India's large and diverse disease population is, equally, an advantage from the clinical research and development perspective
- India's currently low per capita expenditure on drugs and healthcare as a whole is set to change over the coming years. As the health insurance industry matures, expenditure on health care and pharma products is expected to go up in a commensurate manner.

Before the advent of the product patent regime, India managed to create a successful, cost-effective generic pharma industry by first reverse engineering patented drugs and innovating improved production processes. Now, the industry is fast gearing up to take the path of discovery-led research and innovation. Spending on R&D, hitherto rather modest, is slated to change as companies take up the innovation challenge.

Looking to future

The road ahead offers India an enormous opportunity to be a global innovator with an inherently competitive cost and skill base. Indian research and clinical services are already being harnessed by MNC pharma and biotech companies in their own bid to lower drug development costs. Recent out-licensing deals struck by a few Indian pharma and biotech companies indicate early success in discovery-led innovation.

Our innovation-led business strategy at Biocon allowed us to attain our first milestone where we indigenously developed and commercialized the world's most affordable Anti-EGFR monoclonal antibody, BIOMAb EGFR® for the treatment of solid tumours in a variety of cancers. The antibody itself was initially developed by a Third World research institute, the Centre for Immunology in Cuba. Biocon partnered the Cuban researchers and added significant value through large-scale process and clinical development to bring it to the Indian market. This demonstrates that affordable innovation can deliver a novel life-saving drug for cancer patients in the developing world who would otherwise be deprived.

With its low operating costs, improving regulatory environment and its talented scientific workforce, India may well realize, within the next decade its potential and emerge as the region's hub for innovation and product development in bringing new and cutting-edge products to global markets. Moreover, it might have put in place an innovation model that rivals that of the West. □

M M Sharma
Emeritus Professor of Eminence
University Institute of Chemical
Technology, Mumbai

Dons enrich industry

With the opening up of the Indian economy, entrepreneurs have access to world technology. Thus the deeply entrenched view of 'the Best in India' is being replaced by 'the Best in the world.' This will impose heavy demands since any technology that is acquired is, at best, second hand. The acquisition of technology as a 'black box' is full of dangers and companies will find it necessary to take assistance from the academics to shine some light into the black box to gain vital 'know-why'. This calls for academia-industry interaction on a significant scale.

Leadership in innovation will not come without pure science. Intensive work is required in areas like genetic engineering and materials science. Industry is already finding it desirable to enlist the help of academic scientists. This exposure will benefit the academics too. Those working in plants enjoying a monopoly in the sector for long, seemed to believe that they know 'everything' about the technology, plant and even the science associated with their enterprise. They are often hostile to the heretical views of the academics.

No technology is ever mature and we can still witness remarkable developments in the technology of plants developed years ago. In the case of the large-scale ammonia plants, where the basic technology is over 80 years old, we can discern very important developments. On the other hand, academics are also afflicted with a similar disease of assigning to themselves all the wisdom in the area of research in which they are concentrating. There has to be openness and ideas should be put gently and persuasively in order to wean the personnel at all important levels, particularly middle management, from orthodox thinking.

I have had considerable success in increasing the capacity of some fertiliser, acid, petrochemicals and alkali plants, based on knowledge engineering with insignificant or no capital expenditure. The University Department of Chemical Technology (UDCT), Bombay (now renamed University Institute of Chemical Technology, Mumbai) has an impressive tradition of doing consulting work, without using the experimental facilities of the department. This has helped the institution in several ways.

A large number of my former students are working as consultants and a very respectable percentage of faculty members at UDCT are consultants to a spectrum of industries. Unlike in most other engineering institutions, the students here prefer to work for a PhD, forsaking good jobs. This is remarkable as the difference between the salaries in industry and the senior research fellowships is very large and with increasing fees, hostel rents and mess bills, they can barely meet their expenses. But what a pleasure to see this live exchange between industry and academia and academic research work being taken to its ultimate destination!

For academics in engineering and technology, it is a professional necessity to interact with industry in several ways. An effective way to interact with industry is to be a consultant. I have worked on assignments with a variety of industries on a broad range of problems, from extending the potential of existing equipment, to getting better specification product, to totally new R&D-based projects. I have been associated with identification of new projects involving very large investments. As a member of the

Board of Directors of several public sector and private sector companies, I got insight into the working of the 'boardroom'. This enabled me to arrive at strategies which allowed new ideas to be nourished.

Academic research in engineering and technology has a different philosophy than that in pure sciences. The stimulus for research is provided by industrial problems and, of course, both modes, namely, Discovery Driven Research (DDR) and Market Driven Research (MDR) have relevance. However, we have to zealously ensure that the ad hoc methods, more frequently referred to as the 'art', do not overtake the sound theoretical basis.

We should recognise that the art of practice is sterile without theory and in engineering, theory without practice is drab. Thus, contrary to prevalent beliefs, research in engineering is far too demanding and has to marry the cutting edge of science with the harsh realities of commercial practice. An 'outsider' consultant faces additional impediments in India where this practice is of relatively recent origin and largely confined to progressive industries which are largely science based, such as the chemical industry.

Imported technology

Most of the plants operating in India are based on imported technology and many organisations now over 30 years old have witnessed personnel at the top echelons who have risen from the ranks, where the perspective is quite different. It is essential for a consultant, or for that matter, the in-house R&D personnel, to have a friendly turf provided by the plant personnel both for on-going projects as well as those projects which come entirely out of the in-house R&D work. In this context, the role of the top manager and the middle manager is crucial. The consultant should, therefore, have the knack of diagnosing the 'psychology' (or should I say culture) of the company with which he is associated. There ought to be mutual respect between people involved in this exercise. The most renowned chemical companies in USA make extensive use of consultants, even though they have large R&D establishments with a proven track record over several decades. German companies often have as chief executive a person with professorial titles.

The cradle of innovation lies in academia where accumulation of fundamental scientific knowledge takes place. Innovation is the flywheel of technology. We are able to integrate rationality and intuition. The potential for creativity in universities is much greater than has been recognised and we do have 'spiritual' freedom. There is considerable scope for individuality, but we do recognise that group interaction can stimulate, even incite, an individual.

Academics can be utilised fruitfully for brainstorming sessions by industry to obtain independent comments on their own ideas. Here the views will not be biased due to the pressures arising out of hierarchy. Unusual behaviour observed by plant personnel can be presented for comments and the role of academics as puzzle solvers can be gainfully exploited.

Academics are accustomed to unconventional and unorthodox approaches. I could cite an example of a chemical company, where I provided some consultancy without any fee as a member of the board of directors on a two-phase reaction, based on an imported technology. The overseas company had insisted on a certain modus operandi of addition of phases, in a semi-batch reactor, which was contrary to the 'textbook' prescription. I was able to convince the plant personnel, as well as one of the managers of the company, that the correct procedure was the other way round. This suggestion was accepted and the plant gave better quality product in a safer way, with much lower amounts of waste product.

To take another example from this company, in pursuit of much higher capacity, it was diagnosed that the support plate at the bottom of the packed column, attached to the large size reactor, was improperly designed. At a negligible cost of less than Rs 10,000, a large increase in the capacity was realised. At this stage it is appropriate to reflect and state that in retrospect most solutions to problems do look 'trivial'. I have had similar experiences with other overseas companies and I refer to it later in the context of bubble columns (sparged reactors).

Agitated contactors

My early experience was with a textile auxiliary company where I was asked to design a large unit for making a well-known surfactant. To start with, the plant personnel wondered what could possibly be done to improve the quality of this well-known product, made by the company for a number of years. This prompts me to state that no process is ever mature.

There was also the problem of construction material, due to the existence of strongly acidic and basic conditions in the same reactor, and we decided to use, for the first time in the country, polypropylene (PP) backed with fibreglass reinforced plastic (FRP) for a 2m diameter reactor. In those days PP sheets which could be conveniently subjected to FRP strengthening were not available and we had to resort to activation with 'flame'. The discharge of liquid from this reactor was also designed in an innovative way. The key point was high quality mixing where the mild steel turbine impeller, of an improved design, was covered with PP. The quality of this product, with its extremely low acidity, became a hallmark in the industry.

In the '80s we published a state-of-the-art review on mechanically agitated contactors and this led to the generation of many new ideas. One such idea, which proved to be a cost-effective modification of existing mechanically agitated gas-liquid contactors, such as the 'dead-end' hydrogenators, was to employ a 'daughter' impeller close to the liquid interface so that the gas induction is facilitated.

We then showed how gas inducing impellers, which employ a hollow shaft, can be very useful in, say, hydrogenation. My erstwhile collaborators have developed better designs, that have now been adopted. The role of micromixing for fast reactions (even homogeneous) where the reaction and mixing times are comparable has hardly been recognised by industry. We have successfully modified mixer design and improved yields, even in fine chemicals manufacture.

Adiabatic scrubber for HCI gas

An opportunity came in 1966 to design an HCI gas scrubber to give 33 per cent HCI without the use of an expensive graphite heat exchanger. My mass transfer course at undergraduate level came in handy and an adiabatic scrubber, with a calculated amount of air to be introduced, was successfully designed and commissioned. This was the first such unit in India and it made use of FRP. This also demonstrates the prowess of the horizontal transfer of technology!

Sparged reactors

From an early stage, my research work had a strong linkage with equipment-oriented work and bubble columns (sparged reactors), packed columns and plate columns. This grounding in fundamental research, backed up with industrial excursions, provided a rich background for tackling some interesting problems.

A large-sized, multistage, sparged reactor was employed by a renowned company to make an important inorganic chemical where mass transfer of a sparingly soluble gas is accompanied by a slow chemical reaction and the product precipitates out. There was a legacy in using a large number of baffles of a special design and plant personnel considered they had good reasons to adhere to this design almost akin to a passionate attachment. Based on the theory of mass transfer with reaction, I was able to convince them that there was no merit in having so many stages as the backmixing in the liquid phase was not important and we could cut the number of stages drastically, and thereby avoid frequent clogging of the column, resulting in downtime and a progressive reduction in capacity. With the suggested cost-free changeover, the capacity of the plant was increased in a very impressive way and the downtime was indeed drastically reduced. In the same company, modified designs of sparged reactors and packed columns were successfully implemented.

In another instance of a multistage reactor for the production of an organic chemical, where the selectivity of the higher value co-product was important to the economics of the process, a rational design of radial baffles and spacing resulted in a marked improvement. There is no parallel to this design elsewhere. This was based on a PhD thesis of my student who moved to this company and the company made an open acknowledgement of this contribution. The design of baffles and its spacing was based on our work on bubble columns with specific reference to the existence of multiple circulation cells.

The role of backmixing in the gas phase is usually not critical but there are some instances where over 96 per cent conversion is desired. I was confronted with this problem for a large size unit overseas where the difference in the volume of reactors, involving expensive materials of construction, would have been a factor of three to achieve the stated objective. A rational analysis highlighted the real menace of the backmixing in the gas phase and the design was firmed-up without increasing the volume. The proposed new design of radial baffles for handling high concentrations of solids has yet to be tested in the market, but our pilot-scale experiments, which include the use of solid radio-tracers, are supportive of the basic idea. For many air oxidation reactions, where there is no limit on the oxygen content of the outlet gas, and particularly so in the oxidation of inorganic compounds like cuprous chloride and sodium sulphide (black liquor in pulp and paper plants), it is advantageous to adopt the horizontal module. Our fundamental work on such contactors, including the pioneering work on the prediction of the Peclet number in industrial contactors from first principles, which laid the foundation for the above referred vertical sparged reactors, provided a rational basis for the design. We indirectly contributed to this idea being accepted in a large scale petrochemical plant.

Packed columns are extensively employed in industry and usually provide ample scope for getting more out of the existing assets by removing bottlenecks in several ways. In one large size inorganic chemical plant, it was possible for me to show how one tower instead of two could do the job with even better specifications. At first my suggestion was received with cynicism but the plant managers were willing to consider my idea and my persistence paid off. This modification called for a change in the support plate design and column packing, which was a large diameter column (>1 m dia). This prompts me to point out the danger of over-design for gas film controlled packed bed absorbers where such a design can lead to poorer outlet gas specification with respect to the specified solute which may well be noxious and cross statutory limits.

Packed columns
A reputed fertiliser plant asked me to suggest measures to improve CO_2 removal in their plant which employed two towers in a series with different absorbents. It was possible to accomplish the desired objective by improving the liquor circulation rate in the second scrubber. This was based on my knowledge of the effect of the liquid irrigation rate on effective interfacial area.

In another public sector fertiliser factory I was instrumental in implementing stainless steel packing. Initially this was vigorously opposed but when the question of breakage of the packing and the attendant quick erosion in capacity was highlighted the suggestion was implemented with success and the pay-out time was very short.

Let me recall a somewhat hilarious example of a CO_2 bottling plant for aerated drinks, based on an imported design. The terminology adopted by this small unit sounded odd to me but I was able to grasp their problem. This plant was based on burning a fuel containing sulphur, and SO_2 removal, prior to CO_2 absorption, was essential. The liquor being circulated had the right density which the company needed to check regularly. I suspected that the liquor contained a high percentage of potassium sulphate and this was probably responsible for their problems. A quick analysis proved my point. The old liquor was completely discarded and a fresh solution was used: vigilance was kept on the SO_2 removal protocol to be followed. The capacity of the plant, to the surprise of the plant personnel, was more than doubled.

There is a mistaken belief that in columns with random packing, the design of the liquid distributor is not very critical. In an industrial operation, requiring over 35 theoretical stages the specifications of products did not meet the desired levels. There was no reason to suspect the quality of the contemporary packing used. It occurred to me that feed liquid was probably flashing and the liquid distributor design did not recognise this feature. A change in this design led to a marvellous improvement in the specs which were quite tight. Similarly, a small improvement in another unit, which in existing plants can mean a lot, was brought out by reducing the sub-cooling of the reflux.

While on a sabbatical at University of Delaware in 1982, my teaching assistant collaborated with me on absorption of NOx in alkaline liquors project. I had a rather odd conjecture that an increase in temperature may improve the selectivity with respect to the desired product nitrite; nitrate is not welcome. A detailed modelling basically endorsed this idea. A colleague of mine in Bombay pursued this theme vigorously and, excluding modelling pilot plants, data at factory sites was collected. A remarkable improvement in nitrite yield has been realised in existing plants with no additional investment.

Applied thermodynamics
Students generally believed that consulting in this area is unlikely. However, it is well known from examples worldwide how retrograde condensation, retrograde vaporisation, ammonia manufacture, low density polyethylene plants etc., have benefited

immensely from the advice of experts in thermodynamics. The selection of proper solvent for extractive distillation and liquid extraction is now a well-developed subject. Academics have contributed to the concept of supercritical extraction; particularly the use of an entrainer and modification of solubility behaviour has been exploited to solve some difficult separation problems. The role of thermodynamics in processing high pressure natural gas, and in colder climates, formation of hydrates, stand out as outstanding examples.

Our group worked in India on dissociation extraction, a two-phase process which exploits the differences in dissociation constants and distribution coefficients of compounds and where a stoichiometric deficiency of a base or acid is employed to neutralise the more acidic/basic component. A number of difficult separations have been realised: some small scale units have benefited from this strategy as capital investment in the method is minimal. A new strategy was suggested for the recovery of phenols and separation of close-boiling phenols based on the use of calcium hydroxide.

Process innovations

A sound knowledge of organic processes is immensely helpful. Problem-solving often demands a good knowledge of detailed chemistry and engineering aspects. This is all the more so as the impurities being specified in industrial products are approaching vanishing levels and any separation strategy would require a detailed knowledge of products as some impurities might have defied the analytical procedures.

Exploitation of phase transfer catalysis benzyl esters: We were one of the earliest groups to work in this area and we took the 'celebrated' example of benzyl esters based on benzyl chloride reaction with the sodium salt of the desired acid. We were able to show that a cheaper catalyst was more efficacious than that employed. I was not formally invited as a consultant with the first company which made this changeover but they were kind enough to tell us that our idea had worked well.

Triaryl phosphates: We have developed a low temperature two-liquid phase process using a biologically degradable and cheap catalyst based on polyethylene glycol (PEG). This process has been adopted by a small scale unit. However, we were even more delighted when we found a paper from the world renowned company Monsanto that our strategy also worked for thiophosphates where the established method for arylphosphates did not work. It is possible to recover PEG and recycle. This case was also an interesting example of benefits that can accrue from converting a single liquid phase into a two-liquid phase system, where heat removal also becomes delightfully simple.

Role of purge in product specifications: Many plants which were established in the late '60s have expanded considerably and in the meantime the product specifications have become tight and there is competition. A large size unit making a bulk organic chemical faced such a problem where the overall chemistry looked trivial. We had to plough through a fairly elaborate exercise in chemistry which provides clues to generation of impurities albeit at ppm level which gave the undesirable characteristics to the product. When per-pass conversion is not very high, the amount of close-boiling impurities gets accumulated in the recycle stream which constitutes the major part of the 'feed'. A relatively small strategy involving a proper purge rate solved the problem. In the absence of this strategy the plant had to work at a lower capacity with a product which was not as good as that desired by the sales department.

Cationic ion exchange resins as catalyst: The use of heterogenised acidity offers many advantages over the homogeneous catalyst due to avoidance of corrosive conditions, quality product, avoidance of product washing and attendant pollution problems, ease of separation and better selectivity. I have been associated with the successful commercialisation of several products based on alkylation, selective oligomerisation, etc. Some products have been introduced in India and perhaps have few other parallels in the world. Ion exchange resins are quite versatile and more processes are on the anvil for commercialisation.

A novel strategy, based on etherification with isobutylene of phenolic substances, has been developed for the separation of close-boiling substances and this is awaiting commercial exploitation. The general strategy of alkylation-dealkylation for separation of closely boiling aromatics has been developed. This area of work has prompted us to exploit cheap and

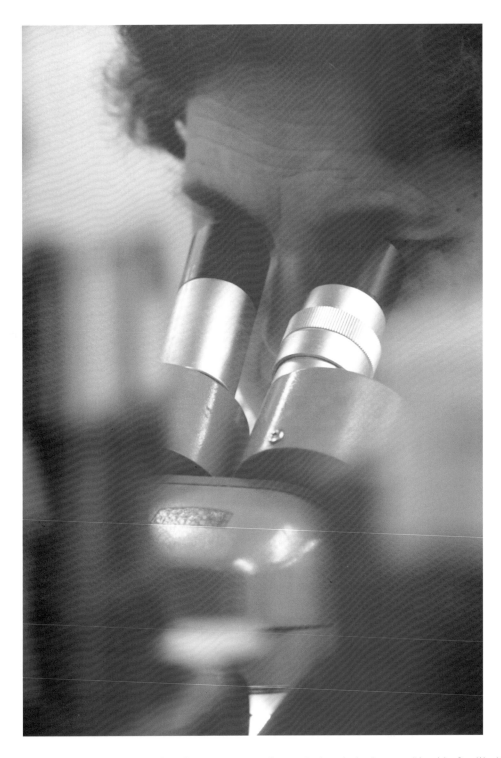

versatile activated clay as a catalyst for alkylation and I am associated with a process which is currently just beginning to be commercialised.

No process stream is a waste and we should treat this stream as feed with a 'negative' cost. There is also a belief that chemical engineers are stewards from cradle to crematorium. It might be more relevant to say that we should be instrumental in closing the cradle to recovery loops. I already had a considerable familiarity with the removal of H_2S from sour gases; this is the most renowned example globally for converting liabilities into assets and over 60 per cent of the world supply of sulphur comes from this source.

My first encounter was through the boardroom of a public sector company, where the manufacture of a specialised aminophenol resulted in a nasty waste stream which was difficult and expensive to treat. This plant was based on imported technology from a well-known company and as far as the Indian company knew, the overseas unit did not have any facility to recover a valuable chemical from the waste stream. I was closely associated with this pioneering project from its very conception.

This project was executed in a period when our effluent discharge regulations were not 'stiff' and there was no statutory pressure to indulge in recovering chemicals. It acted both as a harbinger of other units in India and as a confidence-building exercise. In the same company the treatment of a large volume of effluent from nitroaromatics was based on solvent extraction. This was the first such unit in India with a diameter of about 1 m and although no really saleable product was recovered, it drastically reduced the amount of toxic and refractory components.

Asset, not liability

The waste gases from a phthalic anhydride plant provided an interesting opportunity to convert a liability into an asset. The enactment of air pollution laws would have demanded an expensive incinerator. However, a recovery strategy, based on the simple physico-chemical principle that maleic acid is highly soluble in water and the isomeric fumaric acid is sparingly soluble, provided the basis for the design of an innovative plant where the capital investment was just about equal to that of the incinerator.

The value of the saleable product from this unit is respectable and other units are adopting this strategy. Heterocyclic amines in waste streams are very difficult to treat as these are toxic to microbes. A recovery strategy, based on adsorption on activated carbon, has been developed and this is being adopted for commercial purposes. A similar strategy has been adopted for aromatic sulphonic acids with polymeric adsorbents. In these above cases cheap methanol can be used for regeneration of the adsorbent. Heterocyclic amines have been brought down to levels like a few ppm and in some cases to even 1 ppm. The common strategy for investments in India has been based on the license system and to have indigenous production of items which have hitherto been regularly imported. This strategy is no longer rewarding and new avenues have to be explored. As a

student of the global chemical industry over three decades, I have been able to identify a number of projects for investment with price tags of Rs 10 crores to Rs 200 crores. It may sound odd that academics could be useful in this sector as well. The projects with which I have been associated have been innovative and introduced for the first time in India. I am inclined to believe that the scope will prove more wide-ranging than is currently recognised. In some cases the corporate long-term planning division was created in companies at our behest.

Host institutions

The prestige enjoyed by an institution in industry, where the majority of our students find 'residence', increases when it becomes known that a sizeable number of their faculty members are consultants to a variety of industries. Thus, the credentials of the faculty are accepted and students also feel happy that the subjects they are learning are 'wet', with a good blend of theory and practice. Academic consultants also become very popular as research guides for doctoral theses. Many of my erstwhile PhDs are working in industry and I have had the pleasure of having some doctoral students who gave up lucrative jobs in industry.

An academic institution, which harbours and encourages these 'hands-on' consultants, will attract funds from industry for projects and even outright donations for 'open-ended' research. The UDCT has benefited a great deal from industry's generous contributions.

Speaking personally, I have been able to, in an uncanny way, combine the rigours of organic chemistry and problems associated with chemical engineering, particularly with respect to mixing and separations technology and have been able to solve over the years intricate problems in the pharma, fine chemical, agro-chemical and dyestuff industries. I also dealt with the acute problems associated with crystallisation at the plant level when everything else was fine but the product was not saleable. I was able to do this with the existing equipment and personnel which was more challenging than an *ab initio* solution. The crystallisation problem was solved at no cost to the company, only through knowledge engineering and with the close cooperation of the plant personnel. □

Ashok Jhunjhunwala
TeNet Group
Professor, IIT Madras

Innovation as a way forward

In 1981, I returned to India and joined the faculty at IIT Madras. Madras was the third largest city in the country. I wanted a telephone for my home. I booked the phone and it took me eight years to get it. I wanted to buy a two-wheeler. I was told that it would take four years to get the scooter once I had made the deposit!

In 1984, I wanted to get a PC for my institute. Knowing that it would not be easy to buy one in India, I got some of our alumni to donate it. A PC was purchased in USA and sent to Madras. It took me one year to get it released from customs. To buy a microprocessor chip, costing only Rs 150 required a round trip flight between Madras and Delhi. The fare was equal to four months of my take-home pay.

Many people used to wonder and ask me why I had come back to India.

Now 27 years later, most of the middle class youth will find it difficult to believe what I am saying. This is because India, at least urban India, has changed significantly. Urban India is growing in confidence. Today, we add 7 million telephone lines in a month and are one of the fastest growing telecom markets in the world.

Our tariffs are by far the lowest and affordable by even lower middle classes. People from middle classes can now buy their own two-wheeler and even a four wheeler. The same class can fly all over the country on the no-frills airways. According to a report, *Foresight* of the Economic Intelligence unit of the *Economist* in 2006, India will contribute 12.2 per cent of the world's economic growth from 2006 to 2020 and will generate 142.4 million new jobs. This will be just behind China and USA.

The confidence amongst urban Indians is evident in all walks of life with people excelling in numerous fields. India has made this leap forward using innovations. Innovation is the way forward, as we continue to tackle numerous challenges.

Our knowledge and skills with Information and Communication Technology (ICT) was used very innovatively in the last 30 years. We had skilled and hard working people with us. Instead of allowing them to just leave India and work abroad, we started using the limited number of computers that we had and the meagre connectivity to Europe and USA that we obtained, to do work from India for the West. It was difficult in the beginning. Most Western corporations were very suspicious of what we could deliver from India. They were concerned about the security and the quality. But we did not give up against this initial reluctance.

Soon our efforts paid off and we started delivering world standard work to the western countries. Orders went on multiplying. We used innovative methods to do more outsourced work remotely. Developments in computers and IT technology helped us. Now all kinds of designs could be done on computers and we made use of every opportunity that came our way. Not only did we start getting recognized as the IT services centre of the world, we also went ahead to become the design house for the world. We did not just generate wealth for ourselves; we also created a huge confidence amongst us.

We no longer looked at ourselves as inferior to anyone else in the world. This started impacting all walks of life. As the political process in India started liberalizing and freeing up markets, we began to innovate more. We learned that India has a very large market, but only at the right price point. We innovated to build better products and started providing services to our people at affordable prices. Telecom and airline travel are two examples. But we did much more. We now have the fastest growing wind power company in the world. Five of the twelve most energy efficient cement plants in the world are in India. We have started to become the auto component capital of the world. We are innovating in design and building the most inexpensive car in the world, Tata's Nano. India is on the move.

Going forward

All this, unfortunately, is confined by and large to urban India. Rural India, where 700 million Indians live, is not part of this rapid economic and attitudinal shift. At the same time, our media is flourishing and daily shows the disparities of this 'new India'. Further, our democracy is strong and the 700 million rural voters could vote out a Government which fails to include them in the boom.

Unfortunately, in the post industrial era, there is no viable model in the world for simultaneous rapid development of urban as well as rural areas. But India does not have an option to ignore its rural people. We need to innovate to take rural India along this growth of wealth and confidence. ICT can help. But let us never forget that ICT is a mere tool. It has to be used effectively to fulfill the felt needs of rural India, which are improved access to quality education, quality health care and better livelihoods. Plenty of innovations will be needed to help us achieve these goals.

About 14 million children become eligible for school every year in rural India. But there are very few good quality teachers. While we struggle to rectify this anomaly, ICT can help teach children remotely. It is not an easy task. Just setting up computers and communication in rural areas will hardly help. Delivering quality education to children in villages, where any kind of infrastructure, including electricity is hardly present, and where children get barely enough to eat, will indeed be a challenge. Careful experiments will need to be conducted before scaling up such projects.

This is also true of health care. Doctors hardly practice in Rural India. ICT has to be used to strengthen delivery of quality health care services by local health practitioners. Some remote diagnostics will be possible, but it has to be within the means and grasp of villagers.

Again careful experiments rather than hype creation are required.

Agriculture in India has stagnated over the last 20 years. Once again, ICT can become an important tool to enable the development of intensive agriculture. But ground realities show that making an impact in Indian agriculture is not simple. It requires a number of experiments and plenty of technological innovations.

In the previous two centuries poverty was combated by migration of people from poor regions to those places with opportunities. In the late 20th century, ICT and inexpensive transportation opened up another possibility. Work from the developed regions could be transferred to the regions where the incomes were lower. Thus, manufacturing shifted from the West to the East. Later services started getting delivered using ICT and shifted to countries like India. Many countries used this work migration to initially create some wealth, but soon innovated to become developed nations. Countries like Japan, Korea, Taiwan and China did this in the last century, while one can see India doing this at the turn of this new century.

Rural BPO

Can the same process be used to strengthen rural India? Can work be migrated from urban India to rural India? There is no reason to think that with access to computers and communications, young rural Indians cannot provide ICT-based services to urban India and to the rest of the world. A rural BPO in each village, employing 20 to 30 people, would begin the process of transformation. Yes, there will be initial reluctance.

Questions will rise such as—can the people in villages deliver? Is the infrastructure adequate? What about quality and security? Can we not get work done in more developed towns? The same questions were raised in the West before services migrated to India. We just need to repeat this process again. Similarly, ICT can be used to transfer manufacturing to rural India; especially jobs that do not require heavy machinery and large amount of electricity and depend more on human skill and labour. Distributed outsourced production can thus become a reality. If a significant per cent of the raw material for such manufacturing also comes from rural areas, there will be an even stronger case for manufacturing in rural India. Agro-industry is therefore the most obvious candidate for this.

But where will this development lead to? Getting rural India to catch up with urban India is a mere beginning. The task ahead is even more difficult. Today a country like India consumes less than one 20th of per capita resources as compared to the West (as per International Energy Agency statistics division, India consumed 512.4 kg of oil equivalent of energy per person as opposed to 7794 kg of oil equivalent per person in USA in 2003). But urban India consumes far greater per capita resource as compared to rural India. In other words, urbanization significantly enhances per capita resource consumption.

The post industrial development paradigm has implied far larger per capita resource consumption as compared to that in the pre-industrial era. So far only a small fraction of the population in the world had such high consumption. Even then, there are enough warnings that Nature is retaliating as such larger consumption is making our eco-system unsustainable. What would happen if 1.4 billion people of China and 1.1 billion people of India become a part of this development and their per capita consumption starts matching that of the West?

The answer is obvious. We just cannot go there. At the same time, people in India and China cannot be asked to slow down their efforts to emerge out of poverty and deprivation. Hence this is the time to innovate; one needs to find viable alternative solutions. The biggest innovation today would be to redefine development, which would imply having a 'better life', with much less resource consumption. The knowledge economy of tomorrow has to leave behind the philosophy of the industrial revolution and definition of progress which associates development with higher consumption.

Higher consumption does not necessarily imply a better life. If education, health care, livelihood opportunities, and a minimum infrastructure are provided in rural India, quality of life there will improve. Moving people from rural India to urban India is therefore not an answer. Our way of living and way of working may have to be rethought. Innovation alone can take us forward. □

Kiran Karnik
Former President, NASSCOM

Incredibly innovative India!

The last few years have seen a rapid acceleration in the process of globalization. In the arena of culture and ideas, which began some time ago, triggered by the new information and communication technologies, particularly satellite broadcasting. In India, we have seen this process being telescoped in time, as we went from one—largely controlled—TV channel to dozens and now, hundreds, including a whole host of international channels.

In the sphere of economics, the lowering of tariff barriers has been both the cause and result of globalization. Goods now move around the world almost as freely as they did some centuries ago, and certainly far more easily than at anytime in living memory. In the case of services, the combination of new technologies and globalization has led to unprecedented levels of international trade. As a result of such globalization, there is intense and growing competition. This means that each company and each country has to find its competitive advantage, its niche or unique selling proposition (USP). It is in this context that I see innovation as India's potential USP.

In today's global market place, various products and services from India enjoy different advantages. If we look for a sector in which global competition is the most intense—because the barriers are minimal—it is probably IT software and services. It is the sector with zero to minimal tariffs in all major countries, and while there are some non-tariff barriers—particularly with regard to movement of people—these are comparatively low. In this highly competitive sector India has established itself most strongly and been most successful: not only is this sector India's top exporter, but India is the destination of more IT-BPO off-shoring than all other countries put together. It is, therefore, a good case study to look at India's competitive advantage and see if it is specific to this industry or whether there are aspects that are more broadly applicable.

The abundant availability of English-speaking computer programmers gave India a good start in the global IT business. Through the 1990s, as the technology boom in the West created an ever-growing demand for talent, young Indians made just the right fit. The next stage was wage arbitrage, with computer programmers in India costing a fraction of what they did in the West. Familiar with business needs, thanks to the earlier stage, Indian companies were able to create an 'on-site and off-shore' model, with employees located in customer-premises ('on-site') and in India ('off-shore'). As confidence grew on both sides, the ratio changed and more people worked off-shore (in India), resulting in lower costs for the customer and higher profits for the Indian vendor. One needs to acknowledge this as an important innovation, one that was truly 'game-changing' and created a new business model. This innovation has built well on India's inherent cost-plus-skill advantage and has given India a sustainable competitive advantage.

Beyond quantity and costs, the Indian IT industry soon developed another USP: quality. Meeting quality standards requires a strong adherence to process and, therefore, great discipline. To successfully inculcate this in Indians is quite an

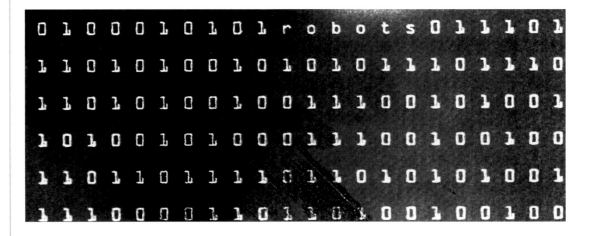

achievement, and is itself an innovation! However, the bigger innovation—if it may be called that—was in the very concept: to adopt an international and credible quality standard and to get Indian companies to meet it. As it turned out, this was overwhelmingly successful, with half the highest quality certifications being from India.

Another plus

In the context of the times, another innovation was the creation of an industry body (NASSCOM) with the goal of making India the preferred source for IT software and services, irrespective of whether these were provided by Indian companies or MNCs. In the days of protectionism, when industry associations were expected to promote domestic companies and try to keep out the MNCs (the nascent/infant industry argument for high tariff barriers), here was an association which actually fought for bringing tariffs on software to zero. Clearly, NASSCOM and the industry understood that if MNCs set up IT operations in India, it will enhance the credibility of India as a source for IT products and services, and that this would ultimately help Indian companies. The success of this strategy is evident today: not only have Indian IT companies survived, but they have grown into huge behemoths and themselves become MNCs.

India's value proposition in IT is now extremely strong: no country can match its triple advantage of delivering cheaper, better and quicker. However, over the next few years, there may well be some locations that begin to match India on one or possibly more of these dimensions. Therefore, to stay ahead, India must develop other comparative advantages, preferably those that its immediate competitors cannot match.

One can think of facets like management, governance, data security and intellectual property rights, as possible India advantages. However, these can and almost certainly will be emulated. What few countries can match is India's potential for innovation.

In the world of tomorrow, it is innovation that is going to be the true differentiator and value creator. As products and services get ever more commoditised, value-addition is going to increasingly depend upon innovative new ideas. Creativity and innovation flower best in situations where conformity is not a norm. In India, deviating from any set rules is the norm! The visible manifestation of this is the indiscipline on the roads, the absence of queues, and the sense of disorganisation and lack of order. The diversity of India is a big factor in creativity and innovation. It is this diversity which gets us used to people wearing different clothes, talking a different language and eating different food. No visitor from Britain fails to notice the houses in our cities—each flaunting a different architecture, design and colour! With this background, thinking different thoughts is not only permitted, but actually encouraged. Clearly, this is in sharp contrast to some countries where things are far more homogenous and even thinking has been strait-jacketed.

The other factor that spurs creativity and innovation is adversity. It is, unfortunately, abundantly available in India. The very many innovations that this gives rise to are visible even in day-to-day living. Innovation is not only about creating something new; equally, it is about finding a different use for existing products. Therefore, converting an unused water-supply pipe into a home, using a washing machine to churn butter milk or a TV set as a fluorescent light: these are as much innovations as is a wind-up radio or a new software package.

With an over-supply of adversity and a rainbow-range of diversity—a combination that is rare to non-existent elsewhere—India is uniquely positioned as a potential hot-bed of creativity. However, converting potential into realization, ideas into specific products or services, creativity into cash requires a conducive eco-system. It is the lack of such a supportive ambience that has, so far, inhibited the translation of inherent capabilities into marketable goods and services. There are many gaps in the overall system, and without closing these, India will never achieve what it is capable of doing.

Funding

One major deficiency has been in the availability of funding. While there is finance available—quite easily, especially in the last few years—for scaling up a successful business venture, and even for going from proof-of-concept to production, there is almost no money for early-stage funding. Backing a vague, somewhat poorly-defined idea is not easy, especially if the originator is young and has little or no business experience. Yet, this is the crucial stage, and support here determines the size of the funnel for future ideas. This 'seed' or 'angel' investment does not take too much money, but is obviously high-risk with very high failure rates.

Fortunately, over the last decade or so, India has witnessed a rapid growth in techno-entrepreneurs who build their business on innovation. Many of the more experienced entrepreneurs willingly volunteer to act as mentors for young starters. An increasing number of those who provide early-stage funding also make available mentoring and networking opportunities. There is, for example, the Indian Angel Network, comprising a group of highly-experienced entrepreneurs, mainly from the IT area. They provide seed-capital and mentoring.

NASSCOM, the association of Indian IT software and services companies, has been providing mentoring through volunteers and also networking opportunities.

It also recognizes innovative companies through high-profile awards which serve to showcase these companies and their innovations. The run-up to the awards is a series of regional events where a large number of companies get a chance to present their innovation and the jury not only short-lists the most promising innovations for the awards, but also provides feedback to all presenters. The purpose is to stimulate and encourage innovation on an extensive basis. NASSCOM, in association with ICICI, is also promoting an Innovation Fund, for providing seed-capital to innovative start-up companies in the technology sector. The government too has a number of programmes for promoting innovation and for funding. These and other institutions—by the private sector, industry associations and the government—are beginning to make an impact.

India's innovation capabilities find an expression in many sectors including manufacturing, biotechnology and at the level of grassroots. A dramatic recent example is the Tata Nano, which—through innovations in design, engineering and manufacturing—will create the world's first really low-cost, mass-produced car.

India will without doubt soon become a major hub for innovation. Those looking at investing in India need to recognize that the real benefit of India's talent pool is not just the combination of scalability, high-level skills and comparatively low-cost, but its innovative capabilities. As the supporting eco-system develops, these capabilities will increasingly see fruition, making India a premier world centre for innovation. The R&D managers the world over will say: Incredible India! ☐

Arun Maira
Chairman
Boston Consulting Group, India

Innovations for inclusion & competitive advantage

India is faced with a dilemma. Should it press the accelerator harder for more growth in the present pattern, and hope that the benefits will trickle down to the masses before the murmurings of inequity amplify into political crises and stall the process of economic reforms? Or can it find another model of development that combines rapid economic growth with rapid inclusion of all sections in its benefits?

Even as economists, politicians and policy-makers grapple with the need to find an innovative solution for India's development, corporate leaders have to steer their companies through the dilemmas they face today. There is much potential demand to be tapped, but how? Vast numbers are hungry for work, but not many of those meet the corporates' requirements.

The Indian economy is amongst the fastest growing in the world. Indian companies are emerging as global competitors across several sectors. They give the highest returns to investors internationally. But this rapid growth is accompanied by worrying concerns about the uneven pace at which the benefits of growth are reaching various sections of society.

There are fears that Indian companies may find it difficult to maintain the rapid growth which investors have come to expect. The companies are running out of the very resource that has fuelled their growth thus far—skilled people at low costs. Salary increases in India, the highest in the world, are putting pressure on business margins. Even though the economy is growing at over eight per cent per annum and corporations say people are difficult to find, ironically unemployment is reported to be increasing!

To keep growing, Indian companies must reach out to segments of the market at the 'Bottom of the Pyramid' and these are more difficult to reach and not profitable to serve with conventional business models. Clearly, innovative solutions are required. Best practices based on conventional ideas will not do.

As Einstein said, the dilemmas one faces cannot be resolved with the same type of thinking (and solutions) that led to those dilemmas. The Boston Consulting Group is examining the solutions that business leaders in India are looking for and discovering from within these dilemmas. It is working with companies to develop new solutions, and with organizations to research the principles and processes of innovations. BCG is working alongside CII to develop the innovation capabilities of Indian manufacturing companies and with Nasscom for IT and ITES companies. With other partners, it is researching and documenting innovations across the country. We recognize that India, as well as companies in India can win only through inclusion.

Our research has highlighted new models that create sustainable competitive advantage. Several companies are pushing the frontiers into new markets and into new sources of critical inputs for competitive advantage. Their pioneering approaches to business strategy and enterprise configuration provide valuable insights.

In the banking and financial services, the competition for affluent customers is intense, while the customers at the lower end of the spectrum remain unserved or highly underserved. This is because the cost of serving this large segment of population is very high under the traditional business model that banks follow, making it unprofitable to develop. ICICI Bank recognized the huge untapped potential of rural India and realized the need for a new business model to derive profitability out of rural sector business. Several hybrid channels were developed for retail customers, e.g. district cluster branches, mandi branches, crop cluster branches, credit franchisees etc. Similarly, for small business customers, specific industry partnerships were created, and corporate linked channel partners were targeted. Partnerships were developed with more than 100 micro-finance companies to provide micro loans.

ICICI Bank leveraged technology extensively to reduce the cost of doing business in rural areas. It incubated and partnered with a technology company FINO (Financial Information Network and Operations Ltd.) to develop a standardized and shared infrastructure to link clients and financial services providers. Offline handheld equipment was provided by FINO to all the micro-finance providers like MFIs, NBFCs etc. with which ICICI Bank tied up. Data from these devices gets transferred through FINO's platform to the ICICI Bank system periodically. This enables ICICI Bank to collect more extensive data on its clients in a cost effective manner. ICICI Bank is also experimenting with biometric cards to provide unique identification of customers.

New model

Developing a new model of working extensively with partners and leveraging technology to access customers, ICICI Bank has become the largest rural and micro loans provider in India. By innovating their business model, the bank and its partners have opened up a large market for themselves. They have also provided access to financial services with concomitant social and economic benefits for a large section of the population.

The business process outsourcing (BPO) companies in India depend on low-cost Indian manpower. As salary levels increase in India and as attrition rates become higher, the competitive advantage as well as the margins of companies are eroded. Genpact is a prime example of a company at the forefront of tapping into non-traditional pools of manpower to resolve this problem. Applying best practices from supply chain management and vendor development to the human resources domain, it has redefined the paradigm of people recruitment and development. By finding new sources of personnel, extending its recruitment

process, and adjusting its training and development systems, it has created a very effective 'people system' for itself. It has launched multiple initiatives to expand its recruitment pools. It hires from Tier-2 and Tier-3 towns which were traditionally considered as not having the requisite talent pools.

Genpact hires over 300 people a month in Jaipur. Genpact also hires students who could not complete college, retired people and housewives. It has begun applying the retail sourcing model to hiring by opening storefronts for recruiting—job stores where candidates can walk-in to apply for jobs and get offers within four to six hours. Genpact has also invested heavily in resources for training and grooming raw talent. The new talent pools are providing Genpact with resources at competitive costs while providing employment to people who were not considered 'employable' earlier.

The Byrraju Foundation has gone a step further and tapped into the rural areas for building a BPO business. Combining social services with a business agenda, the Foundation has opened call-centres in villages in Andhra Pradesh. Thus it has created incomes at the Bottom of the Pyramid and also created a competitive advantage in the BPO business by tapping into lower cost (and lower attrition) manpower resources.

Kegg Farms

The Kegg Farms are a remarkable story of business innovation in India. They are the topic of a case study at the Harvard Business School. Faced with intense competition from larger companies and MNCs in 1992, when trade restrictions were lifted, Kegg Farms decided to create a unique India-specific poultry breed and business. Focussing its R&D on the rural market, it developed a hardy variety of the bird called 'Kuroilers' that could be raised in rural households rather than in poultry farms. This is a great example of scientific innovation being driven down to the grassroots level to derive economic as well as social benefits. Scientific innovation was combined with the evolution of a business model that included NGOs and rural households in a new supply and distribution network. Kegg Farms now services over 700,000 village households in 11 states, supplying 17 million Kuroilers chickens. Kegg Farms has developed a competitive business leveraging rural households and skills and it is providing an additional source of livelihood to hundreds of thousands of rural households.

Five lessons

Our research from dozens of emerging examples of successful innovations in business practices reveals five critical success factors.

1. Partnerships are necessary. The 'last mile' is very difficult and costly to traverse alone. Potential customers are widely scattered in India's rural markets. Also, they do not have sufficient income to buy in larger quantities— they live hand-to-mouth and must therefore buy and consume on almost a daily basis. The cost of reaching out is also high on the resource side: it is easier to recruit at campuses where the cream of Indian youth is concentrated, rather than reaching into less well known schools and smaller towns. We find that companies are overcoming the problems of last mile cost and reach by partnering with others—other companies, local governments, NGOs—to develop new platforms and share the costs and benefits.

This is not easy. Often the potential partners have no experience of working with one another, and must develop trust. New enterprise models and governance frameworks are required.

2. Innovative applications of technologies often provide the breakthroughs—as in ICICI's rural financial services network, and as in the Kegg Farms Kuroiler bird that was developed to meet the specific requirements of villages.

3. Fresh thinking and systemic solutions are required, as in Genpact's reframing of its 'people supply chain'. Such solutions cannot be found by any one function in a business organization; they require collaboration amongst many functions to make appropriate changes within their operations to make the new solution work. Hence, we find that the

CEO's sponsorship and involvement with the innovations is essential—e.g. Mr Y C Deveshwar's passion for the ITC e-choupal initiative, Mr K V Kamath's push for ICICI's rural thrust, Mr Pramod Bhasin's personal involvement with Genpact's search for new resources, and Mr Vinod Kapur's unflinching commitment to his company's rural poultry initiative.

4. Innovation is the key. New products and new services are required. And invariably, new enterprise models seem to be necessary too. Merely becoming more efficient at old solutions and working within old organizational constructs cannot provide the needed breakthroughs.

5. Finally, a willingness to think beyond constraints, experiment with ideas, drive towards action and learn from experience are the keys to innovation. Therefore, the creation of a culture of innovation, and an understanding of how organizations learn new ideas—not merely in labs but also in action, become very important requirements for success.

Agent of good

Through innovative solutions, our business pioneers expand benefits to the less served sections of society while seeking sustainable competitive advantage for their businesses. They believe the purpose of a business cannot be only short-term returns to investors. No matter how hard analysts and stock markets drive them to focus on quarterly results, these leaders also keep an eye on the big picture and on the future. This way, they shape strategies that will avoid risks and create value. As our conversations with many of these leaders showed, their compassion for the less privileged is not merely a matter of good business, but also a matter of the heart. □

Sunil Mittal
President, CII & CMD
Bharti Enterprises

Innovative approach to business

The story of my enterprise says it all: the story of India's recent growth and the spectacular spurt of enterprise in this country.

The past few years have also witnessed outstanding results of innovations in business models, management and technology development. I shall begin from 1976 when I took my first tiny step, looking at some of the successes in my hometown in Ludhiana and in the rest of the country. The new entrepreneurs interested me. I started with a capital of less than Rs 75,000, a princely sum for a student coming out of college, an amount I borrowed from my father. From 1976 to 1981, the economic environment was grim for entrepreneurs. We lived with complex import and export policies and a very difficult industrial licensing regime. Very few people could get industrial licenses, and licenses were required for manufacturing anything, from a pin to a car, and these generally went to people who found favour with the Government. There was no transparency in the system of getting licenses. The entrepreneurs had to look out for small openings in various Government policies. You could turn lucky every now and then by finding a gap and then moving a little faster.

India was taking just incremental steps. Take my own example. Our company began by importing portable generators from Suzuki Motor Company of Japan. These were needed in the electricity-starved nation and these were a hit from 1981 to 1984. I made a lot of money for myself and, more importantly, set up a large distribution system across the country. In 1984, in one fell sweep, the Government of India decided to ban the import of generators. The reason was simple. Two business houses managed to get licenses to manufacture generators, and they asked the Government to ban generator imports. Pleading and lobbying by a young entrepreneur against this move made no difference. So, overnight our business disappeared. These were the times when entrepreneurs were at the mercy of Government policy, and you always had to be prepared, sitting in your hot seat, to plunge into something else as soon as the Government hit you with a change in policy.

The Government was a facilitator, but at another level, the bureaucracy in some parts of the Government, the old forces, impeded economic growth. And there was another factor inhibiting the Indian entrepreneurs. These were the established business houses. Most of the official policies were being shaped by the large corporate entities in the country.

Mahatma Gandhi once said "First they ignore you, then they laugh at you, then they fight you, and then they lose." I kept this in mind as these large Indian titans were trying to squeeze out the small entrepreneurs. The phase (1984–95) when we were being ignored by all these people was good for us because you need to be ignored when you are building yourself. If you come under the spotlight at that point in time, you are likely to be pushed out of business.

We launched our mobile telephone services in Delhi. Some large business houses laughed at Bharti. Here was an entrepreneur who was trying to build a telecom company to provide services which required, as they always said, deep pockets. They said this business was not for the small entrepreneurs. The Tatas, Thapars, Modis and other large companies had also bid for mobile licenses and had secured some. The environment for us and two or three others became rather difficult. But I took inspiration from Gandhi's words that "a small body of determined spirits fired by an unquenchable faith in their mission can alter the course of history." That's what he did. And if he could do it for a nation, we could do it for a company. We could do it in a sector. And that's what we did.

We assembled a world-class team during the period when we were being laughed at; we brought in very large investors from outside India. One of these investors, Warburg-Pincus, made one of its biggest investments in India. And we started India's new telecom story. There was no telecom infrastructure to rely upon. An entrepreneur had to build the basics—the fiber optic cables, the satellite nodes, and thousands of towers across the country—under his own steam. There was nothing that was available from the existing operator. In fact, we were trying to fight the state monopoly in the telecom business.

Reforms

By 1996, when Prime Minister Narasimha Rao, who had pushed in huge reforms, lost the elections, Bharti and others of the new class of entrepreneurs had established themselves on the Indian map. Notable among these were Jet Airways and Zee TV, a media house. Then you had companies which had come up in the IT space, such as Infosys, Wipro and Satyam. All these companies were taking strong shape on the Indian economic map. In fact, when Narasimha Rao lost the elections, most of these companies had become fairly dominant in the marketplace. Atal Bihari Vajpayee became the Prime Minister and his commitment to economic reforms was good news for the business community.

Further moves toward opening up the telecom, IT, aviation and other sectors raised the annual economic growth rate to about six per cent. But this was also the period which saw the fiercest commercial battles. In 1999, the Government of India introduced a new telecom policy which allowed more competition in the marketplace and more players to come in, and this to my mind was the defining phase for most of our growth in those early years. This was the time to break free and move up on the curve and on to the grandstand of the Indian economy. This was also the time when many had to lose out because of the free and open competition. Out of the 25 telecom operators, only three

survived. Some 22 sold out, a few of them even collapsed, and some of them got merged among themselves to form bigger players in the marketplace.

This was also the time when we saw both the Government entities and some of the large private operators come in heavily to muscle out the new entrepreneurial initiatives. And although Bharti had become reasonably big, it had not yet crossed to the point of becoming a permanent, sustainable business player in the market. We saw during this period some intense battles in the telecom space.

That as a result of these battles, one of the finest business models in telecom emerged, is another story. Indian tariffs dropped dramatically. Today, Indian telecom has by far the lowest tariffs that have been witnessed anywhere in the world. Despite these low tariffs the sector is still profitable. That is what is bringing companies like Vodafone to India to come and study this model. This has happened because we had to reinvent ourselves and because of the huge battles that the sector witnessed in those years. New enterprises could not be extinguished. We had to do something very quickly and something which was never done in the telecom industry. We had to build a model which could sustain one-tenth of the normal tariff.

Outsourcing

How did the Indian entrepreneurs do it? How did Bharti do it? We made some dramatic changes in the industry. For the first time in the history of the telecom industry, we did some major outsourcing deals. We put the entire IT side of Bharti in the hands of IBM, right from the desktop and laptop on my desk to the most complex piece of IT, they were all given out to IBM in one single deal, a $750 million contract over a period of eight years. We gave our networks, which were built by Ericsson and Nokia, back to them to manage. More importantly, we told them we would not pay for the boxes, we would only pay for the traffic that came out of these networks.

It was a most unique and unusual model. Some experts laughed at us. How can you put your lifeline into the hands of vendors, and vendors like IBM, Ericsson and Nokia? We told them this is not our life. Out life is our customers. Our life is how to get and retain the customers. Technology for a telecom company is just an enabler. Technology is never owned by a telecom company. The fact is, not many telecom companies believe this particular point even today. They believe that telecom is all about technology. Technologies have changed, and those who have not focused on the customer and focused purely on the business model, have actually gone away. Take the case of AT&T. We all know where AT&T is today, it exists only in the business segment. On the other hand, companies like Vodafone, which were focusing on customers, have progressed and built a company worth $200 billion.

We were very clear that technology was not something we needed to focus on. Technology is something we buy to sell to the customers, and technology is something which Ericsson, Nokia and IBM develop for a living, so let's give it to them because they know it best. The last four years have seen dramatic improvements in the business model insofar as Bharti is concerned. During one visit to Delhi, Arun Sarin mentioned at a press conference that they had come to Bharti to learn this new business model. So we believe that we learned a lot during those years of big battles and managed to establish a sustainable business model.

India's agenda

The path forward for us is clear and determined. India's agenda is clear. New areas of growth have opened up in the field of innovation and R&D. Global corporations, from Intel to Cisco to IBM, are engaging with India by setting up innovation centres and R&D laboratories for getting high-quality results at a very low cost. Skilled manpower is plentiful in India. This is another area where India is going to take pole position.

In the services field, the creative and entertainment sector is becoming important. Most of the new animation films that Americans see are now developed in India. India lost the manufacturing space to China. Having said that, I believe all is not lost. There are pieces of manufacturing which could still be with India. The automobiles sector, especially auto components, is developing very well. Ford Motor Company and several Japanese companies have set up shop in India, and they are helping us develop a very strong components manufacturing base.

We manufacture a lot of steel. We manufacture a lot of cement to meet domestic needs. Most of the essential manufacturing pieces are in place, but as yet there is no dramatic movement in the manufacturing sector which can propel us to the next level. There is

nothing major in electronics components manufacturing in India.

Biotechnology is another area where India is making moves but it is a work in progress. It is early days. India remains very hopeful of progress in biotechnology.

Agriculture is going to be the biggest growth area. It is an area which is getting our attention. With our partners, Sir Evelyn and Lady Lynn Rothschild, we plan to develop farmlands. Here again the model is going to be unique. I am reliving the early days in telecom when we did pioneering activity. The agriculture business too can transform India and more importantly, transform rural India leading to inclusive growth.

Thankfully, India today is feeding its billion people. It even exports some grain. Wheat, rice and major cash crops are in abundance now. We have had a Green Revolution. As you know, we add about 62,000 babies every day, and that's about 20 million people a year, but we still have surplus food grain stocks. When we had half this population, we were living ship-to-mouth.

However some questions demand answers. Are we using our farms, farmlands and our farmers to the fullest potential? The answer is no. We need to move the cropping pattern in India from foodgrains to crops of high value. India is positioned very well to feed the world. India can today use its advantages such as low-cost labour and plentiful sunshine to grow vegetables and fruits to sell to the world. The vision that we and the Rothschilds have for India is to link Indian fields to consumers of the world. Fast delivery of the produce poses a big challenge but it is a challenge that one can rise to.

If we can surpass the 10 per cent growth rate and stay on course for 10 years, India will change for ever. This could happen if Indian entrepreneurs take serious initiatives and put in serious capital to develop the markets.

The growth story of India is enduring. Why do I feel this growth is sustainable? The sheer size of the Indian market. There are 630 million working people in the country. By 2016, this number will move up to 830 million. Amongst the BRIC countries (Brazil, Russia, India and China), India has the highest percentage of people in the working class. With half of its population below 25 years of age, India will continue to attract global corporations who chase human resources. The Western world is aging and it will have to depend on Indian workers and professionals. □

Surinder Kapur
Chairman, CII Mission for
Manufacturing Innovation & CMD
Sona Koyo Steering Systems Ltd.

The next leap forward

India has achieved amazing growth in the last 10–15 years. The manufacturing sector has recorded over 9 per cent growth rate. The growth has been fuelled both by the manufacturing and the service sector. Manufacturing now accounts for almost 70 per cent of India's export. Today, India boasts of 18 Deming awarded companies from JUSE (Union of Japanese Scientists and Engineers), 123 TPM awarded companies from Japan Institute of Plant Maintenance and of having more than 22,000 ISO certified companies. In the auto components industry, India is ranked number one on quality of products supplied, ahead of China and Thailand. Multinational companies have begun to see the benefits of sourcing from India. GM and Caterpillar source radiator caps from Sundram Fasteners—the company that has won GM's best-supplier award for three years. GM sources light equipment from Lumax. Mitsubishi of Japan sources front-axle beams from Bharat Forge, and Federal Mogul of the US sources components from India through a tie-up with the Anand group. These achievements are a reflection of the increasing quality consciousness within India Inc., coupled with its cost arbitrage advantage.

But can this lead to sustainable growth and help create the many more jobs that the manufacturing sector is expected to deliver? No. To take India to the next leap in the manufacturing revolution, our companies need to look beyond the cost arbitrage advantage and attempt to understand the latent demands of the market. They need to be able to design the products quickly that would meet this latent need. This requires an ability to innovate, to stay a step ahead of competition and to expand our markets. Talking of TCS's IT-enabled services; S Ramadorai of Tata Consultancy Services (TCS), India's leading CEO, had once said: "Cost helped us get a foot in the door, quality opened it a little bit more, and now we need innovation to open it all the way."

While contract manufacturing currently provides some growth opportunity, India needs to reposition itself from being a low-cost manufacturer and a service provider to a 'creative product developer' and an 'innovator'. Small steps in this direction have already been taken by various companies at the individual level. As a result, a list of familiar names in US such as Bell Labs, Cognizant Technologies, Enercon, Exxon, GE Industrial Systems, GE Medical Systems, IBM, Intel, Lucent, Microsoft, Motorola, National Instruments, Oracle, SeaGate, Texas Instruments, and Xytel, are operating R&D centres in India. But a culture of innovation needs to spread across the country to make it India's engine of growth in the future.

The CII Mission for Innovation in Manufacturing set up in 2006, is a contribution to this effort to make India an innovation oriented country. The mission's objective is to serve as a facilitator to help 100 Indian companies develop as leaders in innovation and product development over the next three years. More than 30 companies are already following the roadmap laid down by the Mission for Innovation.

Although this target might not seem very ambitious, CII believes that these leader companies can create a much-needed ripple effect throughout the country. To help promote the concept of innovation and its associated processes among Indian manufacturers, CII is developing institutional co-operation with global authorities on innovation processes, such as Deming Prize winner Prof. Shoji Shiba, and Prof. Soumitra

Dutta, Roland Berger Chair, INSEAD. In this direction, CII has already launched the Visionary Leaders for Manufacturing Programme, focused on creating a critical mass of 200 to 250 Visionary Leaders.

Innovation is indeed appropriate to the next phase in the country's development. Just as CII launched the quality movement two decades back, and trained manufacturers in the 1960s in the process control techniques associated with Edwards Deming that had led Japanese manufacturers to such great heights, it has now turned to train people to think as visionaries. CII led the Quality Movement through the unique 'Cluster' concept, making India the first country in the world to adopt clustering for learning quality concepts.

Learning community

Achieving breakthrough innovation is certainly the next step for India's manufacturing industry. In 2004, CII established a new cluster under the guidance of Prof. Shoji Shiba, called the Learning Community. Prof. Shiba came every three months to spend three weeks working with the members of this Community. The four participants of the first Learning Community adopted the Prof. Shiba's 'Swim with the Fish' approach for creating an ambidextrous organization and an organizational architecture in which ideas are not killed. They achieved very exciting results.

As a result of their innovation experiences, the four companies expanded, and five more joined up to work with Prof. Shiba through the Learning Community. To convert innovation into a nationwide movement, this Learning Community has now been extended to a national level through the Visionary Leaders for Manufacturing Programme, being personally led by Prof Shoji Shiba. Some 48 leaders from 22 manufacturing companies are currently attending this programme.

While India is in a great situation, demographically poised to become the world's youngest nation over the next decade, it needs to accommodate between 8 to 10 million new job seekers every year. Moreover, India's manufacturing and innovation strategy, geared of necessity to the goal of employment generation, faces a number of challenges. At the same time that India expands production capacity, both through foreign direct investment and domestic companies enlarging their manufacturing base, it is also saddled with archaic labour laws that cannot be

changed overnight. These labor laws, pending reform, might prove an obstacle to co-operation with institutions at the international level.

For this reason, the formation of the National Manufacturing Competitiveness Council and its development of a strategy for increasing manufacturing's share of GDP to 25 per cent from the current 17 per cent are very important steps. The Prime Minister heads a mechanism for monitoring and measuring performance of the NMCC. This is significant not only in demonstrating high-level commitment but also in making it certain that, in cases where an intervention by the Prime Minister's office is required, it would cut across the ministerial bureaucracy.

Because India needs to create demand through cost competitiveness and to achieve world-class performance through innovation, both the national and the state governments have an important role to play: making changes that support the environment required. The manufacturing culture which is at the core of this, will certainly come about with the programmes that we have put together and the strategies that the National Manufacturing Competitiveness Council has developed.

CII is contributing to this endeavour by running an awareness campaign through seminars, workshops and events with international innovation experts and Indian practitioners. Indian companies need training in the tools and techniques of innovation, since innovation 'doesn't just happen.' CII's Mission for Innovation is working with companies to help them learn the tools and techniques for innovation. A number of skill-building tools are employed in training the companies: Christensen's Disruptive Technologies, concept engineering, TRIZ, the Strategy Canvas as put forward in Blue Ocean Strategy, Whitney's technique for creating concepts, and breakthrough management techniques as developed by Prof. Shoji Shiba.

CII plans to continue forming high-tech clusters, in view of their effectiveness to date, and to bundle its programmes to work systematically as part of a comprehensive approach. The CII programmes give specific attention to the needs of the Small and Medium Enterprises (SMEs), which constitute the real base of manufacturing.

Periodic innovation learning missions for the SMEs are organized by CII to enable them to learn from the experiences of others. A programme focused on creating a critical mass of visionary small and medium enterprises is aimed at imparting skills to them in tools and techniques to help them imbibe innovation in their culture.

Aiming towards building a culture of innovation, CII works with companies, both small and large. And, in this endeavour it is partnering with the government and the academia. CII is working with all stakeholders to pave the way for India becoming a leader in Innovation. □

VLFM Programme

The Visionary Leaders for Manufacturing Programme is a path breaking programme launched by CII aimed at creating a critical mass of Visionary Leaders for India's manufacturing sector. For the first time Government (NMCC), industry (CII) and academia (IITK, IITM and IIMC) have come together to transform India's manufacturing sector. The Programme has also received strong support from the Government of Japan (JICA). It has been recognised by the Prime Minsiter of India as a programme that will contribute to the national level skill-building efforts of the Government.

S S Mehta
Director General
Confederation of Indian Industry

An innovation-centric strategy for growth

The march of civilization since the advent of history has been the effort of mankind to embrace innovation in the context of new challenges. These new challenges are unique to every era, requiring innovative solutions. In the current context, India's unique challenges include:

- Catering to the needs of a mass of population at the Bottom of the Pyramid
- Fuelling growth
- Creating jobs for the millions.

These three challenges translate into a need to harness our innovation potential as a country. That alone will enable us to sustain competitiveness, economic growth, and rising living standards over the long term. A multi-pronged approach in which the government, industry and academia collaborate and cooperate with one another can alone enable us in this mission.

Bottom of the pyramid

The market potential at the Bottom of the Pyramid can be realized if the products being offered embrace the elements of multi-functionality, frugality, simplicity and diversity. What India needs is 'inclusive innovation'—innovative products, knowledge creation and absorption efforts most relevant to the Bottom of the Pyramid—i.e. innovations in healthcare, sanitation, clean water and public services. We need 'thinking-outside-of-the-box' solutions to find new ways of delivering products to the Bottom of the Pyramid. Simultaneously, we need to develop products that might seem aspirational but are actually a necessity in many ways. For instance, a refrigerator is more of a necessity if viewed as something that can help preserve medicines and keep food fresh. If we leave out the ice-making function we can make this refrigerator at a very affordable cost, and that would open up a large domestic market.

In a neighbouring country there is a state-of-the-art 'innovation park' which is inviting huge investments. However, a walk through a village nearby indicates that the lives of the people there are untouched by innovation. The local shops have products made by multinationals for international consumers at affordable prices, but they do not have a single product that has been developed for the local people to meet their requirements. For example, local people use a cycle rickshaw for commuting short distances. Can we develop a solution that builds the cycle rickshaw using local materials, which is easier to maintain in the local conditions and use the skills of the local people?

In India, innovation is required not just for fulfilling an inventor's dream, but so that we, as a country, acquire skills and build competence to innovate every day. Just as we learnt quality as a process with some skill sets, we now need to develop the processes for innovation and build skill sets for their application.

The CII, by setting a target of a 100 companies to innovate, has taken up a challenge. It is beginning to develop this new area of competence.

India is today at the inflection point of a growth trajectory that, given the right impetus could enable the country to gain its rightful position in the global economy.

There is no doubt in the minds of policy makers, politicians, industrialists as well as the common man, that this growth can be achieved only if the manufacturing, service and agriculture sectors all grow in tandem. The contribution has to be fair and equitable. India certainly has the talent and the wherewithal to achieve this growth but only with the right approach and strategy. The strategy has to be innovation driven. We recently read about the need for a 'grass revolution' to bring about the second revolution in agriculture. For the next ten years, if we plant grass and systematically cover the entire non-concrete part of India's landscape, we can stop soil erosion, provide employment, reduce dust levels drastically and also achieve our growth targets in agriculture.

Growth
Manufacturing growth requires application of new technologies. For example, the chemical industry needs to acquire new technologies that can give us pure water across the length and breadth of the country at an affordable price. We need to take nanotechnology to fertilizers and pesticides to minimize their negative impact. For our nuclear reactors we need to produce steel with high resistance to nuclear material that will last long and be safe, because we cannot afford to keep changing reactors as frequently as developed countries do. Our model for growth needs a lot of innovation.

In the service sector, innovation is even more essential as service industry innovations can be copied easily.

Creating jobs
It is the highly specialized service sector that fueled India's recent exponential growth, giving India the status of a growing economy. As in any growing economy, the migrant population from agriculture needs now to be absorbed beyond its own borders. However, India's service sector cannot create jobs for the unskilled millions. It is only the manufacturing sector that can offer an answer to this need and this is where its growth becomes ever more critical and challenging.

In the future, therefore, India needs to harness its innovation potential to the maximum. The next question then is how ready is India to harness its innovation potential. According to a recent survey conducted by Confederation of Indian Industry alongwith Boston Consulting Group, almost 89 per cent of

the manufacturing companies believe that the importance of innovation had increased over the last 10 years and almost 91 per cent of the respondent companies placed it amongst their top three strategic priorities.

Innovation in 'India Inc' today is as big as the Quality movement of the 1980s and 1990s. After going through that movement, manufacturing companies today want to focus on front-end innovation. However, the Indian manufacturing sector is facing what is called the innovation paradox.

Limitations
The first limitation to India becoming an innovation-led country is at the organizational level. The manufacturing sector has undoubtedly recognized the need to innovate. However, Indian companies face a huge gap between formulating an innovation strategy and being able to implement or follow it as a business process. Thus, at the organizational level, companies need to have the right mix of discipline and motivation in order to encourage innovation and obtain results.

The second limitation is at the government policy level. The current government policies do not induce companies to become innovative. The government needs to put in place a policy to encourage innovation.

The third is at the society level. Entrepreneurs today fear failure. The Indian mindset is tuned to reprimanding failure and does not encourage experimentation. Unless this mindset is changed in society at large, many innovative minds will continue to fear ridicule and keep away from innovating.

These three limitations can be addressed through the creation of a framework or a 'supportive eco-system' that enables the innovator to derive benefits out of innovation. Such an eco-system can play a positive role in encouraging innovation. Government bodies, research institutes, academic institutions, investors, industry bodies, manufacturing houses and lawyers need to come together and step up their role in order to provide the right eco-system to encourage innovations.

CII is playing the role of a catalyst for building entrepreneurship and fostering innovation. Realising that India requires innovation as a strategy for its very sustainability, CII launched the Mission for Innovation in the year 2006. This Mission aims to enable at least 100 companies to embrace global processes for innovation and

Economist   Entrepreneur   Scientist   Administrator

product development over a period of three years. To achieve this objective, CII laid out a structured roadmap whereby Indian manufacturing companies would adopt globally benchmarked processes to make innovation a strategy for business growth.

CII introduced some international experts in innovation to the manufacturing sector, such as Prof Shoji Shiba, Prof Clayton Christensen and the Blue Ocean Strategy Network. These experts are now handholding 15 companies through the process of innovation. CII's tie up in the UK and the launch of the CII Raunaq Singh innovation grid are providing other links to the eco-system.

The Visionary Leaders for Manufacturing Programme, launched by CII under the aegis of the National Manufacturing Competitiveness Council and in close cooperation with the Indian Institute of Management, Calcutta, Indian Institutes of Technology, Kanpur and Madras is a unique initiative to skill senior managers from the manufacturing sector. The objective is to enable them to identify and capitalize on the innovation opportunities. More than 20 companies have already enrolled for this programme.

This programme together with the Raunaq Singh Grid are moving in the direction of creating the environment that will help harness the country's innovation potential. □

Bharat Wakhlu
Resident Director
The Tata Group, New Delhi

Fostering the essence of innovation: The Tata Way

Much has been written about innovation and its relevance to human progress. Tomes have also been published on the many variables that encourage innovation in the organized sector. However, what is often forgotten in the process, is that innovation is essentially a human endeavour that, to yield tangible physical outcomes, has to first occur in the minds of people. The first critical steps towards fostering innovation, therefore, require the conscious encouragement of creative thinking in individuals, and in teams of people working collaboratively.

This paper shares a simple template showing how progressive companies within the Tata Group, endeavour to stimulate in-house lateral thinking, as a precursor to breakthrough innovation and adoption of radical new ideas in business.

Belief in change
No society or organization can progress unless a critical mass of people wholeheartedly believes that their thinking and actions can make a difference. This is a fundamental aspect of change. Within their minds, potential change-makers have to firmly believe that they have the power to alter things for the better.

History documents the cases of many societies and cultures around the world, whose collective negation of their power and ability to change things was so deeply ingrained that it resulted in stagnation and even their extinction.

The belief that change is possible and desirable, is therefore something that needs to be encouraged and fostered with determination. This is most relevant to organizations where new entrants are often 'inducted' into the organizational fold with subtle suggestions that they conform and fall in line with the existing rules of business— including that of not asking too many questions or 'rocking the boat'. This insidious approach to enfeebling people saps the confidence of young people in their own ability to bring about change. Often, such people also unwittingly fall victim to the prevailing 'Group Think'.

In the progressive Tata Group companies that are known for their commitment to a creative approach, problem solving and innovation, there is a constant effort to strengthen the employees' belief that change is within their powers. This is done in a variety of ways.

Employees are encouraged to become accountable for outcomes in important areas of the business, where they can initiate change, if need be. They are invited to senior level meetings to share their novel, and often 'out of the box' perspectives for positive change. Resources are provided to them to initiate modifications that they may have suggested. Teamwork for improvement is supported.

It is this emphasis on making capable employees accountable and supporting them in their championing of new ideas that lays the firm foundation for ideation and the right kind of thinking. That foundation in turn, provides the basis for individual and group involvement in innovation.

Once individuals believe that they are in a position to make change happen, and are encouraged by the organization to spearhead improvements of a significant nature as champions of change within its fold, they soon become ready to internalize the next pre-requisite for innovation—having the ability to act as iconoclastic and creative problem solvers, who can take sensible risks that might even deviate from the *status quo*. This is not at all easy to do. Even those who believe in their ability to change and modify things, hesitate to take the path of iconoclastic, creative destruction, especially within the organization.

Given their rigid structures and precise standard operating procedures—all of which are essential to run current lines of business—organizations can be enormously intimidating for someone to think and act differently. Which is why seniors are continuously encouraged (or rapped on the knuckles, if they do nothing!) to support the initiatives of young professionals or change-makers, who might come up with new ideas that no one else may have thought of.

Youngsters

The famous MIT Professor of computer sciences, the late Michael Dertouzos once told a small team of senior Tata executives, that one of the key ways to make a difference in the knowledge economy, is to give youngsters (and he was emphatic: it had to be people in their late twenties or early thirties at best!) a free rein to think of value-creating ideas. The Tata Group has taken this advice seriously, and over the past ten years has consciously endeavoured to support young professionals—including college students working in the teams—to put forth radical, new ideas for improvement and positive change.

Iconoclastic, creative thinking also calls for sturdy Human Resource policies that reward leaders and managers who promote such thinking and ideational risk-taking. Those who are creative and see things differently should not feel alienated, or be treated as 'trouble-makers' during meetings or discussions.

Encouraging the participation of those with diverging points of view is a sure way to boost creative thinking and ideational risk-taking in organizations. Furthermore, providing formal platforms for such people to present their views are a means used by the Tata Group companies to stimulate individual and team creativity.

Individual accountability and the stimulation of iconoclastic creativity and ideational risk taking, as described above, provide the basic grounds for individuals to contribute to value-creation, and serve as champions of change. However, many initiatives that creativity and individual accountability engender, remain confined to the organization itself and are limited to its inner workings.

Innovation, by definition, is the creation of new paradigms and solutions that connects ideas and action with larger societal needs. Innovation is what serves to propel enterprises into new, unchartered directions that yield long-term value and advantage.

To that extent there is a need for organizations to make a conscious leap, from encouraging empowered individuals and teams who serve as champions of change, to enabling them to transfer their essential skills and competencies to real-world problems. Then alone would the competencies stimulate innovation and trigger the quantum jump to something unexpected, valuable and new.

This leap requires a structure and support to connect the right people with issues and 'pain-points' of the real world. The Tata Group provides the structure, and the process for this is in the form of the Tata Business Leadership Awards initiative.

Leadership awards

The Tata Business Leadership Awards (TBLA) is a formal innovation platform that was initiated in 2004. The structured TBLA process is an annual Tata Group event that is open to Tata employees across the group and to students of select business schools. It offers Tata employees and management students a unique opportunity to compete with the brightest and display their innovative abilities and business acumen.

The award also underlines the commitment of the Tata Group towards promoting and encouraging innovation, creativity and raising the value of these capabilities universally, in developing and identifying future leaders.

Employees and students (in teams or three to four) are given strategic, real-life problems or situations relevant to the Group. The teams have to make presentations to senior managers in the Group, and defend their ideas and the business cases that might be developed. The defence is evaluated on parameters such as creativity, clarity, relevance and business value. Employees and students, for the past few cycles of the TBLA, have gone on record to confirm how greatly the presence of the platform, stimulated their ability to be accountable, creative, and willing to think differently in relation to real-world problems.

Tata Companies are encouraged to provide the necessary guidance, and training to senior as well as young professionals to ensure that everybody feels accountable for his or her area of work, and thinks creatively about continuous improvement. The innovative connection with the outside world, where people can use their faculties to think of novel lines of business, is provided very effectively by the Tata Business Leadership Awards process. The Tata Group is confident that by seeding some of the ideas that have emerged in the TBLA forums over the past few years, new and profitable businesses can be created to improve the quality of life of people around the world. □

The new car by the Tata Motors that created excitment across the world.

Reliance Team
RIL

Innovation: Reliance Way

"Have you spent the money?"

This was the Chairman's question every day to the various project leaders, who were driving the implementation of Reliance Petroleum in Jamnagar. He was monitoring the 'burn rate' for investments.

An unusual way indeed, to measure the progress of a project. Perhaps a very effective way too.

This is also quite reflective of the Reliance way if one might call it that.

The Reliance way is driven by an unusual approach to business ideas and their implementation.

The making of the world's largest integrated petroleum plant at Jamnagar is a classic example of this thinking. Apparently consultants who were on the project asked the founder Chairman Shri Dhirubhai Ambani as to which crude he wanted to process in the refinery. Most conventional refineries made this decision first. His answer stunned them: "I do not know; you tell me". What followed posed the biggest challenge: "We do not want a conventional plant. Instead we want a flexible plant that is not dependent on anything or anybody, for anything. We want a giant who would dance to our tunes."

Integrated plant

A simple, sharply defined challenge has created the world's most unique integrated petroleum plant in Jamnagar that employed over 80,000 people to construct the refinery. Its features are mind-boggling and unprecedented in many different ways. It is considered an industrial wonder not only because of its features and scale, but also because of the speed of execution. The refinery was erected in a record time of less than 36 months, when most refineries world over take anywhere close to 60 months. Not only that; the plant was almost completely destroyed by a devastating cyclone. That did not delay the completion. The plant was back in action in a record 12 days.

Just to get a feel for the magnitude of the project, consider this:

- It is on 7500 acres of barren land
- It has 14,000 kms of cabling which is twice the length of the coastline of India
- It has 5000 kms of pipeline which is thrice the distance between Mumbai and Kolkatta
- It has used 100,000 MT of structured steel
- India's largest liquid port terminal
- A 900 MW steam and power plant
- A desalination plant
- An integrated petroleum plant.

Jamnagar in many ways reflects the DNA of Reliance.

Some beliefs are fundamental to Reliance Industries. These beliefs and values emanated from the founder Chairman Shri Dhirubhai Ambani:

1. Whatever is good for India, is good for Reliance Industries
2. Every employee has a right to think for the company
3. Have the courage to trust people
4. Start believing in achieving the impossible, and you will achieve the impossible
5. Hope is our most powerful weapon, self-confidence our biggest asset.

Here are two of his most often quoted statements:

> "I consider myself a pathfinder. I have been excavating the jungle and making the road for others to walk. I like to be the first in everything I do."

> "Imagine a wall before you. If you can't go around it, try and go under the wall or over the wall. If you can't do that, then you must break the wall and move forward."

This sums up the attitude of the entire organization and distinguishes it as well.

For those who study innovative organizations, Reliance Industries is a good example of how innovation is practised in almost everything that they do.

Here are few things that set them apart:

Impossible is an inspiring word: Nothing turns on the leadership at Reliance Industries more than this magical word. Again to quote the Jamnagar example, it was considered impossible to turn barren land into a greenbelt. Today mangoes grown in Jamnagar are sold at Harrods in London.

Hands on thinking, hands off execution: It is characteristic of Reliance leadership. They think everything through and meticulous planning is their hallmark. When it comes to execution empowerment delegation down to the last employee in the chain is clearly demonstrated.

First time it is learning. Second time it is a mistake: Mistakes are never frowned upon; instead they are treated as a learning opportunity. It is one such mistake converted to learning that created the world's largest 'Craft Centre' located at Jamnagar. Cumulatively it has trained 1,50,000 workmen—electricians, welders, carpenters.

Sense of urgency: Reliance speed is legendary. Reliance has mastered project management skills and has turned it virtually into a fine art. It is this sense of speed that restored operations in record time in Jamnagar, Patalganga and Hazira after being affected by cyclones and floods.

Think. Anticipate. Be prepared: Part of meticulous thinking is the ability to anticipate problems. "Every transformation initiative will face resistance. It is our job to anticipate the resistance, take the responsibility to earn the respect of all stakeholders to create a win-win business model."

Dreams and Vision are the most potent fuels in the world: This is an unmistakable Reliance hallmark espoused both by the founder Chairman Shri Dhirubhai Ambani and the current Chairman Shri Mukesh Ambani. To a question on what would be his next big ambition Shri Mukesh Ambani answered, "Rural transformation. Creating direct employment for half a million people in rural India. Creating a supply chain that the world will envy."

Measuring success differently: Developing a metric to measure how much money was spent, is just one example of inspiring people to think and act differently and effectively.

Asking the right questions: Reliance Leadership excels in asking the right questions. The company folklore is replete with examples of deceptively simple questions, leading on to incredible outcomes. Commonsense is the bedrock of such thinking.

"Hard work, timely decisions, speed and ingenuity" says one of the senior managers of Reliance Industries to sum up what Reliance is all about.

It is evident that Reliance Industries is where it is today because of innovation in thinking and execution. Given its ambition for India and its own organization, Reliance leadership has now taken on a major initiative in the innovation domain.

The leadership of RIL recognizes that its biggest competitive advantage and differentiator in the future will be innovation. Innovation has to become the language, the behaviour definer, the culture and the soul of Reliance more explicitly than before.

To achieve this RIL has launched a Reliance Innovation Movement with a charter:

- Growth is Life
- Innovation as a Way of Life
- Innovation Led Growth.

A Reliance Innovation Council has been established to provide the vision for this movement. The Council comprises global business and science thought leaders such as R A Mashelkar (Chairman), C K Prahalad (global strategy leader), Larry Summers (Ex-President Harvard), Nobel Laureates Robert Grubbs and Jean Marie Lehn, George Whitesides (global expert on materials science from Harvard) and Mukesh Ambani (Chairman of RIL). This powerful group of thought leaders will set the innovation agenda. To serve the Council, RIL has set up the Reliance Innovation Leadership Centre in Pune. The mandate of this centre is to implement RIL's innovation agenda which hinges on four key elements:

1. Build innovation leaders of today and tomorrow within RIL
2. Deploy best and next transformational innovative practices that will impact the country and the business
3. Develop new business based on emerging and disruptive technology
4. Strategically deploy a corporate venture capital fund to maximize value.

The Centre will act as a catalyst in providing leadership and support to the business of RIL by harnessing cutting-edge, futuristic but practical, science, technology and innovation initiatives from both within and outside the organization. It will serve as a nerve centre with the sole quest of propelling RIL to the forefront of global business leadership.

Another important organization, the Reliance Research and Technology Centre (RRTC) is set to be created in New Mumbai to support the innovation vision. This is where intensive research and technology development work will take place in state of art laboratories.

Given the Reliance track record of vision, scale and speed, it will be interesting to watch the impact of the Reliance Innovation Movement and its initiatives on the Reliance business and on India. Innovation may never be the same again! □

Rajdeep Sahrawat
Vice President, NASSCOM

A global innovation hub

The TATA Nano truly represents a *'Chak De'* moment for the Indian manufacturing sector. Someone said the Nano's launch was like a shot heard around the world. While nay-sayers from Detroit to Shanghai marvel at the innovations which created the Nano, an intriguing fact which tends to get overlooked is that how could the Indian automobile industry, renowned more for imitation rather than innovation, create a disruptive innovation like the Nano?

Why did the Nano get conceptualised and created in Pune instead of Detroit? According to Ratan Tata, as he observed Indian families riding on two-wheelers, it led him to wonder whether a safe, affordable, all-weather form of transport could be created for such families. Perhaps it was this detailed understanding of the market discontinuity developed by being close to the problem which enabled Ratan Tata's team to create the Nano whereas an automobile designer in Detroit could never have contextualised the problem.

Millions of Indians belonging to the migrant work-force are denied access to the comfort and security of the increasingly sophisticated Indian banking system perhaps simply because they do not have verifiable addresses and means of personal identification i.e. PAN cards, ration cards, voter cards etc. Not having a bank account denies them access to institutional credit and often leaves them at the mercy of the usurious money-lenders. Rather than wait for the archaic banking procedures to change, a private sector bank in India is combining cutting-edge technologies including wireless, smart-cards, bio-metrics etc. to provide a full range of banking services to this ignored market segment.

Having access to a bank account not only fulfils social aspirations but also opens many other opportunities. Interestingly, the bank is not doing this as part of Corporate Social Responsibility (CSR) but because it genuinely believes that its next wave of growth will come from new markets at the Bottom of the Pyramid. Even in today's flat world, it is unlikely that this 'bank to the customer' innovation in a risk-adverse industry like banking could have been created in London or New York, two of the most mature financial markets in the world.

Born out of adversity

It is true that these innovations are yet to prove themselves in the market, but both of them have the potential to disrupt and transform existing paradigms in their respective industries. While these disruptive innovation examples represent completely different genres, product and services, a commonality shared by them is that they were conceptualised and created in close proximity to the problem.

Innovation is often born out of adversity, greater the adversity, greater the probability of innovations. For truly game-changing innovations to succeed, they perhaps need to be created in the context of the problem instead of merely being replicated from a context where the problems are considered as someone else's problem.

In spite of the recent surge in the national economy and the general sense of 'India has arrived', we continue to face severe challenges on many fronts. Complex problems continue to bedevil us. We do not have affordable, world-class healthcare for every Indian, we have high infant mortality and we have yet to provide good quality primary education to every Indian child, increase agricultural yield and eradicate poverty. As many as 300 million Indians live on less than US$1 a day and 45 per cent of Indian children under the age of five are malnourished. Less than a third of India's homes have a toilet and only half of 500,000 villages are connected to the electricity grid. Falling agriculture productivity is threatening to turn India into a net importer of food for the first time since the green revolution.

But these problems are not unique to India. Large parts of the world's population inhabiting Africa, South and Central Asia and large parts of Latin America face similar challenges in education, healthcare, agriculture etc. These are not issues only confined to the developing world but as in the US, several million people with no medical insurance are denied access to good quality healthcare.

Disruptive innovations

Addressing these complex global problems will require disruptive innovations along multiple dimensions as the tried and tested approaches are not delivering.

This is where India has a unique opportunity for becoming a crucible for global innovation instead of aspiring merely to be the world's back-office and front-office. A world-class IT industry, wide array of skills in large numbers, a large science and technology infrastructure, unsurpassed cultural diversity, 'can-do' attitude of one of the world's youngest population, endow India with a unique and unmatched confluence of factors to make this happen. But above all, India provides an environment for incubating these innovations because the so-called 'insurmountable' problems of India actually represent market discontinuities and thereby provide a fertile ground for innovations.

There are already several examples of this. Successful innovations like the Aravind Eye hospital or the Jaipur foot required a context in which they were conceptualised and made successful. The success of the one rupee shampoo sachet required a customer segment which could not often afford the large shampoo bottle and if they were able to purchase it, they often lacked the space to store it.

Transforming India into a global innovation lab is not going to be easy as there are no off-the-shelf prescriptions available. For this to

happen, existing dogmas and 'givens' will need to be replaced by fresh thinking, aversion to failure will need to give way to boldness to experiment and a desire for the disruptive will need to overcome the acceptance of incrementalism. However there are two things which are perhaps more crucial than others.

Firstly, collective national innovation aspirations are needed which transcend the ordinary and provide a galvanising effect. Merely talking of innovation or passing off the trivial as innovation will only result in innovation being consigned to the graveyard of passing fads. In his famous 'land a man on the moon' speech at Rice University, J F Kennedy said it will not be one man going to the moon but the entire nation. This national aspiration motivated individuals and institutions in USA and resulted in game-changing innovations in diverse areas, which otherwise may not have happened. Perhpas we need similar national goals to raise the bar for innovation in India. World-class and affordable primary healthcare for all Indians, quality primary education for all Indian children, bringing a step change in crop yield etc. will require disruptive innovations on multiple dimensions involving both individuals and institutions.

Secondly, the innovation dots need to be connected. Successful innovations are often created through the intersection of multiple technologies originating in diverse industries and institutions and therefore creating sustainable linkages among ecosystem constituents. While common perceptions may point to lack of the maturity of the innovation ecosystem constituents in India, the real issue is the tenuous and transactional nature of the linkages between the ecosystem constituents.

Lack of linkages

Nowhere is this lack of linkages more starkly evident than in the industry—academia interactions, especially at the post-graduate and doctoral levels. While Indian industry often treats its interactions with the academia as CSR, expecting and giving little apart from financial investments, industry-academia interactions in the US have reached a high degree of maturity with both sides having clear expectations from the relationship and more importantly, working collaboratively towards realising the expectations. No wonder that US universities are extremely strong in pre-competitive

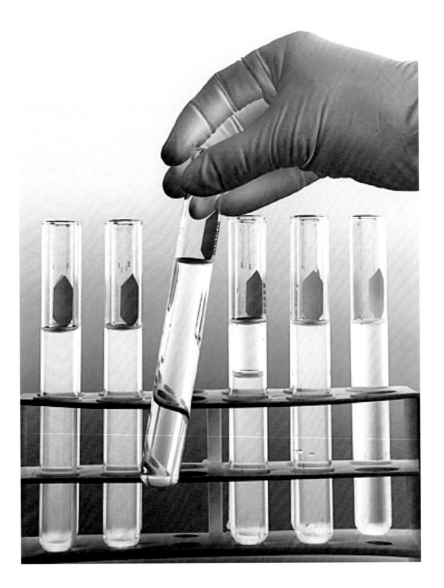

research and are global leaders in producing high quality PhDs in hi-tech sectors including computer science. A famous illustration of this is Google which was created by two doctoral research scholars at Stanford. Similarly, sustainable linkages need to be created between other innovation ecosystem dots including, industry and R&D institutions, IT industry and user industries, young start-ups and large firms etc.

Coming from a civilisation, if not yet from a nation, Indian inventions and innovations in science and medicine have benefited the world immensely. Today, once again there is a unique happenstance when the billion problems of India can become a billion opportunities for innovation which not only benefit India but also perhaps provide succour to the rest of the world. That will truly make the 21st century India's century. *Carpe Diem!* □

M G K Menon
Adviser, ISRO

The present enriched by the past

India has been one of the cradles of human civilisation. Three of the great religions of the world originated in India: Hinduism, Buddhism and Jainism. From India, Buddhism spread right across East and South-East Asia. Many in the world know of India in terms of its philosophy, mysticism, architecture, sculpture and the performing arts. Few are aware that India was also the fountainhead of important foundational scientific developments and approaches. The reason for this lack of appreciation is that there has been no major research or account of the panorama of scientific work initiated in ancient times, a part of Indian tradition that nurtures the culture of today.

Major contributions to science from India range from the decimal place value counting system using nine digits and the zero to the highly developed holistic philosophy and practice of medicine, Ayurveda, so different from the approach of Western medicine. Many developments in mathematics, which today bear the names of Western scientists as their discoverers, were known much earlier in India.

India accounts for many discoveries in astronomy, chemistry, metallurgy, plant systems and work on sophisticated aspects of grammar, linguistics and logic as a part of philosophy. In just over 600 years, from the 12th to the 18th century, over ten thousand books were written in India on science and technology. Indian manuscripts were translated into Persian and Arabic, and a great deal of knowledge travelled outward from India; equally, India assimilated scientific ideas and techniques from outside, displaying the open-mindedness and rational attitude characteristic of a scientific tradition.

In 1918, when the British appointed the Industrial Commission, its testimony stated: "When merchant adventurers from the West made their first appearance in India, the industrial development in the country was at any rate not inferior to that in most advanced European nations." However, with the degeneration of Indian society into a highly fragmented, feudalistic and ritualistic one, and internecine strife in the country, the earlier great traditions of open discussion and rational thinking were submerged under the dead weight of hierarchy, irrational subjective thinking, superstition and the like.

India did not participate in the scientific and industrial revolutions which took place in the West a few hundred years ago, and came under colonial domination. During the colonial period, development of science and technology did take place, but basically to cater to the requirements of the then existing government. And then, towards the later part of the colonial era, over the three-quarters of a century prior to Independence, there was an awakening in science, through the efforts of a large number of outstanding Indians.

This was in some way related to the ferment in Indian society, which motivated the freedom struggle, and many aspects of social transformation connected with it. It was also greatly influenced by interaction with Western liberal thought, and information on the new great developments in science that were taking place in Europe. Many scientists who achieved international recognition were associated with this renaissance. These included: J C Bose, Srinivasa Ramanujam, C V Raman, Meghnad Saha and S N Bose.

Others, like Birbal Sahni and P C Mahalanobis, opened up new areas on their own initiative and created new institutions; and then came, towards the later part of this period, S Chandrasekhar and Homi Bhabha. There were many more, not so well-known internationally, but who were responsible for building institutions, instilling patriotic zeal, and creating an ambience that would encourage the pursuit of high quality scientific research.

India was thus fortunate, at the time of independence, to have a scientific base characterised by dynamism, and an atmosphere of self-confidence. This was in harmony with the élan that characterised Indian society as the country emerged into freedom. This was in contrast to many other countries emerging from colonial rule.

Up to 1947, science was largely carried out in educational institutions, with some of the work being comparable to the best in the world; this would be characterised as 'curiosity driven' research. There was no question of any of this work being applied for national development or to production processes. India did not have at the time any major technological capabilities of the nature and scale seen in the industrialised countries.

National development

The annual growth rate in agriculture was 0.3 per cent. It was also very low in manufacturing industry, with the exception of textiles, certain extractive sectors, and a large steel plant (based on the vision of Jamshedji Tata). It was clear that a major effort was called for to alter this situation. The potential of science to underpin and accelerate national development was not widely appreciated; science was regarded as a separate, academic activity.

It needed the vision of a Jawaharlal Nehru to project the interconnections between science, technology, production activities and development. In 1947, Jawaharlal Nehru, while addressing the Indian Science Congress, had remarked: "So science must think in terms of the few hundred million persons in India." He was clear in his mind on the relationship between science and society, and its relevance for meeting the basic needs of large numbers in society; he never tired of talking about the importance of the 'scientific temper' permeating society to determine its ways of thinking and functioning.

This vision of Nehru's led to a paradigm shift: towards a large-scale enlargement of the scientific effort, its application to meet the needs of society and training of the men and women needed. There was massive development of infrastructure for science and technology, across a wide spectrum. In addition to continuing support for small-scale science, characteristic of work carried out in the educational institutions, the post-Independence period saw the emergence of national laboratories and major scientific agencies covering a broad range of areas and disciplines. While we were not yet into mega science, we were into large projects and extended team work.

Two main thrust areas during the Nehru period were the development of the atomic energy programme and through it, thereafter, the space programme; and the setting up of the large chain of laboratories under the Council of Scientific and Industrial Research (CSIR). Another major growth area, initiated by Nehru, is defence research. The significant growth and diversification of this area took place during the seventies under Indira Gandhi; and it has continued to develop ever since on a confident, self-reliant basis. It was in the Nehru era that the Indian Institutes of Technology (covering science, engineering and technology), and Indian Institutes of Management, were set up for the generation of high level personnel needed in these areas.

Political leadership

Indira Gandhi, who dominated the national scene over a two-decade period between the mid-'60s and mid-'80s, had an approach to science very similar to that of her father, Jawaharlal Nehru, stating: "The challenge before leaders of science and the moulders of national and international policies is how to direct the removal of hunger, want and the diseases of privation."

One of the important areas of success in Indira Gandhi's early tenure as Prime Minister was the effort to significantly increase food production. It came about through a combination of clearcut political decisions, good administrative support, and high quality applied research, which made the fullest use of new developments from abroad which were adapted to local conditions and cultural practices; there was good team work in extension, education and dissemination. This led to the 'Green Revolution'. Not only in the case of grains, but over a wide range of agricultural products, there has been enhanced production, the productivity, and diversification.

During the 1970s and the 80s a wide range of new initiatives were also taken in areas of great importance to the nation's future: electronics, environment, new and renewable energy sources, ocean development and biotechnology. These have become major areas of activity in their own right and bear fruit as we move into the next millennium. From what was only small science of very high quality, the newly emerging nation, devoid of modern technology on any relevant scale, has moved significantly forward over the past five decades. There is now an industrial base to be reckoned with. In science and technology, there is a major infrastructure, and extensive coverage of a wider spectrum of disciplines than most countries in the world. Not only is it a matter of infrastructure and capabilities but also accomplishments of a high order.

The Green Revolution and related developments in agriculture, with the potential of the new developments in biotechnology, give confidence that India can be essentially self-sufficient in the matter of food. The 'White Revolution' relating to dairying, the largest irrigation network in the world, one of the largest chemical industry, achieving contemporary international levels in process systems design and catalysis are some illustrations of what has been accomplished in different areas.

Accomplishments

India's nuclear programme was envisioned for the generation of electricity. The entire range of technologies from prospecting for raw materials to the design, construction and operation of large power reactors is now available on a self-reliant basis. It is based on this infrastructure and capabilities that nuclear tests were carried out in 1974 and in 1998. India's satellites, whether low orbiting ones for remote sensing or geostationary ones for telecommunications, broadcasting and meteorology, have performed efficiently and these are now wholly designed and built in India. The launch capabilities developed steadily have given the nation access to the geostationary orbit. Environment and ecology has gained importance ever since the UN conference on Human Environment held in Stockholm in 1972.

From the local issues of air, water and industrial pollution, to regional and transboundary impact, and environment in relation to health, there is now discussion on global issues such as ozone depletion, and increase of carbon dioxide concentration in the atmosphere (with its implications for energy based on fossil fuels), and consequential climate change. The great importance of biodiversity as a rich resource for the future, and also as a stabilising influence on the Earth's system, has also come to the forefront. India has a good scientific base, including in the use of powerful techniques of modern biology, to deal with this area.

Microelectronics enabled the computer revolution and we are now into the new age of informatics, with computers and communications merging into a single stream, bringing together all types of media relating to information storage, access, dissemination, computation, and analysis. Information Technology (IT) represents a revolutionary tool, which promises to transform every facet of human life and usher in a knowledge-based society in the next century; it will bring about connectivity of each human being on earth to all others. There has been increasing recognition in India of the importance of IT in national development. In a variety of ways, India now has a base to embark on an IT programme that will enable it to emerge as a major global player. The new National Informatics Policy can bring this about.

The wide-ranging and rapidly growing capabilities in IT are the result of efforts in strategic areas such as defence, nuclear and space research. Also in government initiatives relating to software development and database management, parallel computing, digital communication systems, and the rapid growth of the private sector in the field of software, particularly for exports.

Biotechnology

Biotechnology, which has emerged in its modern form from the laboratory into the marketplace, is an area where major investments have been made over the past two decades to create the necessary infrastructure, trained personnel and capabilities. There is no doubt that as we move into the next century, there will be major contributions from India in all the significant areas of application agriculture, health delivery systems and industry.

Another area in which initiatives were taken two decades ago relates to new and renewable sources of energy. This will be an area of decisive importance for India and for other developing countries, where decentralised autonomous systems will make energy available for development without awaiting capital-intensive transmission and distribution systems. This is a field that poses challenges, but also offers great scientific opportunities.

India has today significant scientific, technological and industrial capabilities relating to materials of all types. Since Independence, there has been the growth of ferrous and non-ferrous metal industries, in polymer production expertise relating to catalysts and materials for the nuclear programme, and specialised capabilities relating to managing steel, super-alloys, composite materials, tungsten, magnesium and titanium. It has one of the world's large solid propellant block production facilities. There is also a very high quality scientific base relating to the properties of materials, particularly using the most advanced and contemporary techniques for surface studies, bulk properties, failure analysis etc. This over-all competence constitutes a major resource for advanced will technology programmes in the future.

Future

As we move into the future, it is clear that a policy for science and technology will have to be directed along three lines. The first will be to apply the great powers of science and technology to meet basic human needs particularly taking note of locale-specific situations; these would relate to food, water, energy, employment, shelter etc.

The second would be to embark on major thrusts in the areas of informatics, biotechnology, new and renewable energy sources, new materials and environment-related programmes. In all of these, India has major capabilities, and would find it quite easy to move into top gear.

The third would be to continue with areas of high technology such as nuclear energy, defence research and space science and technology, where self-reliance and capabilities have been built up over several decades. Apart from these there will also be a need to ensure that the finest minds, who seek to work on what excites them most, are provided with the environment and opportunity to pursue their interests with fullest zeal. It is this planned paradigm shift,

which is now being called for, where government has prime responsibility.

One of India's greatest strengths is the large base of highly trained manpower created by its institutions of higher learning. Despite a serious neglect of the education sector, there has been a remarkable and continuing flow of highly skilled human resources of very high quality which has sustained the growth of science and technology in India. The hopes of India for its future will have to be pinned on this rich resource.

In the early stages of its development, because of limited financial resources and shortage of foreign exchange, there was a clear effort to plan the economy centrally, so that the investments could be directed at the core sectors which would constitute the base of future industrial development, such as steel and other metallurgical industries, machine building, and power. There was also an effort to achieve self-reliance and import substitution. A major export-oriented economy was not feasible, since the world had not reached the present state of globalisation; also the large industrial base needed for this had not yet developed. Exports were largely related to such products as cash crops and raw-materials.

Over a period of time, this planned approach became highly bureaucratic, and increasingly constrained by the requirements of innumerable unnecessary licenses and permits. There was also a considerable waste of resources through unbridled growth of subsidies, unjustified increase in public expenditure, and short-term partisan political interests. There was an increasing tendency to underestimate the roles of markets and incentives, and to rely exclusively on the State in the sphere of production.

Change

There has, however, been a major change on the international scene, as well as in India as a result of advances in science and technology, particularly in respect of information technology, and in the transportation of goods and people. We now live in a highly inter-connected inter-dependent world. This has led to the globalisation of markets which tend to look for resources from all over the world, including financial, and brings these together at points where production is most cost-effective and efficient, and then to move the goods to markets everywhere. This calls for a seamless or borderless world for movement of goods, and of people. Tariff restrictions, as well as those on financial flows, and nature of activities, have to be kept to a minimum, consistent with national sovereignty, and the need to raise resources for development, and to support areas specific to each country and its history.

India has embarked on a significant process of reform to move towards this globalisation. The elaborate structure of licensing and permits has been dismantled to a great extent. Market forces are now recognised, and private industries encouraged.

Foreign investment has been welcomed and promoted. There is significant emphasis on exports, and dismantling of controls on foreign exchange transactions. India's role in the globalised economy is expanding. It has to be remembered that India is endowed with highly competent trained human resources in a variety of fields; and the cost of living in India is relatively low. Using current and developing information technology, work is shifting to India from elsewhere in the world: in research, design, systems engineering, software product development and applications. India's policies are not autarkic. This would be against its self-interest and development. It has to be a part of the global community. It will, therefore, continue to import and export on a significant basis. However the scale of its needs, based on its large population, is such that a very large part of its requirements, particularly food and primary materials for energy, will have to be met from production within the country. While it has considerable industrial activity, it is still an agricultural country in terms of deployment of its population.

India is witnessing a great shift towards industrialisation and from rural to urban centres in parallel with the information technology revolution. There will also be a rapid move to a knowledge-based society. Interaction is growing between India's scientific research and capabilities and sectors of production and services. The World Trade Organisation and the new patent regime have created an awareness of the importance of Intellectual Property Rights and their role in the new world order. There is enormous latent innovative capability in the Indian scientific system which could easily fructify into competence of value. This calls for support from other areas such as patent attorneys, patent offices and the financial sector. With the emphasis on exports and global competitiveness, the production sectors in India will increasingly turn to the scientific competence in the country, which is also linked with global scientific enterprise.

As India continues to develop, and increasing numbers become well-to-do, they will move into the market economy on a scale that will fuel further growth. India represents a giant system, functioning as a democracy, moving from a conservative hierarchical society to a flexible, modern knowledge-based one. The foundations laid in creating its present widespread competence in science and technology will stand it in good stead in this transformation. □

V S Ramamurthy
DAE Homi Bhabha Chair Professor
Inter-University Accelerator Centre

An ecosystem for innovation and entrepreneurship

We are on the threshold of a new era in the history of human civilization, an era not only dominated but also driven by science and technology. There is no aspect of human life today that is not touched by S&T in some form or the other. While governments look at S&T as an engine of economic growth, business houses see it as a unique tool for competitiveness and new opportunities. Expenditure on scientific research and technology development are seen as investments with the consequential expectations of returns-on-investment (ROI).

However, exploitation of laboratory knowledge for commercial gains has always been a challenge to countries and institutions. While some countries like the US have built robust ecosystems for a seamless transfer of scientific and technological knowledge into their industries, many others lag behind. The Indian ecosystem is best illustrated by an anecdote. A child was asked by the teacher to name two places on the face of the earth having the maximum distance between them. After struggling for some time, the child approached his father for help. In a frustrated voice, the father replied "the research laboratory and the industry." We do not know whether the father was a scientist struggling to get his invention across to the industry for commercialization or an industrialist who could not get his problem solved by the 'ivory tower' scientists.

The anecdote very neatly reflects the ecosystem in India. Not only are we concerned about this, but we have taken initiatives to bridge this gap and build a favourable ecosystem. The technology transfer chain has multiple links, with laboratory research at one end and the marketplace at the other, with innovation and entrepreneurship in the middle. With increasing vertical specialization in new and emerging domains, globalized marketplace and rigid enforcement of Intellectual Property Rights, a seamless transfer of technologies from laboratory to market, demands new enabling mechanisms. Technology intermediation may be termed as the sum total of all such enabling mechanisms.

Let me start with access to scientific knowledge. It is well known that scientists generally prefer to work in isolation, interacting among themselves. They expect the industries to access their knowledge through their publications, research reports, and at best through technology transfer documents. The industries on the other hand look for a continuing relation, a hand-holding, particularly in an environment of fast changing technologies. Such a polarization can only be bridged by building what one might call 'seamless knowledge corridors'. I am reminded of my younger days in the Bhabha Atomic Research Centre, Mumbai. BARC is a multidisciplinary research organization. There is, in BARC, a long laboratory called the 'Modular Laboratory' that houses a number of their research groups in a corridor nearly half a kilometre long. It used to be said that if you have a problem in science or technology, you simply walk along the corridor and share your problem with every one you come across. By the time you reach the other end of the corridor, you are sure to have come across someone who can solve your problem or knows how to solve it.

Jokes apart, can we build such seamless corridors where both scientists and industrialists tread and share scientific and technological knowledge and expertise seamlessly? Mobility of scientists and technologists among institutions is yet another way of promoting knowledge sharing and transfer. In recent times, many of our leading educational and R&D institutions have taken steps, sometimes hesitantly, to promote closer ties with industry. Sector specific centres of excellence have been established in some of our leading educational institutions in the public-private-partnership mode. Industry sponsored chairs and industry fellowships have been put in place.

The second aspect that I would like to touch on is access to sophisticated instruments and facilities. We all know that present-day scientific research is heavily dependent on sophisticated instruments. More importantly, these instruments become obsolete faster and faster. It would be uneconomical for an industry to invest in such instruments. On the other hand, educational and R&D institutions with no short term ROI expectations can add these to their infrastructure. The national S&T funding agencies have been investing in the creation of several sophisticated research facilities with access to industry and entrepreneurs.

Cost of failure

Another important weakness of the Indian ecosystem is the near absence of safety nets for new entrepreneurs and industries venturing into new technologies. The cost of failure in financial terms is well known. In the US, if you fail in a new venture, you can list it in your CV as proof that you are not averse to taking risks. But in India, if you fail, not even your wife will look at your face, let alone financial institutions and the government. It is only now that one comes across government initiatives like TDB, NMITLI, SBIR etc. Venture financiers are also being seen more often. Professional and legal safety-nets are yet to mature in our country. We have been dreaming of Special Innovation Zones where the ecosystem is favourable to new entrepreneurs and new technology industries.

Last but not the least, even in a world dominated by technology, people hold the key. They are the generators of scientific knowledge, developers of technologies, innovators of products and services, entrepreneurs to build and operate sustainable businesses and above all the end users. It is rare to find a single

individual who can assume all the roles at the same time. Technology intermediators are individuals who act as glue in bringing people having different specializations together towards a common goal. They are not simple managers, they are like conductors in a Western orchestra. Some of their roles in technology development and transfer are enumerated below.

Any high technology product stands on multiple technologies, often from multiple disciplines. A new discovery or a new development in one area may have an important impact on a product design in a completely different area. There is a need for constant watch, for technology leads across disciplines keeping in mind the broad applications landscape. Any research is futuristic. Technology forecasting and assessment is an integral part of technology planning.

Intellectual Property Protection is taking a central place in today's knowledge economy. The scientific community has been sufficiently sensitized to IP protection in recent times.

However, management of Intellectual Property Assets goes far beyond protection of these assets. The institutional assets of any organization are far more than those documented. For example, even in scientific research, successes are well documented, publicized and protected. What about failures? Are they not the stepping stones of success and contribute to knowledge as much as the success? What happens to this asset when people die, retire or simply are poached upon by others? You need people and mechanisms to handle knowledge in its totality, whether they are the generators of that knowledge or not.

Technology intermediation is indeed a complex job that demands not only scientific knowledge but also special skills in managing people and knowledge, for a common goal. They are like oxygen in the air. Their presence is rarely noticed but their absence has profound consequences. It is only in recent times technology intermediation has been recognized as an integral part of technology development and transfer in our country. With the recent initiatives mentioned earlier, our country can build an ecosystem that will make it globally competitive in the S & T driven world of today and the days ahead. □

Arjun Malhotra
Chairman & CEO, Headstrong Corporation

Arun Dang
President, Strategy and Business Advisory

Innovation in the age of discontinuity

Driving through Punjab you may come across a *Jugad*, a flatbed transport powered by a tube well engine. The engine unit is taken out from the tube well installation, fixed into a slot in the flatbed, and linked via a belt drive to the front wheels. It replaces the time-honoured bullock-cart to transport farm produce, commuters and marriage parties complete with blushing brides. Existing capital equipment—the engine unit—gets used during idle hours, there is higher speed and faster turnaround than in the bullock cart and the engine easily returns to running the tube well as priorities dictate. The term *Jugad* has become a colloquial term for "innovation". It signifies improvisation, making do and developing a contraption to suit the need.

The *Jugad* as a product is an unauthorized transport, and would invite the wrath of authorities in Delhi. But there too such innovations flourish, less conspicuously. The next time you see a flatbed cycle rickshaw, another delivery vehicle, look again. Chances are it has the rear half of a Bajaj scooter discreetly strapped to its underside. The scooter engine drives a wheel, which becomes the prime mover of the rickshaw. Back-breaking pedalling goes out, replaced by faster deliveries, quicker turnaround, and more business completion every working day.

Welcome to the marriage of necessity with ingenuity. The survival imperative has forced us to find better ways of doing things with severely limited resources. And the large population has been an asset in two respects—firstly as a source of enormous thinking power and adaptation, and secondly as a large, ready adopter of the benefits of innovation.

Innovation takes place when the human mind is pushed by a stimulus. As India unshackles itself from problems of survival to address opportunity, it becomes a vibrant centre for innovation. Technology and globalization are transforming the world, effecting discontinuous change in the interactions between peoples, places and situations. The past no longer extrapolates into the future. The compulsion to innovate is itself a matter of survival.

Innovation begins in all quarters. We see it in the developed world and the developing one. We see it in legacy-bound organizations, and in leapfroggers. As it builds, we see the power of ideas, and human thought becoming a wealth creator. This narrows the resource gap between existing organizations and the start-ups, in fact transferring some advantage to the new ones. The 20th-century industrial organization is structured to handle repetitive tasks, at increasing scales of operation and across multiple locations. Technological change and globalization question this paradigm. They completely redefine challenges and opportunities, requiring new solutions. Restructuring organizations, products and services has become necessary for survival.

The need is to transform existing mindsets, organizations and practices in order to make them more competitive. The changes are gut-wrenching: even the supervisory role of management is being integrated into the new processes wrought by technology. How can human thinking be productively redirected into the new opportunity areas? Innovation becomes a necessity, even in organizations where it was explicitly discouraged.

Today, non-legacy organizations are able to grow rapidly, changing and aligning with the future. These organizations often face greater challenges, because their target customer is less affluent and/or more aware, hence more focused on deriving best value. The solution lies in leveraging opportunities, making optimum use of latest technologies, and expanding beyond the domestic arena to actualize global integration of resources, markets, comparative advantages and opportunities.

Such organizations succeed as they accept, *ab initio*, that the future is discontinuous with the past, and that past success is no guarantee of future existence. Equally, the next success will not ensure continued success in future. They deal with the uncertainty of the future by building in a capacity to innovate and to carry on restructuring the paradigms, products, services and benefit situations on which they will stake their existence.

India advantage

The purchasing power of the Indian middle class has been well documented. Even if we place its size at a conservative 50–75 million, or the population of the UK or Germany, it is a sufficiently critical mass for development of dedicated products and services. We have seen housing, fashion garments, vacations, financing schemes, teaching institutions and now even automobiles being specially designed around their requirements, preferences and affordability. In effect it's a new market in the global economy, the emergence of which has spurred a whole lot of innovation.

This, though, is just the tip of the India iceberg. The next 250–500 million have lower purchasing power, true, but a whole economy already exists to create and deliver goods and services to them. It's a market economy, with promotion and branding, market segmentation, test marketing, manufacturing, outsourcing, distribution, trade fairs and shopping festivals all happening apace. Its past isolation reduces rapidly as TV and mobile phones disseminate information and physical access improves with better highways and local roads. Margins are naturally lower, but the absolute numbers create a tempting set of equations for the innovator.

The Indian market, present and potential, is a huge spur to pioneering and innovation, to handling unprecedented situations and deriving new frameworks. The scale of opportunity creates a furious pace of activity,

one that draws more minds into its ambit, and sends them out on quests for even more new opportunities. Innovation then extends much beyond opportunism. It goes into product development, engineering, business modeling and structuring, feedback loops and new market creation. These capabilities, once created, become a resource for the rest of the world, thereby creating hubs of innovation in the country.

Unleashed innovation has a habit of not respecting boundaries, of travelling to other fertile ground. Innovation does not travel as products alone. It travels also as an attitude, one that examines existing problems and successes, for further opportunities. The Tata Nano is being sought as a finished product outside India. Its design approach, dubbed 'frugal engineering' by Carlos Ghosn, is an unsung hero of India's software success.

Ghosn's organizations, Renault and Nissan, plan to use 'frugal engineering' to design automotive products in India for global markets. True, Indian engineers come at a lower cost than comparable professionals elsewhere. But additionally, they have the mindset and exposure to deliver 'frugal engineering', an achievement that delivers enormous value in every single unit manufactured, over the entire life-cycle of the product.

The India Advantage has moved way beyond labour arbitrage. It is now the power of the mind, and an environment where large numbers are getting trained to think out-of-the-box.

Story without end?

Innovation is the power of the mind. It is the modern philosopher's stone, able to turn base metal into gold. India uses it for the big domestic market, and now begins to extend it to the global arena where it finds itself. But is it a flash in the pan, or will it sustain itself? The greatest threat to innovation is complacency, an easing of the pressure that drives the mind. Is there a danger of hubris, as India compliments itself ever more loudly?

The answer to this too is found in the large Indian population: there are another 100 persons, or 100 million, snapping at your heels, driven by the same fire in their bellies as you had in your hungry days. The opportunities are only increasing, their motivation only grows, your tasks don't reduce.

In India today, you rest on your laurels at great risk. □

Ashok Parthasarathi
Former Secretary
Ministry of New and
Renewable Energy

Progress in renewable energy

India, like other newly industrializing nations, spent the first 30–35 years after Independence in making incremental innovations, except perhaps for the hybrid seeds for cereal and horticultural crops. However, since around 1980, it began to tread the path of revolutionary innovations. These ranged from the digital telecom switching systems of C-DOT, the CorDect wireless telecom systems developed by IIT, Chennai, the Supercomputers developed by C-DAC and BARC to several new pharmaceutical products including biotech-based vaccines. Innovation was involved in the designing of the fast breeder reactors and the thorium breeding reactor. The manufacturing sector has come up with some outstanding R&D products such as the Tata cars. The challenge before the nation is to extend this drive for technological innovation into the traditional sectors of industry such as textiles, footwear and leather garments, the railways and roadways, the hugely demanding infrastructure sector and above all, in all energy subsectors, particularly coal.

This paper focuses on the promising area of renewable energy sources that has been especially marked by innovative efforts. India started R&D on solar energy systems as far back as 1975 when a pioneering group of physicists and electronic engineers was formed in the public sector company, Central Electronics Limited (CEL). Laboratory work to produce solar cells and panels was completed in 1980. Based on that experience, CEL was asked to execute a national solar photo voltaic (solar electricity) demonstration (NASPED). Designing and manufacturing of an SPV Pilot Plant of 1 MW/year production capacity was undertaken at CEL as the core of NASPED. Using that plant and the solar cells and modules produced by it, complete SPV Power Systems were built for domestic and village street lighting, solar water pumps for irrigation and drinking, SPV-powered radio and TV sets. The SPV energy systems for powering static and mobile wireless communication sets were prototyped and produced in small lots for extensive field and user evaluation. In 1985, the CEL went on to set up a commercial plant of 5 MW/year capacity.

The world's first Ministry of New and Renewable Energy formulated an ambitious plan encompassing various technologies, processes, materials, components, sub-systems, products and services at par with international specifications, standards and performance parameters. The plans envisioned the deployment of indigenously developed and manufactured products and services in furtherance of the national goals of energy security and energy independence. India is among the top rankers in the installation of grid interactive renewable electricity systems. The country has a total estimated renewable energy potential of about 85,000 MW, made up by 45,000 MW from wind turbines installed onshore and a practically limitless potential from such turbines installed offshore; about 2500 MW from small hydro power plants of capacity of 25 MW or less, and 2500 MW from biomass/bio-energy.

Currently sources, renewable, mainly, wind, biomass and small hydropower contribute around 11,300 MW accounting for about eight per cent of the installed power generation capacity from all sources. In addition, 200 MW is generated as captive/distributed renewable power.

Wind energy is one of the fastest growing renewable energy resources with an installed capacity of over 7800 MW, which is the fourth largest in the world. Biogas and solar lighting have reached 4 million and 1 million households respectively for meeting cooking, lighting and water pumping requirements, mostly in rural areas.

As of March 2007, about 2 million solar photo-voltaic (SPV) systems of some 28 different types for rural, remote area and industrial applications were in operation. All of these were designed, engineered and manufactured within the country. In addition, around 2.6 million sq m collector area of solar thermal systems has been designed and deployed to meet domestic and institutional hot water needs and industrial process heat requirements. A major programme is being implemented to electrify 10,000 villages through renewable energy resources by 2012.

Government policy initiatives have facilitated the design, development, manufacture and use of renewable energy systems based on an array of technologies. Many technologies are currently at the threshold of economic viability. Strong R&D capacity and manufacturing base for a number of renewable energy systems/devices, namely, solar water heating system; solar cookers, solar photovoltaic systems, wind turbines and biomass power generation systems have been created in the country. Domestic R&D has enabled wind electric systems of capacities of 1.5 MW and 2 MW to be designed, developed and manufactured in the country and even exported.

Wind power: The 7800 MW of wind power installed and operational includes several wind farms of 50-80 MW capacity. Our leading wind turbine manufacturer M/s Suzlon Energy, a wholly Indian owned company has not only installed and operationalised several such wind farms at home but also set up a 75 MW wind farm in Turkey and is in the final stages of operationalising a 330 MW wind farm in France. It has also operationalised many other such wind farm projects in 10 countries.

Solar photo voltaic power: The largest SPV system in the country is the 25 MW power plant for home and street lighting and a wind-SPV hybrid energy plant to power a large cold store for fish. This project, the largest in Asia, is located on the Sagar Island in the Sundarbans

in the Ganga-Brahmaputra delta 150 km from Kolkata. The beneficiaries are some 12,000 households of fisher-folk. The households are charged Rs 7 per KWh which they are willingly paying as there is no other mode of electrification for the island because it is 10 km from shore. The 25 MW SPV power plant is built up from 25 KW, 50 KW and 100 KW sub-units. The project started in mid 1997 was completed in mid-2003. The modular power plants were manufactured, installed and maintained by India's five top SPV manufacturers—four in the public sector and one in the private sector.

Our largest public sector SPV company, Central Electronics Ltd (CEL) makes 28 different types of SPV systems, all based on in-house R&D and falling in the categories of rural, remote area and industries. These include portable solar lanterns, SPV water pumps for rural drinking water systems, special vaccine storage refrigerators at village Primary Health Centres, SPV power sources for charging the batteries of wireless communication sets for military pickets on the world's highest battle field on the Siachen Glacier in the Himalayas at 16000–18000 feet, and SPV power sources for powering the control and instrumentation systems on offshore oil and gas platforms in the Arabian Sea, 250 km from shore. CEL is also our major exporter not only of complete SPV systems—to some 20 countries including Cuba, Mauritania, Sudan Nepal and Sri Lanka—but also of specialized plant and equipment to set up SPV factories in Syria and Sudan.

Biomass power plants: This is another area in which regular commercial manufacture of systems meeting international specifications, performance levels and costs have been underway in several companies for many years. The complete technology of a locally designed, engineered, field proven and mass manufactured biomass power plant has also been internationally patented and the technology exported to Switzerland.

R&D activities of the Ministry of New and Renewable Energy aim at resource assessment, technology development, demonstration and commercialization. A comprehensive policy on Research, Design and Development, done both in the public and private sectors, is in place. The Government has set up specialised technical institutions. These are the Solar Energy Centre (SEC), Gwalphari, Gurgaon Haryana, the Centre for Wind Energy

Technology (C-WET), Chennai, Tamil Nadu, and the Sardar Swaran Singh National Institute of Renewable Energy (SSSNIRE), Jalandhar, Punjab.

The research, development, demonstration and testing activities in the area of small hydro power and biomass power are supported at centres established in the Indian Institute of Technology, Roorkee, and Indian Institute of Science, Bangalore. SEC provides testing and standardization facilities for our renewable energy industry, helping to provide customer confidence in solar energy systems/devices and new product development.

The Centre for Wind Energy Technology has been playing a vital role in the wind resource assessment programme. It is also the national testing and certification agency for wind turbines. This has greatly helped technology upgradation of locally made wind turbines and also facilitated the export of wind energy equipment.

The Ministry operates a large R&D programme in industry and academic institutions. It spent about Rs 1000 million on projects in some 45 organisations during the Tenth Five Year Plan period 2001–07. The expenditure will go up to Rs 3000 million during the Eleventh Plan now underway. Apart from the official schemes, the companies manufacturing renewable energy products are undertaking their own in-house R&D at levels ranging from 4 per cent to 8 per cent of sales on both production processes and products. This effort is designed to make our renewable energy industry technically and commercially competitive.

The share of indigenously designed, developed and manufactured new and renewable energy systems/devices has continued to increase. Research, design and development efforts are focused on the manufacture of complete systems. The focus of such efforts is on system design engineering and manufacturing at lower costs. The following systems and products are covered:

- Solar Thermal Energy (High Temperature) power generation systems
- Solar Thermal Energy for domestic and industrial applications
- Energy efficient buildings utilizing renewable energy concepts
- MW-scale solar power generating systems
- Increasing the number and scale of major SPV cells, modules and systems manufactured to attain world levels
- MW-scale wind turbine electric generators for low wind regimes

- Biomass integrated gasification combined cycle systems
- Simulators for RE grid-interactive power stations using renewable energy
- Alternative bio-fuel, synthetic and hydrogen systems
- Hybrid systems
- Geothermal and Tidal Energy systems
- Energy intensive storage devices, including those for grid power
- Fuel cell-based systems for industry and transport
- Electric vehicles which have longer range, higher speed and lower cost.

Future

The country has set a goal of 14,000 MW of renewable power by the end of the Eleventh Plan, 2012 from 11,300 MW at the end of the Tenth Plan. The solar water heating and remote village lighting programmes are quite ambitious. Major private-sector companies like Reliance and Moser Baer have announced plans to set up large grid connected SPV power plants of 10–15 MW capacity.

Moser Baer has recently announced that it will be making an investment of 1.8 billion dollars over the next three years to expand the capacity of its 40 MW thin film solar cell manufacturing plant to 600 MW/year, making it the largest SPV production plant in the world. With these initiatives and smaller plant capacity expansion by the five public sector SPV manufacturers, the goal of achieving a 10 per cent share of grid interactive solar power by 2012 and 20 per cent by 2020, looks entirely feasible. As for costs, the last five years has seen the cost of SPV power decline from Rs 20/KWh to Rs 15/KWh. The target for 2020 is less than Rs 10/KWh which will make solar power comparable to power from coal based power in that year.

In alternate fuels such as bio-fuels, synthetic fuels and hydrogen, the aim is substitution of petroleum and diesel by up to 5 per cent by 2017 and 10 per cent by 2032. India has also been pursuing research and development in hydrogen and fuel cell technologies for transportation and power generation. A Hydrogen Development Board has been established to oversee efforts for the development of hydrogen as a renewable energy source for large-scale commercial use.

All possible technologies will have to be explored if the country has to progress towards energy security. □

R Rajamani
Former IAS officer

Prospects in science and technology

Science and Technology (S&T) are not confined to national boundaries and are universal in nature. But in a world besieged by insular attitudes and imperfect competition, the compartmentalization of S&T seems inevitable, and thus we too have to talk of Indian S&T! From India's mixed performance in the S&T sector, we have drawn lessons for the future in a spirit of optimism.

There have been several successes in Indian S&T, especially in the teaching of science in schools and colleges, in experiments in laboratories all over the country in various institutions such as universities; and in both Government-sponsored and private establishments dedicated to S&T. The applications of S&T have been refined in farms, factories and hospitals across the country.

Cataloguing these is not the objective here, but mention may be made of the advances in space sciences and technology, atomic energy, astrophysics and cosmic studies, biochemistry, medicine, biology (including systematic botany and zoology), geology, geophysics and meteorology. Mathematical sciences have had their applications in fields like information technology and so on. Inspiration has come from the work of brilliant individual researchers among whom we can count some Nobel laureates, and also from professors, teachers and leaders of science in several institutions. It has not always been only individual brilliance but also teamwork that has been responsible for many of these successes, the basis on which we can build for the future.

Earlier work over the centuries like the efforts of Bhaskara, Gargi, Susruta, Varahamihira, and work in recent years by people like J C Bose, M N Saha, C V Raman, N L Dhar, P C Ray, Seshadri, Dr Subba Rao, Narlikar, Khorana, Satish Dhawan, Janaki Ammal were based on painstaking observation and toil combined with intuitive flashes and were in the interests of expanding the frontiers of knowledge, whether rewarded or not. In most cases, recognition did not come easy but the ethic of work and service to humanity itself was inspiring enough to urge them on.

But it must be recognised that a large part of the work until Independence (and even later) was not inspired by institutional mechanisms for advancement of S&T, and in cases where they existed, it was in spite of them! In many cases, much depended on the leadership in the university or laboratory or shop floor. But this had its flip side because of the human tendency to jettison the work started by one's predecessor and start anew. An example is the Karimnagar Project started in the Council of Scientific and Industrial Research to take S&T to the rural areas, while also upgrading the skills there. Started by Dr Nayudamma, it later languished, though there are now signs of revival of such an initiative.

The linkages between the university system and other institutions devoted to S&T have also varied over the years and there is no steady exchange of personnel among them. Exceptions are many, however, especially in the field of medical science where the system of teaching hospitals and colleges has ensured real-time feedback to academia on the problems faced by patients and clinical practitioners.

The connectivity between industry, farms and services and S&T institutions has also improved because of the efforts of Government institutions like CSIR, Indian Council of Agricultural Research (ICAR), Indian Council of Medical Research(ICMR), as also privately funded or quasi-private institutions like the Indian Institute of Sciences and Indian Institutes of Technology (IIT's). Innumerable smaller organisations started by civil society have also been engaged in the task of integrating traditional and modern trends in S&T. Yet much more needs to be done in future to strengthen these linkages and connections.

Sustainables

The key is also in learning from past mistakes and failures in S&T. Harping only on successes could carry us up to a point, but we would achieve much more by recognizing failures and choosing those methodologies, experiments and applications that are marketable, serviceable and conducive to the general good. We should encourage those who work towards solutions and not those who foresee only the negatives. We should encourage lateral thinking from childhood and not dismiss anyone as eccentric without testing his or her hypotheses. We should continue to reward achievement without discouraging failure, which may well be the seedbed of future work that will be recognised. We must build sustainable institutions that survive the charisma of leadership, recognizing that they also serve who work silently.

The integration of traditional knowledge and wisdom with the modern has been one of the hallmarks of some of our achievements in fields like pharmaceuticals but this quest should continue. We may laugh at the Jarawa tribal and his ways in the Andaman Islands but we cannot help admiring his instinct (which cloaks an atavistic scientific tendency) when he runs up the hills with the animals and birds even before the advent of the tsunami and much before the modern inhabitant realizes what has hit him!

In a globalizing world where our S&T can ensure creation of jobs and incomes in our country, we should anticipate trends and build on our strengths. We will have to do much more in fields like solar energy and evolve solutions which optimize our strengths and avoid lapsing into the old ways of pure imitation, thoughtless migration of talent and adverse terms of trade. By now, India should have had a solar photovoltaic roof over the electric automobile, continuously charging the battery, driving it long distances and avoiding air pollution, but the corporate sector and scientific establishments seem to be waiting for developments elsewhere to import and copy for which we will pay a high price!

Our future in S&T is secure not only because of the inherent talent we have, but also because of the recognition that we need to increase investments in Research and Development and spread awareness of the fruits of good S&T among students in schools and colleges. We need not lament brain drain or even poor salaries as long as the scientific temper pervades our workplaces, academia and even our drawing rooms. India has enough talent in reserve even after donating some for the international effort in S&T, which is our tribute to its universality. □

S Vardarajan
Former President
Indian National Science
Academy

Total technology development and delivery

It is generally not known that some eminent Indian scientists played an important role in promoting industrial production through research. C V Raman, committed to excellence in all fields and to the autonomy of scientists, created the Raman Research Institute, eschewing government resources and influence. How many people know that he established a small industrial unit in Bangalore, manufacturing and marketing mantles for petromax lamps by installing circular knitting machines for cylindrical cotton products, subsequently soaking the material in cerium salts? The income generated contributed to the functioning of the Institute for 25 years.

In Calcutta, scientists such as U P Basu and P C Ray promoted Bengal Chemicals, Calcutta Chemicals and the Bengal Immunity Company to produce fine chemicals, drugs and vaccines. The Haffkine Institute, with distinguished scientists such as Sir Sahib Singh Sokhey, developed biochemical therapeutics and vaccines. The Pasteur Institute at Coonoor, produced vaccines. The Nutrition Research Laboratories, originally in Coonoor, had many scientists, such as Prof V Ramalingaswamy and Dr C Gopalan, who went on to become heads of the Indian Council of Medical Research. In Jammu and Srinagar, the Drug Research Laboratory, under Col Sir Ramnath Chopra, carried out extensive investigations into the chemical constituents of plants and marketed several drugs through a company which continues to function.

In a spirit of nationalism, scientists trained abroad, such as Dr Khwaja Hameed, started CIPLA, a major pharmaceutical research and production organisation. The Indian Lac Research Institute promoted production of shellac. Prof T R Seshadri, who worked with Sir Robert Robinson in London on the structure and synthesis of natural products used as pharmaceuticals and dyes, created on his return active Schools of Research in Andhra and Delhi Universities, and these have continued to make outstanding contributions. Kasturbhai Lalbhai, an ardent patriot and industrialist in textiles, aware of the problems of import during the Second World War, arranged to train a cousin at the Massachusetts Institute of Technology, USA, and started Anil Starch, producing starch-base and textile auxiliaries. Cellulose Products in Ahmedabad, and Laxmi Starch in South India, represented such offshoots.

Industrialists in Bombay such as Tata, Chinoy, Wadia and Darbari Seth, have all promoted Indian technology and chemical industry. G M Modi in Meerut, Girdhar Lal and Lala Shri Ram in Delhi, diversified into alkali chlorine, and hydrogenated oil industries, as did Seshasayee in South India and G D Birla in Bengal and Western India. Industrialists from Chettinad in South India started educational technology institutions (Annamalai University, Alagappa Chettiar College of Technology) and chemical and fertiliser industries such as Parry and Co, and Southern Petrochemicals. Travancore State with its enlightened policy on education and science also promoted manufacture of fertilisers, rayon, aluminium and titanium. The Princely State of Baroda established a University and promoted modern industries.

Some industrialists of Bombay, such as Sir Vithal Chandavarkar, promoted training and research in textiles, chemicals, pharmaceuticals, dyes and vegetable oils through a new University Department of Chemical Technology. Similar initiatives were taken in Kanpur by industrialists such as Singhania of JK Industries, promoting the Hartcourt

Butler Institute of Technology, Kanpur University, and the National Sugar Institute and in Nagpur by Jamnalal Bajaj through the Nagpur Institute of Technology.

India was an exporter of vegetable oils until 1956. All those engaged in oil milling and vegetable oils produced electrolytic hydrogen for hydrogenated edible fats to supplement milk-based ghee. They were also manufacturers of soaps (Tata Oil Mill, Calcutta Chemical, Modi, Sarabhai Swastik Godrej, Lever). Hydrogen obtained from alkali units and chlorine led to hydrochloride, bleaching powder, chloro-hydrocarbons and PVC with carbide-based acetylene.

Scientific equipment for experimental work was designed and fabricated by scientists with skilled technicians. Raman, J C Bose, and M N Saha made their pioneering discoveries in this way. The construction of a mercury vacuum pump by Venkateswaran led to the Waran pump.

Scientific instruments production was ushered by Toshniwal and Andhra Scientific Company from laboratory experience. Skills in glass blowing and lens grinding were imparted to students.

Scientific equipment

There are numerous instances of total technologies before Independence in local raw material based chemical processes, and isolated cases of scientific measuring equipment, because of the demands for consumables. The manufacture of capital goods other than building materials, small arms and boats was not widespread. Even in buildings, other than bricks, cement and structural steel, items such as ceramics, pipes, valves, sanitary fittings, fans and electrical components, including bulbs, were imported. The exceptions were S L Kirloskar, T V Sundaram, and P S G Naidu, who introduced rotating machinery. Ship building continued in Mazagaon, Surat, and Hubli, although all instruments, engines and equipment were imported.

A significant initiative for the growth and diversification of the chemical industry in western India arose from the close association of Prof K Venkataraman, then Director of the Bombay University Department of Chemical Technology, and Dr Pai, a member of the Allied group of scientists, during the study of records of the German chemical giant Badische Anilin Soda Fabriken, immediately after the end of the war in Europe. Details of the technological processes for the production of numerous

synthetic dyes and pigments for textiles were gathered. Prof Venkataraman continued further research and pioneered the development and manufacture of synthetic dyes. He has recorded these in the 26 monumental volumes on the chemistry of synthetic dyes. The production of synthetic dyes, intermediates and basic raw materials from coal tar by numerous large, medium and small units resulted. Textile auxiliaries, detergents, and emulsifiers, were added to the list with investments by textile manufacturers and their families and employees. Production units were established in outer Bombay and Pune, as well as in many centres such as Vapi, Bulsar, Surat, Ahmedabad, Rajkot and Baroda.

Soon after independence, the need for new technologies and products became apparent. New petroleum refineries with total technology were established in Bombay and Vizag initially and subsequently in other coastal locations in Madras and Cochin. Apart from the discovery of oil from a surface leak in Dighboi, and the later construction of a 0.3 million tonne fractionation unit by the Assam Oil Company, exploration for petroleum in India was not favoured by any foreign company.

Oil exploration

Then came the discoveries of very large petroleum oil and gas reserves in new locations in the Persian Gulf, Middle East, Siberia, Nigeria, Algeria, Mexico, Brazil, Venezuela and in the offshore North Sea. This changed the picture regarding energy availability, storage, transport and usage. The low price initially prevailing with oversupply allowed a vast expansion of petroleum refining, gas fractionation, gas liquefaction and the replacement of coal as a raw material for chemicals and as a source for rail transport, electrical power generation, and as fuel for heat and cooking. As solid coal use needs ash disposal, and the cleaning of flue gases to meet new stringent environmental standards, petroleum oil and gas based technologies made a significant headway. As oil fluids are of uniform composition, the economies of scale in production of chemicals and energy have radically altered. Batch processes are replaced by continuous processes.

The potential role of petroleum was recognised in India by the then Oil Minister K D Malaviya. Supported by Jawaharlal Nehru, the minister paved the way for establishing the Oil and Natural Gas Commission in 1956 for the exploration, production and processing of oil and for conversion of this resource into major chemicals, polymers and fibre products.

Onshore oil and gas discovery in Gujarat in western India led within seven years to the establishment of an inland refinery in Baroda under the government-owned Indian Oil Corporation with Russian technology and equipment; it provided Indian engineers with an excellent opportunity to be associated with the transport of heavy, large equipment, and its erection, joining, testing, commissioning and operation. The Russian agency accepted the concept of total technology delivery responsibility while utilising Indian services. This experience in the Indian public sector oil processing industry has blossomed into a sophisticated capability that is internationally accepted.

At a time when coal was the major resource for chemicals, the sustained efforts of a group of scientists, technologists and engineers at Sindri, situated in the area of coal mines, outlined processes for the preparation of ammonia fertilizers. They formed part of the large Government-owned Fertilizer Corporation of India as a research, development, and design engineering project organisation.

Catalysts

They were able to develop and produce several high quality catalysts for use in the production of ammonia and products such as urea and ammonium sulphate and phosphate. Several manufacturing plants were also established in different parts of India. This experience of local development was valuable. The availability of petroleum gas, fuel oil and naptha made such basic materials more attractive from 1970 onwards, when in co-operation with a major Italian organisation, larger single stream, energy efficient ammonia plants were designed and constructed.

A similar design and project service organisation has been developed by Fertilizers and Chemicals Travancore Ltd. The Council of Scientific and Industrial Research has grown to be the major research and development organisation. Processes developed for batch production of basic aromatic organic chemicals have been absorbed, adapted and improved. The conversion of a laboratory research preparative process needed substantial pilot plants, design engineering and equipment fabrication capabilities. These had to be developed by professional design engineering

project organisations, not available in India during the first quarter century after Independence. There were very few units capable of fabrication of reactors, heat exchangers, furnaces, valves, and instruments and these could not easily be imported due to the need to conserve currency in the two decades after 1960.

During this period of about 15 years, there were many instances of medium size organisations evolving their own processes and products, mainly of a non-capital goods nature, towards self-reliance, self-sufficiency and some export. Most of these utilised natural local resources which had not been well developed or even identified. The country became a major producer of essential oils, natural and synthetic terpenic perfumery and flavour materials utilising, among others, pine oils, citronella, palmarosa, citrus, linaloe berry, geranium, lemongrass and vetiver. The industry has grown several fold with substantial technological advances.

Likewise organisations such as the Indian associate of Unilever identified many unusual seed oils and developed technologies for adding annually a quarter million oils for industrial use. An outstanding example is also the development and growth of non-soap detergent in a bar form in India representing a world-class innovation. There are success stories relating to textile auxiliaries, additives, and modifiers, and food colours and dyes. Others relate to leather and leather goods with strong technological development from the Central Leather Research Institute.

Milk revolution

Another breakthrough was in milk and milk products, covering the full range of animal husbandry, collection from small farmers and processing. Dr V Kurien provided a dynamic leadership and worked out the entire operation, including the production of stainless steel vessels and other capital equipment. A milk revolution was thus ushered in by the Indian Dairy Corporation and the Kaira Milk Producers Co-operative.

The Government of India recognised the increased demand for petroleum products as fuel for lighting, cooking and transport as well as for efficient fertiliser manufacture. The Ministry of Petroleum and Chemicals supported the move to upgrade Indian capabilities by forming a partnership with Bechtel USA. Thus a company named Engineers India Ltd was established. The original objective of building five energy efficient high capacity nitrogen fertiliser plants from 1966 onwards did not fructify and Bechtel withdrew from the partnership transferring its shares to the government. Engineers India concentrated on petroleum refining, petrochemicals, polymers and fibres.

Two other major initiatives by the government were directed to maximise technology delivery from highly co-ordinated Indian efforts. The first was the formation of the fully government-owned Indian Petrochemicals Corporation Ltd in 1969 to produce intermediates for the production of polyester and a major complex including olefins from a naptha cracker and other plants for conversion of olefins to polymers such as linear polyethylene, polypropylene, polybutadine rubber, polyvinyl chloride and olefin based acrylonitrile and its conversion to acrylic fibre.

Production of other major chemicals such as linear alkyl benzene (made only in Spain at that time) and ethylene oxide/glycol was also planned. Only very small quantities of nonlinear polyethylene, PVC and polyester had been produced in the country at that time. The second major decision was in each case to purchase processes and for some items basic engineering only. All common systems for 18 different utilities and processing of effluents and byproducts, as well as the overall integration of the entire complex including storage and safety were assigned to IPCL.

Detailed engineering

The entire detailed engineering, requiring over three million man hours, as well as procurement, inspection, certification during fabrication in supplier plants, construction planning and supervision of erection at site services were assigned to EIL, in addition to basic engineering for some projects and in total utilities and infrastructure. From 1972 the National Committee on Science and Technology formulated strategies to meet needs of self-reliant growth in every sector, under the dynamic leadership of the then Minister, C Subramaniam. Excellent detailed reports resulted from close interactions with hundreds of scientists, technologists, engineers and leaders in education, research development and industry. Such national consultations and commitment to a vision of science-based development led to policies for rapid

achievements. These are reflected in the commitment in EIL and IPCL. The Department of Science and Technology was established to implement the plans.

An action committee on public enterprises was established, under the chairmanship of M S Pathak who also held the positions of Member, Planning Commission, and Chairman and Managing Director, EIL. Several public sector enterprises in each sector were merged. Ailing private units in cotton, jute textiles and pharmaceuticals were acquired by government for rehabilitation. An R&D plan was prepared for such enterprises. A key role was played by Lovraj Kumar, the first Rhodes Scholar from India, who, after association with the oil industry through Shell, joined the Government. He led a group to support EIL and IPCL from the early '60s and functioned as a non-executive member of their Boards. He promoted linkages between public sector companies, universities and research institutions.

The development of IPCL by successfully mobilising a very large number of Indian industrial units to accept challenges for design and fabrication of complex special items of equipment generated high motivation within the company, EIL and others involved. New project teams for each of the 15 projects in both companies accepted near impossible targets and 70-hour working weeks. The operations group in the plant for xylene and terephthalate achieved record production and profit, restoring overall confidence.

Malaviya's role
K D Malaviya patiently absorbed the details of the developments and potential in petrochemicals and arranged an audio-visual presentation to Prime Minister Indira Gandhi, all senior Ministers and Planning Commission Members in the Prime Minister's Committee Room in August 1975. The room, little altered since 1926, had to be provided with electrical wiring for plug points to enable the use of audio-visual equipment. This resulted in the release of financial resources and government interest in the use of polymer fibres for national development in sectors such as water conservation, agriculture, food storage, health and medicine, energy, transport, housing, education, telecommunications and national security.

Earlier these materials had to be imported and there were severe restrictions on such imports. Several new measures were taken, such as the creation of the Central Institute of Plastics Engineering and Technology at Madras, with Regional Centres. A National Committee on Plastics in Agriculture helped to promote the use of plastics by farmers and in water management, food packaging and transport. Plastic and fibre processing equipment manufacture received attention. Large numbers are employed in small units in acrylic fibre knitting and in fabrics and garments production. Employment generation and economic development from these has been very high with small investments.

Similarly a project on polyester filament yarn promoted by IPCL as a new corporation adjacent to the olefin complex added 3500 tonnes of yarn to the meagre 1200 tonnes available in 1978 and made the material available, overcoming shortages and high prices. These initiatives were successful. The polyester yarn and fibre production exceeded one million tonnes per annum in 1998 and prices have been continuously reduced.

The implementation of the IPCL cracker complex projects involved the generation of entirely new capabilities in the country in the fabrication of a wide range of items of equipment to international standards. Several public and private sector engineering companies were given orders for supply of equipment not made by them then, on an understanding that they would obtain know-how and technology. In other cases, IPCL arranged for expertise from abroad and provided large loans to such companies for acquiring machines needed. Stagewise inspection at the production units and constant requalification of welders as well as raw materials such as steel, SS sheets, special alloy tubes, valves, pumps, motors, and flameproof fittings enabled suppliers and fabricators to meet quality standards.

Cracker

Notable among these units are those of Bharat Heavy Electricals Ltd in Tiruchi and Hyderabad, Bharat Heavy Plates and Vessels Vizag, KGF Bangalore, Bharat Pumps and Compressors Allahabad, Larsen and Toubro, Kaveri Engineering, Kota Instruments and Bestobel. Similarly several new Indian groups were mobilised to carry out major projects of mechanical erection, one for each of the 15 projects and additional groups for 18 shared utilities systems. About 800 persons were trained to qualify as Class I welders by IPCL.

Many moved to West Asia to meet very large demands in processing oil and gas and yet about 200 could be available at any time to the mechanical erection contractors. National and private scientific research institutions provided vital inputs.

The Department of Aeronautics of the Indian Institute of Science carried out wind tunnel tests to determine destructive resonance vibrations on models of a pair of towers resulting in a change of distance of separation from the original plan. The Associated Cement Company R&D Centre in co-operation with IPCL developed molecular sieves and arranged to supply them.

The National Chemical Laboratory, Pune, developed basic process designs for manufacture of four acrylate esters by IPCL for which technology from other sources was not available. The joint efforts of NCL, IPCL and EIL resulted in successful production on a large scale of all these despite the risks of corrosion and explosive heat generation in unexpected polymerisation. The Central Electrochemical Research Institute of the CSIR and the Bhabha Atomic Research Centre contributed in corrosion prevention technologies.

Another breakthrough was the development of new high performance catalysts for hydrocarbon reforming and isomerisation. This was achieved through co-ordinated efforts by NCL, the Indian Institute of Petroleum of CSIR and IPCL. These were then manufactured by IPCL and used in several refineries and in IPCL itself. This laid the base for further development, international co-operation and export of technologies in a highly sophisticated and competitive area. Catalysis has also been the interest of the Fertilizer Corporation of India at Sindri, situated amidst coal mines. It has provided major catalysts in the fertiliser industry. Research studies in IISc Bangalore and later in the Indian Institute of Technology, Kharagpur, were very valuable.

India is among the leading countries in homogeneous and heterogeneous catalysis R&D and is providing many technologies in chemical, petroleum, gas, petrochemical, fertiliser, pharmaceutical, and pest control agent industries and for meeting environmental standards in power generation, automobiles, primary metals, metal forming casting, foundry and glass ceramic industries.

Another important development is in the involvement of EIL in separation processes. The Heat and Mass Transfer Division designed valve trays for distillation columns and arranged for their fabrication by Godrej Ltd Bombay from 1975 and installation in units in IPCL and refineries for high efficiency separation and purification of fractions of liquids and liquefied gases. Constant improvements are being made to remain competitive internationally. Molecular sieves for separation and drying have been developed by ACC.

EIL is also assisting in a project on water desalination by membranes in co-operation with the Central Salt and Marine Chemicals Research Institute, Bhavnagar, and Madras Refineries Ltd. Total technology for large scale liquified petroleum gas production in India was accomplished in 1978 by EIL and resulted in the establishment of plants in Uran near Bombay by ONGC and their operation by IPCL personnel. Addition of many such units from Bombay High Gas has led to very high increase in local production of LPG and in the entire equipment supplied from Indian sources.

Recognition of these capabilities got EIL assignments in Algeria and Abu Dhabi as the managers for LPG and liquefied natural gas projects then being executed by US and Japanese companies. An unusual case of technological knowledge and delivery experience was the iron ore water slurry pipeline in Karnataka, transporting ore to Mangalore port for export to Iran from 1977–80. An R&D and pilot project initiated by EIL in the Regional Research Laboratory, Bhubaneswar in Orissa gave some basic insights which could be applied to the Karnataka Project with specifications evolved by Canadian Metchem. These were revived by EIL and the plant has been operated successfully. There are numerous opportunities for such transport of coal, ores and byproducts in non-ferrous metal units. In winter, slurry problems in waxy crude in the Bombay High transport pipelines to Mathura Refinery near Delhi often need remedial measures.

A remarkable institution developed by Prof M S Valiathan, the distinguished medical research scientist and heart surgeon, is the Chitra Tirunal Centre for Medical Science and Technology at Thiruvananthapuram in Kerala on the south west coast of India. The technology wing is renowned for its development of a PVC special polymer bag for human blood collection, storage and transport.

Technology was delivered to a new company for manufacture of one million bags in 1986 at a time when such technology and production was limited to Japan and Korea. The technology has revolutionised blood availability for critical use and has allowed increased production to five million bags per annum. Technology is being transferred to other developing countries. Equally brilliant has been the evolution of design, fabrication and testing to meet the highest international standards, of the Chitra Heart Valve, and its manufacture in India.

CIBA recognised the potential for new drugs from natural material after the extraordinary success of it's Reserpin. The company started a major modern research centre in Bombay 1961. It was inaugurated by Pandit Jawaharlal Nehru in the presence of several Nobel Laureates, including Robert Robinson, Vladimir Prelog, Robert Woodword and Alexander Todd. Under the direction of Prof T R Govindachari, who had worked with Roger Adams, a brilliant team of organic chemists and biologists at the centre trained a large number of researchers.

The centre did not continue, but its scientists worked in research institutions related to the fine chemicals industry. India has built up significant capabilities in the sectors of synthetic drugs, agrochemicals, speciality chemicals, synthetic dyes, and textile auxiliaries. The Indian Institute of Chemical Technology, Hyderabad, the NCL, and the Central Drug Research Institute, Lucknow, have demonstrated expertise in hydrogen cyanide, and cyanuryl chloride.

State support

Technological capability is achieved through state support and by creating an appropriate investment climate for commercial companies. The contracts given by the government to aircraft and defence systems companies for new developments allowed a large write-off. In many countries, companies are free in any year to decide on the percentage of claim for depreciation of capital assets and deduction from profits. These encourage high-risk high-profit ventures in frontier areas. Governments have prmoted mergers of related businesses to evolve strong national companies, as in aircraft, automobiles, chemicals, telecom and computers in Europe and America. □

C N R Rao
Jawaharlal Nehru Centre for
Advanced Scientific Research
Bangalore

Personal reflections on science

When India gained freedom in 1947, I had just started the first year of college. It was a time of tremendous enthusiasm and expectation. A tidal wave of a sense of fulfilment and determination, and a spirit of nationalism seemed to sweep the country. The leaders at that time, in particular Mahatma Gandhi and Pandit Nehru, meant a great deal, personally, to the people. They talked not only of hopes but of a dream and vision to be fulfilled: the unique destiny of India. There were few institutions for advanced study and research in science and technology, but the situation soon began to change. Nehru had faith in science and technology (S&T) as an instrument of national development. He could not envisage an India where S&T did not play a major role in solving societal problems or in taking the country forward to a well-rounded development. A number of institutions were therefore to be established after 1947.

It was in this ethos that many young people like me went into science and engineering, although a future in S&T was uncertain. When I decided to study chemistry for my master's degree in Benares, it was not clear what place chemistry or science would have in the country's future. There was, however, an implicit faith that the future would bring change and that India would have a large number of scientists and engineers.

After my master's degree in science in the early 1950s, I had to go to the US for a PhD, since there were few good institutions at home. By the '60s and '70s, a large number of institutions had begun to provide excellent training in various fields of S&T. The space and atomic energy programmes had started showing results, as had the agricultural modernisation project. Our efforts in strategic areas, where we were denied technologies and materials, became fairly effective. Indian science and the S&T institutions seemed to have come of age by the '70s. There was still a gap between what was considered sufficient to carry out good research and the real needs of a modern laboratory, but this gap no longer seemed too big to bridge.

The setting up of the National Committee on Science and Technology in the early 1970s during Indira Gandhi's tenure as Prime Minister, was a landmark in science planning. This committee, chaired by Mr C Subramaniam on which I sat as a young member, prepared the first major S&T plan for the country. It was responsible for setting up some of the important new structures, including the Science and Engineering Research Council and the Regional Sophisticated Instruments Facilities. The committee evolved subsequently as the Science Advisory Council to the Prime Minister (SAC-PM), during Rajiv Gandhi's tenure in the 1980s. As Chairman of the Council, I had the privilege of participating in the far-sighted contributions that SAC-PM made, such as setting up the Technology Information, Forecasting and Assessment Council (TIFAC) and the high-tech computer R&D centre, C-DAC, for parallel processing and the organisation of seven major technology missions. After the 1980s, even as the geopolitical and global economic scenarios changed radically, the government, unfortunately, was without any science advisory mechanism for a period.

Globalisation and the pressure of competitiveness brought home the urgent need for a change in the emphasis and the direction of the S&T effort in India. A Scientific Advisory Committee, appointed by the Gujral government, made recommendations on

support for science in educational institutions and on some aspects of the patents regime. The report found an enthusiastic response.

The greatest challenge India faces today is to undertake and develop the type of science and technology which is globally competitive while simultaneously contributing to the needs of the country. I feel this challenge will be answered by the scientific community, if the problems are suitably posed. The demands on Indian science and technology have changed because of the changed economic and geopolitical scenario. Indian industry in the past never made great demands on the R&D systems although some industries benefited from the laboratories' contribution to industrial development. Today, as industry has to turn increasingly to innovation, the need for R&D is crucial and until industry acquires substantive R&D capabilities, the government has a key catalytic role to play.

Also, since one can buy almost anything from the market, the science pursued today must be relevant to the international scene. This is true of our efforts in strategic as well as technology-related areas. There is no point in developing technologies for some unknown user or hypothetical industry; we have to develop technologies that are as good as anywhere else. To add to the complexity of the challenge,

Indian scientists are generally exhorted to work on problems that are socially relevant. I understand the spirit of this argument, but carried too far, it can restrict the scientists working on new ideas. To argue that one must be independent in science would be difficult, for there is also inter-dependence in science. Influences and ideas travel across geographical boundaries, and, when the issues are in the frontier areas, it is not possible to steer free of prevailing trends of enquiry.

Certainly, the problems of society need a larger component of long-term fundamental research. It is important, then, to see that the total scientific effort of a country has the right mix, related to the basic needs of the people, the long-term needs of the nation, and contemporary science. Research efforts today require a high degree of sophistication and interlinkages.

India was looked upon by most of the advanced countries as a recipient of knowledge. Over the years, this image has changed. In fundamental research, there had always been successful informal programmes involving Indian scientists and those in the US and Europe. Among the programmes, the most successful was that with the erstwhile USSR. As co-chairman, along with academician Marchuk, of the long-term collaboration programme between the two countries, I saw the Soviet Academy in its days of glory. The Indo-Soviet programme put in place some sound projects involving technology development. The Indo-French Centre for the promotion of advanced scientific research is another programme which has been eminently successful The Indo-Japan Science Council has been promoting collaboration among scientists.

I would like to relate one or two specific instances of international collaboration to illustrate the type of efforts that succeeded. As the Director of the Indian Institute of Science, I encouraged the establishment of an advanced biotechnology research centre in collaboration with the Astra company of Sweden. Initially set up in the Institute campus, it matured into an independent laboratory and moved out of the campus, and is now doing extremely well. The research laboratory employs the best of Indian scientists, including those from abroad, and carries out internationally acclaimed research in medical biotechnology. Since that experiment, leading industries in the world have come to India to set up R&D units in India to take advantage of the pool of competent scientists and the relatively low costs. For India, it is a useful way to participate in global R&D, and reach out to international investors as well. The Indian software industry serves a large number of companies abroad.

For all the problems, those who have made a sincere effort in research and development have succeeded. Whether I was leading my group in the setting up of the radio telescope or working in advanced materials, we have had satisfaction and success. As the infrastructure for R&D improves substantially, there will be fewer teething problems and greater support for contemporary research.

Over the years, Indian S&T efforts have contributed to many areas, developing indigenous capabilities in rockets, satellites and nuclear reactors. While such big programmes have worked because they secured proper allocations, the universities have not been adequately supported. Yet in spite of severe limitations, fundamental research in India has flowed mainly from educational institutions. Today, there is a realisation that without it being strengthened, the educational sector cannot contribute productively to the S&T efforts or impart the best post-graduate and doctoral training.

Finally, I would like to reiterate that India's standing agenda has been to inculcate the scientific temper among its citizens as part of its commitment to democracy. India's foundational dream has been to contribute, on the one hand, to innovative science and technology at the highest level, and on the other, to the solving of pressing problems of mankind. I consider adequate support to science and education to be the most crucial of infrastructural elements. It is crucial to the fulfilment of the special dream that was articulated in 1947. □

K R Naryanan
(1920–2005)

What underpins science in India

India achieved a high standing in the field of science, technology and industrial production largely due to the vision and wisdom of Nehru. He encouraged and supported science education and research as well as the application of science and technology to problems of development. We tend to overlook this fundamental achievement of long-term significance. How far-sighted Nehru was in giving importance to science and technology! As early as 1937, while addressing the Indian Science Congress, he said, "Even more than the present, the future belongs to science and to those who make friends with science and seek its help for the advancement of humanity." Referring to India, he asserted: "It was science alone that could solve the problems of hunger and poverty, of insanitation and illiteracy, of superstition and deadening custom and tradition, of vast resources running to waste, of a rich country inhabited by starving people."

In 1938, under his inspiration, the National Planning Committee of the Indian National Congress set up a working group on scientific research, and after India became independent, Nehru assumed charge of the Ministry of Scientific and Cultural Affairs in 1949. He was probably the first Minister of Science in the world, though Lord Hailsham who was appointed Britain's Minister of Science in 1963 claimed to be 'the first Minister of Science' in the universe!

The Scientific Policy Resolution adopted by Parliament in 1958, formalised India's commitment to the development of science and technology. The resolution declared the aim of the Government's Science Policy to "secure for the people of the country all the benefits that can accrue from the acquisition and application of scientific method." Let us not forget that the steel mills and atomic reactors, when they were first established, were decried by some as white elephants and mere showpieces. The pioneering role played by Nehru in the advancement of science was a significant contribution. It is possible to find drawbacks in the system of science and technology built up during the Nehru era, but no one can deny the importance of the chain of educational and research institutions, and above all the dissemination of the idea of science and the method of science which Nehru promoted as the basis of a progressive social order.

Mankind today is turning to new realms in search of resources. It is reaching to the depths of the oceans and to the infinity of space in a spectacular outward expansion, and moving inwards, more or less, releasing energy from within the atom, exploring and exploiting, through biotechnology, the inner mysteries of life and devising novel methods of extracting the maximum out of the known resources. It's to the credit of our political leadership and, of course, our scientists, that we have built up a sophisticated infrastructure of science and technology, tried to keep pace with the advances in knowledge and know-how in the world, and are participating in the new adventures of science which provide us with the means of tackling some of the major socio-economic problems of the country.

To give just one example, technology had a crucial part to play in our Green Revolution and in the attainment of basic food self-sufficiency. It has added an important new dimension to our programmes pertaining to agriculture, irrigation, power, communications, health, education and industrialisation. One overriding objective of

Nehru was to build the intellectual and technological infrastructure of the nation in order to ensure self-reliant development. He knew that total technological dependence and political independence did not go together, even though he believed in the independence of nations and in increasing international cooperation. In 1957, during a debate in Parliament on the Atomic Energy Department, he said: "It is very necessary for us not to depend too much on the outside sources. If we depend too much on others for fissionable material, then, inevitably that dependence may affect us in the sense that other people may try to affect our foreign policy or any other policy through that dependence... If we have to depend too much on that central pool which contains very special fissionable materials like Uranium 235 or Plutonium 233 then we shall have to submit to all kinds of conditions." These words proved to be prophetic.

External pressures

It has become necessary to go boldly ahead with our scientific and technological programmes untramelled by outside pressures, and "by offering good conditions of service to scientists and according them an honoured position" as enjoined by the Scientific Policy Resolution. If at this critical juncture we lack audacity and lag behind in our scientific-technological effort we may well lose the most opportune moment for attaining not only advanced knowledge and techniques but influence and status in the world.

Nehru's belief in science was not the result of a blind faith in the march of technology. He had always emphasised the social and the human aspects of science, the need to make science serve many by applying it not only in heavy industries and other sophisticated fields, but in agriculture, small industry, and in innumerable fields relating to the daily life and culture of the ordinary man. He pleaded particularly for the cultivation in society of the temper and approach to science, pointing out the paradox that even great scientists could be, outside the realm of their scientific work, totally unscientific and devoid of the temper and approach associated with scientific method. He once said that while science offered hope to mankind, "more wonderful than Earth and heavens is the mind and spirit of man which grows ever mightier and seeks fresh worlds to conquer." He also declared "Without science you perish: without spirituality you perish." His was the philosophy of 'scientific humanism' based at once on faith in the infinite potentialities of science and in the supremacy of the mind and spirit of man.

When man has plumbed the depths of the oceans uncovering the riches of Neptune's realm, when he has reached the moon, when he has experimented with himself through genetic engineering and clonal reproduction, and when he has invented instruments of mass destruction that can annihilate the human race itself, it is important to reflect upon the philosophy of scientific humanism as a practical guide for survival in the nuclear-missile-satellite age. Leon Trotsky (I hope it is not counter-revolutionary to invoke his name) has dreamt of the perfection of man through a threefold process, viz., technical mastery of nature, social constructiveness, and psychological self-education. He envisioned that through this three-fold development "Man will grow incomparably stronger, wiser, subtler; his body will become more harmonious, his voice more musical. The forms of his existence will acquire a more dynamic theatrical quality. The average man will rise to the stature of Aristotle, Goethe, Marx, and above these peaks new peaks will appear."

Matching development

I do not know how agreeable it would be to live in a world where everybody is a genius. But science has opened up prospects for realisation of the dream of the perfectability of man, provided technological advance is matched by social, educational and psychological advancement. Without this matching development, human beings might well be reduced to the position of glorified automatons in a 'tetragonal' society.

Computers have already begun to overshadow man by taking away from him a variety of organisational and even intellectual functions, and threaten to alienate him from work, from society and from life-experience. Genetics is advancing with such rapidity that 'the technological copying' of man and of creating 'a model man' through genetic technology has become a weird practical proposition. It is well-known that in the field of military technology developments have long ago passed the stage of 'over-kill' of mankind and the destruction of civilisation.

All this is happening without any significant advance in 'the social constructiveness' and 'the psychological self-education of man'. While science and technology is transforming the world into a global village, mankind has advanced very little either in terms of human consciousness or social organisation, which might turn out to be a dichotomy of tragic dimensions. Since science has come to stay and since the world of tomorrow is going to be one of computers, electronics and satellites, "the problem" as Charles Reich has pointed out "is not one of escaping from modern technology but of mastering it." But it may be asked whether man will be able to master modern technology if the pace of its growth is blind advance of genius and inventiveness allied to money and politics, unrelated to the evolution of the social order and human consciousness and untramelled by social responsibility and normative values.

Human enterprise

A distinguished academic, Prof Ervin Laszlo, has answered this question in the following way: "Science can, and no doubt will, continue to pursue paths of pure research, having no other objective but the acquisition of scientific knowledge. But science is a human enterprise, not above concern for human condition. At a time when that condition is seriously threatened, science must devote a sizeable portion of its energies, talents and funds to evolve the kind of knowledge which is of the most urgent human and social significance." While man is mastering nature and adapting himself to nature, he has now got to master and adapt himself to the second nature that he has himself created in the form of a vast complex of science and technology.

The old but still prevalent dangers of floods, famines, hurricanes, diseases, poverty, population pressure, violent conflicts and wars have been compounded by environmental threats arising out of a technological civilisation, and the danger of total annihilation of the human race posed by the proliferating nuclear-missile weaponry.

One cannot say that because of these perils science must stop, for there could be no doubt that on the advance of science and technology and its wide and wise application to human, social and environmental problems hinges the salvation of mankind. But it is necessary and possible to devote greater attention to and

allocate more funds for developing knowledge and know-how which are of the most urgent human and social significance.

If these immediate tasks of eradicating poverty, disease, inequality and injustice are neglected by science in favour of conquests of the planets, and the acquisition of instruments of political, economic and military power, it might well lead to the hegemony of an elite class or an elite group of nations. This technological despotism of the future will be more hideous and totalitarian than anything that has occurred in history so far. Therefore, a satisfactory social and international order, a reconciliation of conflicting interests and the fashioning of common goals and supranational institutions on Earth are essential if man's leap into other worlds is not to produce a nightmare or a terrible end for mankind.

Challenge

For us it is perhaps idle to speak about the infinite benefits or the terrible consequences of science and technology. Almost all of us in India, indeed the vast majority of the people in the world, live without enjoying the full benefits of this knowledge and technology. We are very far away from the world of technological civilisation. But we understand for the upliftment of our people and for the modernisation of our society, it is essential to rely upon science and technology. This fact might give us an opportunity to use science for human and social purposes, to plan our technological development in tune with the human, cultural and social values we cherish. The challenge that we face is not only to catch up with the scientific and technological revolution, but to integrate our values as well as our needs with this inexorable process so that we may build a just, progressive social order in our country and make a contribution to a new and equitable order in the world. If man cannot give a human face and social purpose to science, one may well say of him with Shakespeare:

But man, proud man,
Drest in a little brief authority,
Most ignorant of what he is most assured,
His glassy essence, like an angry ape,
Plays such fantastic tricks before high heaven,
As make the angels weep. □

K R Narayanan, President of India (1997–2002), was at one time the Minister for Science and Technology. This contribution is being reproduced from the first volume, INNOVATIVEINDIA.

IN DEPTH

Raja M Mitra
Analyst

India emerging as global R&D centre

The principal factors pointing to India's potential to be a major R&D power are the size of its educated workforce, entrepreneurial traditions and a significant existing R&D-related institutional infrastructure. On the whole, India has made major advancement in these areas in the past decades. It has a diverse range of public sector R&D undertakings. The central government has been the major investor in higher education as well as in R&D in the country. There are about 200 national laboratories and an equal number of R&D institutes in the central sector and about 1300 R&D units in the industrial sector. The number of people employed in these R&D establishments is estimated to be around 300,000. The other major entities pursuing S&T activities include the university system, comprising more than 162 universities, 32 institutions deemed to be universities and 10 institutes of special national importance.

Despite the government's stated ambitions to foster research, the results have been mixed, with bio-technology and space being examples where significant progress has been made while progress has been limited in areas such as non-renewable energy. Since the '90s there have been numerous changes in the governments R&Ds focus. Spending on defence has increased and the pattern of industrial research has changed. The government has increased its allocation to various scientific agencies. Government R&D is becoming more result oriented and mission-based. This is likely to enhance the effectiveness of government R&D. The linkages are evolving as consortia research is increasing and this will induce the national system of innovation to be a networked one. There has been an increase in demand-pull innovations after economic liberalization due to the intense competition from global firms. In addition, efforts have been made by government and private sector entities to develop closer links between the country's universities and the corporate sector.

Corporate R&D

India's emergence as a major economic, knowledge-based services and R&D power will clearly have wide-ranging local and global consequences. The imperative to specialize and internationalize R&D operations is driven globally by intensified international competition, rising costs of R&D in advanced industrial economies and the scarcity of engineering and scientific manpower. In this context the increasing complexity of R&D and the need for rapid responses to changes in technology, legal and regulatory frameworks and markets are also important.

At the same time, the attractiveness of carrying out R&D in India or in its emerging high-technology industry clusters is increased by the growing availability of innovative entrepreneurial, scientific and engineering skills and manpower at competitive costs, the ongoing globalization of manufacturing processes and service delivery, and substantial and fast-growing markets.

The impact of India's development is poised to be significant in major sectors such as ICT, industrial manufacturing and in other areas such as engineering, energy, agriculture, environmental technology and life sciences. Continued rapid growth is also expected in IT-enabled services, spearheaded by developments in the software industry, coupled with those in ICT hardware and telecommunications.

These services include the higher-end, knowledge process industry niches (e.g. finance, accounting, insurance, education, health etc.). The knowledge process outsourcing industry has considerable growth potential in a wide range of areas. It may well employ more individuals than traditional R&D operations within the next five to ten years.

The development of networks and high-tech industry clusters has been fostered by improved communication and by the internet in particular. The mobility of qualified and talented human resources within India and internationally has also been one of the prominent attractions for high-tech industry and R&D developments in India.

The rapid development of industrial clusters has been a central factor in the growth of the software and IT-enabled services industries in India, especially in the export sectors of those industries. Initiatives by the government to establish software industrial parks were pivotal in this respect. It has promoted development through industrial clustering in IT, biotech, engineering and in other fields. These initiatives include the launching of new special economic zones (SEZ).

R&D towns

Bangalore, Delhi, Mumbai, Pune, Hyderabad and Chennai have so far been the most preferred destinations for R&D in the country. Factors such as the combined presence of foreign companies, research labs and educational institutes have made these locations attractive centres for R&D operations. The benefit of locating to these cities has been demonstrated by the continued, rapid corporate expansion, despite the major local challenges of physical infrastructure bottlenecks, environmental degradation, high attrition rates, wage inflation and social problems.

The development of the software and business process outsourcing industries in India illustrates the importance of skills development and networks. India's initial entry into the software business has much to do with its access to a large pool of low-cost human resources. Subsequently the country also developed a significant number of vendors capable of meeting high quality standards and conducting R&D.

A key feature of the Indian talent scene is that it is much more globally mobile than labour in general. Indians account for more

than 40 per cent of the temporary work visas issued by the United States to foreign workers. Further, the Indian diaspora's long-established success in the US has played a central role in facilitating the flow of talent back and forth between the two countries. In short, the Indian diaspora is playing an increasingly important role in a wide range of knowledge-based industries in North America, Europe as well as in Asian economies.

Challenges for MNCs

India is a major player in the so-called 'global war for talent' in the knowledge-based industries and in research. Generally, foreign multinational companies and major Indian firms recruit and retain much of the top-level talent in India. They typically offer higher salaries and advanced training, combined with attractive international career opportunities— advantages most domestic companies are often unable to match. The demand for skilled human resources is rising in India, illustrating the growing competition for talent within the country and globally.

In many respects, India is still in an early phase of development in the areas of the high-tech industries and international R&D. There exists considerable scope for building on strengths and tackling weaknesses in the national innovation system and the corporate investment climate. Challenges include the critical needs of improving the physical infrastructure and the education system, laws and practices governing labor markets, taxation, land and real estate development, intellectual property rights and general functioning of government institutions at both the central and state level. Moreover, it is essential to build private-public partnerships, expand foreign investment and enhance the role of the Indian diaspora and other forms of international collaboration.

Despite these challenges, India can still emerge as one of the world's principal centers for offshoring of knowledge processing, R&D and high-technology industry investment and trade. Multinational companies are already developing the capabilities of the country to undertake production-supportive and adaptive R&D and design work, as well as developing innovative means of undertaking knowledge processing work. The driving motive is that the cost of not having comprehensive strategies for developing economic and technology relations with India (and China) will prove to be significant, especially for companies with global aspirations.

The fact that more companies (American, European, Indian and others) have increasingly internationally distributed systems for undertaking R&D is part of the globalization processes reflected in foreign trade, investment and human resource developments, covering not only goods production but also services.

It can be argued that India's contemporary trajectory regarding industrial and S&T developments is significantly different from earlier experiences of economic catching-up in Europe and East Asia. Unlike past experiences from Japan and most other countries, offshoring-oriented corporate expansions have been key drivers in the rapid emergence of high technology centres and industries in India since the '90s; the software industry being a prime example.

In addition, development in India's high technology industry is taking place in an era when the internet and a wide range of global and local alliances and virtual networks are crucial in R&D and innovation, as well as more generally for economic and social development.

Confidence

The confidence in India's R&D potential is evident from a statement by R A Mashelkar in 2003: "India has the potential to become the number one knowledge-producing centre in the world by 2025, going by the way things are moving."

India's emergence as a major economic and R&D power is poised to have wide-ranging implications for the people of India and globally. These include effects on trade, investment, employment, the environment and trajectories for national industrial and technological developments.

An Economist Intelligence Unit (EIU) global survey conducted in 2004 found that multinational companies are redistributing their product innovation activities across the globe. Some 70 per cent of the companies surveyed employed R&D people overseas; 52 per cent reported that increasing overseas R&D spending was a priority. When asked to choose the most likely centres for overseas investment, India ranked third (behind the US and China), attracting 28 per cent of the respondents.

Furthermore, the EIU survey found that 70 per cent of companies employing R&D workers overseas considered India a 'R&D hotspot'. EIU

defined a R&D hotspot as "a place where companies can tap into existing networks of scientific and technical expertise; which has good links to academic research facilities; and provides an environment where innovation is supported and easy to commercialize." India is claimed to have many of these qualities.

American firms

US companies have so far led in expanding the production of offshoring services in India. There are however strong indications of a rapid expansion of R&D activities by a large number of stakeholders. This is illustrated by the way British, Canadian, Chinese, German, Swedish and other companies are expanding their operations in India.

In short, in recent years a common perception has been that India can emerge as a major international R&D and knowledge process outsourcing (KPO) power and more effective absorber of existing technologies, products and manager of business organizations. This is reflected in the statements of top corporate leaders, financial institutions, consulting firms, government officials and academics. The optimism exhibited by key stakeholders has resulted in the expansion of R&D operations of foreign and Indian companies, directed at both the local and international markets.

India does have a long way to go before it can claim to be one of the world's principal powers in R&D and innovation. Some scholars question the sustainability of current trends of high economic growth and rapid expansion of multinational corporate R&D investment. Many stress the possible risks associated with uneven development and the sharp socio-economic disparities within the country.

These risks are associated with increased foreign financial and other dependencies, as well as weaknesses in the system of governance at central and state levels. Others point to signs of institutional decay and erosion of the human talent base in some areas of science, including basic, or theoretical.

Future developments critically depend on forceful action by government and corporate stakeholders to build on opportunities and strengths, while simultaneously responding to risks and tackling shortcomings. Despite the challenges, the country appears poised to become an eminent player in R&D and innovation in an increasingly wide range of areas. □

From a working paper by the author for the Swedish Institute for Growth Policy Studies (courtesy itps).

Kirsten Bound
Senior Rsearcher, DEMOS, UK

Interdependent innovation

Alpesh Patel is a talent scout. As one of eight 'dealmakers' commissioned by the UK Trade and Investment's Global Entrepreneur Programme, he scours India for budding innovators to match with UK investors. Patel has learned that to find the best ideas he needs to venture off the beaten track. One excursion took him to a hidden corner of the University of Hyderabad, where an Ivy League-trained professor had developed some promising intellectual property (IP). But what startled Patel was the setting in which the discovery had been made: protruding through the window of the dusty laboratory was a large tree, its growth a force of nature that the university had been unwilling or unable to tame.

India's science is not straightforward. It's a complex mix of factors and forces which can create unexpected results and confound easy clichés. Something significant is stirring in India, and science and innovation is crucial to it. But India's rising is uneven, its trajectory uncertain.

So many Indias co-exist, and all are moving at different speeds. Not long ago, India was a low growth economy and aid recipient. Now it is more open and dynamic, both culturally and commercially. The buzz around science is part of that. Yet underdevelopment still casts a long shadow. Large parts of the country remain impoverished. Indians are more used to juggling these contradictions than Western observers. As Sridhar Mitta, Managing Director of E4E Systems in Bangalore puts it: "Westerners always want to simplify things into black and white—but everything can survive at the same time in India. It is a big place and everything has its own role."

India's growth is being fuelled by the size and reach of its young population: a rapidly increasing graduate base, a newly confident global culture and strong flows of people back and forth from the US and Europe. But its institutions, both public and private, were largely designed for a time before India was open to such dynamic forces, and the task of modernising them has only just begun. Political, religious and class-based divisions make that challenge even harder.

India seems like an emerging giant, and even a threat to established science powers, if one just focuses superficially on the large numbers of scientists and engineers it is producing. But once the variable quality of its education system and the shortages of top talent are taken into account, India's knowledge base looks distinctly fragile.

In *India: the uneven innovator*, a publication that forms part of UK-based think tank Demos' Atlas of Ideas programme of research, we consider how these dynamics might play out in India's future.

We argue that the unique interweaving of ancient scientific excellence, colonial dependence and post-independence nationalism has contributed to a complex, globally connected environment for science and innovation in India today.

We map the main elements of science and innovation in India, showing that systematic links between education, research and commercial activity are relatively sparse, but are indeed increasing, as organisations like CSIR and new institutions like the IIScERs pioneer a more integrated approach. The quality of university education is hugely variable, ranging from excellent to inadequate. Elite institutions like the Indian Institutes of Technology cannot provide all the answers.

We argue that a key determinant of India's ability to compete in the knowledge economy will be its returning diaspora, who bring with them leadership skills and creativity. In the long run, what will matter more is whether these skills filter through to the wider scientific and business community.

Although scientific excellence may have been geographically concentrated in the past, international scientists and business people should widen their attention to India's second tier cities, which may be a pool of important opportunities. In business, the impetus for private R&D in India is changing. From the biggest pharmaceutical companies to the smallest startups, companies are finding new ways to benefit from dispersed global networks of R&D with astounding results.

We do not overlook the tension between the need to meet India's basic needs and the desire to undertake worldclass science and innovation. But we argue that huge opportunities may be available for those who seek to work with the grain of these tensions, which could ultimately be productive if they create new, hybrid forms of science, drawing on the best of Indian and international approaches.

Countries like the UK cannot afford to be complacent as India emerges as a significant player in the new geography of science and innovation. We run the risk of squandering an historic opportunity to contribute to a collective scientific future. Britain needs a new special relationship with India for a new era of networked science and innovation.

With so many variables in play, Indian science and technology could develop in several directions, perhaps simultaneously. The matrix below describes four possible trajectories, based on two dimensions of change: first, the value or creativity of the R&D undertaken and second, the level of interdependence or connectivity. These scenarios are not predictions, but simply provide entry points into thinking about the future paths that India may take.

Imagined futures
Scenario one—equity before excellence:
India is not a global science power. The inadequacies of the Indian science and innovation system—bureaucracy, disjointedness and weak infrastructure—mean that public science underperforms. Economic growth slows and talent flows reverse: returnees start going back to the US. At the same time, the failure of science and innovation to benefit the rural poor foments a political backlash, leading to the election of a populist government focused on intermediate technologies and 'Bottom of the Pyramid' innovations for rural India. Advances in malaria control, water management and climate prediction are amongst the early benefits of this new focus.

The politics of this scenario—innovation India versus agricultural India—are plausible and to some extent already visible. Innovation is widely seen as benefiting an elite rather than the nation as a whole. Much therefore

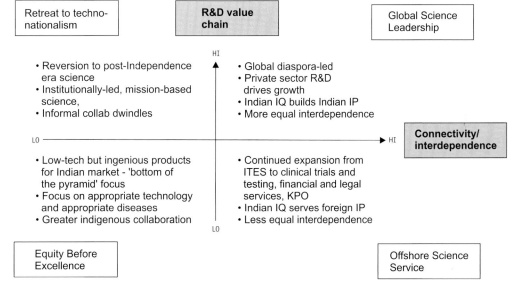

Fig. 1: R&D value chain.

depends on sustaining the fundamentals of Indian growth. As long as India prospers, it will attract people back from the US, and its demographic and educational prospects are essentially strong. At the same time, the fruits of this growth must be seen to be distributed more fairly.

Scenario two—retreat into techno-nationalism: Geopolitical instability in Asia fuels the emergence of ultra-nationalist politics and a reorientation of Indian science towards military competition with Pakistan and China. Science becomes a tool for projecting India's power in Asia, signalling the renewed primacy of post-independent traditions in Indian science, such as space and nuclear programmes. The focus of these programmes is more about international prestige than development. Constituencies and institutions which favour national science in India gain sway. The first indication of this is when Indian scientists withdraw from international benchmarking efforts and rely on parallel national frameworks.

Given how much India has invested in interdependence, economically and politically, the overall likelihood of this scenario is quite low. India's reliance on flows of people and money from abroad give it a major stake in multilateralism and mutuality. But this does not preclude the possibility of techno-nationalism in specific areas, most notably the military.

Scenario three—offshore science service: More innovation by large companies is outsourced to India as part of global innovation networks. Indian IQ works in India but does not yield much Indian IP, which continues to be controlled by Western companies. This scenario is interdependent, but it is unequal. It is a process driven by multinationals who become increasingly adept at managing global processes of innovation. In university and public sector R&D, the same model may apply. European and US partners could do the theory and modelling, while India does the development and 'blue collar' research. Elements of this scenario already exist, and it is likely to form part—if not all—of whatever the future unfolds.

Scenario four—India as global science and innovation leader: India increasingly masters its management of interdependent relationships. It is eminently capable of leading global innovation networks, or acting as an

equal partner within them. India starts to create new standards and platforms, which means that it is not just servicing global innovation networks, but actively leading them. Crucial to this is the improving quality of fundamental research and capacity for innovation in Indian clusters and companies. India, or at least a growing part of it, will increasingly be on equal terms with Silicon Valley, Boston, Munich and Cambridge. This scenario is eminently plausible. But there is still a long way to go.

A science power, but not as we know it

During the Cold War, science had a particular national significance—linked to the arms race, defence technology and the 'national interest.' Today, the complexity of scientific problems, specialisations, expense of equipment and ease of communication have all contributed to the rise of international collaboration. World class science is as much about participation in global networks as it is about belonging to a world class 'national' system.

Power is no longer a 'once and for all' acquisition. Rather than embarking on a quest to become a superpower, India is learning to exploit soft, transactional forms of power to its advantage. Khilnani describes India as a 'bridging power,' a country that exploits its capacity to be the 'essential connective tissue' to its advantage. India's future strength in science and innovation will come from its ability to utilise the power of its networks: to combine the sheer numbers of its technical workforce with the dynamism of its entrepreneurial diaspora, to mix ancient and modern knowledge.

India is both an economic powerhouse and a country crippled by budgetary deficit; it faces huge development challenges even as parts of the country integrate into the global knowledge economy. India is not trying to beat the West at its game, but instead create its own. Its emergence as a science power is easy to caricature but harder to characterise. We ignore how India is changing the world at our peril.

We have examined the dynamics that are shaping India's scientific future. The likelihood of each of the above scenarios depends on India's response to them. We end by revisiting the dynamics, discussed in this report, of a set of strengths and weaknesses, and finally by offering a set of recommendations for UK policymakers.

Eight strengths

1. The democratic dividend: India is the world's largest democracy. This brings constraints in terms of directing research and resources, but India's democratic status remains a source of strength, not weakness, in three main respects. First, democracy is part of India's soft power. It makes India an attractive partner rather than a competitive threat. India's relationship with the US hinges on its status as a democracy able to act as a 'counterpoint to China'. Second, India has a vibrant civil society. Its huge NGO sector and long tradition of public debate performs a crucial scrutinising function and sets a public interest test for science and innovation. Third, democracy helps to sustain creativity and innovation. The relationship between democracy, innovation and economic growth is not straightforward or linear. Nevertheless, in the long-term, a democratic climate and the social values that underpin it provide the freedom to innovate and think creatively on which scientific success depends.

2. India's talent ocean: India's talent pool is boosted by around 2.5 million graduates in science, IT and engineering every year. At the top end of the education market, graduates from the Indian Institutes of Technology are sought after worldwide.

India's population is growing younger, and will overtake China as the world's most populous country by 2040. The size of this talent ocean is a familiar part of the Indian success story. But we still have little concept of the scientific potential that might be created simply by virtue of scale. The current configuration of scientific research and innovation activities in Europe and the US, and the business models that underpin them, reflect certain historic realities about cost and the availability of human capital. The rise of India does not so much threaten Western dominance of those activities as make possible entirely new ways of organising science, and on a totally different scale.

3. Discount discoveries: There are now around 150 multinational R&D centres in India benefiting from the comparative low costs of research in India. Drugs trials can be undertaken at only 60 per cent of the cost in Europe. This brings advantages of speed to Indian science, and the ability to run more trials or design more prototypes for every research dollar that is being spent. Innovation is simply cheaper in India.

4. The sun never sets on 'India': The Indian diaspora is a worldwide network of over 20 million people. A significant proportion of these are highly skilled professionals and scientists, many of whom are now returning to the country to provide leadership and management experience. They are creating waves in the upper echelons of Indian science that are now beginning to spread throughout the system. What is important in this story is not just the reversal of brain drain to brain gain, but the constant and multiple connectivity that is driving Indian innovation and entrepreneurship. This is significant not only as a source of scientific influence, but also political and economic power.

5. Multiple R&D hotspots: Indian success in science and technology was in the past limited to a select few cities. But established R&D locations such as Bangalore are now facing significant challenges from 'second tier cities' such as Pune and Ahmedabad. This is beginning to create healthy inter-state competition for a piece of India's knowledge economy action. New institutions such as the Indian Institutes for Education and Research, could provide a crucial new source of multidisciplinary excellence in these emerging cities.

6. The software story: a powerful role model: The story of software success in India is now well known. It has revolutionised opinions and images of India in Europe and the US. More importantly, it has changed India's own view of its potential. The folklore that surrounds Indian success in Silicon Valley and the profile of Bangalore in the global media is driving Indian self-confidence in science. If the country can do it in IT, then why not in other fields like biotechnology? This confidence has also played a fundamental role in enticing multinational R&D centres and Non Resident Indians to invest in India. IT is only the end of the beginning of India's story in the knowledge economy. India's investment in new models of networked innovation and outsourcing is likely to reap results elsewhere.

7. New dynamism in the private sector: Private sector innovation is a crucial part of any knowledge economy. Previous to 1991, India was a closed environment where innovation was seen as unecessary. But the Indian private sector is now coming alive. Faced with increased global competition, certain sectors are beginning to undergo an innovation overhaul. Particularly interesting is the pharmaceutical sector, which has seen a 400 percent rise in R&D in the past 4 years. This trend has accelerated since compliance with WTO regulations since 2005. The capacity to comply with IPR increases the attractiveness of India as a site for FDI and reduces anxiety in collaborative relationships.

8. Multiplying linkages: India is open to creating as many strategic alliances as possible, not only with the US and Europe but also with China, Australia, Japan and other Asian nations. The crucial test for India will be whether it can get as good at building domestic innovation linkages as international ones. It also has the potential to combine traditional knowledge (e.g. ayurveda) with modern techniques in new and surprising ways.

Eight weaknesses

1. Disjointed innovation: In India, research and education have been historically separated, limiting connectedness between the creation of ideas and their dissemination. Innovation often happens despite formal co-ordination mechanisms rather than because of them. India has a fairly poor track record in commercialising ideas, due to the absence of well-understood pathways to take ideas from the lab to the market.

2. A follower but not a leader: It is difficult to say with certainty that India will be the place where big discoveries will come from, because so far, there's little precedent for it. India is getting better at incremental innovation, but its strengths in outsourcing and 'service science', provide no guarantee of building the capacity to be a genuine science pioneer. In spite of India's meteoric rise it is still vulnerable to being marginalised in global innovation networks.

3. Testing times—the variation in educational quality: Looking below the top line statistics reveals a system of higher education that is hugely variable in quality. The Indian Institute of Science in Bangalore and the 'deemed universities' of CSIR labs may meet global requirements, but many universities have an

inadequate infrastructure for science teaching and research. It can be difficult for potential collaborators to judge the quality of Indian universities and pick appropriate partners. University lecturers' wages are tightly regulated, making it hard to incentive and reward research. There is also still a long way to go for basic education mobilize incentive to be brought up to scratch. World Bank data shows that the literacy rate has risen from 58 per cent to 68 per cent since 1985 for men, whilst for women it has risen from around a third to just under half. India faces huge challenges in terms of equity as well as excellence.

4. License Raj lives on? The curse of red tape: Cumbersome regulations still surround new businesses, and the World Bank's list of countries where it is easy to do business ranks India at a miserable 134th, below the West Bank, Syria and Gabon. Regulations surrounding science are sometimes contradictory. The bureaucracy that tightly controls wage scales also makes procurement of new equipment in universities a great challenge. One of India's advantages is its rule of law and independent judiciary. But India's systems of governance also face significant challenges. The World Bank rates India low in its rankings for successfully tackling corruption. India also topped the latest 'Business Bribe Payers Index' released by Transparency International, the anti-corruption NGO.

5. Still a tough deal for entrepreneurs: The climate for entrepreneurs in India is now more positive, particularly since the success of Indian entrepreneurs in Silicon Valley. As the venture capital industry grows, experienced innovators are benefiting. But first-time entrepreneurs still get a hard deal. Gaining approval for loans can be difficult and a new wave of technology incubators are only now getting started.

6. Walking the tightrope of stability: India's demographic boom is a strength, but it also presents huge governance challenges. India is home to 40 per cent of the world's poor. This creates an intense pressure to create jobs. The threat posed is exacerbated by the mix of religious communities represented in India, and the regional disparities between rich states like Karnataka and Kerala and poor states such as

Bihar. The conflict between India and Pakistan over the disputed territory of Kashmir has made this one of the most heavily militarized zones in the world. Tribal wars between local tribes and Maoist Rebel Naxalites plague the central state of Chattisgargh. Some have said that it is pure magic that holds India together.

7. Built to last? Infrastructure ills: More people means more pressure on India's creaking infrastructure. Millions of people do not have access to adequate sanitation systems. In science hubs like Bangalore, road systems are at breaking point. With the government failing to act fast enough, the private sector is taking the strain, but the government needs to provide faster answers to these long term problems.

8. What you see isn't what you get: Contradictions come as standard in India. Statistics are often unreliable and hard to fathom. But chaotic systems produce results. Ideas can be found in the most surprising places. Visitors are shocked to find venture capitalists working from offices next to slums, or interesting IP created in a lab with a tree growing through the window. This is one reason why so many multinational R&D managers are returnee Indians—they are more able to understand how India works. □

Demos is one of the UK's leading independent think tanks. The Atlas of Ideas is a major programme of research into science, innovation and globalisation around the world. All reports, including *India: the uneven innovator* can be downloaded for free at www.atlasofideas.org

Anuja Utz
World Bank

Promoting inclusive innovation

Most discussion on India's innovation system focuses on formal R&D efforts and the formal part of the economy. However, a cross-cutting, multi-pronged strategy is needed to make India's innovation system better meet the needs of the common people. This note outlines some mechanisms to support innovation efforts that can help improve the productivity and livelihoods of people in India's vast informal economy. Much is known about basic nutrition, sanitation, preventive medicine, environmentally friendly technologies, cheap mobile phones and the like. But further innovation can indeed improve delivery of a wide range of public services by harnessing collaborative efforts among various formal disciplines and programmes to focus on the poor. Not only is it necessary to reduce the cost and increase the availability of goods and services, but more importantly, it is necessary to open up sustainable livelihood and productive income-generating opportunities for the vast number of people left out of the system.

The innovative ability of the weaker sections of society is constrained by insufficiently developed skills, inadequate access to public services, to markets and to assets on fair terms and their inability to handle associated risks. Enhancing skills through better delivery of basic training for the informal sector is a key step. Innovation by opening up access to new and existing technology can help create more and better-paying jobs. This has not received enough attention. In addition to strengthening poor people's capabilities, solutions will involve strengthening incentives, policies and institutions. Part of the solution is to create stronger institutional infrastructure that enable the interlinking of public R&D entities, industry, universities, NGOs and global networks. The poor can assist by organising themselves into groups. In Andhra Pradesh, for example, community-based development initiatives have led self-help groups to develop mutual insurance schemes, lending and savings operations and marketing strategies for new agricultural products. This acticle illustrates the potential of new and existing technologies in opening some of these opportunities.

Efforts for the poor
India has to harness, increase and redirect formal innovation efforts to better meet the needs of the economically weaker sections of society. Pro-poor, early-stage technology development and commercialization by the formal sector has to be encouraged. This could possibly be done through preferential matching grants to collaborations among public R&D entities, industry, universities, NGOs and global poverty alleviation networks.

The historic Green Revolution is perhaps the clearest example of such an effort and its beneficial synergies. Agricultural R&D is crucial to generating additional income and employment for the poor. Given the limited scope for expanding agricultural areas, increases in productivity, profitability and competitiveness will be the main sources of agricultural growth—led or triggered by innovations and applications of science in agriculture. Flows of knowledge and innovations play a critical role in this paradigm shift. To attain global competitiveness, more attention should be given to harnessing advances in frontier sciences in priority areas. Thus, support for basic and strategic research is critical. The collaboration emerging between research entities and the private sector, promoted by the National Agricultural Innovation Project.

Building on R&D: India's large, diverse public R&D infrastructure has the potential to address more of the problems of the poor. The bulk of India's public R&D infrastructure is mission oriented to defense, space and energy, with much less applied to problems of agriculture, industry and health. Much more can be done to orient the considerable capabilities of this large public research system to address the needs and problems of the poor. Some of this harnessing is occurring in mission-oriented programs such as space and a number of initiatives are under way in biotechnology, medicine and industrial R&D (box 1).

Stronger incentives and funding are needed to harness the potential of public R&D and university-enabled initiatives. Available mechanisms to increase the focus on inclusive innovation include institutional mandates, prizes and public awards and targeted funding. The government should encourage research institutes, universities and other publicly funded learning institutes to do more to address the needs of the poor—for example, through competitive research grants. Prizes and public awards could be given to research teams and institutes that produce relevant innovations. Mechanisms—including widespread dissemination and funding—should be offered to scale up, demonstrate and disseminate these innovations to people in the informal sector.

Encouraging private sector: There is even greater potential to harness the research capacity of the private sector to address the needs of the poor—as shown by the growing number of Bottom of the Pyramid initiatives. Global networks provide another source of formal R&D to meet the needs of the poor. The best-known of international public goods R&D efforts is the Consultative Group for International Agricultural Research (CGIAR), which was behind the green revolution. There are also major initiatives in medicine and pharmaceuticals, environment and other areas in which India should continue to participate, such as in the Global Research Alliance.

The government should consider allocating more funds to encourage formal creation and commercialization efforts that focus on the challenges facing the poor. It could establish a pilot Inclusive Innovation Fund to support formal R&D by public R&D entities, the private sector, universities and NGOs aimed at the needs of the informal sector, on a matching grant basis. Initiatives should focus on the underserved community—the more than 800 million Indians living on less than $2 a day (box 2). Many solutions developed for poor Indians would also be applicable for the 4–5 billion poor people worldwide. Thus, firms can develop and pilot in India products and services that then may be marketed globally. In addition, the government could provide financial incentives and awards to research teams, institutes and universities that produce relevant innovations, as well as dissemination and funding mechanisms to scale up, demonstrate and disseminate innovations to people in the informal sector.

Box 1: Public Research for Development

Using space technology for development. Advances in space-based Earth observation technology and its applications have the potential to integrate diverse sciences to provide economic security and better living standards. For example, Sujala, a watershed development project in Karnataka, has created hope for 1,270 villages across five districts, relying on high levels of community participation and scientific planning tools like satellite remote sensing, geographic information systems and information technology (Muniyappa, Ranganath, and Diwakar 2004). Similarly, under the Rajiv Gandhi National Drinking Water Mission, more than 2,000 ground-water maps covering about 45 percent of the country (mainly problem zones) have been prepared and more than 24,000 wells drilled (Mohandas and Reddy 2004).

Preventive medicine. The new anti-tuberculosis molecule (LL-4858 Subotern) by Lupin is an example of network innovation through a public-private partnership. The Council of Scientific and Industrial Research supported this project through the New Millennium Indian Technology Leadership Initiative (NMITLI). The molecule has the potential to not only treat tuberculosis but also significantly reduce treatment time, and is compatible with combination therapy. The molecule has been tested on mice and guinea pigs and has been proven very effective. An investigational new drug application has been made. Once cleared, the molecule will go through clinical trials (Bowonder and others 2006).

Source: Anuja Utz and Carl Dahlman in Unleashing India's Innovation: *Toward Sustainable and Inclusive Growth*, edited by Mark A. Dutz, World Bank, 2007.

Box 2: Bottom of the Pyramid Initiatives

Solar energy for the poor. The Solar Home Systems program, launched as a three-year energy pilot in Karnataka by the United Nations Environment Programme and the Shell Foundation, works with two major Indian banks and nine agricultural subsidiaries to make loans to rural households seeking to buy solar lighting. By September 2005, the program had provided more than 100,000 people with reliable, affordable electricity for the first time.

Mobile telephones. Ultra low-cost handsets are being produced by Nokia and LG, reflecting the 5 million new mobile phone connections being added each month in India.

Simputer. Amida's Simputer is designed to enable word processing and e-mail, regardless of language. Prices for the computer range from $240–480. It was developed for use in rural areas and for applications such as microfinance and e-governance.

Microlending. The SKS smart cards project is a microfinance project catering to marginal farmers and agricultural workers. SKS Microfinance is an innovative nonbanking financial company that has a variety of loan products, encourages membership of women, and provides loans of $100 or less. So far it has loaned about $57 million to more than 200,000 people. ICICI Bank has lent more than $10 million to SKS and led multiple initiatives to provide affordable banking services to the poor. The bank has partnered with SKS, n-Logue, and others to co-locate automated teller machines with rural Internet kiosks. It has also created a network of 8,000 self-help groups, each with 20 female members, to create microfinanced businesses.

Hypermarkets and access to cold storage supply chains for poor farmers. Over the 2007–10 period, Reliance Industries—India's largest private sector company, an oil, petrochemicals, and textile group—intends to build a nationwide retail network of 2,000 supermarkets and 1,000 larger hypermarkets based on a distribution supply system, an integrated "farm to fork" logistics supply chain. Reliance will not enter the farming business. Instead it will be the "off-taker of last resort," relieving farmers of risk. It plans to revolutionize both farming and retail by investing $5.7 billion by 2011 to modernize both farms and stores, connect them through a distribution system guided by the latest logistics technology, and create enough surplus to generate $20 billion in annual agricultural exports.

Direct-to-home distribution network. Consumer goods firms such as Hindustan Lever are seeking new ways of doing business among the rural poor. Its Project Shakti recruits women to self-help groups that offer tiny loans—microcredit—to support a direct-to-home distribution network. The project already reaches 80,000 villages, and by 2010 expects to employ 100,000 "Shakti entrepreneurs," covering 500,000 villages.

Low-cost Internet connectivity for poor villages. Indian Tobacco Company's e-Choupal initiative has equipped more than 6,000 villages with computers and satellite connections to the Internet—part of its agribusiness procurement network. Farmers can use the computers to check prices for their products and sell online, freeing them from middlemen who take a big cut of farm earnings. Once a commercially viable way has been found to provide a village with an Internet connection, it has many other potential uses, including for e-government, sales, education, and entertainment.

Drishtee.com. This initiative delivers fee-based e-governance, education, commerce, and insurance services to rural populations in northern and northeastern India. These services are delivered through more than 700 kiosks owned and operated by local entrepreneurs. The International Finance Corporation's Grassroots Business Initiative is providing Drishtee with a grant to establish 50 new kiosks in Meerut, Uttar Pradesh.

Sources: Usher 2003; Shell Foundation 2003; Tata 2007; Economist 2005a, 2005b, 2005c, 2006; Sharma 2004; Bellman 2006; Prahalad 2004; Moreau and Mazumdar 2006.

Promotion

A second approach to promote inclusive innovation is for India to better promote and diffuse innovations by grassroots entrepreneurs. The largest, best-known non-government programs are the Honey Bee Network (HBN) and the Society for Research and Initiatives for Sustainable Technologies and Institutions (SRISTI). The two largest government programs are Grassroots Innovation Augmentation Network (GIAN) and the National Innovation Foundation. The government has also set up the Traditional Knowledge Digital Library (TKDL) to prepare a computerized database of indigenous knowledge on medicinal plants. Grassroots innovation networks support efforts where traditional knowledge and innovative products emerge at the individual or collective level.

The grassroots innovation networks used to be evaluated and supported. Although there has been a lot of activity on grassroots innovations, there has not been much assessment or quantification of how they have contributed to improving the livelihoods of people in the informal sector. What little evaluation has been done mostly lists activities and number of innovations. There is virtually no information on costs or impact of the innovations. This despite the fact that some have even been licensed in India and abroad. Conceptually there are some models for promoting inclusive innovations (box 3).

Five challenges

High transaction costs of scouting and documentation, need for value addition, need for commercialization, need for finance and unclear IPRs. High transaction costs are inevitable in programs that support a large number of widely scattered informal innovators who have accumulated knowledge from years of trial and error, or incremental innovations in existing tools or agricultural practices. What is needed is good monitoring and evaluation to support grassroots innovations considered to be making positive contributions by a new pilot inclusive innovation fund. There issues in the question of pro-poor IPRs. How can India deliver the benefits of IPRs to poor citizens living traditional lifestyles? Any attempt to craft a traditional knowledge IPR framework that rewards functional knowledge from traditional communities will require revolutionary thinking and bold experimentation in both legislation and administration. Box 4 examines possible system structures for traditional knowledge IPRs.

Helping informal sector

A third approach to promote inclusive innovation is for India to help informal enterprises better absorb existing knowledge. A main recommendation is for government programs to more effectively promote

knowledge absorption in the productive sector and extend the reach of markets to the common man.

There is growing realization that a rural development strategy is needed to focus on increasing farm incomes and rural nonfarm employment. The recent National Agricultural Technology Project has piloted a more market-oriented extension approach built around demand-driven market assessments, farmer organizations and bottom-up governance. In particular, the extension component has successfully piloted farmer-centered, market-driven extension services with close links to researchers and farmers known as Agriculture Technology Management Agencies (ATMAs). ATMAs improve coordination among line departments, encourage public-private partnerships for technology testing and extension and strengthen institutions for monitoring and evaluation at the state and national levels (box 5).

Support to markets

Support networks can help low-income workers raise productivity and incomes by teaching more efficient production methods. Informal enterprise, formal microenterprise and SME production chains of goods and services suffer from low-quality inputs, stock seasonality and accumulation, weak capital machinery, unavailability of prototyping and facilities for experimentation, lack of information on and exchange with markets—including for exports—and poor knowledge of how to manufacture goods.

Creating networks of entrepreneurs and giving them better access to modern training, knowledge, quality assurance and quality control training and finance could lead to them providing high value to customers—increasing productivity as well as incomes. Trader-entrepreneur networks are also important, including traders and

wholesalers up to exporters, master-craftsperson traders and guild masters. Recognition is needed for their roles in minimizing transaction costs, channeling market information, enabling informal contracting and close monitoring of least costs, providing finance and providing designs and inputs and sometimes even skilled staff. Among the clear advantages of producer cooperatives, professional organizations and other NGOs is that they have lower direct personnel and infrastructure costs than do formal organizations carrying out similar functions. More important, they often have or can create or access informal networks that can facilitate their work—and their impact can be significant. The government as well as the private sector would do well to learn from their experience.

The government should consider providing additional programmatic support to markets and networks at the cluster level—with a focus on helping informal enterprises better absorb knowledge. The development of linkages calls for the emergence of new partnerships among traditional knowledge systems, NGOs, user ministries, associations of village industries, panchayat raj institutions and rural Indians. Socially driven pro-poor innovations should also be encouraged. This is where companies have to go beyond the pure profit motive to develop goods or services to deal with the needs of the poor, such as basic literacy, preventive medicine and health-care (box 6). □

Box 5: The Experiences of Agriculture Technology Management Agencies

India's ATMAs provide for decentralized, participatory, farmer-driven extension services and have institutionalized bottom-up planning processes through the preparation of Strategic Research and Extension Plans—based on participatory rural appraisals and Block Action Plans. The program relies on a group approach based on village groups, as well as training of volunteer farmers. ATMAs support private extension initiatives by contracting NGOs to conduct extension responsibilities in selected areas, using farmer-to-farmer extension services provided by individuals or through farmer organizations, and forming partnerships with input providers (of seeds, fertilizers, crop protection chemicals) for demonstrations and farmer training. In most districts, farmers and other stakeholders have a sense of program ownership.

ATMA successes include diversification of production systems for higher income (for example, cultivation of high-value crops including flowers, fruits, vegetables, and medicinal plants), better natural resource management, integrated pest management, organic farming, well recharging, integrated plant nutrient management, resource conservation technologies, and development of new enterprises such as cashew processing, beekeeping, dairying, value addition through processing and group marketing. Farmer interest groups have mobilized men, women and young people to join common interest groups, such as producer groups for flowers, fruit, milk and other products, as well as marketing groups for seed.

Training farm leaders in technology and leadership skills is important. Strong farmer organizations can be a positive link in the cost-effective provision of extension support to small and marginal farming communities, as well as an alternative to privatization of extension service. Farmer Advisory Committees are operational in most project blocks and are recognized by government line departments. However, internal conflicts between ATMA priorities and departmental responsibilities persist, and extension staff require considerable motivation to work in a farm advisory role with multiple funding sources.

Source: Janssen 2006.

Box 6: Indian Initiatives for Corporate Social Responsibility

Education: The Computer-Based Functional Literacy (CBFL) Program (www. tataliteracy.com) tries to overcome illiteracy through the innovative use of information technology. It uses a mix of teaching software, multimedia presentations and printed materials to teach uneducated people to read in a fraction of the time it takes to do so using conventional means. The project focuses exclusively on reading; people in the program can acquire a 300–500 word vocabulary in their own language within 30–45 hours spread over 10–12 weeks. *The Infosys Foundation* (www.infosys.com/infosys_foundation/learning.htm) has set up more than 10,150 libraries in rural schools, as well as well-equipped libraries in Hubli and Bangalore with the latest books in high-tech streams—such as medicine and engineering—that can be accessed by underprivileged students. It has also collaborated with the Center for Environment Education, Bangalore, to train teachers in science and the environment; 15 camps have been held in the 2004–06 period, and 1,000 teachers trained. *The Azim Premji Foundation* (www.azimpremjifoundation.org) is dedicated to universalizing primary education in India. It works under a Learning Guarantee Program, building a voluntary spirit of accountability among schools, communities, and government functionaries, and studies factors that influence learning. *The Byrraju Foundation* of Satyam Computer Service broadcasts English and math classes through satellite links and radio towers to more than 200 government-run schools (Corcoran 2006). With IBM's help, it has put computers in 54 rural primary schools and supports vocational programs for plumbers, electricians and dressmakers. *NIIT's Hole in the Wall* experiment started in 1999 by introducing a kiosk housing a high-speed, touch-screen computer in a wall in a New Delhi slum, and showed that children can master navigating the Internet within hours (Orvis 2006). Since then, more than 150 computers have been installed in some 50 locations in Delhi slums and rural India. *TARAhaat* (www.tarahaat.com) is a franchise network of 37 ICT centers that provide e-education, communication, and governance services to the poor. They also sell innovative products such as fuel-efficient cook stoves, lighting systems, and solar power devices.

Health and preventive medicine. Distance Healthcare Advancement is an initiative of Philips India to deliver high-quality, low-cost diagnostic distance health care for the underserved (www.philips.com/Assets/Downloadablefile/05-DISHA-15354.pdf). It partners with Apollo hospitals, which provides doctors and specialists for free consultations; the Electronics Corporation of India (a government organization that supplies the satellite dish); and with ISRO (Indian Space Research Organization), which places the satellite in orbit.

Linking farmers and rural population through information technology. Indian Tobacco Company's e-Choupal (www.echoupal.com) is the largest infrastructure network serving villages, farmers and rural markets, reaching more than 3.5 million farmers in over 31,000 villages through 6,000 kiosks in at least six states. Village Internet kiosks managed by farmers enable the agricultural community to access information in their local languages on the weather and market prices, disseminate knowledge on scientific farm practices and risk management, facilitate the sale of farm inputs, and sell farm produce from the farmers' doorsteps. Real-time information enhances farmers' ability to make decisions and aligns their farm output with market demand and secure quality and productivity. Aggregation of demand for farm inputs gives them access to high-quality inputs from established manufacturers at fair prices. As a direct marketing channel, e-Choupal eliminates wasteful intermediation, significantly reducing transaction costs (Das Gupta 2006). *Microsoft's Rural IT Initiative, Saksham* (http://www.mission2007.org/saksham_tm.pdf), is aimed at delivering the benefits of IT to rural India. It will partner with Drishtee, Jai Kisan and n-Logue to roll out kiosks across the country: 50,000 are planned over the next three years. And the *Byrraju Foundation* has created two IT centers (known as GramIT), with 100 kiosks each in Andhra Pradesh. The foundation covered the initial costs: $110,000 for computers, wireless networks and worker training. GramIT withholds some wages for the 1 per cent equity that each worker will hold in the local business in two years. It is estimated that each job generates as much revenue as five acres of good land (Corcoran 2006).

Creating opportunities by starting new businesses (www.ifc.org/gbi). The Bharatiya Yuva Shakti Trust (BYST) identifies underprivileged young entrepreneurs and provides them with collateral-free financing over three years. Funding is supplemented by targeted mentoring monitoring, and networking. BYST has engaged with the Indian corporate sector. Its Mentor Development Program will expand its mentor network to 30,000 over the next five years, affecting 90,000 enterprises run by young entrepreneurs in India.

Source: Anuja Utz and Carl Dahlman in *Unleashing India's Innovation: Toward Sustainable and Inclusive Growth*.

---

*This article is a short version of Chapter 4: Promoting Inclusive Innovation by Anuja Utz and Carl Dahlman in *Unleashing India's Innovation: Toward Sustainable and Inclusive Growth*, edited by Mark A. Dutz, World Bank, 2007.

Finnish Innovation
Fund Report

Innovators' progress

Anil Ghosh has a small, and tidy office not far from the entrance to the building. He's wearing a chemical-stained lab coat and has wispy grey hair and thick glasses. He's small and slight but has a powerful voice and manner. When anybody else enters the room from the company, there's no doubt that Ghosh is in charge. He grills us about our project, why we're there, what it's going to achieve, and tells us that he's fed up of delegations coming to see him wide-eyed at what Chemgen Pharma has achieved and how advanced they are. He tells us how he was awarded an NSF grant for his work at MIT in 1977, "I could compete with the best then, so why don't people think I can compete with the best now in India?"

In his early career Ghosh worked in university labs and for a number of the large drug companies in Europe and America on drug discovery. He says even then he knew he wanted to start a research lab in India, it was just that at the time he didn't know how.

He tells us that he also founded Chembiotek, another Contract Research Organisation (CRO) company just down the road. He left and started up again because he wanted to move up the value chain, he wanted to be doing more advanced research and eventually to be developing new drugs and owning the intellectual property. "I knew I wanted to have a better lab than Glaxo" he says with a smile.

"In this business, imagination is just as important as knowledge" he says, and that is where the Indian education system is letting down the future of science and technology in the country. But he has no doubt, India will become a new centre for drug discovery and he will make a lot of money out of it. The last 10 years have seen India gain greater access to learning about all parts of the value chain. This is partly because the Indian middle classes have attracted the attention of almost every global consumer company and will continue to do so.

It has been estimated that the affluent consumer market in India grows by nearly 20 million people per year. This makes small amounts of growth in consumer markets in Europe and North America pale in comparison. There is money to be made, especially if you can establish your brand and good reputation early. The decision by multinational consumer brands to begin operations in India was described to us as a 'no brainer' more than once.

This means that as well as shifting back office and manufacturing to India, most consumer MNCs have marketing and strategy personnel in India.

Even if it is taking place informally and outside of particular companies, this increasing concentration of knowledge in India about an increasing array of business stages is strengthening Indian potential for developing new successful technologies to be sold either at home or abroad.

One indicator of this is that design in India is beginning to take off as well, as MNCs discover the inexpensive but well regarded consultancies such as Elephant Design. The Indian Government is also increasing funding of the National Institute of Design.

The commentator Niti Bhan writes, "In the international economy, China is a commodity player. India's promise lies in its control of cultural particulars. And by this I mean, India understands and participates in the culture of the First World West in ways China does not."

These are all examples of India moving up the value chain and increasingly taking control of the creative elements of developing new technologies, over and above the 'coolie' tasks epitomised by manufacturing, call-centres and contract research. While the more mundane, lower value services have fuelled Indian economic growth, in the next 10 years we can expect India to increasingly move from 'coolie to creative'.

Global Indians

Rakesh Mathur is a global Indian. He is a graduate of the Indian Institute of Technology in Mumbai. He left Intel to strike out on his own in the early 80s. His most successful venture, a comparison-shopping service called Junglee, was acquired by Amazon in 1998 for $241 million. Since then, he's been a founder of three technology start-up companies and has been an early stage investor in several other companies.

His ventures include Webaroo, which he felt important to run from India, "It's the cost and the leverage most of all I suppose; here, if you raise $5 million you can make five times the mistakes!" Rakesh sees Webaroo as a "disruptive force" in the mobile search market.

Rakesh visits India at least once a quarter, and is proud to have "hired more IITians than Bill Gates in the past year!" He says the software story in India isn't really the phenomenon that people think it is. "So far India has just been grabbing the low-hanging fruit—but Indians are realising that this isn't the most juicy! Now things are being invented here for the first time—we need to ignore the washing machine stage that has been so profitable for China, and concentrate on the rockets and anti-gravity boots!"

Global Indians like Rakesh are an important factor in the country's success. There are an estimated 20 million Indians outside the country, which is a small percentage of the total population, and an even smaller group are what could truly be called global Indians, travelling widely and with strong networks into innovation networks, but they have a large impact in finance, entrepreneurship and research and development.

Continental Airlines started direct flights between Newark and Delhi on 1 November 2005. American Airlines began direct flights between Chicago and Delhi two weeks later. Delhi to Chicago has become the longest direct flight in operation globally, requiring two sets of pilots (one set sits in first class until half way through the flight) to get around working time agreements which normally prevent any flight over 12 hours. Use of Boeing 777 planes, where much of the plane is adapted for business and first-class accommodation suggests that airlines are aiming the flights directly at multinational companies. American suggested during the buildup to the inaugural flight that they expected most of the standard-class seats to be filled by people of Indian origin visiting family or traveling as tourists.

First flight

Finnair's first direct flight from Helsinki to New Delhi began in November 2006, further opening up Finland to the potential flow of global Indians. However Indians living in Finland that we met said there had been times when they felt uncomfortable and they thought there were many barriers to Indians living in Finland, even for short stays of a number of months or a few years. Unlike the UK or other large European countries, Finland doesn't have the critical mass of Indians to foster a thriving community and develop a unique Finnish-Indian culture in the same way as an Anglo-Indian culture has developed in the UK.

Non-resident Indians (NRIs) used to be regarded as deserters in India. Now this group carries a huge burden of hope and expectation as the social class which will transform India. They are providing otherwise rare leadership and management skills, financial and risk capital and success stories that are driving momentum in Indian science and innovation. Where other countries rely on an innovation system linking research to business, India relies on an innovation cadre—a diaspora of global Indians.

And as wealth in India increases and more Indian firms play on the global stage, the number of global Indians is sure to increase. They may only number in the thousands but global Indians play a disproportionate role in innovation and will continue to do so.

Indian IQ for Indian IP

Behind Srini Rajam on the wall of the Ittiam boardroom are two certificates he is proud of. Ittiam were chosen as one of Red Herring's top 100 Asian Companies in 2005 and are the world's most preferred Digital Signal Processing company—that's the electronics and software that makes portable devices like digital cameras, video players and mp3 players work.

In front of Srini on the table are a selection of toys he has readied to show us. He scoffs at the iPod we're using to record the interview. "I hate them" he says with a laugh. "Our player is much better than theirs."

A phrase we heard a number of times was 'Indian IQ for Indian IP'. This is the driving force behind companies such as Ittiam who don't aim to do any manufacturing, instead they develop technologies and then license their inventions to household brands. Their USP is speed to market. If a manufacturer like LG or iRiver wants to develop a new product, they can either set off on their own R&D which might take two years or they can license Ittiam's technology which they could have in the shops in months.

In a fast moving arena as consumer electronics, more companies are choosing to use Ittiam. Srini had a long career with American giant Texas Instruments, which was the first of the tech companies to open up in Bangalore back in the 1970s. He progressed through the company, working in the US and then returning to India to eventually become Managing Director for TI in India in 1995 – a role he held for 5 years. But he knew what he really wanted to do and in 2001, with six other colleagues he set up Ittiam.

"We wanted to do something that was beyond just entrepreneurship. We thought that India needed to create giants of its own. That it needed companies with drive and passion, even nationalism."

The history of the generic drugs industry in India shows how intellectual property rules can shape business success. Exports by Indian companies to Africa, especially Cipla and Ranbaxy, helped drive the annual price of antiretroviral treatment down from $15,000 per patient a decade ago to about $200 in 2005. They also simplified therapy by putting three AIDS drugs in one pill.

The battle for the neem tree

Neem is a fast-growing tree in the same family as mahogany, native to India, Vietnam and Laos. It has been used by Indians for its medicinal and health providing properties for centuries.

However, several patents on the use of neem were taken out by international companies and this led to an international group, spearheaded by the Indian environmentalist Dr Vandana Shiva, taking the case to the European Patent Office, claiming you can't patent ancient knowledge and calling it 'bio-piracy'. She told the BBC, "We wanted to reveal what bio-piracy is, this patenting of indigenous knowledge and bio-diversity. We thought a patent that's held by the biggest superpower of the world and one of the biggest chemical giants would be an effective patent to take on." The patent was revoked in 2005.

The question is what is the best way for the value of the neem to be spread to ordinary Indians? Dr Ramesh Saxena, head of the Neem Foundation in India, has pioneered the use of neem as a natural pesticide in South Asia, the Philippines, East Africa and Australia. He believes it can have an impact on some of world's greatest problems including malaria, dengue fever, AIDS and human population growth. However, he warns that India has to act fast to realise neem's potential and profit from it as China and Brazil are rapidly overtaking India, each cultivating millions of neem trees every year.

The clash between different groups over the best route to reap the benefits of India's intellectual property can seem paradoxical to outsiders and is still in a flux. We can expect further change in the years to come.

In a piece for the Wall Street Journal, Richard Wilder and Pravin Anand claim that, "India is rapidly evolving into Asia's innovation centre, leaving China in the dust. Its secret weapon? Intellectual property rights protection. New Delhi has taken big steps to protect these rights, and the results have been dramatic." □

Extracts from Sitra Report 71, Courtesy Finnish Innovation Fund Sitra

Recognise innovators, says CII

Executive summary of Innovate India: National Innovation Mission

Innovation has been defined as the intersection of invention and insight that leads to commercial and social value. In India, there are many instances where innovation, as defined, has occurred and is occurring. However, these are not enough, given the size of the country and the number of problems India is grappling with as it embarks on a path of rapid, sustainable and inclusive growth. Higher growth in India is the outcome of its productive energy, of which, there were many instances prior to 1991. However, industrial delicensing in 1991 unleashed this energy. To sustain the consequent growth, we now have to unleash India's innovative energy, taking it beyond sporadic instances and making it integral to all productive activity.

A careful analysis of the innovations suggests that the translation of new ideas into value generation is not a simple process. Though innovation starts with the idea and ends with value, there are a number of intervening steps that an innovator has to go through. There are no roadmaps that a person with ideas can follow to reach one's destination. Hence, to nurture innovative ideas, it is essential to have an innovation eco-system that opens up a large network of roads on which an innovator may possibly travel.

In other words, instead of directing innovation, the ecosystem has to enable it. A number of enablers can be identified and they cover, among others, institutions, laws, infrastructure, mind-sets, incentives and culture. For instance, while outstanding researchers may happen in spite of the system, the level of an average researcher improves with a good research environment. In this context, the number of PhDs in India is far less than it should be and dwindling. The research environments in universities and institutes must attract researchers back into their fold and employment opportunities for such PhDs must be made comparable to what they can otherwise get.

Not only should we produce more PhDs in existing disciplines, we should get some of them in new disciplines also. This will mean the development and implementation of new courses that will develop skills required in the future. One example is the new initiative being talked about regarding a services science syllabus. Some of the best minds in the best universities and organizations are taking exploratory steps in this direction. We need to develop and adopt some of our own.

Focus on our problems and solutions starts at the schooling stage—freedom and encouragement to try, nurture experimentation and out of the box thinking, and allow failure. This mind-set of experimentation must extend to skill generation and its continual upgrading. Vocational training and modular courses are therefore important too. Capacity for imparting education and skills must be augmented while allowing for competition amongst the providers.

An innovator must be empowered to experiment and fail. It is not enough to make entry easy for start-ups with venture capital and small business loans, though they are essential. Simultaneously, the social and economic costs of failure must be brought down. Failed entrepreneurs must be able to exit easily. Labour from these units must get support during transition. While flexibility in reallocating resources is desirable for all producers, it is a must for start-ups and young firms where the failure rate is high.

Innovation works best if groups of people, or organizations, come together and innovation is no longer restricted to the laboratories of large organizations.

For such collaborations to succeed, two things are essential. First, proper recognition has to be given to all those who participate in an innovative venture—be it in research, commerce or in social initiatives. India should think innovatively on a patent regime that supports open collaboration. Shared patents such as patent commons are one example.

Second, to maximize the number of individuals and organizations participating in the process, common platforms need to be built so that a collaborator can move in and out of the process seamlessly. The operative word here is "open"; no one knows from before who one's collaborator will be. Defining and developing standards for

technology and services will enable people to work on common platforms, reduce duplication of effort and enhance compatibility.

One such common platform stems from e-governance: filing online tax returns encouraged small businesses to embrace information technology for taxes and then beyond to other aspects of their businesses boosting efficiency and transparency. Such innovation leadership, especially from the government, has multiplier effects.

This eco-system of open networks, private or public, has to be supported by a base network or an Indian Innovation Network. We recommend a paradigm shift in the nation's goal-setting (like what happened in 1991 when the economy was opened up) that is not to 'drive' innovation but instead generate an attitudinal change in people's mindsets like greater tolerance to failure, going off the beaten track, looking for solutions encountered in daily life, etc. It will also encourage the public, government and other organizations to create an innovative eco-system in whatever they control. Most importantly, it will foster experimentation.

Simply put, if we do not innovate, we perish. □

An IPR Journey

Indian industry is becoming acutely aware of intellectual property rights.
Crompton Greaves filed 118 IPRs in the year 2007, the highest number of IPRs filled in the country by any Indian engineering manufacturing organization. The IPR movement, which started in the organization three years ago, has made rapid progress from under 10 IPRs in 2005 to over 100 IPRs in 2007.
This IPR journey began three years ago with a clearly defined Technology Vision to enhance its IPR wealth. An action-oriented IPR roadmap was created to realize this vision which included:
• Awareness promotion at every level
• Creation of an IPR structure to monitor and promote the movement
• Establishment of a system to identify and promote innovation culture
• Motivation initiative to reward and recognize inventors.
Over 1000 personnel were trained at various levels and 25 IPR coordinator worked across the company's manufacturing divisions to identify and create the innovations. The Managing Director of Crompton Greaves motivates, recognizes and rewards every inventor at a glittering function every year. The high level of involvement of top management, supported by a declared Technology Vision, has made this IPR record possible.

Step 1 Establish IPR cell at Corp level, 25 IPR coordinators
Step 2 Create awareness across the organization at various levels
Step 3 Ensure products are infringement free
Step 4 Ensure innovative features existing in present products are protected through IPRs
Step 5 Apply special focus to examine that the new development of products and processes have IP potential right at the beginning
Step 6 Establish an innovation development system and tools such as TRIZ
Step 7 Establish systems for IP portfolio management and IP valuation.

SPACE

Marking a new stage in India's space programme, *Chandrayaan-1* seeks a better understanding of the Moon, its origin and evolution. Indigenously developed payloads, through topographical, chemical and mineral mapping of the lunar surface, hope to unlock some of the mystery of the Moon and of the Earth from which it broke away.

GSLV launch

K Kasturirangan MP
Director, NIAS, Bangalore
Former Chairman, Space Commission
M B Rajani
Research Scholar, NIAS, Bangalore

Soaring higher and higher

Some unique features have marked India's space endeavour and continue to do so. Its inspiration, rather unusually, came not from military objectives but from a masterly vision coupled with the keen interest of a large community of scientists engaged in geophysical and astrophysical research. At that time, the programme led by scientists was directed to interact with the user agencies and the intended beneficiaries of space technologies—the common people. The goal set for the first phase was developmental. Awareness of the commercial and security implications of the space programme evolved later.

The scientific pursuit soon acquired an additional dimension. Space science and technology came to be seen primarily as tools for national development in areas ranging from meteorology, agriculture and mass education to telecommunications, resource mapping and urban development.

With a rare mix of idealism and pragmatism, cosmic physicist Vikram Sarabhai sensitised the political leadership of the day to the immense potential in terms of socio-economic benefits of an endeavour that was seen by many as an esoteric activity.

Thumba on the coast of the Arabian Sea at the southern tip of the peninsula was chosen as the site to launch sounding rockets. Its location on the geomagnetic equator provided a very good opportunity to conduct studies of the upper atmosphere and ionosphere whose physical and dynamic characteristics are considerably influenced by the location.

The scientific community catalysed the agencies responsible for services to make use of space technogies in different sectors. ISRO ensured the establishment of an extensive infrastructure in different states to make use of the remote sensing data for developmental purposes. Scientific workers came in close touch with the agencies starting to use space technologies. The dialogue began. Several schemes drawn up by scientists in response to the feedback demonstrated the social and economic impact that high technology could have on the lives of the common people.

An outstanding example of such two-way exchange was the innovative Satellite Instructional Television Experiment (SITE). It enabled the tribal communities in remote corners of the country to see for the first time in their lives a moving image on the television screen. This, in a country with a 100-year-old film industry.

The space programme also led to the development of high technologies in response to certain needs, as national security and commercial interests began to define limits of international co-operation. Indian planners also grew in there awareness of the security and commercial dimensions of space technologies. The embargoes on the export of technologies by the 'space haves' only speeded up the indigenous development of innumerable products and processes that would be needed for satellites, launchers and earth observational systems. Innovations shaped the project in this phase.

Sarabhai's emphasis on self-reliance enabled the scientists and technologists to face and overcome numerous challenges that cropped up in acquiring and applying space technologies. His wide vision guided the Indian space programme that evolved through three major phases. The first phase related to initiation of activities with the objective of proof-of-concept evaluation (1960–1970), followed by the experimental phase of realizing end-to-end capability demonstration (1980s) and led finally to the operational phase providing routine services (1990s and beyond).

Having acquired significant capabilities for the domestic needs, ISRO also turned its eyes toward the market in space technologies. It established Antrix Corporation to promote commercial use of the space assets of ISRO and to help Indian space industries achieve global competitiveness. Global marketing of IRS data, launching of four foreign small satellites by PSLV, leasing of INSAT transponder capacity to commercial operators including INTELSAT, supply of spacecraft subsystems and mission support services of Indian ground stations are some of the highlights of the Antrix space business.

Alliances

The corporation established an alliance with Europe's leading satellite manufacturer, EADS Astrium, to jointly manufacture communication satellites using the INSAT bus for selling in global markets. In the initiation phase, working closely with potential user communities was the essence of the endeavour. It entailed utilising foreign space systems and configuring the ground system to suit the national needs and conditions. This phase witnessed the development of the first satellite launch vehicle SLV-3, with a capability of orbiting the 40 kg class of satellites in the low earth orbit. In the second and experimental phase, a major exercise was undertaken to create an end-to-end capability in the design, development and in-orbit management of the space missions. Of course, for the users, the associated systems on the ground were also developed and managed.

Systems with limited capability, realized within stringent cost and time controls, characterized this phase. Two experimental satellites Bhaskara-1 and Bhaskara-2 for remote sensing and the Ariane Passenger Payload Experiment (APPLE), for communications, represent the missions undertaken in this phase. This phase also witnessed the development of the Augmented Satellite Launch Vehicle (ASLV).

In the next and operational phase, major space infrastructure was created over the last two decades. Such infrastructure broadly falls into two classes: one for communications, broadcasting and meteorology, through a multi-purpose satellite system Indian National Satellite system. INSAT is one of the largest domestic satellite communication systems in the world. The other is the Indian Remote Sensing satellite series. IRS system comprises some of the best satellites in the world for generating information on natural resources. The programme has developed capabilities to produce world-class satellites and launch vehicles and to apply them in diverse areas relevant to national development.

Both IRS and INSAT satellites, through a multitude of applications, have benefited the country in various areas of national development. INSAT satellites are the mainstay for television broadcasting and provide connectivity to more than 1100 TV transmitters. They also network radio stations, provide rural area communications, business communications and tele-education and tele-medicine services. They are also used to relay cyclone warnings, gather meteorological data, assist weather forecasting for emergency communication support during disasters and providing search and rescue support.

Applications

The imageries and data from the IRS satellites are used for vital applications such as locating zones for availability of ground water in habitations having no access to drinking water, monitoring agricultural crops, providing advisories to coastal fishermen on potential zones for fishing, planning water shed, rural development and waste land management programs as well as disaster management support. The remote sensing programmes demonstrated in a dramatic manner the application of space technologies for groundwater exploration, wasteland mapping, forecasting agricultural produce, identification of potential fishing zones, weather and climate studies as well as environment impact assessment and monitoring.

The space launch vehicles are aimed towards providing autonomous launch capability to orbit these classes of satellites. India's Polar Satellite Launch Vehicle (PSLV) is well proven through eight successive successful flights and it provides the capability to orbit remote sensing satellites of the 1.4 tonne class in polar Sun synchronous orbits. The Geo synchronous Satellite Launch Vehicle (GSLV), capable of launching 2 to 2.5 tonne class of INSAT satellites, has been operationalised with three successful flights in a row, making

India one of the six countries in the world to demonstrate capabilities for geo-stationary satellite launch.

In the field of exploration, the programme opened up valuable opportunities for planetary studies, high energy astronomy and research programmes related to middle atmosphere, upper atmosphere and ionosphere.

Technology development was taken up with zeal in the face of difficulties and denials thrown up in the way of procuring systems and components, for this wholly civilian programme. The satellite experts developed alternate versions of configurations for applications in the areas of remote sensing, communication and space science research and the needed trail of backward and forward linkages.

It was an innovations-driven pace that only quickened the impulse for self-reliance in key technologies. The space programme also acquired experience in developing unique organisational and management skills for implementing mega projects.

Front ranking scientific investigations are being carried out in the fields of astronomy, atmospheric sciences and long-term climatic research, using satellites, balloons, sounding rockets and ground-based instruments. India has embarked on an ambitious planetary exploration programme, the flagship mission being *Chandrayaan-1*.

The conception and implementation of the country's space plans bears the imprint of Sarabhai's vision. It manifests India's self-confidence, ability to think big and think ahead. It reflects the aspiration to explore new areas of knowledge and also the determination to place such knowledge at the service of the people.

Relevance: Space technologies can and do provide solutions to developmental problems	
NEEDS	AREAS WHERE SPACE TECHNOLOGY CAN HELP
Improving Food Security	• Watershed management • Optimal land use strategy plan • Control of land degradation • Drought mitigation and proofing • Recovery of irrigation systems • Monitoring of crops and cropping systems • Ground water targeting • Siting water harvesting structures • Fisheries forecasting
Infrastructure development	• Road connectivity analysis • Selection of sites • Land use mapping/monitoring • Urban mapping • Community information kiosks • VSAT communications network
Health and Education—bridging gaps and improving quality	• Tele Medicine Network • Tele Education Network
Disaster Management and Response	• Cyclone warning • Flood damage assessments • Flood plain GIS/flood zoning analysis • Drought monitoring • Land slide zoning
Environment management	• Vegetation monitoring • Forest mapping, aforestation plans • Coastal zone regulation monitoring • Mining impacts • Urban sprawl and land use monitoring • Monitoring desertification. • Weather watch • Water conservation and management • Atmospheric pollution monitoring

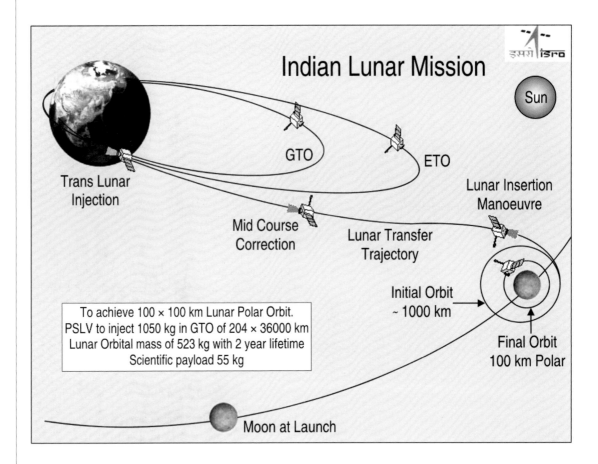

Space research in India has become deeply intertwined with many facets of the national developmental endeavour. Social objectives will continue to be the main driver of India's space programme. This implies consolidating and extending the capabilities of the present remote sensing and communication space infrastructure.

At another level, India will seek to ensure that it retains access to space and is not left out in the race to build cost-effective space transportation systems. In future, the Indian space programme planners will have to look beyond the core sector which as of now, has substantial social component but is limited in its strategic, commercial and international cooperation elements.

One major step in this direction is to secure private sector participation not only in providing downstream services but also in owning and operating satellite systems as well as providing launch vehicle services. This would need consortia of industries to produce state-of-the-art, cost competitive satellites on one hand and manufacturing of launch vehicle and providing launch services on the other hand. Of course, the private sector's participation will involve issues related to technology transfer from the ISRO and the use of its infrastructure for testing and other related requirements. It will also involve issues relating to confidentiality and national security. In this context, the private sector has to take a major initiative, while as an enabler; the government has to prepare a policy framework.

India has the capacity to play an increasing role in manned space missions, the creation of space habitats, lunar bases and planetary exploration; all within the ambit of a global partnership framework like the present model for International Space Station. India could also play an effective role in global missions like that for disaster management, monitoring and understanding climatic and weather systems and developing new concepts. It is both timely and appropriate for India to embark on this next step in space. □

To the Moon! Why not?

The Moon mission evolved from the past scientific activities as well as the technology base of rockets and satellites developed primarily for application oriented activities.

It is interesting to recall that the American experience in its early remote sensing programme of also derived valuable inputs from its early planetary programmes. This was natural since the pioneering planetary exploration missions had developed sophisticated techniques for imaging from space at different wavelengths, along with analysis techniques and methods for interpreting the images. The Indian remote sensing programme, built on similar techniques, has matured into a world class effort. Thus, at this juncture, we are in a position to use this experience in planetary exploration.

There have been instances where much justification was demanded by critics for initiating a new programme since the intangible benefits that they could deliver were not creadible enough. For *Chandrayaan-1*, we went through an elaborate process of consultation with the scientific community, academia, political leaders and the media.

Some of the basic considerations that influenced the decision for a mission to the Moon are:

First and foremost, we have yet to understand the origin and the evolution of the Moon. It is strange that so little is understood about the nearest celestial object! Hence there is renewed interest in the astronomical, physical, chemical, isotopic, geological and geo-chronological aspects of lunar exploration.

Chandrayaan-1 will address some of the basic questions.

Secondly, a small nucleus of scientists engaged in planetary research would receive a new impetus with a committed long-term program. Since the early 1960s several groups in India have been carrying out research in planetary sciences, using telescopes and laboratory simulations. Study of cosmic ray effects on meteorites was pioneered by Prof D Lal and Prof N Bhandari. When the lunar samples from Apollo and LUNA missions arrived here, the early investigations at TIFR were extended to the rocks and dust from the Moon during 1972–81.

Of equal significance is the fact that *Chandrayaan* is expected to provide unique opportunities to upgrade several areas of technology. Examples include that of dealing with a challenging mission scenario, higher levels of refinement in the trajectory computation and orbital manoeuvres, newer strategies for guidance and navigation, and deep space communications.

India intends to participate in international planetary missions in the future. The creation of a cadre of young scientists, and demonstration of the various relevant technologies and techniques, are critical to achieve this goal.

K Kasturirangan

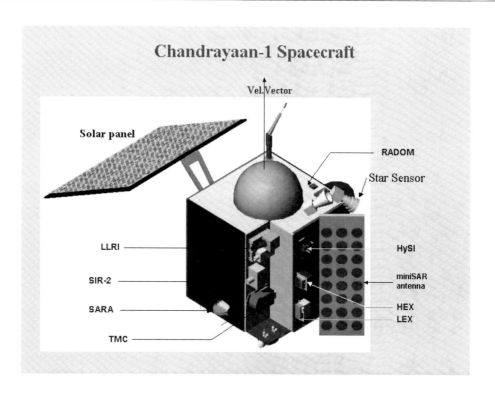

Chandrayaan-1 Spacecraft

114

K Jayaraman
Correspondent *Nature*

India's aspirations in space

India's ambitious space exploration plans remind me of one of the most poignant photographs in the archives of the Indian space research organization (ISRO). The picture shows India's first communications satellite APPLE being taken to the launch pad on a bullock cart (see photo). The year was 1981. Sceptics then asked why a nation without even good roads needed satellites.

As a reporter, in 1992, I heard similar comments while watching ISRO's first homemade liquid rocket engine VIKAS being static tested in one of the Arianespace facilities in France.

"Launching communication satellites requires big rockets and their development calls for huge investment that India cannot afford," an Arianespace official whispered into my ears. "Why does India want to spend on building rockets when it would be more economical to have its satellites launched by us?"

But planners starting with Vikram Sarabhai, the founder, and Satish Dhawan, the architect of India's space programme thought otherwise. They knew that key to space supremacy, in the long run, was self-reliance. "Dependence will retard progress and we have to invest if we want to be self reliant," space scientist Udipi Rama Rao was fond of saying. Rao steered ISRO during the critical phase of the Indian space programme through a time when the agency's ambitions were high but funding was low. That policy of self-reliance has been the hallmark of the country's space programme from early 1960s when young Indian scientists fired their "toy" rockets from the midst of coconut groves in Thumba, a fishing village near Thiruvananthapuram in southern India.

"Our propulsion [technology] started with a tiny motor of 75 mm diameter with 2 seconds burn duration and 4 kg propellant mass in 1967," recalls B. N.Suresh, until recently director of the Vikram Sarabhai Space Centre (VSSC) in Thiruvananthapuram.

ISRO has come a long way since then. The motor that VSSC now makes for ISRO's advanced version of the Geostationary Satellite Launch Vehicle (GSLV-Mk-III) has a diameter of 3.2 meters and a propellant mass of 200 tonnes—one of the biggest in the world. GSLV-Mk-III, which is slated to make its debut in 2009–2010, will have the capability to place payloads of 4 tonnes in geostationary transfer orbit (GTO) against the current version of GSLV that lifts 1800 kg to GTO.

The other launcher in ISRO's stable—the Polar Satellite Launch Vehicle (PSLV)—can place a 1600 kg satellite in polar orbit. It has been used to launch as many as four payloads in a single mission. While the GSLV has so far made three successful flights, the PSLV has launched 9 remote sensing satellites and a weather satellite for India as well as small satellites for Belgium, Germany, Korea, Argentina, Indonesia, Italy and Israel. ISRO's satellite programme has been equally impressive. Its first satellite, the 40 kg Aryabhata, launched by the erstwhile USSR, was a plaything compared to the communication satellites that make up today's Indian National Satellite (INSAT) network—the flagship of ISRO. India currently uses foreign launchers only for its heavy INSAT satellites but this dependence too will end once GSLV-Mk-III is ready in 2010. The Indian spacecraft technology has been well recognized globally: ISRO grabbed two contracts for communication satellites from EADS-Astrium, the European consortium. The ISRO-made satellites will be used by EUTELSAT, the European satellite network. And, jointly with the Russian space agency, ISRO is developing a satellite for Russia's global navigational satellite system GLONASS.

ISRO's triumphs in the four decades are particularly remarkable considering it had to function in a 'technology denial' regime and with an annual budget of around US$600 million—three per cent of what US space agency NASA spends in a year (the budget went up to $760 million for the year 2007–08). Restrictions on technology transfer imposed by the US after Indian nuclear tests in 1974 and 1998 forced ISRO to reinvent technologies it could no longer buy. "It was a blessing in disguise," says Krishnaswami Kasturirangan, former chairman of ISRO. "It spurred all-round indigenous effort by ISRO—in association with academia and industry—to develop the complete range of technologies for launch vehicles and satellites."

For instance, ISRO embarked on developing the cryogenic engine on its own in 1993 after Russia, under US pressure, refused to transfer the technology to India. On November 15, 2007, the indigenous cryogenic upper stage was successfully tested for full flight duration of 12 minutes. "The flight of GSLV with home grown engine will take place in 2009–2010," says Gopalan Madhavan Nair, ISRO's present chairman. It took nearly 14 long years and Rs 3.36 billion ($82 million), but ISRO is happy it has, at last, its own cryogenic engine.

In the long run, the efforts of indigenization have served ISRO and India well. Today, nearly 90 per cent of Indians can watch television; listen to weather forecasts and disaster warnings thanks to the INSAT network of seven satellites with a total of 175 transponders—the biggest civilian system in the Asia-Pacific region. ISRO's satellites are also having an impact at sea. OCEANSAT-1 monitors the chlorophyll content of oceans and the sea surface temperature. ISRO scientists use the information to identify fishing zones. ISRO, which has built more than a dozen remote

sensing satellites, presently has a fleet of six in operation, including the Cartosat-2 launched in January 2007 that can take pictures with a spatial resolution of one meter. The global sales of imagery from Indian remote sensing satellites (IRS) generate US$6 million in revenue to Antrix Corporation.

Within India, scientists have used the IRS pictures to combat deforestation, monitor desertification, predict crop yields and identify groundwater on a scale not attempted anywhere else in the world. "The IRS program has been the most cost-effective," says the first ever economic analysis of India's space programme. A study released in 2007 by U. Shankar of the Madras School of Economics in Chennai says that ISRO has already recovered one-fifth of the $222 million investment it made so far in remote sensing satellites through sale of their data products. "In the absence of IRS satellites, the country would have spent $124 million in purchasing the same data," says Shankar. "While the direct and indirect gains from the IRS program are substantial even now, in the long run, the economic gains will outnumber the figures many times over." The study justifies the investment by arguing that ISRO saved money that India would have otherwise spent on launching its satellites from abroad. For instance, ISRO saved up to $50 million by launching its last four remote sensing satellites.

ISRO is ahead of other space-faring nations in being more innovative about using its satellites for national development. Its $20 million "Edusat" satellite launched in 2004—exclusively for teaching—beams educational programmes to 30,000 classrooms. It is a precursor for a nationwide space-based educational service to be put in place by 2010, says ISRO. And ISRO's rapidly expanding telemedicine network also promises to revolutionize health care delivery to rural areas where 80 per cent of Indians live (but are served by only 2 per cent of the nation's doctors.). The INSAT network currently links 264 hospitals in towns and cities with health centres in villages. Enthused by its popularity, ISRO intends to launch satellites 'Healthsats' for health care. None of these would have been possible had India relied on foreign launchers and purchased satellites.

Difficulties

But it has not all been smooth sailing. India's first rocket, the Satellite Launch Vehicle (SLV), crashed into the Bay of Bengal in 1979. Two "augmented" SLVs met with the same fate, and an explosion in an ISRO facility killed six in 2004. ISRO's workhorse, the PSLV, made nine successful launches in a row after its first flight in 1993 crashed into the sea. "Failure is common in space business and we learnt from each," Nair told reporters after the July 2006 disaster when the third GSLV carrying the telecom satellite Insat-4C went up in smoke.

ISRO's quest for self-reliance has recently been extended to other areas as well. It is building an Indian Regional Navigation Satellite System (IRNSS) of its own at a cost of $320 million to reduce the country's dependence on the Global Positioning System (GPS) satellites operated by the US Department of Defense. Consisting of a constellation of seven satellites, IRNSS is expected to provide position accuracies in a region centered over India and extending to adjoining countries. ISRO, in collaboration with the Airports Authority of India, expects to implement this regional navigation by 2014.

Out of necessity, ISRO initially viewed space technology primarily as a tool for national development. It has since matured as a credible business organization with services to provide in international market at competitive prices. Italy's astronomy satellite Agile launched in April 2007 was the first major commercial contract bagged by Antrix. Israeli spy satellite

TecSAR, launched by ISRO on January 21, 2008, was the next. "These deals have raised the image of PSLV as a reliable launcher," says K.R. Sridharamurthi, executive director of Antrix. The Israeli space telescope TAUVEX is next on the list of foreign payloads, while Canadian and French payloads are on the wait list. With its first ever commercial contracts for two telecom satellites for EUTELSAT already in hand, Antrix is looking for potential buyers of ISRO's time-tested remote sensing satellites. "Till now we have only been marketing the imagery obtained by our remote sensing satellites," said Sridharamurthi. "We now want to offer the satellites themselves."

In anticipation of increased demand, ISRO is setting up an additional satellite building and testing facility in a 100 acre plot in Bangalore. With this expansion to be completed in 2009, ISRO's production facility can handle six satellites at a time against two or three at present. ISRO's business prospects are set for a boost with the entry into service of a second launch pad in the existing space complex in Sriharikota Island on the east coast. Commissioned in 2007, the Rs 4 billion launch pad with state-of-the-art facilities is "one of the best in the world," says Kasturirangan.

New launch pad

This new launch pad is already the centre of activity with the planned Moon mission later this year. The 525 kg lunar orbiter *Chandrayaan-1* will have a mission life of two years during which it will create 3-dimensional maps of the Moon's surface at a resolution of between 5 and 10 meters, something that has never been done before. It will also map the distribution of minerals and look for water. The Moon mission led to a major engineering creation: the 250-tonne 32-metre diameter parabolic dish antenna on the outskirts of Bangalore—to communicate with *Chandrayaan-1*—is the largest of its kind designed and built in India. "The deep space antenna is going to serve not only the Moon mission but, at a later date, the mission to Mars," says T Krishnamumar, the ISRO scientist in charge of this project. The Mars mission awaits government approval but ISRO has firmed up the second Moon mission, *Chandrayaan-2*—that will attempt a soft landing.

Narendra Bhandari who heads ISRO's planetary exploration programme is thinking about *Chandrayaan-2* and even beyond. "There are two aspects which are futuristic but of foremost interest for ISRO," he says. One is helium-3, considered to be an ideal fuel for fusion available in lunar soil but extremely rare on Earth. The other feature is the presence of organic molecules in abundance in comets, "some of which, if harnessed, can have commercial implications." Bhandari says future missions by ISRO—besides Mars Orbiter—may include an asteroid orbiter and a comet fly by. ISRO scientists are already working on an astronomy satellite called "Astrosat" and a scientific satellite named Aditya that will study the Sun with an advanced telescope during the peak of the solar cycle in 2011.

While engaged in planetary exploration, for the next two decades, ISRO will focus on reducing launch costs. The per kilogram launch cost of $27,213 by Indian vehicles according to Shankar's study, is already lower than the average cost of $33,348 for America's Delta-2, Europe's Arianne, and Russia's Proton. "But we intend to reduce the cost further," says Nair. Towards this end, ISRO has undertaken the development of a reusable launch vehicle (RLV). According to Nair, an RLV "technology demonstrator" will be test flown before 2010.

Whilst guided by the motto of self reliance, ISRO is keen on foreign collaborations that are mutually advantageous. The "Megha-Tropiques" project to study tropical weather jointly with Centre National d'Études Spatiales (CNES), the French space agency, is one of these. *Chandrayaan-1* carries instruments from the US, UK, Germany, Sweden and Bulgaria. ISRO's second mission to the Moon, *Chandrayaan-2* in 2011–12 will be done jointly with Russia, and ISRO's new agreement with NASA signed in January 2008 in Washington calls for Indo-US collaboration in "planetary exploration."

ISRO also has schemes especially for space scientists of developing countries. Under one scheme, ISRO trains scientists from third world countries in different applications of space technology, bearing all costs except air tickets from their home countries. ISRO has also announced plans to build and launch a remote sensing micro-satellite named Third World Satellite that will beam imageries for use by select developing countries. It is slated for launch in 2009.

But the Manned Mission Space programme is one project that ISRO wants to do by itself without foreign collaboration. Nair says his agency would like to keep the programme "totally indigenous." Russia had offered its space module for training Indian astronauts,

but ISRO, says Nair, "would want to develop its own technology as in the long run we want to be self reliant." Former ISRO Chairman U R Rao fully agrees. "Despite growing cooperation with the US, it is essential for India to develop its own capability in space," he says.

ISRO took the first step towards a manned mission in January 2007 by putting in orbit its first recoverable space capsule and retrieving it safely after 12 days. In the next phase, ISRO has earmarked Rs 500 million ($12.5 million) of its budget for "developing a fully autonomous orbital vehicle to carry a two-member crew to low earth orbit and safely return them to earth." The project, yet to be formally cleared by the cabinet, would, in the first phase, cost 2.2 billion dollars to put an Indian in orbit by 2014, and at least twice as much in the second phase to land him or her on the Moon by 2020. If approved, India will join the select club of the United States, Russia and China that run manned space missions.

Such a decision had not been anticipated by Vikram Sarabhai. At the early stage of the space programme, he had said, "India does not have the fantasy of competing with the economically advanced nations in the exploration of the Moon or planets or manned space flights." But leading space scientists, including U R Rao, think Sarabhai's statement is not relevant after what all has happened in the past few years. "Even if India wants to build space solar power stations in future you need to send humans to space to assemble solar panels."

Nair says a manned mission is the next most obvious thing to do since ISRO has "more or less fulfilled" the primary objectives envisaged at the beginning of the space programme. He cites three reasons for pushing forward human presence in space. Firstly, it may become essential for planetary exploration, which beckons future mankind. He also believes manned missions will have spin-offs and enthuse talented youngsters to pursue science and technology as careers. Thirdly, he says India can afford a manned mission with its current GDP growth rate.

Officially, ISRO is not competing with China, which in 2003 sent an astronaut into space. But it is generally believed that an acknowledgement by ISRO that it is losing ground to its bigger neighbour China has spurred its scientists to think the unthinkable. And if ISRO keeps up its tradition, it may put an Indian on the Moon by 2020! □

Srinivas Laxman
Journalist

An ambitious voyage

A launch countdown is in progress at India's vast spaceport, Satish Dhawan Space Centre, Sriharikota. In the mission control room, scientists and engineers are glued to the computers monitoring the enormous amount of data which is flowing in continuosly from the launch pad. Hundreds of people have gathered everywhere anxiously waiting to watch a historic mission takeoff in a few minutes. On the terrace of the Brahma Prakash hall, which turns into the media centre during a launch, a large number of mediapersons have assembled to record the much-awaited flight, which if it succeeds will mark a major milestone in India's space programme.

Soon the countdown hits the zero mark and the highly-proven four-stage brown and white Polar Satellite Launch Vehicle (PSLV) lifts off with a thunderous roar having as its passenger a hi-tech orbiter. For a change, the permanent home of this Indian spacecraft will neither be the geo-stationary orbit 36,000 km above the equator which is occupied mostly by communication satellites, nor the polar Sun-synchronous orbit which is often used by remote sensing satellites. This orbiter will have an entirely new destination to which no Indian spacecraft has been earlier. Its destination: the Moon.

India was now headed for the Moon. The distance: 3,86,000 km away from the earth.

The mission is slated for lift off later this year.

How will India get to the Moon?

Soon after take off, the Moon-bound spacecraft will be placed in the geo-stationary transfer orbit (GTO) with its closest point to the Earth being 240 km called perigee and the farthest being 24,000 km called apogee. Here, after executing a few critical manouvres, the altitude of the spacecraft will be further raised with the farthest point from the earth being 1,000,000 km. Its nearest point to the earth will remain the same which is 240 km. Now, it will be readied for its journey to the Moon, a distance of 3,86,000 km, which is expected to last for five-and-a-half days. At one point the spacecraft will be transferred to the lunar orbit, which the director of ISRO's telemetry, tracking and command network centre, S K Shivakumar, said will be the nail-biting moment of the entire mission. Called the lunar orbit insertion (LOI) the commands from the centre have to be flashed for a precise number of seconds to the spacecraft. "A slight deviation can completely doom the mission," he said. After this the spacecraft will be placed in a 1000 km polar orbit around the Moon for evaluation purposes, and then gradually lowered to 200 km before it reaches its final orbit of 100 km above the lunar surface. The Rs 386 crore mission will last for two years.

A worldwide network of ground stations belonging to ISTRAC and the space agencies of the US, Russia and Brazil will track the craft. ISTRAC's ship borne terminal will also be deployed at a suitable location.

The spacecraft is cuboid in shape weighing 1304 kg during launch and 590 kg at the lunar orbit. It will be powered through a single-sided solar array which will provide power during all phases of the mission. In case of a solar eclipse the spacecraft will be powered by lithium batteries.

The rocket which will carry the spacecraft will be an upgraded version of the PSLV which was first tried out when it ferried the Kalpana-1 weather satellite to the geostationary transfer orbit in September 2002. The PSLV carries remote sensing

satellites to the Sun synchronous orbit. This was the first time it took a satellite to the GTO. The significance of this is that the Moon-bound spacecraft will be initially placed in the GTO by the PSLV.

The exciting story of this flight had its beginnings in the 90s when Krishnaswamy Kasturirangan headed the space body. In the application-related space programmes like remote sensing which helps in important areas like urban development, agriculture and coastal management, and communications, India had performed satisfactorily. He was happy that in these two important areas India had literally become a world leader. Even a powerful space-faring nation like the US was buying pictures taken by India's remote sensing satellites. The ISRO chief was convinced that the time had come for the Indian space agency, with its talented pool of scientists and engineers, to embark on a mission which was really challenging and exciting.

His colleagues shared his view that India had the capability to go in for a major space mission which would establish the country's credentials as a big space-faring nation. The question was what type of a project should this be? The space chief realized that future space programmes of most nations focused on space sciences. This would mean largely launching inter-planetary flights. He felt that for India to remain in the forefront of the space sector, it

too had to seriously explore the possibility of going beyond the geo-synchronous orbit of 36,000 km and fly further into the solar system. The question then was where could India go? He knew that there was a lunar renaissance taking place, with the US planning to return to the Moon, and Japan, China and the European Space Agency planning unmanned scientific lunar missions. So why should India lag behind?

Kasturirangan was convinced that India had the capability to embark on such an ambitious flight. Now, he wanted to test public response. The forum chosen for this was a programme organized on May 11, 1999 at a five-star hotel in New Delhi to mark the first anniversary of the nuclear weapons tests at Pokhran. Kasturirangan spoke at length about the achievements of India's space programme. Then he threw a bombshell: India was exploring the possibility of launching an unmanned mission to the Moon. The audience, comprising a large number of VIPs could not believe what they had heard. They were dumb-struck. Not surprisingly, the response was extremely favourable. Most of them felt the Indian Moon mission would enhance India's standing in global scientific circles.

Encouraged by the response, Kasturirangan took the lunar proposal to various scientific bodies for their opinion and approval. India's flight path to the Moon crossed various organizations with all of them unanimously giving their approval. For instance, in October 1999 the Moon programme got the go-ahead from the Indian Academy of Sciences and in February 2000 it received the green signal from the Astronautical Society of India. The Parliamentary Standing Committee cleared it in April 2002 which was followed by the approval of the space commission in June 2003. During this time a National Committee for Lunar Exploration was formed which completely backed the project. The veteran space scientist, George Joseph, told me sometime ago during an interview: "We were already late with regards to Pokhran. The same thing should not happen to the lunar mission," he said.

And then, on August 15, 2003, Prime Minister Atal Behari Vajpayee announced India's plans to go to the Moon during his Independence Day address and named the mission "Chandrayaan" which in Sanskrit means Moon craft. The announcement triggered widespread excitement in almost every part of the country especially among the younger generation. Kasturirangan asked: "Can we afford not to have a Moon mission now?"

The project did face some criticism with a small bunch of scientists pointing out that the Moon mission will not yield any useful scientific data and should therefore be scrapped. But, their opposition was brushed aside and the government decided to go ahead with the programme.

The decision to go to the Moon has to be seen in the context of a statement which was made by the father of the Indian space programme, Vikram Sarabhai. In the early 60s when the Indian space programme was started at a fishing village called Thumba, close to Thiruvananathanapuram airport, Sarabhai declared: "There are some who question the relevance of space activities in a developing nation. To us there is no ambiguity of purpose. We do not have the fantasy of competing with the economically advanced nations in the exploration of the Moon or the planets or manned space flight."

A number of space scientists feel that his observation has no relevance since there was a global race to the Moon in order to harness its resources and also set up a habitation in the long-term. They feel that in this competitive era India cannot afford to lag behind.

With the Indian Moon mission now a reality, its scientific objectives were defined. The role of the project was primarily aimed at a high

---

Scientific Objectives

The *Chandrayaan-1* mission is aimed at high-resolution remote sensing of the Moon in visible, near infrared(NIR), low energy X-rays and high-energy X-ray regions. The objectives will be

- To prepare a three-dimensional atlas (with a high spatial and altitude resolution of 5-10m) of both near and far side of the Moon.
- To conduct chemical and mineralogical mapping of the entire lunar surface for distribution of elements such as Magnesium, Aluminum, Silicon, Calcium, Iron and Titanium with a spatial resolution of about 25 km and high atomic number elements such as Radon, Uranium & Thorium with a spatial resolution of about 20 km.

Simultaneous photo geological and chemical mapping will enable identification of different geological units, which will test the early evolutionary history of the Moon and help in determining the nature and stratigraphy of the lunar crust.

Mission Objectives

- To realise the mission goal of harnessing the science payloads, lunar craft and the launch vehicle with suitable ground support systems including DSN station.
- To realise the integration and testing, launching and achieving lunar polar orbit of about 100 km, in-orbit operation of experiments, communication/telecommand, telemetry data reception, quick look data and archival for scientific utilization by identified group of scientists.

---

resolution remote sensing of the Moon and preparing a three dimensional atlas of both its near and far sides. The Indian mission will also conduct a chemical and mineralogical mapping of the entire lunar surface for the distribution of elements such as magnesium, aluminum, silicon, calcium, iron and titanium. This study apart from benefitting the people on Earth in the long run will help in analyzing the evolution of the Moon. It will also hunt for water. The data transmitted by the lunar orbiter will be analysed at the National Science Data Centre which has been set up ISRO's new
deep space network at a village called Byalalu near Bangalore.

Chandrayaan project director Mylaswamy Annadurai told a meeting of planetarium officials at Nashik in January 2008 that the Moon is useful because it contains a million tonnes of helium-3, which, if harnessed, can help in solving the Earth's energy problems. "Moon contains 10 times more energy because of helium-3 than all the economically recoverable fossil fuels on the Earth." He said that in the past the interest in space and the Moon was driven by scientific curiosity. Now this voyage of discovery will give way to "a voyage of profit," he told the gathering at Nashik. Sometime ISRO chairman G Madhavan Nair at a meeting held at the Bhabha Atomic Research Centre in Mumbai said that helium-3 can power nuclear reactors which in turn can solve the Earth's energy problems.

Well known lunar expert Paul Spudis has described the Moon as "a scientific laboratory of extraordinary facility, richness and benefit." In a report which he prepared about the advantages of going to the Moon, he said, that it could also be a stable platform to observe the universe. He says that scientists have estimated that each pole of the Moon contains nearly 10 billion tonnes of water, enough to launch a fully-fuelled space shuttle daily for over 39 years.

Alan Binder, principal investigator of NASA's Lunar Prospector unmanned mission to the Moon in 1998 says that the Moon has resources which can be used to build a lunar colony and industrial complex. "There is a revival of interest in the Moon all over the world because nations have realized the economic importance of the Moon for the future of humanity," he said.

According to NASA, there is a global interest in the Moon for a number of reasons. Some of these are:

• The Moon is an ideal place where astronauts can learn to live and work in a difficult environment before flying to more distant destinations.

• Advanced types of space suits and rovers can be tested on the Moon.

• Astronauts on the Moon can learn to operate crucial life support and power systems which are needed on Mars.

• The impact of the absence of normal gravity can be gauged on the Moon.

In an interview, Annapurna explained that some of the previous lunar programmers by other countries "were limited in characterising the Moon in the sense that the data were only from samples on representative locations and the observations were not detailed enough to make an in-depth study." The Indian mission to the Moon should be seen beyond the scientific results it produces. "We have many more meaningful places in the Moon to be explored that were untouched by NASA's Apollo missions to the Moon," he said.

According to him, studies have shown that the Moon could serve as a source of economic benefit to mankind and could be of strategic importance. "The Moon can be both a beacon and a focus for the next generation of space exploration which will accrue new and important benefits, to the people of all nations," he said.

The man who has been entrusted with the task of taking India to the Moon says that with the advancement in technology and miniturisation, it is now possible to observe the Moon as close as possible with better resolutions,

About the challenges which he faces, he said: "We have to look at all the systems afresh. Even while adopting a simple system that has a heritage from INSAT or IRS (Indian Remote Sensing Satellite), we have to weigh which one is more suitable, IRS vs. INSAT to the lunar environment. Additionally as *Chandrayaan-1* is carrying nearly one dozen scientific instruments from equal number of institutions, an unprecedented situation for any project director, all care has been taken while accommodating the instruments," he said.

Regarding the most challenging and difficult aspect of the flight to the Moon, he said technically speaking achieving the lunar polar orbit itself will be a challenge, considering the success rate of lunar missions both by the US and Russia is only around 70 per cent. "Additionally, thermal management of the satellite in lunar orbit of 100 km around the Moon will also be quite challenging," he said.

When ISRO firmed up the Moon mission, it decided that there would be a total of 11 scientific payloads and the project will have an international flavour. To achieve this, it made what is known as an "Announcement of Opportunity," inviting foreign participation in the mission. The response indeed took ISRO by surprise. Despite the fact that it was India's maiden mission to the Moon, ISRO was flooded with a large number of proposals for lunar experiments from various space agencies of different countries. "We were truly taken aback by this huge response," remarked a senior ISRO official, who added that initially there were more ideas for experiments from foreign countries than from India.

The foreign proposals were evaluated at the Physical Research Laboratory in Ahmedabad headed by J N Goswami, who is the principal scientific investigator for the mission. A few were shortlisted and finally, six lunar experiments were chosen which conformed to the requirements of the Indian mission. Of the six, two were from NASA, three from the European Space Agency and one from Bulgaria.

Indian payloads

- Terrain mapping camera: this will map both the near and far side of the Moon and prepare a three-dimensional atlas. This has been developed by ISRO.
- Hyper spectral imager: The data from this equipment will provide details about the mineral composition of the Moon and also the deep crater regions. Also developed by ISRO.
- Lunar Laser Ranging Instrument: It will determine the accurate altitude of the spacecraft above the Moon's surface. It will also obtain an improved model for the lunar gravity field and supplement details from the terrain mapping camera and the hyper spectral imager payloads. Developed by ISRO.
- High energy X-ray spectrometer: It will attempt to detect radioactivity. Developed by ISRO.
- Moon Impact Probe: Weighs 29 kg.

The probe was introduced on the suggestion of former President APJ Abdul Kalam who was keen that India should make its presence felt on the surface of the Moon. The announcement about introducing this probe was made at a lunar conference which was held at Udaipur on November 22, 2004. It took many space scientists by surprise and quiet a few questioned its last minute inclusion which added to the weight of the spacecraft. But, a sizeable number also backed the idea that the landing of the probe on the lunar surface will reaffirm India's position as a growing space power.

According to ISRO, the probe will ride piggy back on the top deck of the main orbiter and will be released at a pre-determined time, after the orbiter reaches its final 100 km orbit above the Moon. It will crash land at a particular location on the Moon. Flying at a hypersonic velocity, it is expected to take about 20 minutes to hit the Moon's surface once it detaches itself from the main orbiter.

The probe will determine technologies for future soft landing missions (*Chandrayaan-2*) and explore the Moon from a close range. It will be equipped with a radar altimeter, a video imaging system and a spectrometer.

Foreign payloads

- Chandrayaan X-ray spectrometer: It will help in mapping the Moon. Earlier, it successfully operated in Europe's first mission to the Moon, Smart 1. It has been mainly developed by the European Space Agency.
- Near infra-red spectrometer: It will address issues related to the surface aspects of the Moon, explore space weathering and survey mineral lunar resources for future landing sites and exploration. It has been developed by the Max Plank Institute for Solar System Science in Germany. It is a contribution of the European Space Agency.
- Sub Kev Atom Reflecting Analyser: It will help in imaging the Moon's surface. Jointly developed by the European Space Agency and the Swedish Institute of Space Physics.
- Radiation Dose Monitor Experiment: Its main role would be to study the radiation environment in the Moon and evaluate the radiation hazards while exploring the Moon through the *Chandrayaan-1* mission. This data will help in planning future manned missions to the Moon (India has not totally ruled out the possibility of embarking a manned lunar mission around 2020). This has been developed by the Bulgarian Academy of Sciences.
- Miniature Synthetic Aperture Radar: It will detect water ice in the permanently shadowed regions of the lunar poles. A contribution through NASA.
- Moon Mineralogy Mapper: It will assess and map the lunar mineral resources. It is through NASA.

While an agreement between ISRO the European Space Agency and Bulgaria were signed on June 27, 2005, in the case of NASA it was firmed up in 2006 as some issues had to be sorted out. After the decks had been finally cleared, it was President George Bush himself who made an announcement about NASA's participation in the Indian Moon mission during his visit to New Delhi in March 2006. Subsequently, NASA administrator Michael Griffen came to Bangalore and signed the formal agreement on May 9, 2006, relating to the two NASA payloads which will be flying on *Chandrayaan-1*.

Griffen remarked to the media after signing the document: "The mission you will conduct some 40 years after humans saw the Moon close for the first time, will greatly advance our understanding of our closest neighbour and

---

Tracking the Moon tracker

A tiny village, Byalalu, which is about 40 kms from Bangalore off the Bangalore-Mysore highway is surrounded by hills, has a few houses which have no electricity and power most of the time. On many days the villagers have to walk to a nearby well to collect water. Despite the backwardness of their village, the local people seem a happy lot.

Their village occupies an important place in the world space map. After evaluating a number of places, ISRO decided set up the deep space network in this village which will play an important role in the field of communications in the Indian Moon and Mars missions. It is saucer-shaped and is free of any type of radio interference.

On a visit to the village, I saw two antennas, one of 32-metre and other of 18-metre diameter. The smaller one has been acquired from Germany, while the bigger one has been jointly made by the Electronics Corporation of India Limited and Bhabha Atomic Research Centre.

The nearly 135-acre deep space network complex which has been established at a cost of Rs 100 crores consists mainly of a technical complex, the antenna complex building, the Indian Space Science Data Centre (ISSDC) and a guest house. The ISSDC is the main centre for storing the scientific data transmitted by the lunar orbiter. From here it will be distributed for scientists in India and abroad for analysis. I was taken inside the hi-tech technical complex which has among other facilities an operations area, a satellite communications zone, a telemetry hall, an electronics laboratory, a video conference room and a VIP room.

According to ISRO officials, high performance processors will allow the decoding of low faint signals from deep space. The deep space network is also equipped with precision timing systems. All operations are designed to be carried out locally from a single computer or remotely from the network control centre at the ISTRAC in Bangalore.

Dedicated communication links connect the deep space network to various participating agencies of the *Chandrayaan-1* mission, both in India and aboard. From the lunar orbiter the signals will first flash to the antenna, then to the technical complex and from there to the telemetry, tracking and command network centre at Bangalore and vice versa. The whole process will take just a few seconds.

Officials asked me to climb right on top of the 32-metre antenna which I did. It was really a risky and precarious climb through the steep ladders. Once on top I felt I was on the Moon!

The Chandrayaan flight is expected to be intellectually very rewarding and encourage research in the field of planetary sciences in Indian universities. In the US, during the Apollo missions to the Moon between 1969 and 1972, many students opted to study science and mathematics. "We hope the Chandrayaan mission provides a similar inspiration to our students too," remarked a space scientist. He said that it should encourage students to participate in future Indian planetary missions by going in for physics and mathematics.

---

represents a very impressive technical achievement. NASA is honoured to be a participant on this mission," he said.

According to NASA the data obtained from the Moon Mineralogy Mapper could be of practical use to future astronauts who may have to live and work on the Moon for extended periods of time.

American geologist, Carle Pieters, who has been selected by ISRO to participate in the scientific investigations of the Moon Mineralogy Mapped said, "I feel honored that the project funded by NASA has been selected by ISRO. I am really excited to work on this ambitious project." ISRO has not levied any fee to the foreign space agencies for carrying their payload on Chandrayaan, but stipulated that they had to share their data with India. Goswami, who is the principal scientific investigator to the Chandrayaan mission said in a presentation about this project that the Moon is scientifically very important because it is the

only planetary satellite which is in the inner solar system.

He says that while studying the Moon's history the special regions of interest would be its polar regions, the South Pole Aitken region and some selected basins and craters. "*Chandrayaan-1* is a science-oriented mission which is geared for technology and the use of the Moon as a future gateway for exploration," he stated in his presentation to a gathering of space scientists.

Second mission to the Moon

"*Chandrayaan-1*," will not be India's last flight to the Moon because in 2011–2012, ISRO will launch a second unmanned mission to the Moon called "*Chandrayaan-2*."

This joint Indo-Russian flight will have a landing platform with a Moon rover. This rover will move on wheels on the lunar surface, pick up samples of soil or rocks, carry out a chemical analysis and transmit the data to the orbiting spacecraft. This in turn will relay the information to the ground station.

An agreement signed between ISRO and the Russian Federal Space Agency (Roskosmos) in 2007, says that while ISRO will develop the orbiter, the Russian space agency will be responsible for the lander and the rover. The Russian-made rover will weigh between 30 kg and 100 kg, depending on whether it will be a semi-hard or soft landing on the Moon. The rover will have a one-month life span, but the total operating life of the orbiter will be two years. Kanpur IIT wanted to provide the rover, but India opted for the Russian one during the Prime Minister Manmohan Singh's visit to Moscow in November 2007.

Then to Mars

The Indian Moon missions have been described as the beginning of more ambitions interplanetary flights by India.

In 2012 when the second Indian Moon mission, "*Chandrayaan-2*," is set to take off from the Satish Dhawan Space Centre, Sriharikota, another exciting flight will perhaps be readying to lift off. The target: Mars.

The journey from Sriharikota to Mars is expected to take anything between six and nine months. The cost: Rs 3 billion.

Madhavan Nair has said that the Indian Mars mission could be launched around 2012 and the rocket will be the three-stage Geo Synchronous Satellite Launch Vehicle.

That this project is not a fantasy or dream of ISRO is also amply evident from the fact that it forms a part of the space agency's 11th five-year plan. Goswami said that scientists have already started informal discussions about the flight to Mars and provide inputs to ISRO. "We are studying the best science which can be done on Mars in the international context. We do not want to repeat what others have already done," he said. According to him, the areas of research will be Martian atmosphere, its ionosphere, the dust storms, its magnetic fields and the Martian weather. "It will be an orbiting mission which will image the surface of Mars," he said.

Former ISRO chief K Kasturirangan said that an Indian mission to Mars has to be a natural follow up to the lunar flight. "It will be a natural evolution to India's planetary exploration programme," he told this writer.

Kalam has set a very ambitious plan for the Mars mission. He wants the unmanned flight to eventually lead to a manned mission with the first Indian landing on the surface of Mars by 2030. □

त्वं सोम प्र चिकितो मनीषा त्वं रजिष्ठम् अनु नेषि पन्थाम्।।
O Moon, we should be able to know you through our intellect.
You enlighten us through the right path.

Rigveda Part - 1/91/1
(about 2000 years B.C.)

Pallava Bagla
Correspondent *Science*

An inviting destination

The Moon has always held pride of place in the Indian ethos, and holds meaning and significance for millions of people of diverse religions, communities and cultures across the length and breadth of this country. The 21ˢᵗ century however, will enrich this relationship as a series of Moon missions will follow *Chandrayaan-1*. An Indian soft lander and rover may be on the Moon by 2012. Thereafter a manned mission in space possibly by 2014. An Indian craft will land an Indian on the Moon perhaps six years later. The Moon as a destination will then on become merely a starting point for journeys to Mars and beyond. Aditya, a mission to study the Sun, is to be launched in the next four years.

India is truly set on a voyage to Moon, Mars and beyond, to the edges of the solar system. India is no stranger to human civilisation's unending quest for knowledge, and this latest programme will place the country squarely among the scientifically advanced nations that seek to answer the unanswered, that search the unexplored frontiers and that tirelessly work to keep the flame burning—shedding light on the dark unknowns. With a host of unanswered questions—the true origins of the Moon, the possibility of exploiting the natural resources on the Moon on a commercial basis in times to come—these lunar missions have a lot to accomplish, finding clues and contributing to the global knowledge system.

After Sputnik was launched back in 1957 by the Soviet Union, India began to configure a home-grown space programme, with initial emphasis on the application of technology for meeting the developmental needs of the people.

Having used the space technologies to address society's needs, it became necessary to think of other dimensions of the space programme. With its mature space research programme, India was able to plan one of the most intense lunar exploration missions of the world in three decades. Some 30 years after man first set foot on the lunar surface, a new Asian race has started for reaching the Moon. China recently launched its maiden probe to the Moon called Chang'e-1 named after a Chinese goddess who, as mythology goes, had flown to the Moon. Japan launched its heaviest lunar probe called Kaguya in October 2007. The US is to follow.

Questions are raised about a country riddled with large-scale poverty such as India wasting resources on a scientific mission to the Moon. In the context of *Chandrayaan-1*, Prime Minister Manmohan Singh gave a reply: "We have to walk on two legs, to deal with the fundamental problems of development and at the same time set our sights sufficiently high so we can operate on the frontiers of science and technology. In the increasingly globalized world we live in, a base of scientific and technical knowledge has emerged as a critical determinant of the wealth and status of nations and it is that which drives us to programs of this type."

Political leaders and academicians, physicists and civil society, felt this way even sixty years ago, when India was beginning its now vibrant and diverse space research programme. Back in 1968, the father of the Indian space program Dr Vikram Sarabhai said: "We are convinced that if we are to play a meaningful role nationally and in the community of nations, we must be second to none in the application of advanced technologies to the real problems of man and society, which we find in our country". Today, with the many small and big ways in which space research and technology is touching our lives, Sarabhai's testimony stands vindicated. And the Moon mission is a major milestone of this remarkable journey.

Chandrayaan-1

How exciting it would be to obtain a 3D atlas of those regions of the Moon that hold scientific promise! And a chemical map too—through investigation of the distribution of various minerals and chemicals on the Moon. Expected to cost roughly Rs 386 crores, *Chandrayaan-1* is an unmanned orbiter or a lunar satellite that holds immense promise, not to mention scientific curiosity and advanced knowledge. "The objective of the lunar mission is to derive maximum scientific knowledge about the Moon" says G Madhavan Nair, chairman of the Indian Space Research Organisation (ISRO). The Polar Satellite Launch Vehicle (PSLV), India's own 44-meter, over 300-tonne workhorse was transformed into a new avatar for the Moon probe that weighs about 550 kg in lunar orbit. It has enough space for about 100 kg of scientific payload. The remote sensing satellite that it will place in a polar orbit will map the lunar topography and conduct X-ray and gamma-ray spectroscopic studies from a distance of 100 km from the Moon's surface. The Moon probe is expected to last two years or more; most other missions have much shorter life spans.

When the mission was being planned, the then President of India, APJ Abdul Kalam suggested adding to the payload a 25 kg lunar impact probe or impactor. This tiny free falling rocket will, on command detach itself from the satellite, hitting the Moon surface. It won't land softly but will strike the lunar surface at high speed. The probe is likely to throw up lunar dust, which will then be analyzed instantly and the chemical composition beamed back to the orbiting satellite.

More than the value of the chemical data, the impactor will ensure that India's flag, which it carries, is placed for eternity on the lunar soil. The Indian tricolour will remind the world of India's desire not to be left out from the community of nations which may benefit from sharing the rich resources of the lunar surface.

Given India's technological prowess and skill, international collaboration and partnerships have always characterized a lot of scientific research in India. That's why India allocated a total of 10 kg in weight for payloads from other countries. Six payloads from NASA, the European Space Agency and Bulgaria were being given a free ride to the Moon by the Indian space agency.

Initially among others, one American instrument called MiniSar was selected. Then as New Delhi and Washington began to intensify scientific and technological cooperation and the Bush administration began to remove some irritants in the field, ISRO chose another US payload called Moon Mineralogy Mapper to be part of this prestigious mission. The proposal for the second US payload initially ran into the usual problems related to the US administration's penchant for imposing conditions when any sophisticated instrument is to be transferred to a country that is not part of some US-led club or another! These were not acceptable to India. However, after negotiations, an agreeable text was arrived at and a Chandryaan specific agreement was inked. Nair says "we did not compromise our interests" and finally both NASA and ISRO managed to hammer out a mutually compatible memorandum of understanding.

The two countries have to hammer out the agreed text of a complex umbrella agreement called Technology Safeguards Agreement (TSA) and the Technology Assistance Agreement (TAA) that would allow India to commercially fly American satellites using our Indian rockets. Both these agreements are a must before any American space technology can be shifted to India. Nair says "these are teething troubles which are likely to be overcome as long as there is an intention to co-operate". New Delhi has assured the US that 'sensitive and guarded American technologies' will be protected by India with utmost diligence. Before *Chandrayaan* was launched, Dr Michael Griffin, Administrator of NASA, had expressed his delight at the prospects of such bilateral cooperation. Referring to some concern and frustration in India with the US export control rules and laws, he said "those controls are frustrating for us". However, he added that the US was very concerned about the proliferation of missile technologies around the world

The US scientific payloads riding on an Indian launcher has a symbolic significance too. It also represents a sort of role reversal as

India offered a free ride to instruments fabricated in the Western countries!

Indo-Russian Moon mission

A key highlight of Prime Minister Manmohan Singh's visit to Russia in 2007 was the announcement of a joint Indo-Russian mission to explore the Moon using an orbiter and a lander/rover. It does not entail sending a man to the Moon. India's second mission to the Moon called *Chandrayaan-2*, likely to be launched in 2011–12, will be a joint Indo-Russian effort, which will include the two countries jointly developing a 'lunar rover', a robotic vehicle that will move around on the Moon's surface after achieving a soft landing. Incidentally, there is no Russian collaboration in *Chandrayaan-1*, where the US has a significant presence.

ISRO and Russia's Federal Space Agency (Roskosmos) have signed an agreement on joint lunar research and exploration. G Madhavan Nair, Chairman, ISRO, and A Perminov, Director, Roskosmos, signed the agreement in Moscow on November 12, 2007. ISRO will have the prime responsibility for the orbiter and Roskosmos will be primarily responsible for the lander/rover. A few scientific instruments from other space agencies may also be accommodated on these systems. *Chandrayaan-2* will be launched on India's Geosynchronous Satellite Launch Vehicle (GSLV) around 2011–12 time frame. This agreement is a major milestone in the long-standing cooperation between India and Russia in the area of space.

India and Russia have a robust collaboration in space and India's first astronaut Rakesh Sharma lifted off in a Russian Soyuz rocket in 1984. Russia has also supplied the cryogenic engines used by India to heave its heavy communications satellites into space from Sriharikota.

India is today at the cutting-edge of technological research and development—and the mission to the Moon will become a highly visible feature of the country's technological profile. □

Scientific Payloads

Chandrayaan-1 is an Indian Mission to the Moon. The indigenously developed payload/experiments are:

TMC: Terrain Mapping stereo Camera (TMC) in the panchromatic band, having 5 m spatial resolution and 20 km swath

HySI: Hyper Spectral Imaging camera (HYSI) operating in 400-950nm band with a spectral resolution of 15nm and spatial resolution of 80m with a swath of 20km

LLRI: Lunar Laser Ranging Instrument (LLRI) with height resolution of about 10m

HEX: High Energy X-ray spectrometer (HEX) using Cadmium-Zinc-Telluride (CdZnTe) detector in the 30-250 keV energy region with spatial resolution of 40km

MIP: Moon Impact Probe (MIP) as piggyback on the main orbiter of the Chandrayaan-1 spacecraft which will impact on the surface of the Moon

ISRO solicited proposals from international community also. Six experiments were selected for inclusion in Chandrayaan-1 mission. These are:

C1XS: Chandrayaan-1 X-ray Spectrometer (C1XS) through ESA -a collaboration between Rutherford Appleton Laboratory, UK and ISRO Satellite Centre, ISRO. Part of this payload is redesigned by ISRO to suit Chandrayaan-1 scientific objectives.

SIR-2: Near Infra Red spectrometer (SIR-2) from Max Plank Institute, Lindau, Germany through ESA

SARA: Sub KeV Atom Reflecting Analyser (SARA) through ESA, from Swedish Institute of Space Physics, Sweden and Space Physics Laboratory, Vikram Sarabhai Space Centre, ISRO. The Data Processing Unit of this payload/ experiment is designed and developed by ISRO, while Swedish Institute of Space Physics develops the payload.

RADOM: Radiation Dose Monitor Experiment (RADOM) from Bulgarian Academy of Sciences

MiniSAR: Miniature Synthetic Aperture Radar (MiniSAR) from Applied Physics Laboratory, Johns Hopkins University and Naval Air Warfare Centre, USA through NASA

M3: Moon Mineralogy Mapper (M3) from Brown University and Jet Propulsion Laboratory, USA through NASA

Source: ISRO

© Pallava Bagla

Narendra Bhandari
Basic Sciences Research
Institute, Ahmedabad

Birth of the Moon: ISRO seeks the story

For long had the scientists at the Indian Space Research Organisation waited for the day! Starting late, three decades after the first human set foot on the Moon and about 50 Moon missions that followed the momentous event; it was a highly challenging task for ISRO to design a meaningful science mission. Meaningful because much remains to be observed and explored, notwithstanding the six manned missions, and the availability of hundreds of kilograms of lunar samples from nine locations for laboratory studies. The origin and early evolution of the Moon remain to be well understood.

The first plan, approved in 2003, envisaged an orbiter mission to the Moon. It brought many planetary scientists and space engineers together as the Moon Mission Task Force constituted by ISRO. Thus *Chandrayaan-1* set ISRO on a very ambitious programme for a long-term planetary exploration of the Moon and other planned planetary missions.

ISRO began, about half a century ago, with the clear mandate of developing space technology and its applications for the benefit of society. Vikram Sarabhai, who defined the vision of ISRO, had thought out his priorities clearly and was determined that "India should be second to none in the applications of advanced technology to the real problems of man and society". To meet these requirements, two sets of satellites, *IRS series* for remote sensing of natural resources, and *INSAT series* devoted to communication and other similar purposes were developed. To achieve this end, two types of rocket, the Polar Satellite Launch Vehicle (PSLV) and the Geostationary Satellite Launch Vehicle (GSLV) were developed by ISRO over the last two decades.

With the successful launch of PSLV in 1994-95, it appeared feasible to launch a fly-by or orbiter mission to the Moon and some inner planets. But the scientific mission had to wait. Urgent national requirements called for several thematic satellites such as *Cartosat (1 and 2), Metsat (Kalpana-1), Edusat, Resourcesat, and Hamsat* to be given priority. These, devoted to cartography, meteorology, education, telemedicine, e-governance and disaster management, were duly launched, and only a few missions could be devoted to astronomy and atmospheric studies.

Having met, to a large extent, the various national goals related to remote sensing and communication, Dr K Kasturirangan, then Chairman of ISRO, initiated a new and challenging planetary exploration programme towards the end of the last century. He believed that in a few decades, when India takes its place as a developed nation, we should not feel that we missed the opportunity of expanding our horizons of knowledge into the frontiers of space.

The formation of the Moon is intimately related to accretion of Earth, its early evolution and the origin and evolution of life on this unique planet, so far known to be the only one in the universe to harbour life. The 'Giant Impact Hypothesis', about how the Moon was formed, proposed that a large asteroid, about a tenth of the mass of the earth, hit the early Earth 4.5 billion years ago with immense impact, and ejected a large amount of earth material in an orbit around it. This material quickly joined together in an accumulative process to form the Moon.

Whereas this hypothesis explained, to a large extent, the Moon's orbital, physical, chemical, isotopic and geochronological data, in particular the isotopic and chemical similarity of Moon rocks and the Earth's mantle, it was not altogether satisfying. It had inherent difficulties in the sense that the problem of the origin of the Moon was transferred back in time to the problem of the large impactor being formed of the same source material as the earth. Since such large impacts are very rare, this hypothesis also introduced a vital element of 'chance' in the formation of the Moon; it was not a logical consequence of the 'standard' process of formation of planets and satellites from the solar nebula. It was recognized that future explorations of the Moon should address this problem of the Moon's origin and also the formation of numerous large lunar craters since. Because of their proximity, Earth and Moon, are both subjected to the same interplanetary events and surely, the Earth should have undergone similar violent and catastrophic events in its history.

Out of the various available options, such as orbiter, lander or sample return missions, ISRO decided to opt for the orbiter because of the advantage it has in providing global and synoptic database. A long mission, lasting about two years was thought necessary for complete coverage of the Moon. This period is the longest of any mission orbiting the Moon so far. It is a difficult proposition, considering large gravity anomalies on the Moon, which deflect the orbiter, requiring frequent correction of its orbit to save it from crashing down on the Moon. This can be done by having large amounts of fuel on the orbiter for frequent correction of its orbit. Using ISRO's expertise in remote sensing, it was also decided to have several new types of detectors, including two X-ray spectrometers, one for low energy fluorescent X-rays and the other for high energy X-rays to map radioactivity (thorium).

The Moon has extreme temperature variations, not only diurnal from day time to night time, ranging between about $+130°C$ to $-120°C$, but also spatially; some regions at lunar poles are expected to be at $-230°C$. This results in de-gassing of the hot lunar surface by day and movement of volatiles to be deposited eventually at the lunar poles where they remain for a long time. It was proposed that these processes would be studied with the high energy X-ray spectrometer, especially gamma rays coming from the decay of radionuclide lead-210 at 46.5 KeV. This window had not been studied earlier. It was also important to map the minerals at high spatial resolution and for this a hyperspectral imager, with a new

wedge type lens for continuous spectral measurements from visible to near infrared (400 to 900 nanometers), was preferred. In view of these considerations, *Chandrayaan-1*, a cuboid, with each dimension of 1.5 meters, was designed to have several cameras working in the optical, near infrared and X-ray spectrum ranges.

Chandrayaan-1

Chandrayaan-1 is a lunar polar orbiter for remote sensing of the Moon from a nominal altitude of about 100 km. The primary objective of this mission is to carry out a topographic, chemical and mineral mapping of the Moon with a high spatial resolution. It will collect data for a period of two years (2008–2010), during which the whole Moon will be mapped in visible, near IR and X-rays, with a detailed study of the lunar poles, which will be observed during every orbit. It is expected that the chemical, mineral and radioactivity distribution on the Moon will be useful in determining the stratigraphic relationship of various litho-units, which should provide crucial information on the evolution of the Moon in its early stages, the transport and deposition of volatiles, and the presence or absence of water-ice on lunar poles. These studies should also enable us to have a better understanding of the resources available on the Moon. Some prime targets on the Moon, such as lunar poles and some craters in the large basin on its reverse side, have also been identified for detailed study.

Chandrayaan-1 has eleven payloads. To achieve the goals set for this mission, four baseline payloads were conceived, which include Terrain Mapping Camera (TMC) for stereo imaging, Laser Ranging Instrument (LLRI) for altitude determination and gravity modeling of the Moon, Hyper-Spectral Imager (HySI) for mineral mapping, and a High Energy X-ray spectrometer (HEX) for radioactive mapping. These are the Indian payloads designed by various ISRO laboratories, namely Space Applications Centre, Laboratory of Electro-optics, ISRO Satellite Centre and the Physical Research laboratory. For the chemical mapping of some basic elements like magnesium, aluminum, silicon and iron, it was considered advantageous to have a state-of-the-art X-ray fluorescence spectrometer, a British instrument designed for European Space Agency's SMART-1 mission. ISRO and Rutherford Appleton Laboratory therefore agreed upon a joint collaborative study of X-rays characteristic of the elements present on the lunar surface.

Considering the mass and power designated for various instruments on board *Chandrayaan-1*, there was scope for a few additional payloads apart from the five instruments mentioned above. International collaboration and cooperation have been a key element of ISRO's policy from the very inception of the Thumba Rocket Launching Station, which dedicated as it was to the United Nation, offered to launch foreign payloads. It was therefore decided to invite foreign proposals for *Chandrayaan-1* mission. Several good proposals were received. A few of these were accepted, in particular those which enhance the possibility of meeting *Chandrayaan-1's* main objective—complete chemical, mineralogical and topographic mapping at high spatial resolution. The five additional payloads constitute significant international participation in *Chandrayaan-1*. Four of the international payloads are: a Miniature Imaging Radar Instrument (mini-SAR) and Moon Mineral Mapper (M^3), both from the USA, an Infrared camera (SIR-2) from Germany (ESA), and a Radiation Monitor (RADOM) from Bulgaria. A Sub Atomic Reflecting Analyser (SARA) is a joint payload of Indian and foreign groups, chiefly Sweden, and will measure neutral particles in Moon's environment.

Impactor

The additional capability of the augmented PSLV, to carry some more mass to the Moon, was used for a Moon Impactor Probe. The impactor has some imaging and other analytical instruments (e.g. mass spectrometer) and will make observations during its descent before crash landing on the Moon on a predetermined site. A part of the objective of the impactor is technological, preparing for future soft-landers on the Moon. These eleven instruments make *Chandrayaan-1* a very ambitious mission, fully equipped with a large variety of sensitive instruments to meet its goals. There is some degree of redundancy between the Hyperspectral Imager, Infrared Spectrometer and Moon Mineral Mapper, but considering the importance of mineral mapping, this was considered desirable.

Another opportunity for international collaboration and cooperation arises from the fact that there will be several orbiters around the Moon with some overlapping period of observation. Japan's *Selene* (now christened

Kaguya) was launched in September 2007 and China sent its Moon orbiter *Change'E-1* in October 2007. They will be in orbit for about a year or possibly longer. *Chandrayaan-1* and USA's *Lunar Reconnaissance Orbiter* are scheduled to be launched some time in 2008. Thus these orbiters will have overlapping periods of observation during 2008–2010. As a result, apart from the international collaboration on instrumentation on *Chandrayaan-1*, data-sharing and further co-ordination between some of these missions is also possible; one mission may benefit from the data of another and suitably modify its observations. Further, there are several possibilities for in-orbit collaboration because some of the instruments on these missions are similar and have similar objectives.

Unknown frontier

The Moon will continue to remain an object of study for a long time, untill the process by which it was formed in orbit around the Earth is fully understood. Its history is intimately related with that of the Earth and the more we learn about the Moon, the better we will understand the early history of the Earth. A long-term plan to follow *Chandrayaan-1* for exploration of the Moon and other planets, their satellites, asteroids and comets is currently being formulated by ISRO. This opens up new and challenging possibilities to explore the unknown frontiers of space around us.

It must be noted that many of the instruments flown on *Chandrayaan-1* were only recently developed, requiring significant research and development. Some of these were flown for the first time on this mission to obtain better spatial resolution. These include the detectors used in instruments for mineral and radioactive mapping. Thus innovation has been the prime driving force of ISRO's planetary missions. Such innovation promises a better understanding of the evolution of the Moon and its resources, should we need them in future for habitation on the Moon; or for going to other planets, or even back here on Earth. The other point is related to the way international collaboration has strengthened the mission by providing multiple ways of resolving a problem. We hope that this mission will provide some pieces to the jigsaw puzzle of the origin of our mother planet and its longtime companion, and the features that made it possible for life to originate here. □

U Sankar
Madras School of Economics

The rupee goes farther in space

The modest investments in India's space programme have yielded very attractive returns. This is a frontier area in which India has demonstrated its comparative advantage. The economics of India's space programme will make India an attractive source for the users of space-related products and services.

The Indian Space Programme began in 1962 with the creation of the Indian National Committee for Space Research under the chairmanship of Dr Vikram Sarabhai. The objectives of the space programme have been:
- self-reliance in the development of space technologies (to enable independent access to space); and
- capacity-building in the development and application of space technologies (to enable socio-economic development).

The conception, design, testing and application of the complex technology tailored to India's development needs required the creation of new institutional structures, programmes and cooperative agreements among government and private agencies to translate this vision into reality. The fact that the Space Commission was directly under the Prime Minister enabled the Commission to effectively steer the programme with long-term direction and a sound policy framework.

Dr K Kasturirangan has commented on the evolution of the programme. The focus in the first decade was on vision development and initiation. The 1970s saw the programme using foreign space systems to put into effect innovative development applications such as Satellite Instructional Television Experiment, the Satellite Telecommunication Experimental Project, and the testing of satellite-based Earth Observation Systems (EOS).

The experimental phase dealt with the realization of end-to-end systems at an experimental level. Some important programmes were (a) launching of Bhaskara satellites in 1979 and 1981 to gain experience in developing operational remote sensing (RS) systems, (b) Ariane Passenger Payload Experiment, 1981, for development of satellite communication systems, and (c) launching of Satellite Launch Vehicle and Augmented Satellite Launch Vehicle during 1980-1994 to provide a basis for planning, configuring and implementing strategies for development of operational launch vehicles. The operational phase began with the launch of communications satellite INSAT-IB in 1983.

The activities executed by the Indian Space Research Organisation (ISRO) may be grouped under four heads. The Indian National Satellite (INSAT) programme is an agency of the Department of Space, the Department of Telecommunications, Doordarshan, All-India Radio and the Indian Meteorological Department. All the four satellites in the INSAT-1 series were obtained from abroad and were sent into space by foreign launchers. Indigenous production started with INSAT-2A. ISRO manufactured five satellites under the INSAT-2 series, four under the INSAT-3 series and three under the INSAT-4 series. All these satellites saw foreign launches. Kalpana-1 was launched by India's Polar Satellite Launch Vehicle (PSLV) and EDUSAT was launched by India's Geo-synchronous Satellite Launch Vehicle (GSLV).

INSAT is now the largest domestic communication satellite system in the Asia-Pacific Region with 10 satellites carrying 199 transponders. EOS provides remote sensing data in a variety of spatial resolutions and spectral bands, meeting the needs of various applications. The planning, development, operation, and application of EOS are coordinated by the National Natural Resource Management System. At present EOS has six satellites placed in polar sum-synchronous orbit. India has the capability to conceive, design, test, launch and operate RS satellites.

Space transportation includes the manufacture of satellite launch vehicles to place INSAT, EOS and scientific satellites in the requisite orbits. In 1994, PSLV successfully placed an Indian Remote Sensing (IRS) satellite, IRS-P2 in the polar sun-synchronous orbit. With the successful launch of GSLV in 2001, India became one of the six space-faring nations in the world with the capacity to launch satellites in the geo-synchronous transfer orbit.

Space science research is being carried out in various ISRO laboratories. Until 2000, the output targets of ISRO were influenced largely by government /public sector user agencies' requirements. The Satellite–Based Communication Services (SATCOM) Policy of 2000 and the policy for RS-based value-added services envisaged the opening of the space industry to the private sector. To assess the prospects and cost-effectiveness of commercialization of space services, ISRO commissioned a study on the economic aspects of India's space programme through the Madras School of Economics. This report has been published as a book.

Cost-benefit analysis

A social cost-benefit analysis framework is useful for investment decisions in space activities as well as for evaluation of costs and benefits to society. The output basket of a space programme consists of private goods, social goods, public goods and intangibles. R&D expenditures in space technologies generate spillover and spin-off benefits that accrue to society as a whole. Development of space technologies is a complex and risky endeavour.

Economists agree that any public project must meet the criterion of lowest possible cost. As regards benefit measurement, the approach depends on the nature of the good, policy goals and market conditions. The social cost for each product should indicate its social scarcity value. Besides gauging the social benefits for different products, the decision-maker should ask the following questions. (a) Is the production of a particular product socially desirable? (b) What's the subsidy component implicit in the price of the product? (c) For the programme as a whole, do the social benefits exceed or fall short of the social costs?

The Government of India incurred a sum of Rs 13,434 crore (book values) on the space programme from its inception till 31 March 2001. The percentage shares, sector wise, are: INSAT 39.2, Earth Observation 14.7, Launch Vehicles 36.4, Space Science/R&D 6.2, and others 3.6. The percentage shares in the experimental and development phases were 10.6 and 29.3 respectively. The total space expenditures, at 1999-2000 prices, is estimated at Rs 19,111 crore. The civil space expenditure as a percentage of gross domestic product in 2001 was 0.08 for India, while the corresponding figure for USA was 0.14.

Following the European Space Agency's approach (1999), our study classified space activities into two stages, namely (i) design, development, testing, manufacturing, and launch of spacecrafts into desired orbital slots (construction stage), and (ii) application of satellite services to different uses (exploitation stage). At the construction stage, the methodology used is cost-effectiveness along with indicators of self-reliance and measurement of spin-offs. At the application stage, the goods are classified under private goods, social goods and public goods. The benefits are measured in terms of revenues, social benefits, cost and time savings, and value of information.

INSAT System: Economic costing (cost of capital at 12 per cent) of all five satellites in the INSAT-2 series and INSAT-3C and INSAT-3E is reported in our study. The costing procedure for INSAT-2E, the heaviest and most technically advanced satellite in the INSAT-2 series, is given here. INSAT-2E has both communication payloads (10 low power C-band zonal coverage and 9 high power C-band wide coverage transponders) and meteorological payloads (Very High Resolution Radiometer and Charge-Coupled Device Camera). It was launched in 1999. It has an expected life of 12 years.

The procedure for estimation of capital cost for each payload entailed the following steps: (a) estimation of costs attributable to 2E; (b) classification of the costs under (i) payload cost (ii) platform cost (iii) other spacecraft related cost and (iv) launch, insurance and transportation cost; (c) computation of the present values assuming a discount rate of 12 per cent; (d) allocation of the present values of the capital costs between communication and meteorological payloads; (e) computation of present value of each payload; and (f) computation of annualized capital cost for each payload. Table 2 gives the annualized payload capital costs.

INSAT–2E payload: annualized capital costs

Rs Crore

Item	Book Value	Capital Cost at 10%	Capital Cost at 12%
Low-power transponder	1.73	3.70	4.45
High-power transponder	1.94	4.15	4.99
VHRR	8.05	17.27	20.74
CCD	5.89	12.58	15.09

It is possible to assess India's comparative advantage in transponder production, because comparable transponders are globally traded. The quoted annual lease charges comparable to the low-power transponder in 1999–2000 varied between US$1.3 million for Thaicom and $1.7 million for Loral; the corresponding variation for comparable high power transponder was between $1.7 million for Lyngemark Satellite-1 and $2.2 million for Pan AM SAT.

Assuming 10 per cent spare margin, annual operating cost of Rs 0.96 crore, an exchange rate of 1 US$=Rs 42, a dollar discount rate of 7.5 per cent, and 10 per cent discount on the quoted prices, the annual quoted lease charges for the low power and high power transponders in US dollars are 1.11 and 1.24 respectively. Thus, the estimated lease change for the low-power transponder is only 85.2 per cent of the charge for Thaicom transponder; and the estimated quoted lease charge for the high-power transponder is 73 per cent of the charge for Lyngemark Satellite-1.

The cost advantages of the transponders will be higher if we assume a rupee discount rate of 10 per cent. A similar exercise done for INSAT-3C and 3E satellites has confirmed India's

comparative advantage in the manufacture of communication transponders.

The existing information base is inadequate to measure IRS payloads' economic costs. It is also difficult to demonstrate India's comparative advantage because each RS satellite is unique and the relevant cost data is not in the public domain. However, comparisons of approximate costs of IRS-1D with French SPOT-4 and US LANDSAT-7, indicate that the production cost of IRS-1D is lower.

Launch vehicles

Development of the launch vehicle is the most challenging task because of the technological complexities and export restrictions. Launch vehicle development helps in acquiring independent access to space; it also leads to critical manpower benefits and spin-off benefits. The study found that based on book values, the development costs of both PSLV and GSLV are lower than the costs of comparable vehicles in the US or France. At present, the production cost of GSLV per kg of launch is higher than that of Ariane space. PSLV has had eight consecutive successful launches since 1994. It has become a work horse for ISRO.

PSLV-C8 successfully launched Italian astronomical satellite in April 2007. After three successful launches one after the other, GSLV – F02 could not place INSAT-4C in orbit on July 10, 2006. The successful launch of INSAT-4CR by GSLV-F04 on September 2, 2007 restored ISRO's confidence. If the launch of GSLV-Mark III with 4 T capacity payload in 2008 is successful and average annual launches increase to six during the Eleventh Plan, the prospect of India gaining entry into the commercial launch vehicle market will be bright.

Self-reliance and spin-offs

Apart from capacity building in the high-tech area, the space programme yields many indirect and spin-off benefits. About 500 industries were associated with ISRO in 2004–05 and the flow of funds to industries was Rs 1263 crore. Till March 31, 2006, ISRO transferred 275 technologies to industries. The spin-offs resulting from ISRO's contracts with firms engaged in the joint development of technology/process/materials are improved product quality in non-space applications, improvement in quality standard, development of critical manpower and access to new markets.

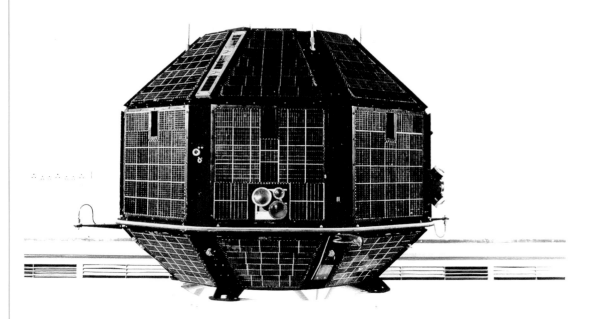

Costs and benefits during use

INSAT system: The cumulative costs in book values till October 31, 2002 are: All India Radio Rs 153 crore, Doordarshan Rs 1500 crore, telecommunication Rs 837 crore and meteorology Rs 236 crore. The revenue realized in 2004–05 was Rs 145 crore—Rs 50 crore from lease of nine transponders to INTELSAT, Rs 45 crore from private TV operators, and Rs 50 crore from Very Small Aperture Terminal (VSAT) operators. AIR, Doordarshan, DoT and IMD do not pay for ISRO's transponders.

The geosynchronous satellite is a superior medium for broadcasting—superior to any terrestrial technology—because the cost of sending a message to thousands of stations within a transponder's footprint is no more than the cost incurred in sending a message to any one station. It is the only choice for places with hostile terrain or poorly developed area. With the emergence of Direct-to-Home TV operators, the demand for Ku-band transponders is increasing. ISRO hopes to raise Rs 50–55 crore annually from the lease of its INSAT-4CR transponders to DTH operators and other agencies.

The niche areas in the switched telecom network are remote area communication, alternative media back-ups, and portable terminals for disaster management, prospecting, and satellite search and rescue service. There is a rapid growth of closed user groups based on VSAT networks in government (NICNET, ERNET), stock exchanges (BSE and NSE), and corporate networks (Tata, ITC, Reliance and others), and networks like Satellite Instructional Television

Experiment, Training and Developing Communication Channel, EDUSAT, tele-medicine, village resource centres. The social benefits are in the areas of cost savings, national security and preparedness for emergencies.

Most meteorological services are regarded as public goods. The contributions of satellite technology are (a) data from inaccessible areas (b) new types of observations (c) new concepts of data assimilation in models and (d) generation of fast and reliable data. The main areas of application are: forecasting, agro-meteorological services, disaster warning and mitigation, floods forecasting, and oceanography.

Remote Sensing: The expenditure on operational missions till March 31, 2001 was Rs 1,008 crore. The expenditure incurred on data reception, processing and application was Rs 554 crore. Revenue from the sale of data was Rs 160 crore, and from sale of IRS services about Rs 50 crore.

The advantages of RS are synoptic coverage, multi-spectral capability, multi-temporal capability and digital capture of data. RS is an exclusive tool for estimation of snowmelt run-off, rapid assessment of areas affected by natural disasters, and mapping of inaccessible areas. It is a substitute tool for conventional methods in mapping of land use, urban land use, preparing groundwater prospect maps, coastal management plan etc. It can complement area and crop forecasting. RS provides enhanced and timely information. As of now, most applications based on IRS data have been in government projects whose aims are development of backward areas, equity, and generation of information to evaluate and monitor natural resources.

The economic and social benefits that accrue to society were estimated by case studies like the Rajiv Gandhi National Drinking Water Technology Mission, the National Waste Land Inventory Project, and the Integrated Mission for Sustainable Development, preparation of forest maps and working plans, and identification of potential fishing zones.

Potential cost savings attributable to the RS technology are in the range Rs 8,000 crore to Rs 10,000 crore. It is true that potential savings occurs over time. The estimates are based on extrapolations from samples. But the estimated potential benefits in relation to the actual cost of the IRS programme are very large; it is reasonable to conclude that the economic and social benefits would exceed the costs of the EOS programme.

ISRO could realize the objectives of developing satellite communications and RS technologies, and gaining independent access to space in a cost-effective manner. It has drawn ambitious proposals for the Eleventh Plan (Government of India, 2007).

In space communications, the main goals are to augment transponder capacity from 199 to 500, develop high power Ka–band satellite and group systems, and build Navigational Satellite Systems and related services.

In EOS, the main goals are to improve imaging capabilities and continuity of data through thematic services—land and water resources, cartography, and ocean/atmosphere; development of advanced microwave imaging capability; and establishment of National Natural Resource Data Base.

In space transportation, the goals are to operationalise GSLV Mk III with 4T launch capacity; and develop payload recovery, re-entry and manned mission technologies. In space science, *Chandrayaan*, will give basic science and research the needed thrust.

At the exploitation stage, there are many innovative applications. After reviewing space applications in different sectors, I can make two suggestions for improving efficient utilization of space technologies and enhancing their social and economic outcomes. First, the public sector user agencies must pay for space technologies and services (or ISRO must give the imputed costs) to enable user agencies to incorporate social costs in their decision-making and achieve economic efficiency. Second, the goals must be specified in terms of outcomes i.e. benefits accruing to consumers or producers or to society as a whole.

To achieve such goals, bottlenecks and inefficiencies at different stages of the supply chains must be identified to resolve 'last mile problems' in delivering services. □

Govind Swarup
National Centre for Radio
Astrophysics, TIFR, Pune

Radio telescope: An early saga in innovation

Man has always wondered about the origin and evolution of the Universe and looked up into the sky to seek an answer. Soon after the completion of the 100-inch telescope in the 1910s, it became clear that there exist in our Universe a large number of distant galaxies, each consisting of numerous stars, located far away from our Milky Way. In 1929, Hubble made a remarkable discovery: the farther away a galaxy is located from us the faster it is moving away. This led to the Big Bang Model, according to which the Universe was extremely small in the very beginning and has been expanding ever since.

In early 1930s, Karl Jansky at Bell Labs in USA made a stunning discovery that radio waves, in the form of random noise, are being emitted from the direction of our Milky Way. No astronomer in the world took notice of it, except Grote Reber, an electronic engineer and a radio ham, who built a 32 ft dish in his back yard, using wood and GI sheets, during the late 1930s and mapped radio emissions from our galaxy. In the late 1940s and early 1950s, using sensitive radio techniques developed during World War II, Australian and British scientists discovered many extremely powerful sources of radio waves associated with some of the distant galaxies in the Universe. Observations have indicated that at the centre of a radio galaxy is located a black hole, millions of times the mass of our Sun. Over the last 60 years the new window of radio astronomy has led to many outstanding discoveries, such as pulsars, molecules in space, quasars and microwave background emission, revolutionizing our understanding of the Universe.

The Ooty radio telescope

By the late 1950s Martin Ryle from the University of Cambridge in UK had catalogued some 200 radio galaxies whose number indicated a preponderance of weak radio sources. Assuming that the weaker sources are located much farther away compared to sources of higher intensity, Ryle supported expectations of the Big Bang model, in contrast to the predictions of the Steady State model proposed in 1948 by Fred Hoyle and colleagues. According to the Steady State model, as the Universe expands, matter is created continuously and therefore the source density is expected to remain the same everywhere. This led to a raging controversy.

In order to distinguish between the Big Bang and Steady State models of the Universe, soon after the formation of a radio astronomy group at the Tata Institute of Fundamental Research (TIFR), in 1963, I proposed measurement of accurate positions and angular sizes of a large number of weak *radio galaxies* by observing their occultations or eclipsing by the Moon. Suitable sensitive radio interferometers were not available anywhere in the world at that time. Considering the advantage of India's proximity to the earth's equator, I proposed construction of a 530 m long and 30 m wide steerable parabolic cylindrical radio telescope, to be located on a hill at Ooty with an inclination of 11.3 degrees in the north-south direction so that the long axis of the radio telescope becomes parallel to that of the earth. This design allowed tracking of the Moon for about 9.5 hours every day by mechanical rotation of the long axis of the radio telescope. During 1970s, the lunar occultation observations made at Ooty provided arc second resolution for about 1000 weak radio sources for the first time in the world. Our data supported the Big Bang Model. The Ooty radio telescope (ORT) has also been very useful for studying pulsars, ionized gases in our galaxy and the structure of many celestial objects including the centre of our galaxy. Using the method of interplanetary scintillations, ORT is currently making a systematic study of high speed ejections from the sun that is occasionally very harmful to satellite equipment and also disturbs the earth's ionosphere and radio communication.

Big Bang Model

According to the Big Bang Model, the Universe had extremely high energy density in the beginning, and expanded very rapidly soon after. At its epoch of seconds and minutes, when the temperature of the Universe was about 10 billion to 1 billion degrees, the standard laws of nuclear physics predict that electrons, protons and neutrons arise in the Universe forming about 75 per cent hydrogen, ~25 per cent helium and only a tiny fraction of light elements. Subsequently when the Universe cools to about 4000 degrees Kelvin, the aggregate of electrons and protons combine, resulting in the formation of cold hydrogen clouds that subsequently collapse gravitationally to form stars and galaxies. Since the Universe is expanding rapidly, photons emitted at the above epoch of 'recombination' are red-shifted (Doppler shifted) giving rise to a microwave background radiation of ~2.7 degrees Kelvin. Its observation by Penzias and Wilson in 1965 gave a strong support to the Big Bang Model. The Nobel Prize was awarded to them in 1978 for this discovery.

The above scenario may seem very weird to a layman. As we know, observations of our surroundings leads to curiosity that results in theories, predictions and finally experimental verifications. Over the last 50 years, numerous ground and space based telescopes have provided a very strong support to the Big Bang Model. Recent observations of distant Type I Supernovae explosions of stars that are considered by theoreticians to have the same intrinsic luminosity and particularly of the 2.7 K microwave radiation by the WMAP satellite, have led to a surprising conclusion that visible matter in our Universe is only ~5 per cent of the energy density in the Universe, ~25 per cent is in the form of dark matter and ~70 per cent consists of dark energy giving rise to an accelerating Universe. Many investigations at the very frontiers of astronomy are being

carried out or are planned at various observatories in the world using telescopes operating at x-rays, UV, visible, infrared and radio wavelengths to further probe the mysteries of the Universe.

GMRT

According to the Big Bang model, galaxies form through the gravitational collapse of the primordial neutral hydrogen condensates. These neutral hydrogen (HI) condensates emit line emission at a wavelength of 21 cm (1420 MHz) that gets red-shifted to meter wavelengths (~100–300 MHz) with the expansion of the Universe.

In 1984, I proposed construction of the Giant Metrewave Radio Telescope (GMRT) for searching for HI condensates from the early Universe at metre wavelengths and for many other important astrophysical investigations that are best studied at long wavelengths, such as observation of the pulsars that arise when stars collapse after their nuclear fuel gets exhausted. Pulsars are associated with Neutron stars and were discovered by A R Hewish in 1967 who was awarded Nobel Prize in 1974 along with Martin Ryle. This was the first Nobel Prize in the field of astronomy. Since then eight astronomers have received the Nobel Prize, including Prof S Chandrasekhar in 1930s, for his theories predicting the occurrence of white dwarfs, and black holes in the Universe.

GMRT consists of an assemblage thirty fully steerable parabolic dish antennas, each 45 m in diameter. A novel and economical design was chosen for these antennas. The reflecting surface of the dishes is made of Stretched Mesh Attached to Rope Trusses, which we have nicknamed SMART design. The welded wire mesh consists of fine (0.55 mm) stainless steel wires which were chosen in order to cut down wind loading. The wire mesh was specially developed for the GMRT antennas by a firm in Mumbai. The firm has subsequently exported similar meshes for applications at the Arecibo Telescope in USA and the Mauritius Radio Telescope.

The GMRT antennas are located in an array stretching across about 25 km. With the rotation of the earth, the relative orientations of these antennas change with respect to the celestial coordinates and thus a 25 km aperture is synthesized. Over the last twenty five years, radio astronomers in several countries have developed many ingenious image processing techniques, which allow self-calibration of the instrumental and atmospheric errors. Thus, GMRT allows us to make images as if it were a perfect parabolic dish antenna of 25 km in diameter! State of art RF and digital electronics have been built for the GMRT by a dedicated team of NCRA engineers and scientists, making it a very powerful instrument. Due to several innovations in design, the total cost of the GMRT was only Rs 46 crores, a fraction of that of similar instruments in advanced countries.

The GMRT is located about 80 km north of Pune. This site was selected so as to be far away from various radio transmitters. The GMRT is designed to operate in the frequency range of about 38 MHz to 1430 MHz. It is the world's largest radio telescope operating in this frequency range. The GMRT is complementary to radio telescopes located elsewhere in the world that are designed to operate at cm wavelengths in order to be able to image celestial radio sources with a resolution of less than one arc-second. On the other hand GMRT giving a resolution of 2 arc-seconds at 21 cm has been specifically designed to operate at longer wavelengths requiring much higher collecting area than the cm wave radio telescopes. A relatively lower degree of man-made radio noise in India has allowed us to exploit of the metre-wave radio spectrum. At long wavelengths, it is required to construct antennas which are appreciably larger in size, though not of high precision. Thus the lower labour cost in India provides an advantage for competing internationally.

GMRT has been operational since 1999. It is a versatile instrument, being used for studying a wide variety of celestial objects. Many important results have been obtained concerning radio emission from the sun, pulsars, supernova remnants, micro-quasars, the centre of our galaxy and HI in dwarf galaxies, HI studies of distant Lyman-alpha clouds, giant radio galaxies and quasars, etc. GMRT is being used for astronomical observations by hundreds of scientists from India and more than 20 countries in the world, including those from many prestigious institutes such as the

Universities of Cambridge, Oxford, Leiden, Berkeley, Stanford, and others.

Puzzles of the Universe

There are many important questions at the frontiers of astronomy today. I highlight only some of these. When did stars first form, soon after sufficient cooling of the primordial clouds of hydrogen and consequent reionization of the neutral hydrogen? What is the origin and evolution of cosmic magnetic fields in galaxies? What processes give rise to the formation and evolution of galaxies, radio galaxies, quasars and other objects in the Universe? What is the nature of the mysterious dark matter and dark energy in the Universe? Can observations of pulsars with milli-second periods help to test predictions of the theories of strong field gravity? Over the last few years, astronomers have detected existence of planets around more than 250 stars and that number is likely to increase many fold over the next decade. If intelligent life exists elsewhere in our galaxy, would it be possible to detect the leakage of radiation from their radars and transmitters, even if they are not sending coded messages to us?

The rapid development of electronics in recent years have led seventeen countries, including India to propose construction of a very ambitious radio telescope, called the Square Kilometer Array (SKA), having sensitivity and performance capability of more than 50 times that of any existing radio telescope in the world. A site with quite a low degree of man-made radio noise in South Africa and another in Western Australia has been short-listed for SKA. More than 30 laboratories in the world are working to develop various aspects of the design of SKA. India could make a major contribution to the highly challenging requirement of software for the SKA.

We can say with confidence that the saga of discoveries in astronomy is likely to continue for decades to come. Also extreme conditions in many celestial objects will continue to provide a unique laboratory to physicists, chemists and biologists. □

B G Anandarao
Physical Research Laboratory
Ahmedabad

Stargazers have an eventful decade

The spiritual rhetoric of *"What emptiness do you gaze upon!"* in Gurudev Rabindranath's Gitanjali aptly evokes the preoccupation of an astronomer striving to bring excitement out of the apparent vacuum of the sky.

Since my article on this subject 10 years ago in the first volume of *INNOVATIVEINDIA*, much water has flowed down all the sacred rivers of India. This paper lists some of the major scientific achievements and enumerates the new facilities that have come up. It also tries to give a foretaste of programmes that will be coming up in the near future. Needless to say, this is necessarily more subjective than exhaustive. Astronomy and astrophysics in India have had a fruitful decade in terms of discoveries made and facilities created. Scientists in these fields have set up useful facilities, done good work and invited international collaboration.

Optical/near-infrared astronomy

Two major facilities were established during the last few years. The first is the Himalayan Chandra Telescope (HCT), a telescope of 2 m diameter, at Hanle in Ladakh (Jammu and Kashmir). The main reasons for going to such great altitudes are to have a reduced water vapor columnar content for better transmission of cosmic infrared radiation and a dust free environment, as well as a large number of cloud-free nights for observations. This telescope, remote-operated from Hosekote, near Bangalore, currently has two focal-plane instruments: a medium-resolution visible spectrograph and an infrared imager. This facility was created by the Indian Institute of Astrophysics (IIA), Bangalore.

The second major facility in the optical/near-infrared wavelengths is the Girawali 2 m telescope near Pune set up by Inter-University Centre for Astronomy and Astrophysics (IUCAA) for encouraging observational astronomy among university teachers. This telescope is already equipped with a visible spectrograph and an infrared camera is being commissioned. The Mt Abu 1.2 m infrared telescope, operated by the Physical Research Laboratory (PRL), also acquired an infrared camera and spectrograph during this period.

A number of new and exciting facilities will open soon in the country. These facilities will be of great value to Indian astronomers both in terms of acquisition of technological know-how as well as cutting-edge science. The future facilities include a 3 m class telescope at Devasthal in Himachal Pradesh by Aryabhatta Research Institute for Environmental Sciences (ARIES), Nainital. A new ultra-stable high-resolution Echelle spectrograph is being built at PRL to detect planetary systems around nearby stars (extra-solar planets). The Udaipur Solar Observatory (USO) of PRL will soon be commissioning a sophisticated 50 cm solar telescope with a variety of instruments for studying the Sun at high spatial and spectral resolutions.

Radio astronomy

The Giant Metre-wave Radio Telescope (GMRT) at Khodad near Pune, after becoming operational to its fullest potential, has already yielded a number of very important results on galactic and extra-galactic astronomical sources. The consequence of this success is that Indian radio astronomers may well play a significant role in the upcoming major international facilities such as the Square Kilometer Array (SKA) for radio observations at very high spatial resolution in frequencies 100 MHz - 25 GHz to be set up in Australia/South Africa.

Ground-based high-energy astronomy

Highly interactive high energy gamma-ray photons from cosmic sources undergo secondary emission processes while traversing the Earth's atmosphere. These secondary radiations can be detected by using ground-based light collectors equipped with detectors spread over very large areas. Such gamma-ray observatories were set up by the Tata Institute of Fundamental Research (TIFR) at Pachmarhi in Madhya Pradesh and by the Bhabha Atomic Research Centre (BARC) on Mt Abu and at Hanle. In addition to these facilities, IIA is planning to set up an ambitious gamma-ray observatory at Hanle for studying high-energy events (flares) from the Sun.

Space astronomy

The first Indian solar physics satellite called SOXS (Solar X ray Spectrometer) was successfully launched by the Indian Space Research

Organisation. Its soft x-ray spectrometer has been functioning well and a number of interesting results were obtained during intense solar flares.

Chandrayaan-1, the Moon mission, is a dream project. Its main scientific purpose is to further our understanding of the origin and evolution of the Moon through mineralogical and chemical mapping of its surface at high spectral and spatial resolution. ASTROSAT is a multi-wavelength astronomy mission covering x-ray, ultraviolet and optical wavelength bands. The UV telescope on-board the satellite is expected to achieve an unprecedented 1-2 arc sec spatial resolution in a field of view of 0.5 degree. For the first time in India the x-ray payloads include imaging capability in x-rays. The two projects have very prestigious international collaborations on instrumentation and science goals. These satellites, in all probability, will be launched in 2008 and usher India into an era of space exploration.

Another upcoming space mission, aptly named ADITYA, has been planned for studying the dynamics in the inner and outer coronae of the Sun.

Further in the future, ISRO is planning several small payloads meant for space science. Proposals are being considered for an

infrared astronomical spectroscopic payload and x-ray polarimetric payload.

Science results

Let us now list a few science results of significance. These results are mostly from Indian observatories/facilities; it maybe noted that some had contributions from observatories/facilities elsewhere in the world through scientific collaborations.

Some of the most important results in **radio astronomy** are:

(i) the discovery of a Binary Pulsar having a period of a few thousandths of a second with a possible black hole companion, indeed a rare coincidence;

(ii) the discovery of the most distant (at a red-shift of ~ 1.0) Giant Quasar with jets from its central engine extending up to about a few million light years;

(iii) a direct estimate of magnetic fields in a Supernova Burst in a nearby galaxy from spectral energy distribution in radio frequencies; and,

(iv) the detection of a giant flare in a 'Magnetar,' enabling an estimate of its distance. Magnetars, first discovered in 1979, are highly compact neutron stars with very powerful magnetic fields (of the order of giga-teslas compared to the micro-teslas of Earth's magnetic field). The magnetic field dissipation yields bursts of very high energy radiation from these objects.

Some upcoming scientific projects in radio astronomy using the existing facilities include,

(i) the study of neutral hydrogen to understand the distribution of neutral gas in external galaxies; and,

(ii) detection of neutral hydrogen in the very early Universe (during the epoch of re-ionisation).

X-ray astronomers like their optical/infrared counterparts have, by and large, concentrated on variability of sources, which in itself does not involve sophisticated technologies. With these innovative ideas, the astronomers have made an impact on the world of astronomy.

Some of the most important scientific results in the field of **X-ray astronomy** are:

(i) the detection of quasi-periodic variability involving oscillations of shock fronts created by bursts of X-ray emission from mass accreting black hole candidates, called Micro-Quasars. This has led, for the first time, to a very detailed study of characteristic features and classification of such events;

(ii) an estimation of magnetic fields from cyclotron line spectra in X-ray Pulsars;

(iii) detection of quasi-periodic oscillations from Ultra-Luminous X-ray Sources (a new breed of astronomical objects emitting high energy radiation, located away from the centres of galaxies and having very high luminosities. Their nature/origin is not yet understood); and,

(iv) the discovery of the time-lag between low and high energy excess X-ray emissions from active galactic nuclei (AGN - extra galactic sources with extremely bright yet very compact central regions, believed to be powered by super-massive black holes).

Some of the significant results from **optical and infrared astronomy** are as follows:

(i) Studies of Nova phenomena at Mt Abu Observatory using near-infrared spectroscopy yielded several significant results, such as enigmatic depletion of hydrogen in the companion mass loss (called Helium Nova—the first of its kind to be discovered); peculiarities in molecular and dust formation in mass outflows and in shock wave properties. Novae are eruptive/explosive episodic phenomena that occur in binary stars due to mass accretion from a companion secondary star on to the compact primary star; the enormity and subsequent evolution of these events depend upon the physical nature of the binary components.

(ii) Detection of molecular hydrogen knots and jets from a high mass proto-star using infrared imaging showed indirect evidence for the formation of high mass stars by accretion process in a similar way to the formation of low mass stars. This is an alternative mechanism to formation by capture or coalescence of two or more low-intermediate mass stars.

(iii) Molecular hydrogen detection at high red-shifts using Lyman alpha systems opened up opportunities for studying the nature of phenomena (such as star formation) in the very early Universe. Lyman alpha systems are basically very distant quasars (with large red-shifts) having hydrogen emission lines in UV, superposed on which occur a forest of absorption lines from intervening objects (galaxies at lesser red-shifts, for instance); and,

(iv) Gamma Ray Burst (GRB) observations from Nainital Observatory (by scientists from ARIES and Raman Research Institute (RRI) furnished some important inputs to the evolution of after-glow phenomena. GRBs are now believed to be explosive phenomena that last for very short time scales at energies much larger than the most energetic supernovae. The phenomenon occurs first at very high energies in gamma rays, causing an intense shock wave that heats up matter around, which in turn gives rise to the after-glows seen in X-rays, visible, infrared and radio regions. Although the exact processes are not yet understood, it is believed that GRBs are extra-galactic and represent stellar phenomena.

Driven by the survival instinct, Indian astronomers have shown considerable innovation. They have had a fruitful decade. They have realized most, if not all, of what was expected from the facilities they had created. They can now look forward to a bright future.

The challenge now is to attract young minds to the wonders of astronomy. Science administrators must know that replenishment of scientific personnel is an on-going process which must be sustained. This in turn requires the creation of state-of-the-art facilities. □

EARTH

D R Sikka
Former Director Indian Institute
of Tropical Meteorology

Advances in atmospheric science

India's geographical position and weather make it especially suitable for climate research, so critical to the future of the planet. The Indian Meteorological Department has a very long tradition of useful systematic research that has shown that Indian scientists are contributing to the challenges thrown up by climate change.

Like the river Ganges, the Monsoon is the protagonist on the country's cultural and economic stage. The grey clouds and rumble and thunder and the harbingers of festivity and well being. India's weather and climate are governed by the two seasonal monsoons—the southwest summer monsoon from June to September, and the northeast monsoon from October to December. The bountiful sunshine and fresh water through precipitation in the two monsoon seasons are the natural endowments that have shaped our history, culture, music, folk-lore and dance forms. Expectations are raised for a bumper crop if rains are timely and good, and dismay looms large if those hopes of rain are not fulfilled, for drought brings economic loss and hardship.

The river systems of India draw their waters from monsoon rains and when floods breaking their banks, they enrich the soils of the farmlands of India. The ancient sages ascribed rain and connected weather-related phenomena to different presiding deities, the most important of whom was the Sun God (Surya Devata). The saying that "from Sun come the rains" is mentioned in different forms in the Vedic and Smriti literature. There is evidence that the ancients had knowledge for making wind measurements (through flags hoisted on wooden poles), and rain measurements by using certain kinds of rain gauges *Varsha Mapan Yantra*, but knowledge of variations in these weather elements was based more on speculation as precise scientific measurements were not available. Poet Kalidasa in his classic work *Meghdoot*, using the existing empirical knowledge, traced the path of the summer rain clouds from Central India to the Western Himalayas, which is in agreement with present day knowledge about the near-surface wind flow over the region. In the 6th century the emphasis changed from belief in the control of weather by presiding deities to an investigation of the phenomenon of rain. Varha Mihira, a scholar in the court of Ujjain, authored an encyclopedic work known as Brihat Samhita, which documented, for the very first time, ancient methods of weather forecasting based on astro-meteorological considerations. He writes:

Food is the elixir of life/And food comes from rains/So let us investigate the rains.

The arrival of Europeans on our shores heralded a new era of scientific thought, supported by observation and precise measurement through instrumental aids like the barometer, anemometer, thermometer and hygrometer. Scientific observation of weather parametres over the Indian Ocean helped to in make connections between rainy seasons and the changing moods of prevailing winds blowing from ocean to land in summer and from land to ocean in winter over the Indian region. The India Meteorological Department (IMD) was then established in 1875 with a mandate to observe, understand and diffuse the knowledge gained, as well to predict, if possible, the weather and climate of India, so crucial to shipping, transport, and agriculture and for administering the British Indian Empire.

The Department, under the pioneering stewardship of British meteorologists, focused energy on setting up an extensive meteorological observational system. Using the data thus systematically gathered, they made some outstanding scientific investigations on the weather and climate of India. A tradition of systematic storage of data and use of that data to investigate, understand and predict weather and climate variability was thus firmly established in the formative years of the IMD. That tradition continues to this day.

The tradition of updating the data in innovative ways by applying available technology has resulted in a well-maintained tank of climatological observations on India for the past 125 years. This has been recognized as a unique source and marker for understanding climate variability on annual to decadal scales, providing insight into weather and climate research in India. The early scientific investigations also produced some outstanding insights into rainfall and patherns in India. Findings on regional components of the summer monsoon, monsoon phenomenology such as its onset, active and break spells, and empirical prediction of weather disturbances on short-time basis (one to three days), have remained illustrious examples of research in that heady period of early scientific meteorology of India.

Monsoon forecasting

These studies also laid the foundation for long-range summer monsoon forecasting over most of India, and winter rains over northern India, by applying statistical techniques based on physical connections between rains and useful predictors. The search for precursors for long-range summer monsoon forecasting resulted in the discovery of three planetary scale pressure oscillations by 1920: viz. the Southern Oscillation (SO) the North Atlantic Oscillation (NAO) and the North Pacific Oscillation (NPO). The SO and the NAO are currently the subjects of intensive studies for climate prediction worldwide. These have remained important precursors for long-range Indian summer monsoon forecasting.

Equipped with a network of observatories, Indian scientists started investigating tropical cyclones in the Indian Ocean, convective thunderstorms, floods and droughts. With Independence new vistas opened up as rapid development was the central thrust of the Five Year Plans. Meteorology was to play an important part in this national endeavour.

Until 1980 IMD laid stress on improving its observational systems at surface and upper air levels as well as in space. The surface observational network was enhanced and the upper air network of pilot balloons and radiosonde observatories considerably expanded. Different kinds of radars began to keep a watch on hazardous weather developments along coastal and interior parts of India. With the collaboration of the Indian Space Research Organisation (ISRO), rocket technology was used in the 1970s and 1980s to provide information on the structure and variability of the upper atmosphere up to an altitude of 70 km. Data from space-based platforms for continuous watch on the evolving weather in the form of INSAT geostationary satellites and land resource satellites have provided important support to IMD's operations from 1980 onwards. India also developed its own ocean satellite in the mid-1990s to provide information regarding biological productivity in northern Indian Ocean. Parameters relevant to studies of ocean-atmosphe coupling to modulate weather and climate were also offered by the ocean satellite.

ISRO will launch an advanced INSAT system—Climate Sat and special satellites like MEGHA-TROPIQUE, will be launched under an Indo-French collaboration for deriving atmospheric, oceanic and land-surface parameters for weather and climate related needs. In the last decade, India has placed an ocean observing system consisting of XBT lines, met-ocean buoys and ARGO Floats over the northern Indian Ocean. This will monitor parameters of the restless ocean up to a depth 500m. IMD currently has an approved ambitious plan to further enhance and modernize observational systems based on various recent technologies; these will not only provide observations but also communicate the observations for weather monitoring and prediction swiftly through the INSAT communication facilities.

Now that observations of the required density and accuracy are thus available, data gaps over the Indian landmass and adjoining oceans are expected to be filled up. Through appropriate assimilation procedures, the data will be used to provide adequate information to weather prediction models and improve the accuracy of weather prediction over India in short (1–3 days) and medium (3–10 days) temporal ranges.

Research done at the Institute of Tropical Meteorology (IITM) in Pune has won national and international acclaim in several areas of atmospheric science, including weather forecasting, climate and climate modeling, monsoon variability, hydrometeorology, atmospheric modeling, climate change, atmospheric chemistry and physics, boundary layer studies, upper atmosphere and atmospheric electricity. This research has found applications in such areas as monsoon forecasting, climate forecasting and climate change assessment, water resource management, dispersal of pollutants and understanding processes in tropical thunderstorms.

The National Institute of Oceanography (NIO) in Goa does research in physical, chemical and biological oceanography. The research vessel, *Gaveshni*, was used for over two decades to collect data from the oceans. At present the *Sagar Kanya*, *Sagar Poorvi*, *Sagar Pachmi* and *Sagar Sampda* and other vessels are in use for ocean-atmosphere research. Such efforts have been supported by qualified atmospheric scientists being produced by many universities and the IITs. The Indian Air Force and the Indian Navy have their own meteorology branches.

The National Centre for Medium Range Weather Forecasting (NCMRWF) plays an important role in using Atmospheric General Circulation Models (AGCMs) for weather prediction to establish an agro-met advisory service in India on the medium-range scale. Networking of institutions for weather and climate research became possible under the Indian Climate Research Programme (ICRP). The programmes organised under the ICRP provided new and useful data for observational and modeling monsoon studies. These studies have brought credibility to Indian scientists working together on focused research programmes designed and implemented by pooling the national resources of infrastructure and scientific talent. A convergence of research and operational organizations for atmosphere-ocean science has also come about under the ICRP.

India began the tradition of collaboration in international monsoon-related field programmes in 1957 by participating in the International Geo-Physical Year (1957–58) and the opportunity was used to build observational systems under IMD, which were further expanded between 1960 and 1980. India hosted the International Indian Ocean Expedition (IIOE) in 1963–66, Indo-Soviet

Monsoon Experiment in 1973, the Monsoon-77 Experiment in 1977 and the Monsoon Experiment (MONEX) in 1979. India has bilateral scientific programmes with several countries.

Indian scientists have contributed to various monsoon studies. India participated in the International Indian Ocean Experiment (INDOEX) carried out through international collaboration from 1996 to 1999 to understand the sources and transport of pollutants from land to the equatorial Southern Indian Ocean during the winter monsoon season. Work by Indian and other scientists has created awareness about sources and transport of chemical constituents of anthropogenic aerosols on their climate.

The polluted aerosols have been found to stabilize the atmospheric boundary layer, cooling at the surface, warming the lower troposphere, dimming of the Sun (solar radiation), and brightening of the sky (diffuse radiation). As suggested by some modelling studies these have hydrological consequences and a possible impact on monsoon climate in the present climate change scene.

Findings about Monsoons

The data generated by the extensive observational network and research have led to important findings in the phenomenology of monsoonal weather and climate over India.

Among other things, scientists have gained an understanding of the low-level cross-equatorial jet, its dynamics and its working as a conduit for carrying moisture across India, its linkage with the onset of the summer monsoon and its fluctuating strength with sub-seasonal oscillations of rainfall over India during the summer monsoon season.

Empirical and dynamical models for predicting storm surges that accompany tropical cyclones when they strike coastal belts of India, have been some of the significant contributions made since the 1970s to warn coastal populations against an impending disaster.

Studies on monsoon low-frequency modulation on sub-seasonal and inter-annual scales have received international attention since 1980.

There is interest in the role of sea surface temperature (SST) in controlling organized convection over tropical oceans and the interplay between the near-equatorial oceanic heat source and the land-locked heat source over central and northern India on one hand and surface hydrology on the other.

Studies have covered the linkages of monsoon performance with the coupled ocean-atmosphere El Nino—Southern Oscillation (ENSO) phenomenon in the equatorial Indo-Pacific Ocean belt, the Indian Ocean Dipole Mode and EQUINO Mode in near-equatorial Indian Ocean with the performance of the Indian Monsoon system.

Research on dynamic long-range prediction using AGCMS with the help of high performance computers has been ongoing since the 1990s.

The atmosphere-ocean research community in India has been using its research for a variety of societal applications dealing with weather and climate impacts and providing advance warnings of hydro-climatic disasters.

Atmospheric and oceanic modelling

When the advanced countries took to numerical weather prediction (NWP) models, India did not have either the trained manpower or computers. Research in NWP began at IITM, Pune and IMD, Delhi, in the early 1970s. IMD acquired its first computer in 1976 and initiated an operational NWP model in an experimental mode in IMD. IIT Delhi joined the effort to develop the NWP system. A group in IIT Delhi, under Indo-French collaboration, had acquired an AGCM with an innovative scheme of stretched co-ordinates, which allowed enhancing spatial resolution over a desired region. Moved by the success story of medium-range weather forecasting in Europe, India established NCMRWF with an in-house Super Computer Cray X MP. The aim was to provide tailor-made forecasts up to 3–5 days for agricultural advisories for a targeted cluster of districts in the country. The scheme has been quite successful because, in addition to the weather scientists at NCMRWF, agricultural scientists at the State Agricultural Universities also participated in the preparation of forecasts and dissemination of the products to the end-user agricultural community.

NCMRWF now uses a very high resolution AGCM with data assimilation scheme (including satellite observed data) to predict global weather up to five days. The boundary conditions from the model are used to drive further high resolution regional models (meso-scale models) to produce more refined forecasts up to 20–30 km scale over India. In order to reduce uncertainty in weather forecasts, a new technique was evolved in advanced countries in the last 5–10 years. They use a multi-model

ensemble (MME) forecast system. IMD and NCMRWF scientists are now engaged in developing an MME system for India. IMD and other research centres in India also produce operational forecasts, and the NWP technique is used by universities to train their scholars.

Even a private sector venture, which claims to add value to weather forecasts to suit their special clients, is using a high resolution model with data received on the internet from USA. In USA and Europe there are several well known private companies that use the data and products from their national weather agencies to sell their value-added products. Several of the specialized products of the national weather services from advanced countries are now available on the internet for utilization by the private sector so that tax payer's money on weather services is utilized by a wider community of public and private sectors. The time has come for India to also develop a public-private sector partnership to fulfill the rising demand of specialized weather services.

Several Indian research groups have acquired such AGCMs (climate models) and have skillfully adapted them to predict the seasonal performance of the monsoon rains averaged for India as a whole. Experimental use of such models till the present day, have had limited success as research done in India showed that the monsoon is influenced not only by surface boundary forcings (SST and snow) but also by internal dynamics. This is because rains over India are influenced by low-frequency scale fluctuation (10–20 day and 30–50 day scales). Nevertheless, use of AGCMs or coupled GCMs has great power and further research may well enhance the use of modelling for monsoon prediction on a monthly to seasonal scale.

Ocean modelling has also taken root in some research organizations in India and researchers are using innovative ways to test the use of such models for ocean state prediction. The availability of ocean state data through XBT profiles, met-ocean buoys, ARGO floats and moored ocean buoys, means that the data can be assimilated into ocean models and for validating the ocean-state forecast. Operational use of ocean-state forecast products has tremendous potential for shipping, fisheries and in other areas. Such an operational ocean state forecast model is now being actively developed at the Indian National Centre for Ocean Information System (INCOIS) at Hyderabad.

Monsoon science, which has received much global attention, has advanced enormously due to satellite data, field observations and application of computing power and mathematical representations. Infrastructure in the IMD and in other research institutions has been added in the last four decades. Development of a hydro-meteorological long-range prediction system continues to be a primary need of the developing Indian economy. India needs more precise prediction of high impact disastrous weather events, as well as of weather and climate variability under the present climate change and water scarcity scenario. This scenario is influenced by variable monsoons, extent of glacier melt due to global warming, reduction in agricultural productivity due to weather and climate related agricultural risks.

Observational studies

The fact is that India's weather and climate are determined by the coupled ocean-atmosphere-land system, linked with the neighbouring mid-latitude and the warm tropical Pacific Ocean as well as global scale atmospheric circulations connected with the southern Indian Ocean and Pacific Ocean, and even the North Atlantic Ocean. We need to vigorously pursue observational studies with expanding satellite coverage, innovative modeling of weather and climate, for understanding, prediction, and adoption of emerging atmospheric technologies for environmental monitoring.

A global partnership in the study of the Earth System has to be multi-dimensional and highly interdependent as changes and variables have to be monitored on all spatio-temporal scales. For research purposes, therefore, the Indian ocean-atmosphere community needs to be well connected globally as well as regionally. India should remain a major partner in ongoing global and regional research programmes on atmospheric sciences so as to play an important role in monitoring, understanding and predicting the changes on planet Earth. Internationally co-ordinated research has a great potential for seamless atmospheric predictions covering new-scale high impact forecasts on inter-annual and even decadal scales. It will provide projections for climate change on a regional scale.

GEOSS aims at using the space platforms of several countries to provide online data on a variety of parameters considered essential for monitoring the Earth System. GEOSS provides a global co-operative mechanism to combine *in situ*, airborne and space-based observations and India should make the most of this mechanism.

Geographically, India is one of the important hotspots for climate change. It is being affected by melting glaciers, dwindling monsoon performance and a rise in extreme events. We have an interest in the mega projects on coupled land-ocean-atmosphere modelling, assimilation of satellite radiance data into weather prediction models, reduction of weather and climate related risks for agricultural systems, reduction of risks due to rising anthropogenic aerosols and air and water pollution in climatic and societal contexts, modelling for air-quality prediction over India and climate change.

For implementing such mega projects, a consortium of research organizations needs to be established for co-ordinated studies on the Asian Monsoon System, which involves the planet's greatest shifts in the rainfall regime on an annual scale.

In the 21st century we have entered a new era of global and regional risks but we also have opportunities where policy and management decisions regarding environmental issues depend critically on good monitoring and prediction systems. Much is at stake for India as its economy is growing fast. Weather and climate information and prediction systems have much to offer that is relevant to policy issues and decisions to sustain the development effort. These challenges can be met only if the observation systems on land, ocean, atmosphere and space are maintained and enhanced, and if research organisations are nurtured and expanded.

India's active participation in international programmes would contribute to solving our own weather and climate-related prediction issues and give greater visibility to India's growing capabilities. We must think globally and act locally.

In today's knowledge-based society, huge investments in financial, infrastructural and human resource development are crucial if we are to meet the coming challenges. India must continue to remain an important partner in the global endeavour for scientific excellence in understanding and predicting future changes on planet Earth. □

Means to measure

The India Meteorological Department (IMD) had, by 1947, established workshop facilities at Pune and Delhi to provide surface and upper air weather instruments for its observational stations. The Instruments Section, as it was called, acquired radars discarded by the military at the end of the World War-II, and deployed them innovatively for meteorological research. To meet the expanding needs of civil aviation, it got weather radars and upper air wind measuring devices from Japan, France and USA.

The IMD scientists were trained to service these sophisticated facilities that were constantly upgraded as the public sector electronic industry expanded. IMD signed contracts with the Society for Microwave Engineering (SAMEER) in Mumbai and Bharat Electronics, Bangalore, to develop radio-theodolites and multi-met weather radars respectively. This was an innovative project for detecting dangerous convective weather as well as for measuring winds. Electronic experts at IMD, Pune, developed other special equipment such as radio-metersonde and ozonesonde needed to measure the distribution of outgoing long-wave radiation and ozone.

IMD has begun to use Doppler Weather Radars for tropical cyclone detection on their coastal network. ISRO joined IMD and developed a Doppler radar which has been successfully operating at their SHAR Centre. ISRO engineers have also developed an automatic weather station (AWS) for surface meteorological measurements which is being tested.

A big success in induction of advanced technology for meteorological purposes was the launching of INSAT-I, a geostationary weather satellite in the early 1980s. This has led to a satellite series that can be used both for communication and for photographing clouds in IR and visible channels. An innovative system was introduced by IMD to use the INSAT for disseminating disaster warnings among coastal communities in the path of an approaching topical cyclone. The advanced INSAT-D system will provide temperature data along with cloud imagery in IR, visible and water vapour channels. India also has plans to launch satellites for atmospheric aerosol and trace gas studies.

There have been several other sophisticated technologies developed in India for *in situ* atmospheric probings. These include the Mesosphere-Stratosphere-Troposphere radar (MST) for probing wind from near-surface to 80 km height; the wind profiling system developed by SAMEER and installed at Pune; electric field mills for studies on atmospheric electricity; spectrometers for measuring trace gas and ozone by scientists of the IITM, Pune. In addition, IMD developed radiation measuring equipment and the National Aerospace Laboratory (NAL), Bangalore, developed transmisso-meters for IMD's airport visibility measuring network.

The IMD is modernizing its atmospheric observational systems to mesh with sophisticated technologies. It will design mobile wind profilers and mobile radars and acquire aircraft for weather reconnaissance. These will obtain targeted observations for weather monitoring and prediction, particularly over the seas for tropical cyclone genesis and movement.

The use of space platforms for monitoring the restless Indian Ocean has brought about big changes since the launch of India's Ocean Sat in the late 1990s. The data from Ocean Sat is used, not only for oceanographic and meteorological studies, but also to provide a satellite-based service to Indian fishermen.

The joint efforts of oceanographers, meteorologists, remote sensing specialists and fishery scientists, have brought about a unique service called the Potential Fishing Zone (PFZ) advisory. The PFZ forecast is issued three times a week by INCOIS, Hyderabad, except during periods when fishing is banned and on cloudy days, thus adding societal value to ocean remote sensing. The National Institute of Ocean Technology (NIOT) in Chennai and INCOIS, Hyderabad, have jointly installed an ocean observing system consisting of met-ocean buoys and ARGO floats. This is yet another success story in the history of oceanic and meteorological services.

D R Sikka

Julia Slingo
Director of Climate Research
National Centre for Atmospheric
Science, UK

Weather knows no boundaries

The Indian summer monsoon provides nearly 80 per cent of India's rainfall, and over the years India's economy and societal infrastructures have become finely tuned to its remarkable stability. So it is not surprising that India has a long and rich history in observing and researching the monsoon and in attempting to forecast it. The UK has played an important role in these endeavours, ever since Henry Blanford was charged with establishing the Indian Meteorological Department in 1875. It was Blanford who initiated proper country-wide monitoring of weather, and this has continued uninterrupted to the present day, providing scientists with an unparalleled record of climate variability and change. He also began the publication of the Department's scientific results and made long-term weather forecasts using the link between the nature of snow in the Himalayas, atmospheric pressure and rainfall in India.

From there on followed several decades of distinguished scientific research, subsequently under the guidance of Sir Gilbert Walker, who discovered the Southern Oscillation, identified its influence on the monsoon and set up the first empirical seasonal forecasting system. These traditions of scientific endeavour continued throughout the 20th century and enabled India to develop the science and a deep understanding of the monsoon system and the various factors that influence it. We now know that the influence of the monsoon reaches far beyond India and may even affect the climate of Europe.

India's strong roots in monsoon meteorology have been manifest in their successful programme of empirical seasonal forecasting, which has so far proved more skilful than dynamical methods using numerical models of the climate system. Climate change, however, poses new challenges that the traditional methods of empirical forecasting cannot tackle. Vulnerability to small changes in monsoon rainfall is already very high, and the possibility that the monsoon may become less stable as a result of climate change, clearly has serious consequences for India.

In terms of the fundamental disciplines of meteorology and oceanography, India has a strong base on which to build as it begins to tackle the interdisciplinary challenges of predicting what climate change will mean for India and its people. As yet India does not have a strong programme in numerical modeling of the climate system and this urgently needs to be built. India recognises this and is currently restructuring its climate research and prediction activities. International collaboration will be vital at this time so that India can build capacity by drawing on modelling expertise that already exists in countries like the UK. This will accelerate progress in climate change prediction and enable India to bring its strong disciplinary base to bear on serious deviations in the performance of all climate models in this critical, yet challenging, region where the ocean, atmosphere, lowlands and mountains all interact.

In addition to future climate change, predictions of year-to-year and within-season variations in the monsoon (e.g. active/break cycles) are required now, and it is anticipated that changes in these variations may constitute the most profound effects of climate change. Climate models currently are limited in simulating within-season variability, its associated weather and extreme events. The all-round failure to predict the 2002 drought, even by the most sophisticated models, is a notable example of our limited knowledge of processes leading to extreme monsoon anomalies. Reliable predictions and clear articulation of the associated uncertainties are crucial if India is going to be in a position to take well-informed decisions about the future investments required to protect its people, their livelihoods and infrastructures from future vagaries of the climate as the planet warms.

In early 2006, the Royal Society sent a delegation of its leading climate scientists to India to explore ways in which a sustainable and long-term partnership with the UK could be established. From that emerged a major programme of collaborative research which has been funded by the British Council through its UK-India Education and Research Initiative (UKIERI). The aim of the collaboration is to combine India's detailed knowledge of the monsoon with the UK's capability in climate prediction, so that, together, we can significantly accelerate the development of skilful monsoon forecasts. At the same time, we seek to develop the methodologies to use these forecasts much more effectively to enable India to adapt to and mitigate the impacts of climate change, especially in the areas of water resource management, ecosystem functioning and crop production.

India has increased its funding for climate prediction and climate change research substantially, and has invested significantly in new, high performance computing platforms. While this is a welcome recognition of the fundamental importance of climate prediction for India's economy and sustainability, and demonstrates a real desire to work at the leading edge of climate change research, it also represents an enormous challenge for India. Financial resources and computing hardware are only part of the story. The real dilemma facing India is how to develop its climate prediction capability as quickly as possible given a very limited talent pool to draw on.

As in many other countries, young people are not being attracted to science because the financial rewards are not great, and a shortage of skilled personnel presents a real problem for India. It is hard to see what the short-term

solution should be, but there is no doubt that partnerships with leading research groups in countries, such as the UK, may help to overcome these difficulties and serve to develop the long-term skill base through appropriate training and knowledge transfer activities. It is gratifying to see that India has already decided to take the UK Met Office weather and seasonal forecasting system rather than develop its own from scratch, a decision that will save, effectively, hundreds of person years of development time. The sharing of joint infrastructures such as these also has other mutual benefits. The use of common tools enables much greater and more meaningful scientific collaboration, and the expertise of Indian scientists in understanding monsoon processes can be directly translated into model improvements, of value to the UK and India alike.

It has been argued that one of the reasons that climate change prediction and research in the UK is so strong is because the government-funded and academic community activities are well coordinated and increasingly aligned to a common purpose. Until very recently, climate research in India has been rather fragmented, and although the recent restructuring will bring greater cohesion, there is no doubt that even greater coordination of national activities will bring significant rewards. In an era when climate change science starts to cross so many boundaries in terms of its relevance and impacts, the need for a well-integrated programme of research and development becomes even more essential.

In the 19th century, Henry Blandford saw India as an ideal place to study, and hence understand, the complexities of atmospheric physics. As he put it,

> Could we but find an isolated tract of mountain, plain and ocean ... girdled round by a giant mountain chain that should completely shut in and isolate some millions of square miles of the atmosphere, resting on a surface vast and varied enough to exhibit within itself all those contrasts of desert and forest, of plain, plateau and mountain ridge, of continent and sea, then the progress of meteorology would be assured.

Now in the 21st century, it is that same diversity that provides such an immense, but rewarding challenge to climate change science. □

V K Joshi
Science Journalist

Earthquakes: Monitoring the earth's mood

They were killers in the past, they are so today. Earthquakes have left their mark on history, mythology, geology and seismology. The author provides glimpses into some of the great earthquakes that have rocked India, into scientific studies on earthquakes and earthquake prediction.

A major earthquake rocked Delhi 287 years ago—on 15th July 1720. Says Moghul historian Kaifikhan in his treatise *Muntukhabul-Ul-Lulab,* "It was Ramzan. People had assembled in mosques to offer prayers when Shajehanabad was shaken by a massive earthquake. Hundreds of people lost their lives. Shock waves continued to scare people for the next 40 days".

The Killari earthquake of 1933 in Central India provoked almost similar language. Said Prabhas Pande, an eminent seismologist and director, earthquake geology, Geological Survey of India, after inspecting the damage: "A few dozen hours ago some 1,000 people perished in one of the most devastating earthquakes of Central India."

The story has always been the same. The National Disaster Management Authority says that six major earthquakes since 1990 have taken 23,000 lives and destroyed property whose worth is incalculable. Earthquakes are intrinsic to the earth's environment and—as history shows—a regular and deadly killer.

Earthquakes in myth and history

All mythologies bear out the age-old association of earthquakes with human beings. People of old regarded them as supernatural phenomena. Hindu mythology has it that Lord Vishnu and his consort (Mother Earth) relaxed on the head of the serpent 'Sheshnag'. The earth rocked when the serpent shook his head.

Men of religion may regard earthquakes and volcanic eruptions as manifestations of divine retribution. Scientists know that quakes occur because of stresses and strains in the earth's unstable interior; and from gases and heat escaping through the crust.

The top portion of the Kutub Minar at Delhi tumbled during an earthquake on 1 September, 1803, that rocked the Mathura-Delhi region. Dr Thomas Oldham of GSI, doyen of the science of seismology in India, believed it would have been an earthquake of 6.5 Richter magnitude. The annals of GSI kept detailed accounts of all major earthquakes that struck the subcontinent from 1819 onwards.

The detailed study of the Assam earthquake of 1897 by Sir R D Oldham, illustrious son of Dr Thomas Oldham, created a history of sorts. He published his work in 1899. Later, C F Richter while writing his book, *Elementary Seismology* in 1958, considered Oldham Jr's memoir 'as one of the best source books in seismology'. It was this work that provided the guidelines for identifying the highest grade XII of the modified Mercalli scale, which is used to describe the effects of an earthquake at a given place. Yet another first for Oldham was the recognition of the longitudinal (P) and transverse (S) and surface (L) waves on the records of seismographs—which form the basic concepts of modern seismology. The first seismograph in India was installed in 1899 at the Colaba observatory in Mumbai.

The earthquakes that ravaged our planet in the past have left tell-tale marks which geologists have deciphered. These marks are described as seismites. The study of such marks, the concept of Palaeo-Seismology or the science of earthquakes, is catching up fast in India too. Seismites help to work out the hazard potential of an area.

India was being rocked by earthquakes much before the collision of the Indian and the Asian Plates 20 million years ago, says Rajat Majumdar of Geo-und Umweltwissenscahften, geologist from the Ludwig-Maximilians Universitat, Munchen, Germany, in a paper published in *Sedimentary Geology*.

Rajat and his research associates found that some layers of rocks (ranging in age from 1,600 million years to 2,100 million years) of the Chaibasa Formation of Eastern India were deformed. These rocks were apparently underlaid by volcanic rocks which were conclusively 2,100 million years old. (It is established that a high-magnitude earthquake liquefies and even deforms the rocks.) In short, the rocks of the Chaibasa Formation were being deposited in a basin affected by active volcanism. Earthquake and volcanism go hand in hand.

Reports pour in almost daily from some part of India or other of evidence of trembling earth from bygone eras. Recent GSI studies have shown the presence of seismites from Yamuna Valley, Uttarakhand, Baspa Valley, Himachal Pradesh, and Madurai in Tamil Nadu and Shillong in the northeast.

New vistas

The emerging science of the study of seismites has opened many new vistas on past earthquakes. For example, B S Sukhija of National Geophysical Research Institute (NGRI), Hyderabad, observes that as a consequence of the Shillong earthquake (M 8.7) of 12 June, 1897 a fault movement caused the shift in the course of the Krishnai River, a tributary of Brahmaputra. On the basis of his studies, Sukhija concluded that such devastating earthquakes in the Shillong Plateau can recur in 500 years. With 1950 as the reference year, he has evidence to prove that major earthquakes did occur at interval of 500, 1000 and 1500 years before this year. Sukhija also studied the Killari (Latur) area of central India. He says this area was not rocked for the first time in 1993, but damaging earthquakes had taken place in the area some 200 years too.

An earthquake that struck Kutch in Gujarat in 1819 left a mound-like structure in the channel of Pharran River. It was found that this mound formed due to liquefaction, was 80 km long and up to six metres high at some places, and was

locally named 'Allah bund'. The teams of geologists of GSI investigating the Kutch (Bhuj) earthquake of 26 January 2001 found a number of liquefaction features in the form of sand blows, ground fissures, mud craters and subsidence craters etc.

Recent studies

"The great Assam earthquake of 12 June 1897 reduced to rubble all masonry buildings within a region of NE India roughly the size of England..." wrote Roger Bilham and Phillip England in *Nature* (2001). Both are experts in plate tectonics and earthquake mechanisms.

The Shillong Plateau virtually 'popped up,' say Bilham and England. Their surmise is based on the latest studies which show that the northern edge of the northern Shillong Plateau rose violently more than 11 m during the rupture of a 110 km long buried fault. Plateau uplift in the past 2–5 million years has caused the Indian Plate to contract locally by 4±2 mm/year. This implies reduced risk for Bhutan but increased risk for densely populated Bangladesh.

Indian seismologists and structural engineers were professionally skilled far earlier than those of other nations. The Quetta earthquake of 1930 inspired railway engineers to construct earthquake-resistant houses. They had developed such designs long before counterparts in other countries had even thought of them. But it was the general apathy or ignorance of known construction norms in earthquake-prone areas that led to the terrible disaster that rocked Gujarat in January 2001.

People of Gujarat learned lessons the hard way. After 2001, the government took no chances. The reconstructed townships are earthquake-safe—or so it is claimed. Only time will prove this, however. Kusala and C P Rajendran of the Centre of Earth Science Studies, Thiruvananthapuram, have collected evidence from monuments to establish that Gujarat could not have suffered a disaster as grave as that in 2001 since the 9th century AD. They strongly recommend a thorough study of hidden faults in the Kutch-Saurashtra region to assess their seismic potential.

Likewise, active faults and sub-surface ruptures haunt the Himalayas too. After the earthquake that shook Kashmir on 8th October 2005, S K Singh of Instituto de Geofisca, Mexico, and his co-researchers from India Meteorology Department, Department of Science and Technology, and National Geophysical Research Institute, Hyderabad, detected a near sub-surface slip of about five metres. A database for the past 120 years available with the GSI shows that many earthquakes of magnitude = 4 have shaken the area earlier too.

V C Thakur of Wadia Institute of Himalayan Geology, India, has also reported similar near - surface ruptures. He says that in the mountain segment south of the Great Himalaya and between the Sutlej and Indus rivers, three large earthquakes of magnitude = 7.5 have occurred during the last 450 years. These are from east to west, the Kangra—1905, the Kashmir—1555 and the Muzaffarabad—2005. In all these quakes, the ground was ruptured, he claims. He has recommended a watch on the un-ruptured portions of the frontal Himalaya, like the Chamba-Doda sector and the Simla-Garhwal sector. He has strongly advocated mapping of active faults in these areas.

D D Joshi, a young seismologist of GSI, also reports an active fault in Chamba. This place falls in the western extremity of Kangra re-entrant, a major structural feature of western Himalayas, he says. The re-entrant has shown a shortening of the earth's crust by 23 km during the past 1.9 to 1.5 million years. In other words, the shortening has been taking place at a rate of 14 ± 2 mm/year. It means the region is under constant stress and faces a threat of major earthquakes in future.

Where we stand

What's the status of today's knowledge of earthquakes? We may consider ourselves well informed. The newly formed Department of Earth Sciences (CSIO) of the Government of India has taken up earthquake precursor studies. Till now, these studies were carried out by individuals who measured changes in the ionosphere, the geothermal gradient, and geochemical changes in the quality of spring waters prior to earthquakes. The problem with such studies is that they haven't been scientifically endorsed yet as dependable. Changes in all these parameters do take place for reasons other than earthquakes as well

An array of seismographs and accelorographs offers a ray of hope in predicting earthquakes in high-hazard areas like the Himalayas. Various institutes have deployed a network of these instruments for weak and strong motion seismic studies in the Himalayas, say B K Sharma and his co-researchers from the Central Scientific Instruments Organization, Chandigarh, in a recent special publication of GSI.

Over the past one and a half centuries, we have evolved from primitive seismographs to the present-day digital multi-channel seismographs linked via GPS and satellite to the microprocessor. The idea is to get information the moment a tremor starts. High-speed computers store the data and simultaneously process and analyze it. If a stronger tremor is anticipated, scientists monitoring the information are alerted.

At present there are 31 Weak Motion Observatories in Himachal Pradesh, Chandigarh, Kurukshetra (Haryana), Uttarakhand, Assam, Itanagar, Manipur, Gangtok and Andhra Pradesh. In addition there are 164 Strong Motion Observatories spread over Himachal Pradesh, Uttarakhand, Northeastern region and Sikkim. The only drawback, says Sharma, is that these observatories do not have a data-sharing arrangement.

Considering the size of the Himalayas and the active tectonic set-up, the number of observatories is meager—but a good beginning has been made.

Risk assessment

A precursor study has yet to find favor with the scientific community; an effort is therefore needed to identify hazard-prone areas in India. Microzonation of certain risk-prone areas has already started. The Geological Survey of India has already carried out such studies in Delhi, Dehradun, Jabalpur, Ahmedabad, Siliguri, Guwahati and Vishakhapatnam. There is a strong need for such studies in all the metros and densely populated urban areas, especially those with high rise buildings.

Risk assessment studies of individual areas considered hazard-prone will be the next step required. As the earthquake waves pass through various sub-surface media, they manifest themselves in different ways. The ground-shaking varies accordingly. Thus, the densely populated Ganga-Yamuna interfluves, hitherto considered safe, may have pockets where an earthquake may cause liquefaction. Such phenomena would mean a serious risk for high-rise apartments coming up on the densely populated flood plains of rivers. In rocky terrains like Mumbai, the high-rise buildings of Powai may require a design different from those in Colaba, depending on the magnitude of the tremor.

In high-risk areas, the structural designs of buildings have to be not only site-specific, but building-specific as well, says Prabhas Pande. A hospital building, for example, may always be crowded with people. It should be designed to be earthquake safe. Even the approach roads and bridges en-route have to be constructed accordingly.

Since the trembling of the earth is a continuous process, the data collected for hazard or risk assessment has to be updated continuously. Public awareness campaigns are always welcome. During the long gaps between two earthquakes, people become lax. An earthquake catches them unawares. Japan carries out regular exercises even in busy Tokyo. The earth needs to be monitored constantly so that we keep abreast of the mysteries of depths and solve them. Earthquakes are in a sense the eco-cardiograms of the interior of the earth. R.A. Daly wrote in 1928: "Man is learning to harness for his enquiring use the very wrath of the earth; the tremblings of our vibrant globe are used to X-ray the deep interior." □

2001 Gujarat earthquake: damaged Bhadra tower (1411 AD) in Ahmedabad. Photo: GSI.

2001 Gujarat earthquake: Swanky Shivalay Apartment, Ahmedabad, crumbled. Photo: GSI.

ATOMIC
ENERGY

Anil Kakodkar
Chairman, Atomic Energy
Commission & Secretary
Department of Atomic Energy

Pathway to energy independence

The ongoing national debate on the opening up of international civil nuclear cooperation for India has led to greater awareness and interest in nuclear energy today than at any time in our history. Clearly, the issues of sustainability of energy resources in India, and for that matter, worldwide, and global climate change have brought nuclear energy centre stage, while the world still grapples with related security challenges and perceptional concerns related to safety and waste management. It is in this context that rapid economic progress in India has driven the international realisation of the importance of a faster rise in the share of nuclear power in India.

Three-stage programme

India has all along pursued a path of self-reliance in its development of nuclear science and technology. While remaining fully committed to self-reliance to ensure freedom from vulnerabilities of any kind and to retain autonomous capability in choosing our own development and deployment options, we have always remained positive about foreign collaborations that do not compromise these principles. For example, India chose the Pressurised Heavy Water Reactor (PHWR) option for domestic development based on its suitability under Indian conditions. It went ahead with the uranium mine at Jaduguda in spite of its very low-grade ore, and at about the same time set up the Tarapur Atomic Power Station as a turnkey project supported by the USA.

Today our indigenous three-stage nuclear power development programme (Fig. 1) has matured to the level of world class capability in PHWR technology, with all aspects of its fuel cycle and heavy water production in the commercial domain.

Three Stage Nuclear Power Programme

Stage - I PHWRs
- 15 - Operating
- 3 - Under construction
- Several others planned
- Scaling to 700 Mwe
- Gestation period has been reduced
- Power Potential = 10,000 MWe

LWRs
- BWRs Operating
- 2 WERs under construction

Stage - II
Fast Breeder Reactors
- 40 Mwth FBTR - Operating
  since 1985 Technology Objectives
  realised

- 500 MWE PFBR-Under Construction

- Power Potential = 530,000 Mwe

Stage - III
Thorium based reactors
- kWh KAMINI - Operating
- 300 Mwe AHWR-Under development
Poswer potential is very large
Availability of ADS can enable early
introduction of Thorium on a large scale

Fig. 1: India's Three Stage Nuclear Power Programme

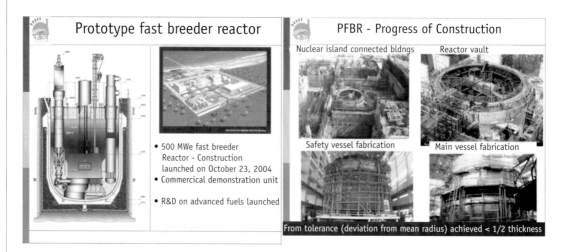

Fig. 2: PFBR under construction at Kalpakkam, Tamil Nadu

More importantly, we have now reached a stage of taking up even Fast Breeder Reactor Technology and its closed fuel cycle in commercial deployment mode (Fig. 2 PFBR under construction at Kalpakkam, Tamil Nadu). This is an area in which at present only two or three other countries have similar capabilities. There is now a widespread realisation of the need for large-scale fast reactor deployment on account of its potential to make fuller use of uranium and thorium for energy production, and also for utilization/disposal of fissile materials produced in thermal reactor systems. Finally, when it comes to thorium, we are perhaps unique in having developed our own capability, and we are now ready to start constructing a 300 MWe Advanced Heavy Water Reactor (AHWR) which will produce two thirds of its energy output from thorium. I am certain thorium utilization will become a matter of global importance when there is a realisation of the inevitability of nuclear recycle. A closer analysis of the global resource position and upcoming needs suggests that this will happen sooner rather than later.

Meeting demand

We have so far done well in the development of robust nuclear power technologies. However, deployment of our three stage nuclear power programme is necessarily a step-by-step process to be followed sequentially. Since our domestic uranium resources are modest, the commercial exploitation potential of the PHWR technology, which is now fully commercial, is limited to 10,000 MWe. Furthermore, we have to allow for gestation periods for maturation of technologies for Fast Breeder Reactors and Thorium-based reactors. The indigenous

programme, which is backed up by sound R&D capability, will thus open up the vast energy potential with our own uranium and thorium resources in the long run. Our estimates are that we should be able to reach a level of around 200 GWe of nuclear installed capacity by the middle of this century on the basis of indigenously available uranium. Our thorium resources would enable this level of capacity to be sustained for a few centuries.

While there is confidence that the above-mentioned goals will be realised, the demands on the energy front are much higher. Estimates are that we will need electricity generating capacity of around 1300 GWe by 2050 and that we would continue to face shortages of around 20–30 per cent even after accounting for optimistic estimates for all available energy resources.

More importantly, the energy crisis will hit us even more severely in a few decades from now unless we find large enough energy resources within the country, or tie up their imports from the external energy market characterized by scarce energy resources.

We thus have a twin challenge of enhancing the share of nuclear power in the near term and bridging the energy deficit in the long run. The answer to this lies in the enhanced result-oriented domestic uranium exploration efforts on one hand, and possible access to external inputs of uranium on the other. Our current efforts are targeting both these fronts. We must recognise that the generation capacity based on uranium can be multiplied through deployment of a fast reactor. This multiple could be as high as 20 in the case of beginning mode with PHWRs, and around 8 in the case of beginning mode with LWRs. Thus the domestic three-stage nuclear power development programme, when fully developed, will enable multiplication of nuclear power generation capacity even with imported LWRs using low enriched uranium.

It is estimated that 30–40 GWe additional capacity in the form of PHWRs or LWRs will not only provide the additional electricity that is so desperately needed in the near term but also bridge the long term shortage through energy from recycled uranium with multiplier effect through fast reactors. The actual capacity of LWRs that will need to be acquired depends on our success in domestic exploration efforts and viable economics of imported nuclear power systems when compared to available alternatives.

Strategic autonomy

It is important at this stage to recognize two important factors. The first one relates to the inherent basis of our pursuit of autonomous three-stage nuclear power developments, which must reach its logical end without any external interference. This is as important as the autonomous pursuit of our strategic programme. In fact, the two are inseparable. The second one relates to the fact that global uranium is also finite. The current assessment indicates that by around 2030, the entire currently known world uranium resources will get tied up for reactors built by that time. Further growth would anyway need to be supported by fast breeder reactors unless significant additional uranium is found. It is thus crucial that we maximize our access to uranium within this time frame. This will be helpful in the short as well as in the long terms.

Our priorities for technology development and principles for international civil nuclear cooperation have to be based on the logic outlined above. Luckily, right from the beginning, we have adopted the philosophy of a closed nuclear fuel cycle. This is now getting recognized as an inevitable global option.

Our achievements in fast breeder reactor technology and our success in commercially robust PHWR technology, both backed by their respective fuel cycle technologies, have earned us the status of a country with advanced nuclear technology. This industrial capability, along with our demonstrated nuclear weapons capability and our time-tested behaviour as a responsible country, makes cooperation with India free of proliferation concerns. Further, we

have been adopting IAEA safeguards on reactors and nuclear fuel supplied from outside. This can continue in the future. Our freedom to pursue R&D to take care of all our national interest is however paramount and cannot be compromised.

Growth of fast reactors in the initial phase would be dependent on plutonium feed from PHWR spent fuel. During this time we need to complete the development of metallic fuel and its fuel cycle to realize shorter doubling time. This is important as this will be the prime determinator of the growth rate of nuclear generation capacity at that time. This development is the main focus of fast-reactor related R&D at IGCAR and BARC.

Further, enhancement of burn-up and improvements in recycle technology are other thrust areas that are being pursued at these centres. It is a matter of some satisfaction that when the world is searching for a fourth generation reactor that will meet the criteria of economics, safety, sustainability, proliferation resistance and waste management, our AHWR design meets all of these with its innovative configuration based on currently known basic technologies.

Advantages

AHWR systems have minimum dependence on active systems, relative immunity from excursions and a long operator forgiving period (as long as 3 days). Further, thorium offers some unique advantages in terms of proliferation resistance, fissile material burning, relatively smaller minor actinides issues and stable fuel matrix.

AHWR is a technology demonstrator to enhance our experience base with thorium utilization technologies. This also forms a bridge between PHWR technologies of the first stage and the requirements that may unfold in the third stage. While thorium offers many advantages, it does not support any significant growth of power generation capacity. There may be differences between several thorium options, but by and large, they all remain close to self-sustaining mode primarily due to the basic nuclear characteristic of thorium. A sub-critical thorium system, driven by an accelerator that produces a strong enough neutron source, offers a way of improving the growth rate. Such accelerator driven systems will also enable an improved capability for transmutation of long-lived radioactive waste. We thus have in principle the possibility of a self-consistent reactor system that would largely minimize the long-lived waste problem and support the growth of nuclear power generation capacity with thorium.

Accelerators are also important tools for basic research. Fortunately, DAE laboratories have a good background in terms of building systems and sub-systems for large accelerators. Although the challenge of accelerators for use in ADS is a big one, we can, through our sustained efforts, realise this goal. Such efforts are useful for pushing frontiers both in terms of energy as well as basic research.

The day is not far off when nuclear power will be seen as a primary energy source, rather than just a source of electricity. This will mean availability of technological capability to use nuclear energy for high temperature heat for pyro-chemical or pyro-metallurgical processes, or for production of hydrogen or some other fluid fuel form, which could also serve as a carrier of energy as well as a convenient energy form for transportation. This requires development of high temperature reactors capable of operating at around a 1000°C. Also, we need to develop technologies for thermo-chemical splitting of water, high temperature electrolysis and solid

oxide fuel cells necessary for ushering in a hydrogen economy era. All these constitute elements of current R&D activities in DAE.

While nuclear fission has the potential to provide much higher levels of energy as compared to fossil energy, rising living standards worldwide may need even larger energy sources. Nuclear fusion that powers the sun, which supports the entire living environment on earth, can also be a source of energy right here on earth. The scientific and technological developments enable us to say with confidence that we will be in a position to produce fusion energy in a sustained fashion.

The International Thermo-nuclear Experimental Reactor (ITER) is the largest scientific project aimed at this objective. India is a member of this mega international effort (Fig. 3). We would be contributing to this project in kind by making hi-tech equipment costing around Rs 2500 crores within the country. This will not only enable a hands-on experience for our industries in hi-tech areas like superconductivity, large electromagnets, high power RF. and microwaves, and cryogenics, but also help to leap forward in our national fusion technology capability by at least 20 years.

Fusion energy

India is a member of ITER group

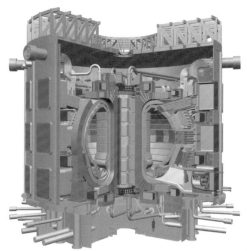

Schematic of the prototype fusion breeder reactor

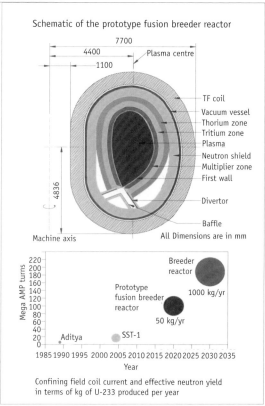

Fig. 3: Indian Fusion Programme

Respect for Mother Earth is embedded deep in the Indian mind. We are now faced with the dilemma of meeting the developmental aspiration of the Indian people, one sixth of the world's population, at a time when global environment is at the edge of a cliff. The exploitation of our planet Earth by the rich and powerful industrialised countries has very little to meet the needs of a vast majority of poor and weak people. We therefore have to meet our present and future needs with minimum exploitation of Earth's resources. This is where the several million-fold higher calorific value of nuclear fuels assumes importance. The strategy outlined above can credibly translate this concept into a reality. We have, in fact, come a long way on this path.

Yet much more needs to be done. The scientific and technological capabilities realised so far and the sound research infrastructure provide sufficient ground for maintaining that India can resolve the challenge posed by this dilemma, and solve not only its own problem but actually be a path-finder for the developing world as a whole. □

The Sun God

President Chirac, European Commission President Barroso, excellencies, ladies and gentlemen,
I would like to begin with a Shloka from the Rig Veda, one of our ancient scriptures.

सप्त त्वा हरितो रथे वहन्ति देव सूर्य। शोचिष्केशं विचक्षण

Seven Steeds harnessed to thy car bear thee, O thou farseeing One, God, Surya, with the radiant hair ...

Our ancestors intuitively grasped the importance of the Sun as the Ultimate Provider and Sustainer of Life on Earth! What they perhaps did not foresee is that one day their progeny would imitate the sun right here on earth to cater to vastly increased energy needs!

India is proud to be a partner in this enterprise of getting the man made star—ITER—off the ground with our shoulders to the wheel ... like one of the seven mythological steeds pulling on the carriage of the Lord Surya—the Sun!

Today, we take a momentous step towards realization of our common goal to seek a clean source of energy of a magnitude capable of supporting a decent quality of life for the entire humanity. Fusion has the potential to provide abundant and clean energy based on resources available everywhere without significant ecological issues associated with mining of earth's resources. It is this context that the Indian delegation is very happy to be a part of this historic human scientific endeavour.

Speaking specifically about India, in spite of being one of the top five electricity producing countries, we still have very low per capita electricity consumption. The objective of electrification of all villages is yet to be realized. Studies indicate that even to reach a modest target of per capita generation of about 5000 kWh, total annual electricity generation has to go up about 11 to 12 times. While immediate increase would inevitably come from fossil fuels, nuclear energy has to play a significant role in the coming decades.

We have an ambitious programme to tap fission energy based on closed fuel cycle approach. However, considering the size of our country and rapid growth in economy, even that is not likely to be sufficient in the long term. There is thus a need to look at new technologies such as fusion that provides even larger energy potential. We have been pursuing fusion science and technology programme at our Institute for Plasma Research, Gandhinagar. Our scientists have already designed and fabricated two tokamak devices Aditya and the steady state superconducting tokamak SST 1. Many technologies of relevance to the forefront of fusion research have been developed by our scientists and engineers in collaboration with our industries. We thus bring to the table a combination of strong commitment from the government and special scientific and technological skills, which are of relevance to ITER and to fusion research.

An extract from the address by Dr Anil Kakodkar, Chairman, Atomic Energy Commission, in Paris in 2006, on the Joint Implementation of the ITER project.

Pallava Bagla
Correspondent *Science*

Indo-US atomic tango: Seeking to make amends

The protracted negotiations for the Indo-US nuclear deal demonstrated that it is not always easy to undo the injustices of the past. In a radically altered post Cold War strategic situation, both India and the US have largely come to terms with the reality and are determined to put the past behind them. Atomic energy is one area in which this mutual desire has dramatically manifested itself. However, when two democracies want to take a U-turn, an individual's fiat cannot order it.

That is why the Indo-US civilian nuclear deal, endorsed by the top leadership of the country, threatened a nuclear fall-out in the political arena. The deal angered the nuclear non-proliferation lobby in the US. In India, it angered two distinct sections. There are those in New Delhi who are ideologically opposed to America and then there are those who want the Indo-US ties to grow but cannot forget or forgive America's past attempts to restrain India's technological empowerment. They just want the Government of India to be cautious while entering into any agreement with the US. They cannot be faulted because history happens to be on their side.

Those pleading for caution have bitter memories of India having been pushed into the nuclear dog house. At US bidding, the nuclear haves ganged up to impede the transfer of sensitive high technologies that India needed for its development. These embargoes were imposed in the garb of stopping proliferation of nuclear weapons.

India's 'sin' was its refusal to sign the flawed Nuclear Non-Proliferation Treaty (NPT), which had set January 1, 1967 as the date by which any country that had exploded a nuclear device, got a nuclear weapons status. The USA, Russia, France, Great Britain and China got in and then made all efforts to ensure their hegemony was never broken.

The first country outside this holy NPT framework to explode a nuclear device was India, when in the summer of 1974, the sands below Pokharan shook, loudly proclaiming to the world the arrival of a new nuclear kid on the block. Ever since, all kinds of sanctions against technology transfer were clamped on India. These sought to cripple India's space and nuclear facilities and deny to Indians the benefits of nuclear power. India was outlawed from the global nuclear community.

A global cartel called the Nuclear Suppliers Group (NSG), now a group of 45 countries, was created essentially to box India into a corner and by its own admission, the NSG was created following the explosion in 1974 of a nuclear device by a non-nuclear-weapon State, which demonstrated that nuclear technology transferred for peaceful purposes could be 'misused.' Much to India's distaste it became a nuclear untouchable and several unrelated civilian sectors had to pay a heavy price as well.

Fuel and spare part supplies for India's nuclear reactors were suddenly stopped, so much so that at times it became hazardous to keep the Tarapur nuclear power rectors running. In the eighties, India was denied the permission to import a Cray Super Computer for its weather forecasting needs and the reason given was that it could be used to design atom bombs. Later, the country was denied technology to manufacture Cryogenic engines needed to hoist communication satellites using locally made rockets. The list is endless.

Higher barriers were being placed against India merely to contain the development of the high-technology sectors in India. But the more the technology was denied to India, the more determined to overcome these embargos did the Indian scientists, supported by the Indian government, become.

The embargoes were overcome not by flouting them or by buying stuff from the so called 'nuclear Wall Mart', but by sheer dint of hard work; whatever was denied has been slowly built locally. Sanctions only delayed the development of these technologies, they did not scuttle whole projects. India is the only country where the American sanctions regime produced the opposite results for which they were put in place.

Embargoes

The restrictive regimes became overbearing when in 1998 the sand dunes of Pokhran were emblazoned once again with the sound and fury of another 5 nuclear weapons tests. Not being coy like last time when the country had dubbed the test as a 'peaceful nuclear explosion', in 1998, India aptly declared itself a 'nuclear weapons state'. The then US President Bill Clinton exclaimed "we will fall on them [India] like a ton of bricks" and the sanctions regime became very strict with 'presumption of denial' being the guiding principle for every request for sourcing simple spare parts like computer chips and chemicals. The heat was faced even by Indian scientists; several were removed from American laboratories. Nuclear scientist R Chidambaram was denied a visa to visit the US to attend a scientific meeting.

Then the White House decided to have a relook at India's nuclear programme and aspirations. It questioned the traditional policy in this regard as friendship with India became its strategic priority. One of the results was the civil nuclear cooperation initiative. When the deal is signed, sealed and delivered, it will end India's nuclear winter. The move accommodates India within an unofficial non-proliferation umbrella while it retains the nuclear weapons. The US recognizes that in the last 60 years, India never broke any international norms, or violated any global treaties.

The technology denial regimes targeted at India are now being disbanded. President George Bush magnanimously called India "a responsible state" among those with "advanced nuclear technology." He was compelled to take note of India's sizeable and credible nuclear power programme based heavily on home-grown technology.

Much to India's delight the very same country that spearheaded the moves to establish these obstacles is today at the forefront of dismantling them. The world indeed has come full circle and a grave historical wrong is being sought to be undone. While the new friendly approach of successive US Presidents has helped, their desire to break the nuclear deadlock was the result of a fait accompli presented by the Indian nuclear scientists who vowed not to be defeated by the technology denial regimes. They managed to create an infrastructure and a bank of knowledge in a field that got neglected in the US because of environmental concerns over nuclear power.

While the Indian nuclear scientists and nuclear engineers demonstrated their expertise, the Government drew up plans to substantially increase nuclear power generation. Once this landmark nuclear deal is inked, the floodgates to nuclear commerce with India will be opened. The official estimates envisage nuclear power generation of 30,000 MWe by 2022 and 63,000 MWe by 2032, which translates into India seeking to invest at least 100–150 billion dollars in this infrastructure sector alone in the next 25 years. It seems this giant pot of gold is attractive enough for countries to remove the several hurdles so that trade in high technology could begin once again with India.

Unique plan

The global nuclear community could not fail to grasp the significance of India's unique plan to build commercial reactors that run not on uranium but on a lighter element, thorium-232. India has relatively little uranium but one of the world's largest reserves of thorium—about 225,000 metric tonnes. Thorium does not fission, but when irradiated with neutrons from the fission of a source material like uranium 235, some of the thorium becomes uranium 233, which does fission and can sustain a nuclear reaction.

India's embarked in 1958 on an ambitious three-stage plan to exploit its thorium reserves. Stage I required building pressurized heavy water reactors that are powered by natural uranium and yield plutonium as a byproduct. Stage II kicks in after sufficient plutonium has been extracted from spent cores; it is converted to fuel for fast-neutron reactors which can enhance the utilization of natural uranium (through conversion to plutonium) by around 70 times. Fast reactors can in addition be used to irradiate thorium and produce U 233 as a byproduct. In the third stage, Advanced Heavy Water Reactors (AHWRs) would burn a mixture of U-233 and thorium, generating about two thirds of their power from thorium. Other nations—including the US, Russia, Germany and Israel—have studied the route but have not attempted to use it to generate electricity.

At present, India has reached a level of maturity in the Stage I of its grand strategy. It has built more than a dozen reactors that run on uranium fuel and two Boiling Water Reactors employing enriched uranium fuel at Tarapur. These first-line plants now produce 3900 MW of electricity. India hopes to generate 10,000 MW of nuclear power by 2010 and 20,000 MW by 2020 as estimated by the Department of Atomic Energy.

Stage II began in the sleepy township of Kalpakkam in southern India. There, a public sector company wholly owned by the Department of Atomic Energy, the Bharatiya Nabhikiya Vidyut Nigam Limited, began the construction of a 500 MW fast breeder reactor that will use fast neutrons to produce U233. In its core, the rector will use a 'seed' fuel containing uranium and plutonium oxide; this source will send neutrons into a surrounding blanket, producing U-233.

Nuclear market

India promises a huge market for the order-starved nuclear power industry of the developed world. Its own nuclear technology business has the potential to go global. The global nuclear community has come to realize what India has to offer in this field. That is why it is being invited to join international projects and that is why it is being heard with attention.

All this was clearly evident at the General Conference of the International Atomic Energy Agency (IAEA) in Vienna September 2007. At the meeting, where 140 countries were represented, Anil Kakodkar, Chairman of India's Atomic Energy Commission, was probably the most sought after person, second only to the Director General of IAEA Mohamed. Elbaradei. There was no nuclear country worth its 'atomic' weight that did not hold a bilateral dialogue with the Indian nuclear chief.

At the annual gathering of nuclear experts, there was much excitement over the big ticket Indo-US deal. Every nation that has nuclear technology or material to sell is waiting for the huge Indian market to open up. So India was

the 'flavor of the season' in Vienna. Notwithstanding the degree of self-reliance in technology achieved by India so far, India cannot increase its nuclear generation speedily and gains access to unhindered uranium supply. Of course, India is not going to be able to import atomic reactors soon. In Vienna itself at the time of IAEA meeting, there was no dearth of India-baiters and the hardliners of the Nuclear Suppliers Group.

In the IAEA building in Vienna, one becomes more aware of the importance of India's nuclear record. The IAEA owes its existence in Vienna to the foresight of the father of the Indian nuclear programme Homi J Bhabha whose casting vote half a century ago brought the global nuclear watch dog to Vienna. Bhabha's statute shares pride of place alongside that of US President Dwight D Eisenhower, the man who coined the phrase 'atoms for peace' and of Marie Curie, the double Nobel Laureate who discovered radioactivity. India is a permanent member of the IAEA Board of Governors, again recognition of India's capabilities.

That India today has the largest number of nuclear reactors under construction anywhere in the world—eight power plants are in various stages of construction—is just one reason for the world to view India leading the nuclear renaissance.

Fast breeder

An audience of 500 top nuclear policy makers heard India's plans of setting up the first commercial prototype fast breeder reactor, a 500 MW unit by 2010 at Kalpakkam. Only Russians, French and Japanese have come anywhere close to harnessing the powers of the breeder reactor. The US tried and gave up and now under the Global Nuclear Energy Partnership (GNEP) programme, they are just beginning to explore the possibilities of using breeders as a way of extracting more energy from the scarce uranium reserves in a once-through mode.

The three-stage Indian atomic energy plan wherein the country hopes to extract every ounce of energy from all nuclear materials (uranium, plutonium and thorium) in what is called a 'closed fuel cycle' is now beginning to be acknowledged as the robust way forward for the world to sustainably harness nuclear energy not just over decades but several hundred years.

India's plans for utilizing thorium as a source material to harvest nuclear energy evokes a lot of admiration from the world nuclear community since no other country is doing any great research in that direction. That India has a full fledged thorium based reactor already designed namely the Advanced Heavy Water Reactor makes India a global leader in a high-technology sector. The thorium rectors could make India energy independent, not just energy secure. These promise at least 300,000 MW for the next 250 years.

In an amazing twist in the tail, even as India craves for the import of nuclear power reactors, Indian officials made an unprecedented pitch for getting the international instruments needed for exporting small power reactors, a technology that India has mastered. With support from at least a dozen countries, India got a resolution adopted that IAEA should promote small and medium power plants for countries with smaller electricity grids. These plants are also useful for supplying fresh water through desalination of sea water.

The controversy at home over the Indo-US civil nuclear deal did not stop the Indian delegation making a leap in faith by suggesting we are already thinking of exports. Bhabha who died in a plane crash in the European Alps, not too far from Vienna, must be benevolently smiling, seeing India everywhere in the 21st century atomic dance. □

THE WHITE HOUSE

PRESIDENT GEORGE W BUSH

United States and India: Strategic Partnership

White House News

We have an ambitious agenda with India. Our agenda is practical. It builds on a relationship that has never been better. India is a global leader, as well as a good friend. ... My trip will remind everybody about the strengthening of an important strategic partnership. We'll work together in practical ways to promote a hopeful future for citizens in both our nations.

President George W. Bush, February 22, 2006

CIVIL NUCLEAR COOPERATION: The United States and India have reached an historic agreement on civil nuclear cooperation. The agreement addresses India's surging energy needs for its growing economy. This will also ease the burden on other countries as the world's energy needs continue to rise.

- The U.S. and India have agreed to pursue civil nuclear cooperation to allow India to cooperate and trade in this key area.
- India has agreed to take steps that will bring it into the international non-proliferation mainstream, including placing its civilian nuclear facilities and programs under IAEA safeguards and adhering to the guidelines of the Nuclear Suppliers Group and the Missile Technology Control Regime.

Baldev Raj, S C Chetal,
P R Vasudeva Rao &
R Natarajan
Indira Gandhi Centre for
Atomic Research, Kalpakkam

Fast reactors for energy security

Fast Reactors form the second stage of the three stage nuclear power programme envisioned by Dr Homi Bhabha. As the link between the first stage involving utilization of natural uranium and production of plutonium and the third stage where uranium 233 would form the main component of the reactor fuel, fast reactors will play a vital role in our country's programme. Fast Reactors have unique capabilities such as efficient utilization of uranium and production of additional plutonium which could be used for setting up more fast reactors, thus catalyzing the growth of nuclear power in the country. The utilization factor per unit mass of natural uranium for electricity production is over 100 times in a fast reactor compared to pressurized heavy water reactors. The total electrical potential from fast reactors for India, based on indigenous uranium availability is over 40,000 GWe-year. Thus, fast reactors constitute a very important energy source for achieving energy security for our country. In addition, fast reactors also provide an attractive option for incinerating minor actinides and long lived fission products which are generated in nuclear fission.

Fast reactors have been in existence in the world for over 50 years. The highest rated fast reactor built (1200 MWe) was Superphenix in France. BN-600 in Russia of 600 MWe rating is the highest rated fast reactor currently in operation. Fast reactors are also in operation in France (Phenix) and Japan (Joyo, Monju) and China is currently building a fast reactor. A 800 MWe fast reactor is under construction in Russia. Over 380 reactor years of operating experience have been accumulated on fast reactors around the world. However, because of the concern of proliferation, utilisation of plutonium in reactors was not given due attention in the last few decades by many countries and as a result the fast reactor programmes in many countries have been slowed down or stopped. However, India has had a sustained interest in fast breeder reactors because of the key role they would play in nuclear electricity generation. As a result of focused research and development, manufacturing technology development and the experience gained from the successful operation of the FBTR, India is today one of the few countries in the world which possess mature fast reactor technology with closed fuel cycle. With the construction and commissioning of the Prototype Fast Breeder Reactor in the year 2010 followed by four more fast reactors before 2020, we can expect that India will be among the leading nations with rich experience in fast reactor technology by the end of the next decade.

In India, fast reactor technology and the associated fuel cycle technologies are being pursued on a mission mode by the Indira Gandhi Centre for Atomic Research, in close collaboration with BARC and other units of DAE as well as a number of academic and research institutions and industries. We have accumulated experience in all facets of the fast reactor programme including sodium technology, structural mechanics, thermal hydraulics, instrumentation, non-destructive testing and in-service inspection, materials engineering and manufacture, backed by a strong R&D base in chemistry, physics, materials science and technology, and safety. The Indian industries have played a significant role in achieving the stringent manufacturing tolerances required for the fabrication of components of PFBR. All these factors have generated confidence in

Fast Breeder Test Reactor (FBTR)

The Fast Breeder Test Reactor (FBTR) was commissioned in October1985 at IGCAR, Kalpakkam and has been operating successfully since that time, barring two events, viz. a fuel handling incident in 1987 and minor sodium leak in 2002. The Reactor is a loop type sodium cooled reactor with a unique plutonium rich uranium-plutonium mixed carbide fuel as the driver fuel. The reactor was constructed with technical know-how from France and inputs from French industries. Its design was based on the French experiment reactor Rapsodie. However, several major design modifications have been introduced, including the incorporation of once-through sodium generators and turbo-generator. The mixed carbide fuel for the reactor was fabricated at BARC. The Mark-I fuel in FBTR (with 70 per cent plutonium content) has performed well and has reached a burn-up of 156 GW/t. without any pin failure in the core. The operation experience of the reactor, including the experience gained from the two incidents mentioned above, has been useful in establishing fast reactor technology in India and in demonstrating indigenous capability in overcoming the problems. Many modifications have been made in the reactor instrumentation, which have contributed to reliable operation. Sodium pumps in the reactor have registered a cumulative operation of over 580,000 hrs without any major problems. There has also been no leak in the steam generator of the reactor.

Presently, the safety status of the reactor is being assessed with a view to extend its operational life by another 10 years. The reactor is being effectively used for several irradiation experiments in fast flux, and will play a key role in the development of alternate fuel and reactor materials for the fast reactor programme, in the coming years.

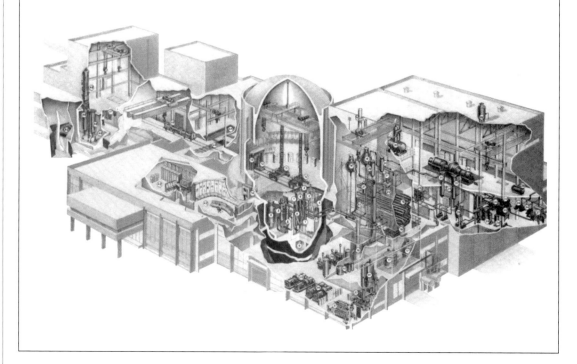

India's capability to develop a robust fast reactor programme towards contributing to the energy requirements of the country.

The Fast Reactor programme can only be successful if the fuel cycle is closed, that is, the valuable fissile materials in the irradiated fuel are recovered and reutilized in reactors. The fuel cycle technology for fast reactors involves unique challenges due to the high concentrations of plutonium encountered and the high burn-up seen by the fuel. It is therefore a matter of pride that India has achieved maturity in the production of the unique mixed carbide fuel for FBTR and also has developed the technology for fabricating the oxide fuel for the PFBR. The irradiated carbide fuel discharged from the FBTR has been reprocessed after relatively short cooling times. The carbide fuel has not been reprocessed in this scale in any part of the world. To close the fuel cycle of PFBR, a fast reactor fuel cycle facility is under construction. This is co-located with the PFBR to avoid transportation of plutonium under public domain, allow better physical control of fissile material, and bring in economies.

Prototype Fast Breeder Reactor (PFBR)

PFBR is a 500 MWe capacity pool type reactor with 2 primary and 2 secondary loops with 4 steam generators per loop. It will use uranium, plutonium mixed oxide fuel with 2 enrichment zones (21 per cent and 28 per cent PuO_2). The plant has been designed for a life of 40 y with at least 75 per cent load factor to be successively enhanced to 85 per cent. The fuel is designed for a peak burn-up of 100 GWd/t. A comprehensive programme on materials development is underway to enhance the burn up to as high as 200 GWd/t.

The design for long reliable operation of components operating at high temperature for design life, design of mechanisms operating in sodium and argon cover gas space, design to accommodate sodium leak and sodium water reactions, seismic design of interconnected buildings, pumps, shutdown systems and thin shells with large sodium mass & fluid-structure interaction effects, in-service inspection and repair of reactor internals are some of the challenges addressed in a comprehensive way for the PFBR, on the basis of strong theoretical and experimental investigations.

The design reflects the international FBR operating experiences of about 380 reactor years including 22 years of successful operation of FBTR. Peer reviews by national and international expert teams, science based R&D output derived from in-house efforts as well as a large number of collaborative projects established through synergism among DAE units, academic institutions, R&D establishments and industries, have added to the high confidence in the design, construction and operation of PFBR.

In the domain of manufacturing technology, the development of many intricate and large size components such as large size thin walled vessels made of stainless steel with tight tolerances (order of wall thickness), grid plate etc., was completed through a detailed technology development exercise before undertaking the construction of the reactor. This has helped immensely in sensitising the Indian industries, assessment of the achievable manufacturing tolerances and in specifying the realistic time and cost estimates for the project. This strategy and the achievements have amply demonstrated the capabilities of Indian industries to manufacture high technology nuclear components within a reasonable time frame. Thus, there is a high level of confidence that the PFBR will be commissioned on schedule, in September 2010.

The success of PFBR is not only important for India in establishing a firm base of fast reactor technology, but is in fact important also for the international community. This is because, today, only Russia and India are in the process of building commercial fast reactors. Three medium sized reactors would be in operation, around the world (the other two being Monju/Japan and BN-600/Russia) by 2010. PFBR will be one of the state-of-art fast reactors in the world beyond 2010. The experience in the construction and operation of this reactor would have an impact on the fast reactor development in global arena.

REACTOR VAULT　　　　27/09/07

While the PFBR and the next four reactors will be based on oxide fuel, future fast reactors will use the metallic fuel alloy as the fuel, which has better "breeding" potential. The enhanced breeding will result in availability of more plutonium which would promote construction of fast reactors at a higher pace. A comprehensive R&D programme on metallic fuels has already been initiated at IGCAR and BARC and it is expected that all the fast reactors to be constructed beyond 2020 will be based on 1000 MWe metallic fuel reactors. With the rapid growth that would be made possible by the metallic fuel, it is expected that by the year 2052, approximately 190 GWe power will be produced through fast reactors using metallic fuel in the core, constituting about 15 per cent of the total installed electrical capacity in the country, at that time.

Sustainability, economics, ensuring highest safety standards, reducing radioactive waste and resisting nuclear proliferation are the main criteria governing future nuclear systems abroad. 12 nations have combined their R&D efforts to achieve these goals by setting up the Generation IV International Forum. There are very good chances of worldwide renaissance of nuclear power in the near future due to the impact of global climate change caused by emission of greenhouse gases and crude oil prices stuck at higher levels. One can expect growth both in thermal and fast reactors. It is significant to note that four out of the six

reactor types chosen for development under the Generation IV programme are fast reactors. The reactors are expected to be built after 2030.

The International Project on Innovative Reactors and Fuel Cycles (INPRO) being steered by the International Atomic Energy Agency has also recognized the important role which would be played by fast reactors for meeting the energy requirements in the coming years. A joint case study on Closed Nuclear Fuel Cycle with Fast Reactors (CNFC-FR) has taken up the identification of an innovative fast reactor and fuel cycle that would incorporate features, which will enhance safety, economy, proliferation resistance and sustainability with minimum impact on the environment. Thus, fast reactors are set to emerge globally as an important source of nuclear energy to meet growing energy demands. Fast Breeder Reactors will vastly enlarge the energy resource base of India because of their capability to utilize uranium resources effectively.

The realization of economic and safe electric power through fast breeder reactor with closed fuel cycle is maturing at a rapid planned pace in India. India is destined and committed to play a leading role in enhancing the contribution of nuclear energy through Fast Breeders with closed fuel cycle route, while satisfying all the sustainability parameters namely economics, safety, resource management, waste management and minimum degradation of environment. □

R K Sinha &
S Banerjee
Bhabha Atomic Research
Centre

Thorium: Key to energy independence

Thorium, discovered in the year 1828, is about three times more abundant than uranium. India has, according to current estimates, one of the largest and richest deposits of the rare earth thorium-phosphate mineral monazite, amounting to 2,25,000 tonnes of thorium (metal). In contrast, the currently known deposits of uranium in the country amount to 61,000 tonnes. These deposits are of an inferior grade.

Thorium, by itself, cannot be used as a nuclear fuel since it does not contain any fissile isotope (unlike uranium, in which the fissile isotope U^{235} is available to the extent of 0.7 per cent). Thorium can, however, be used together with fissile material (such as U^{235}, Plutonium or U^{233}) to serve as nuclear fuel.

Thorium utilisation

The question is often raised why, if India has so much thorium and a shortage of uranium, it does not deploy thorium immediately. The answer lies in the special physics characteristics of the key elements that play a role in nuclear energy generation. Natural uranium, which contains only 0.7 per cent of the fissile isotope U^{235}, can be most productively used in a PHWR to produce energy as well as plutonium. With a given amount of plutonium, the fastest way to multiply the installed nuclear generation capacity is to use plutonium-uranium based fuel in Fast Breeder Reactors with short doubling time. At a later stage, when enough installed capacity has been reached, the urgency to grow at the fastest pace no longer exists and the uranium resources approach depletion, thorium needs to be progressively introduced in the Fast Reactors to generate U^{233} for use in the third stage. An ad-hoc approach to deploy thorium prematurely on a large scale is bound to slow down the pace at which the indigenous Indian nuclear energy programme can grow. In a scenario where thorium is extensively deployed together with plutonium in PHWRs or other thermal reactors, without getting through the FBRs, it may even lead to complete exhaustion of the available fissile resources (neither U^{235} nor plutonium being available), with plenty of thorium left unused.

Indian experience

Research and development in areas relevant to thorium utilisation have been ongoing in the Indian Department of Atomic Energy from its very inception. BARC began its work on thorium-related activities as early as the late 1950s. The DAE later set up Indian Rare Earths to prospect for thorium in different parts of the country, and vast deposits of thorium were discovered in Tamil Nadu and Kerala.

U^{233} separated from irradiated thorium serves as the fuel for our 30 kW(th) KAMINI reactor in IGCAR, which has been in operation since 1996. Currently, this is the only reactor in the world working solely on thorium-based fuel. Thorium bundles have been used in our Pressurised Heavy Water Reactors in the early years of reactor operation with a fresh core to achieve the flattening of power distribution in the core. So far, 232 nuclear fuel bundles containing thorium with a total weight of about 2800 kg. have been irradiated in these reactors. In these reactors, power has been generated by U^{233}, which is produced in-situ in these bundles. One of the test fuel assemblies in FBTR operating at Kalpakkam also contains U^{233}. Thorium oxide – plutonium oxide based fuel- has already been irradiated in CIRUS and DHRUVA in the past. Two of the research reactors built at BARC and de-commissioned, Purnima-II, Purnima-III, also used U^{233} based fuel.

Fuel cycle technologies

The use of thorium in reactors demands the development and optimisation of several technologies different from those used for conventional uranium based reactors. U^{233} cannot be chemically separated from U^{232} which is present in the spent fuel. U^{232} has got certain decay products which are highly radioactive and progressively get built up after the separated U^{233} is stored for a while. For this reason, even with fresh nuclear fuel bearing U^{233} one has to develop solutions for working with radioactivity, implying use of remotised equipment and shielded facilities. Fabrication technologies for Th–U^{233} MOX fuel have, therefore, focussed on challenges arising from this consideration. Some of the new technologies that have reached different levels of maturity include coated agglomerate pelletization, pellet impregnation, gel impregnation, co-precipitation, and sol-gel microsphere pelletization.

Reprocessing thorium oxide fuel also presents unique challenges. These challenges arise mainly out of the inherent stability of thorium oxide and attendant difficulties in its dissolution in very strong acids, which is a first step in the solvent extraction based reprocessing process. Laboratory based experiences have demonstrated the feasibility of adopting certain unique solutions to address these challenges. These solutions include use of certain additives in the fuels to achieve easier dissolutions of the spent fuel and use of micro-waves during the dissolution process.

Innovations in reactor technologies

Advanced heavy water reactor: There is no commercial power reactor operating in the world using thorium-based fuel. Advanced Heavy Water Reactor (AHWR), a 300 MWe technology demonstration reactor producing nearly two-thirds of its power from thorium, has already been designed in BARC. This boiling light water cooled, heavy water moderated, vertical pressure tube type reactor is designed to produce nearly two-thirds of its power from thorium.

AHWR incorporates several advanced passive safety features consistent with the requirements stipulated for the next generation nuclear reactors. Passive safety depends on natural phenomena such as gravity, natural convection and stored energy. The AHWR will be one of the first ever power reactors employing natural circulation, also known as thermo-siphoning, for cooling of the reactor core under all conditions. In case of any accident, water stored in a huge overhead tank inside the reactor building will ensure core cooling for three full days, without any human intervention. Besides, the safety of the reactor will not depend on the operator's actions alone. The reactor will have three shut-down systems including one to take care of postulated 'insider threat' scenario. Although the AHWR will be built in the near-term, the technologies in the reactor will be relevant for an entire era when thorium will be the main fuel for a generation of reactors. Several large engineering test facilities have been set up and used in BARC to validate the design of the new systems and sub-systems of the reactor. A critical facility for AHWR has been already constructed at BARC. This facility will be extensively used for experimental validation of the Reactor Physics design of the AHWR.

Several key elements of AHWR design have been examined by the Indian Atomic Energy Regulatory Board (AERB) in a new mode called 'Pre-licensing Design Safety Appraisal'.

Compact high temperature reactor (CHTR): The CHTR is being developed in BARC as a platform to launch a focussed programme for the development and demonstration of technologies associated with two applications: (a) Compact power packs with long life cores for deployment in remote areas; and (b) generation of high temperature process heat for generating hydrogen by water splitting reactions.

The CHTR, being developed to generate 100 kW(th), uses U^{233}-Thorium based particle type fuel, berylium oxide moderator and graphite as reflector. The reactor, designed to produce heat at 1000 degrees C, is cooled by molten lead-bismuth alloy. The key challenges in the development of this reactor lie in the area of materials and coatings that should reliably survive the aggressive high temperature environment. The preliminary design of the reactor has been completed and the necessary development work is being carried out in a structured manner.

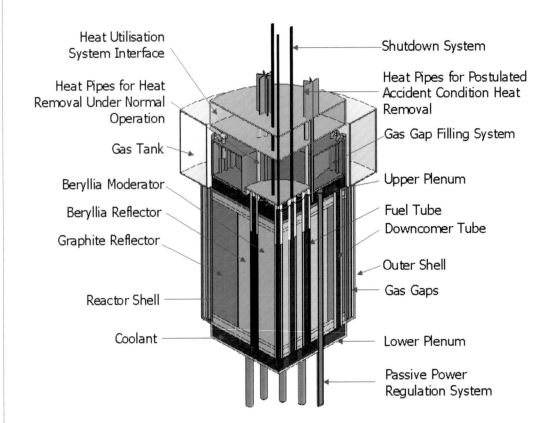

Heat Utilisation System Interface

Heat Pipes for Heat Removal Under Normal Operation

Gas Tank

Beryllia Moderator

Beryllia Reflector

Graphite Reflector

Reactor Shell

Coolant

Shutdown System

Heat Pipes for Postulated Accident Condition Heat Removal

Gas Gap Filling System

Upper Plenum

Fuel Tube
Downcomer Tube

Outer Shell

Gas Gaps

Lower Plenum

Passive Power Regulation System

Compact High Temperature Reactor

A Model of the Advanced Heavy Water Reactor

Fulfilling the growing Indian energy demands requires a two pronged approach. The first one is to achieve energy security speedily, and the other is to meet the growing energy demands consistent with growth of the Indian economy. In the near term, it entails dependence to a significant extent on imported energy resources. For a large country like India, however, it is economically as well as strategically important to achieve energy independence that can insulate the country from any supply shocks. This philosophy forms the basis of the long term approach.

It has been shown that for India to reach and sustainably maintain the status of a developed country without depending upon huge imports of energy resources, the use of thorium in a closed nuclear fuel cycle is essential.

Thorium, together with solar and other renewables, has therefore a vital role in achieving energy independence for India. □

Bikash Sinha
Director
Variable Energy Cyclotron

Adventures in Quarkland

On 16th June 1977, the internal beam of the Cyclotron at Calcutta was sighted. It was a remarkable manifestation of the essential innovative spirit of Indians. There was no electricity during the day and if at all during the night, only intermittently. The political tension prevailing at that time erupted in violence, disrupting the essential routine of life. All the young scientists and engineers used to report to work at night and go home in the morning; so, the cyclotron at Calcutta was the only one of its kind, a nocturnal cyclotron.

The industrial infrastructure was not robust enough to sustain the high level of technology required to build a complicated machine like a cyclotron. The pioneers had, for instance, difficulty in finding a suitable manufacturer for the all essential Resonator Tank. Garden Reach Ship Builders was approached. They said flatly that they built water- tight ships but had no experience about building tanks which have to be air tight, maintaining a high order of vacuum (10^{-6} Torr). The tank has to withstand the tremendous pressure from outside.

However, they built it and it is still working very well indeed. This is just an example and many other examples can be cited. In the early eighties some of us wanted to build a detector to be used at the Super Proton Synchrotron (SPS) for detection of photons as signals of Quark Gluon Plasma supposed to be formed after collision of two nuclei typically at an energy of 200 GeV/nucleon (One thousand Million electron volt, MeV makes one GeV).

The hadrons, protons and neutrons of an atomic nucleus at this awesome energy melts to its fundamental constituents (most elementary building blocks of matter, known to date) quarks and gluons, referred to as Quark Gluon Plasma.

The universe, as per standard wisdom, consisted of quarks and gluons, a microsecond after the Big Bang.

Clearly, the adventure and the romance of building such a detector, now known as Photon Multiplicity Detector (PMD) is truly inspiring but was not easy. The sheer size and the complexity daunted us. The demand on the precision was even more daunting.

The design was done in India. The Cyclotron Centre (Calcutta), University of Rajasthan, University of Jammu, University of Chandigarh and other institutions of India joined in and the group, in a very short time built PMD consisting of 55,000 pads consisting of plastic scintillator 2 cm x 2 cm, arranged in a rectangular fashion with some geometric constraints required by the very design. Optical fibres were inserted diagonally in each pad to pick up the possible signals of QGP photons.

It has been an overwhelming success, unprecedented in India particularly on this scale. One needed all kinds of creative innovation to mount this detector. Curiously enough the best suggestions came from the youngest. PMD is now a legend, a part of the Indian phenomenon in the world scenario. Almost overnight, as it were, a country which was at best tolerated or used turned into a key player in the world theatre!

This kind of science and associated precision technology which, remained dormant so far, came out of the closets and flourished. There was no looking back.

The same PMD, went through major metamorphosis and fundamental design change was introduced, a special design called 'honeycomb' design was implemented and then shipped across the Atlantic for the famous 'STAR' detector of the Relativistic Heavy Ion Collider (RHIC) a the Brockhaven National Laboratory. With this new PMD at STAR, the STAR hasn't stopped twinkling, sometimes with a flash (photons) dazzling the world.

Meanwhile, on home ground we moved on from the room temperature cyclotron to the most advanced form, the superconducting cyclotron using Niobium Titanium superconducting wire.

Hunting for a suitable company who could build our cryostat was a real adventure. We moved from north to south, from east to west. We approached the most well established manufacturer but ultimately drew a blank. In spite of all our determination we failed to find a suitable company to build the cryostat in India.

Eventually we got it done by Air Liquid, France but not without hiccups. Large scale management of liquid helium was yet another challenge.

Finally, in January 2005, the magnet become superconducting at a temperature just around 4.20 Kelvin. Fantastic! The superconducting state was maintained for months together. The whole of January 2005 felt like a carnival. Quietly we had made a quantum jump from room temperature technology to large scale cryogenic technology.

Saha Institute collegues, in the meantime, got excited with the ALICE detector to be installed at the Large Hadron Collider (LHC), CERN. Interestingly enough, they were particularly excited with the dimuon spectrometer of the Mum Arm part of the ALICE (on the right hand side, of the collision point if one is looking at the detector from the front).

Collegues, who remained dormant or busy with routine jobs, suddenly were inspired. They went on to design the now famous 'MANAS' chip for the muon arm. A foundry at Chandigarh (Semi Conductor Complex, India) came up enthusiastically and offered to build the hardware. The MANAS chip after much debate became the centrepiece of the muon arm and accepted as *the* chip worldwide.

Now all the mounting work is done and it is the first of its kind before any other country. Last time, walking in the shadow of ALICE and marveling at the magnitude and immaculate precision with which the work was done, I felt like Alice in Wonderland with the Quarkland beckoning on the horizon.

At home, going from room temperature cyclotron to the superconducting cyclotron gave us the confidence that we can do it; we are master innovators; we are as good as others if not even better sometimes; we build our best on our home turf; we give our best to the world. It has been a long voyage of adventure and triumphant success. □

P K Kaw
Institute for Plasma Research
Gandhinagar

Plasma work takes India to a frontier area

The Institute for Plasma Research (IPR), set up by the Government of India in 1986, is the premier Institute in the country fully devoted to the study of plasma science and technologies and also plasma applications such as thermonuclear fusion using magnetically confined plasmas. It is an autonomous institution funded by the Department of Atomic Energy and is located on the banks of Sabarmati river in Gandhinagar, Gujarat. It has an overall staff strength of about 450 scientists, engineers, technical support staff, students and administrative personnel.

The most important application of plasma science is that of energy production using thermonuclear fusion. India has enormous needs of environment friendly energy production, since our citizens have a poor quality of life, primarily because of scarcity and high costs of energy. Thermonuclear fusion is a possible long-term answer to our needs as it is a nuclear process for which the fuel is plentiful, radioactivity is minimal and there is no danger of terrorist threats etc. It is the nuclear process which fuels the Sun and in which light elements like deuterium and tritium are allowed to fuse and form heavier elements like helium with a loss of mass and release of energy. The energy comes out in the form of kinetic energy of nuclear fragments like alpha particles and neutrons, which either get trapped in the deuterium-tritium mixture keeping it hot or come out and are trapped in appropriate solid blankets producing heat, which can then be used to run the standard turbine cycle for the generation of electricity.

In December 2005, India was inducted into partnership of the International Thermonuclear Experimental Reactor (ITER) project. ITER is a prestigious international experiment involving Europe, USA, China, Russia, Japan, South Korea and India. The objective is to set up an international fusion reactor experiment producing about 500 MWatts of fusion power for the first time anywhere in the world at a cost of about 5 billion euros in about 10 years time. ITER will be assembled in Cadarache, France and will have hardware from all the participating nations. As a full partner, India has committed to supply about 10 per cent of the hardware for this prestigious international experiment, after design and manufacture by Indian industries.

This hardware has nine packages which includes items like a 28 m tall, 28 m dia outermost vacuum envelope of ITER, the cryostat, sophisticated ion cyclotron heating and neutral beam diagnostic systems, cryoline and cryodistribution systems etc. This work will be spearheaded by IPR scientists and engineers, who were also highly instrumental in bringing this prestigious project to India. The Government of India has set up an Empowered Board to monitor this project which will have an outlay of about Rs 2500 crores in the next ten years.

IPR is also leading the overall National Programme of Fusion Research. This involves scientific programmes on the existing tokamaks, work on the ITER experiment, a prototype technology development project which will fill in the technological gaps in our ability to make full reactor scale components of a fusion reactor system and a program of R&D in fusion reactor materials and technologies which involves interaction with universities, IITs, industries, other research institutions etc. With this preparatory work, IPR should be able to start the work of designing an Indian DEMO (prototype demonstration fusion reactor producing electricity) in about ten years.

The human resource development programme of the Institute is based on a training component of one year followed by a PhD programme in fundamental plasma science. We have invested a good deal of effort in setting up research programmes in fundamental plasma sciences. We have set up and are setting up experiments on dusty plasmas, electron-positron plasmas, non-neutral plasmas, large volume plasmas, plasmas in a pure toroidal magnetic field, quiescent multi-cusp plasmas etc. In each of these experiments, we are studying collective nonlinear physics of plasma modes, which is central to our understanding of plasmas in all practical situations.

We are also engaged in computer simulations of nonlinear phenomena in plasmas which aids our ability to quantitatively interpret the phenomena that are observed in the fundamental science or fusion experiments. Computer modeling also helps us in designing future experiments and fusion reactor machines. Therefore, a development of computer modeling and simulation techniques is an integral component of the programs of the Institute.

A third major component of work at the Institute is devoted to industrial applications of plasmas. We have set up the Facilitation Centre for Industrial Plasma Technologies (FCIPT) on a separate campus in the Gandhinagar Industrial estate. This centre has succeeded in the development and transfer of a number of industrial plasma technologies to industries. Thus the plasma nitriding technology, important for hardening of surfaces in wear-resistant tools, gear-wheels etc has been transferred to a company in Pune. The technology for plasma pyrolysis of hazardous medical waste has been transferred to a company in Ahmedabad.

The technology of improving the weavability of Angora wool has been developed together with National Institute of Design, Ahmedabad and passed on for utilization to Himachal Pradesh Wool Board. The Centre has also developed highly sophisticated coating technologies for ISRO, prototype fast breeder experiment in Kalpakkam and a host of specialized components for other private and Government agencies.

Thus the Institute is doing pioneering work in plasma science and technologies with applications to fusion energy production and industrial plasma systems and is helping the country to remain at the cutting edge of the developments in this important field. □

S K Jain
Chairman and Managing Director
Nuclear Power Corporation of India
Limited & Bharatiya Nabhikiya
Vidyut Nigam Limited, India

Nuclear power enterprise

Self-reliance has been the hallmark of the Indian nuclear power programme. Nuclear power in the commercial domain in India has gone through the phases of technology demonstration, indigenisation, standardization, consolidation and commercialisation. India has reached maturity in front-end technologies (that is, exploration, mining, processing of ore, fuel fabrication, heavy water production) as well as the back-end technologies of spent fuel reprocessing and waste management. Today, India has a sound R&D base to meet any high technology challenge of a fast-expanding nuclear power programme. NPCIL has demonstrated the capability for building and operating nuclear power plants. The nuclear power plants in the country have so far generated about 270 billion units of electricity. The second stage of the three-stage programme is launched through the prototype 500 MWe Fast Breeder Reactor being constructed at Kalpakkam in Tamilnadu.

Technology demonstration

As a first step towards establishing the techno-economic feasibility of nuclear power plants in India and to operate and maintain the nuclear power stations in the regional grid system, two reactors were imported from the USA. These boiling water reactors, set up at Tarapur in Maharashtra, were supplied by General Electric Company, USA, on a turnkey basis and were commissioned. These reactors have served their intended purpose well and continue to be in safe and reliable operation at capacity & availability factors of over 90 per cent, even after nearly 38 years of their being commissioned. These reactors are also a source of cheap electricity, currently at 94 paise per unit.

The foundation for the first stage of the three-stage programme was laid with the start of construction of RAPS-1&2, the first Pressurised Heavy Water Reactors (PHWRs) set up in technical collaboration with Atomic Energy Canada Limited. Indian engineers and scientists made significant contributions to the construction and commissioning of this plant. Even in RAPS-1, some equipment and components were manufactured in India. When the Canadian cooperation was discontinued in 1974, the commissioning of RAPS-2 was undertaken entirely by Indian scientists and engineers, including the fabrication of critical nuclear components like end-shields, steam generators and calandria.

Challenges for industry

While the nuclear power programme was being shaped in India in the 1960s and early 1970s, Indian industry was nascent. Some small and medium-size thermal power stations, some fertiliser and cement kilns, boiler drums and simple chemical reactors were the kind of manufacturing and fabrication jobs undertaken by Indian industry at that time. The industry was new to the fabrication techniques and exacting code standards and requirements for nuclear components. Efforts were directed at building an industrial base, which could support the stringent requirements of quality demanded by the nuclear industry.

In addition, the initial design and development activity in many cases was started in our laboratories and later passed on to Indian industry. Special test facilities were created for qualifying products manufactured indigenously, e.g., the testing of large primary heat transport pumps and motors. Facilities available for the qualification of electronic components and reliability analysis were extensively used. There was also considerable interaction in the field of metallurgy for material evaluation and qualification.

Shops and tooling for manufacturing large reactor components like calandria and end-shields, which require precision machining, were developed by the joint efforts of the then PPED (now NPCIL), BARC and different industries.

Developing manufacturing facilities for coolant channel components made from zirconium alloys was one of the most challenging tasks. Nuclear Fuel Complex (NFC), Hyderabad supplied these coolant channel components for all the PHWR units except the first one at RAPS. The complete manufacturing cycle of these tubes has been evolved at NFC.

Indigenisation

The indigenous content in RAPS-1 was only about 55 per cent, which increased to about 75 per cent in RAPS-2. When the construction work on the twin-unit PHWR station Madras Atomic Power Station at Kalpakkam commenced in early 1970, several major modifications and upgrades were undertaken. Significant among these were the partial double containment in the reactor building and improved design and materials for reactor components. The design, manufacture of components and equipment, construction of plant and its commissioning were done entirely through indigenous efforts. RAPS-1&2 and MAPS-1&2 provided a very valuable experience in almost all fields of design, manufacturing, construction, commissioning and operation.

Standardization

Based on the operational feedback, it was decided in the mid-1970s to standardise future 220 MWe stations. The design of the nuclear components required major modifications in line with what were then the latest code requirements to improve reliability and safety.

Narora in Uttar Pradesh was selected for setting up the first of the standardised 220 MWe units. A significant number of developmental works were carried out in-house to meet the design, safety and quality assurance requirements. These included a full double containment in the reactor building,

shell & tube type steam generators with egg-crate type tube supports, design and use of advanced material like Incalloy 800 as tube material, reactor components and primary coolant pumps with improved design, emergency core cooling system and resin fixation systems for waste immobilization. Furthermore, it was the first nuclear power station in the country to have a closed loop condenser cooling system with cooling towers. The Narora units were built and operated successfully after solving a number of operational problems. The experience gained gave immense confidence and paved the way for setting up a series of standardised 220 MWe units at KAPS and later units.

Expansion

In the late eighties, construction of four 220 MWe units was taken up concurrently, two in Rajasthan (units-3&4) and two in Kaiga (unit-1&2) with even better features like compact layout, dome in dome type double containment with the steam generators fully inside the primary containment. Their operational performance at high availability and plant load factors matching world standards were certainly signs of the maturity of 220 MWe PHWRs in the country.

The design for the next generation PHWRs of 540 MWe size was conceived and implemented at Tarapur units 3&4. As the 540 MWe reactor core was large, zonal control systems comprising light water columns for finer reactivity control were designed and introduced for the first time in Indian PHWRs. The construction of the reactors of 540 MWe capacity at Tarapur (TAPP-3&4) was completed seven months ahead of schedule in 2005-2006. The completion of the first of these units in less than five years was an international benchmark. In parallel, four more units of 220 MWe, at Kaiga 3&4 and RAPP 5&6 respectively were also launched in 2002 to enhance the existing capacity. While Kaiga-3 has already been completed (in five years) and is in operation, the other three are at an advanced stage of completion and expected to be in commercial operation during 2008-2009.

Achievements

The performance of Indian nuclear power plants compares favourably with international benchmarks. Sustained efforts in operation and maintenance, development and nurturing of

Innovations in renovation & modernisation

En Masse Coolant Channel Replacement (EMCCR): The earlier design of PHWRs used a zirconium alloy (Zircalloy 2) for coolant channels. It was considered the best available material at that time. However, experience showed that in view of the modification of material characteristics, especially the reduced mechanical strength due to hybridisation under radiation during service, it was necessary to replace coolant tubes after 10 to 12 effective full power years. These coolant channels constitute the core of a nuclear reactor and their replacement is akin to heart transplantation in human beings. The job of EMCCR at RAPS-2, the first attempt with indigenous technology, was successfully completed in record time and all the coolant channels were replaced by an improved coolant tube material, Zirconium with 2.5 per cent Niobium. This was the first time in a developing country, and only the second time in the world, that such a highly complex technical project was completed. The job was completed using indigenously developed tools designed for remote handling. Similar EMCCR work has been accomplished at MAPS 1&2 and NAPS-1, is underway at NAPS-2 and is planned at KAPS-1.

En Masse Feeder Replacement (EMFR): Flow assisted corrosion leading to thinning of the carbon steel feeder elbows at the outlet of the reactor was noticed in some Canadian PHWRs in 1996. A study and assessment carried out in-house showed that there was no significant thinning of feeders in Indian PHWRs. This reduced degradation was attributed to good chemical control and better operational practices in Indian reactors. A decision was taken to replace feeders in earlier PHWRs RAPS-2 and MAPS-1&2, which had long been in service in order to extend their life. Hence, at MAPS-1 the Enmasse Feeder Replacement (EMFR) was carried out along with the EMCCR work. This was the first time anywhere in the world that feeders had been replaced in a PHWR. EMFR has also been carried out at NAPS-1 and is underway at RAPS-2. India has thus acquired expertise in in-core jobs.

Unique Problems Addressed: While operating these reactors, a number of challenging problems have been satisfactorily addressed with the support of in-house R&D and industry.

- In 1981, a light water leak developed in one of the end-shields of RAPS-1. These leaks were successfully repaired.
- In RAPS-1 a leak of heavy water and helium cover gas emanating from the reactor cover called Over Pressure Relief Device was detected in 1994. This leak, in a highly radioactive area and difficult location, was successfully repaired using remote tools and a special metallic seal made of a metal with low melting point, developed and tested indigenously.
- At MAPS, a very unique problem surfaced during 1989-90 when its moderator inlet-manifold was damaged. As a short-term rehabilitation measure, its flow and the moderator lines were re-routed. The plant could operate with this arrangement at 75 per cent full power. Later, a new innovative design modification using sparger channels was implemented for the first time in the world, and the units brought back to their original rated capacity of 220 MWe.
- In 1990, cracks in the core shroud of the boiling water reactor (BWR) were detected in the USA. In view of this, it was decided to carry out a core shroud inspection of BWRs at TAPS using specially developed remote tools like the Grapple Operated Manipulator and an underwater CCTV system. This job was successfully accomplished. Life extension of TAPS-1&2 was carried out in 2006, enabling it to operate for many years in future.

qualified human resources at various levels constitute a unique strength of the country today. In the year 2002, Kakrapar Atomic Power Station was adjudged the world's best operating nuclear power plant among the PHWRs the world over. Kaiga-2 recently completed 529 days of continuous operation. Prior to Kaiga-3, many other Indian reactors KAPS-1, NAPS-2 and RAPS-4 also registered continuous operation of nearly a year. The biennial shutdown durations have also been reduced to about 20 days through effective planning and management of shutdown activities. NPCIL units have been operating consistently at high availability factors of about 90 per cent.

The safety track record of 277 reactor years of operation is evidence of the strong commitment to safety and demonstrates the strong safety culture of the Indian nuclear industry. In Indian nuclear power plants, the radiation dose to occupational workers has been a small fraction of the limits prescribed by Atomic Energy Regulatory Board (AERB), the regulatory authority. The release in the environment has been an insignificant fraction of the prescribed limit. It may be noted that the limits prescribed by the AERB are more conservative than the international limits set by the International Commission on Radiation Protection.

On the construction front, the gestation period of reactors has been brought down to five years. The achievement of criticality of TAPS-4, 540 MWe PHWR at Tarapur, Maharashtra, a first-of-its- kind reactor, in less than five years set an international benchmark and is yet more evidence of the country's strength.

India has developed comprehensive capabilities in all aspects of nuclear power and reached a state of technological and commercial maturity. It is now poised for large-scale expansion. Nuclear power is currently competitive at locations away from coalmines but is likely to become location neutral in the near future. The electricity markets in the country are evolving and the world is entering a nuclear renaissance. India has many opportunities to seize and nuclear power companies need to adopt new strategies in the emerging scenarios. □

Author acknowledges the assistance of Shri N Nagaich, Chief Engineer (CP&CC) and B V S Sekhar, Additional Chief Engineer (Corporate Planning) in the preparation of this paper.

V C Sahni
Director, RRCAT, Indore
P K Gupta
RRCAT

Lasers for varied uses

Raja Ramanna Centre for Advanced Technology (RRCAT) is a premier R&D laboratory of the Department of Atomic Energy devoted to the pursuit of lasers, accelerators (especially synchrotron radiation sources) and related technologies. It was founded in 1984 as "Centre for Advanced Technology" at a new campus in Indore. Later it branched off from the parent institute, the Bhabha Atomic Research Centre (BARC), Mumbai, where most of the early activities had begun in these areas. The new centre has grown rapidly and today it has about 1300 staff members.

Over the years the Centre has developed several laser systems that include copper vapour lasers (CVLs); CVL pumped dye lasers; nanosecond and pico-second solid state lasers pumped by flash lamps or laser diodes, high power cw and pulsed carbon dioxide lasers and more recently semiconductor diode lasers. These laser systems have also been used for many applications. The following is a short account of these developments.

Flash lamp or diode laser pumped solid-state lasers, with a broad range of characteristics have been built. These include, multimode Nd:YAG lasers with power outputs of up to 400 W at an optical efficiency of ~ 50 per cent; intra-cavity frequency doubled diode-pumped systems providing highly stable (better than 5 per cent energy stability) average power outputs of greater than 100 W at green wavelength; an end pumped diode pumped $Nd:YVO_4$ laser system for laser marking applications.

One particularly novel application relates to successful use of a Nd:YAG laser systems (250 W average power, 2–20 ms pulse duration, 5 kW peak power, 1–100 Hz rep rate) for in-situ cutting of coolant channels in a pressurized heavy water reactor (PHWR). In older PHWRs, the coolant channels need to be replaced after about two decades of operation. There are 306 such channels in a reactor each bound at the end by two bellow attachment rings. To replace them, the welded bellow rings have to be detached and mechanical cutters were being used earlier for this operation. It was a cumbersome operation taking a long time. With the multi-port fibre coupled industrial Nd: YAG laser based system and the required fixtures and tools developed at RRCAT, the time required to cut one bellow ring was brought down from about an hour to a few minutes. The system can also be utilized for re-welding the bellow lips.

After a trial at Kakarapar reactor, this system was deployed at Narora Atomic Power Station unit-1. All 612 bellow lips joints could be handled in eight days whereas usual cutters would have taken a few months. Apart from saving time and the resulting economic gains, the radiation exposure of personnel was greatly reduced. Spurred by this success, such systems have been used for the dismantling of a fuel subassembly of the fast breeder test reactor at the Indira Gandhi Centre for Atomic Research, Kalpakkam and for post irradiation examination of burnt fuel sub-assemblies. Similar smaller laser systems had been built earlier for a range of jobs, such as precision welding of Brachy-therapy and radiography capsules for the Board of Radiation & Isotope Technology, laser welding station for heart pacemaker and so on.

Continuously operating CO_2 lasers with powers of up to 20 kW and transversely excited atmospheric (TEA) pulsed CO_2 lasers with average power output of up to 500 W have also been developed. Such high power lasers are routinely used for various applications that include cutting, welding, surface hardening, surface alloying, surface cladding, metal forming and rapid manufacturing. Important applications include high precision cutting of iron sheets for fabricating magnets for accelerators, welding of dissimilar metals and alloys, various auto-components, nuclear fuel end plugs; surface alloying of different types of steel and titanium alloys for improving their wear and corrosion characteristics; surface cladding of turbine blades of Ni-super alloy with stellite and steel with colmonoy. The 500 W TEA CO_2 laser has been used for separation of gram quantity of ^{13}C isotope.

Elemental and kinetically enhanced Copper Vapour Lasers (CVL) with average power of over 50 W and compact CVL, with hydrogen bromide into discharge, have been developed. These have been used to pump tunable dye lasers, for generation of coherent UV radiation and for material processing applications. Coherent UV radiation is being used for high-speed fabrication of fibre Bragg gratings for sensor applications.

User requirements

In addition, many laser units and laser-based instruments have been made for specific user requirements. These include, development of a prototype unit of a state-of-the-art diode end-pumped green laser photo-coagulator for the treatment of diabetic retinopathy, laser markers that can write on virtually any material, nitrogen laser fluorimeters for uranium prospecting and for monitoring of effluents, laser based metrology system for quality assurance of nuclear fuel pellet and remote inspection of radioactive components, laser based land levelling system on the request of Ministry of Agriculture for better water usage. For mass production, technology of such systems has been transferred to industry.

As part of basic studies the high power nanosecond to femtosecond laser systems built in house and procured commercially are being used to carry out R&D on various aspects of high temperature and high-density plasma produced by lasers. Very high peak brightness X-ray sources have been built and used for single shot x-ray microscopic imaging of biological samples with high spatial resolution

and several equation of state studies have been performed. A 10 TW Ti:sapphire laser system that can generate intensity at target of $\sim 10^{17}$–10^{18} W/cm^2 has been used to accelerate electrons of up to 70 MeV energy. Studies are also on in the area of linear and non-linear optical response of a variety of materials. Many ultra fast experimental techniques, like Z scan, pump probe, degenerate four wave mixing have been developed and used to investigate ultra fast dynamics and nonlinear response in materials. Quantum wells and quantum dots of a variety of semiconductors of interest for photonic applications have been grown using pulsed laser deposition. Facilities have also been built to grow multi-layers, super-lattices and multi-quantum wells of conventional III–V semiconductor materials, GaN and other group III nitride thin films. GaAsP and InGaAs diode lasers operating in 730 nm to 950 nm spectral range have been fabricated using these facilities.

Atom properties

RRCAT is pursuing the use of lasers to cool and trap atoms and investigate their properties. It is doing R&D on the use of lasers for biomedical applications. Extensive studies have been carried out to understand the difference in fluorescence from normal and malignant human tissues and a clinical evaluation of the approach, for in-situ detection of cancer of oral cavity, has been carried out at Government Cancer Hospital, Indore. The system has now been installed at Tata Memorial Hospital, Mumbai for further evaluation. Optical Coherence Tomography setups have been developed and used to image fish eye and micro-structures of human skin and animal models with axial and lateral resolutions of ~10 μm and 20 μm.

A laser micromanipulation set up built at RRCAT has been used for many studies that included first demonstration of 3D orientation of intracellular objects, laser assisted injection of genetic material or drugs into cells, malaria diagnosis with laser tweezers, guidance of neuronal growth cones with asymmetric laser tweezers etc.

Some of the studies carried out at RRCAT in the area of bio-photonics have been featured in the *Optics & Photonics News*, a magazine of Optical Society of America. □

A M Patankar
Head, TT&CD, BARC

Churning synergies out of nuclear research

The development of atomic energy capability in India is a saga in itself. The philosophy of self-reliance—pursued with the highest degree of conviction and determination—resulted in a number of developmental programmes being taken up at BARC and other DAE units in nuclear science field. These efforts also led to a large number of Non-Power Applications (NPAs) and spin-offs providing high-tech processes, products and technologies useful to industry and society. This paper on NPAs and spin-offs, features a sampling of the benefits accrued through the from BARC-DAE's Technology Demonstration, Deployment and Transfer Programme.

This is a significant story of the Indian endeavour to create synergy through collaborations and it is an example of innovative development. The three-stage Indian nuclear programme was launched with Homi Jehangir Bhabha's vision of the steps to self-reliance. Thereafter the continuing work put in by Indian nuclear scientists through intensive research in the fields of nuclear science and engineering, has not only brought the first stage of the nuclear power programme into the commercial domain, but has also taken the second stage to the threshold of the commercial and in indeed the third stage, to its final phase of design completion. This has generated a very high level of competence encompassing the nuclear power and non-power applications (NPAs) of nuclear energy with a whole wealth of spin-offs of technologies.

All these have been of direct relevance to increasing productivity, employment generation, economic viability, eco-compatibility, and most important, in creating a highly innovative scientific and technical human resource of very high quality and competence in a number of fields. BARC, while pursuing its research and pushing the frontiers of knowledge, has been ever conscious of the need to explore ways and means of converting the knowledge base into large sections of deployable technologies which benefit the lives of people.

Important contributions have been made to the public domain through the innovative applications of BARC-DAE technologies jointly by our developers and individual entrepreneurs, private industry and PSUs. This led to the establishment of many industries, high-tech services and businesses and to the promotion of large economic activities in different fields.

Every day, in a variety of ways, our lives are touched by technologies developed due to R&D programmes in nuclear field. Some of our common consumer products are off-shoots of nuclear research, for example, domestic water purifier brands and Fluoride Detection Kits for ground water. We also rely on items of agri produce, food processing and medical technologies, such as groundnut, black gram, Krushak, spice irradiator, Bhabhatron, blood irradiator, Hydrogel and a host of sterile medical products through radiation such as syringes, bandages, voiles, caps, implants, eye-ointment and cotton, etc. The products all trace their origins to the Indian nuclear programme. These examples merely suggest the breadth and diversity of NPAs and spin-offs. Through the BARC-DAE efforts and buttressed by those of entrepreneurs, hundreds of products and processes are in use in daily life.

Technologies transferred

BARC and DAE units in the endeavour of developing nuclear technologies in India have successfully transferred some hundreds of processes, products and technologies in various fields of science and engineering such as chemical, material, lasers, optics, medical, environmental, E&I, C&I, automation & robotics, computers, accelerators, agriculture & hydrology etc. Many of these technologies have been transferred to large number of parties along with demonstration and deployment activities. Some of the prominent products, processes, high tech services and technologies provided to industry in recent years are as follows:

Cobalt-60 Teletherapy Machine BHABHATRON
Burn and Injury dressing HYDROGEL
Domestic Water Purifier DWP
Fluoride Detection Kit for ground water FDK
Instrumented Pipe Inspection Gauge IPIG
Supercomputer System ANUPAM-AJEYA
Impedance Cardio-Vasograph ICVG/NICOM
Personnel Monitoring Service PMS
Krushi Utpadan Sanrakshan Kendra KRUSHAK
Biodegradable waste based bio-gas plant NISARGRUNA
Sludge Hygienisation Research Irradiator SHRI
Shape Memory Alloy Sleeves
NIBP Monitor
Isotope Hydrology
Plasma Pyrolysis System
Laser based Land Leveler
Digital Medical Imaging System

BARC has set up procedures for technical collaborations with outside organizations, patenting of inventions and spin-off technology transfers to industry. Spin-off technology transfer procedures are simple and interactive. Technologies are announced on the website www.barc.gov.in and prospective takers respond with their techno-commercial details. Suitable applicants are selected and technology is offered. Considering the efforts and investment required to develop a commercial product, the cost of technology transfer is kept as affordable to local industries, so that they continue to promote the products based on these technologies. Brief information of few of the important technologies is presented below.

Cobalt-60 Teletherapy Machine Bhabhatron:

High energy radiation emitted by radioactive isotope of cobalt is used in the treatment of cancer. Radiation shrinks and/or prevents growth of cancer-affected cells by damaging their structure. Since radiation can destroy the surrounding healthy tissues as well, it is necessary to deliver only the prescribed amount of radiation precisely to the affected region, limiting the exposure to the adjacent tissues to the minimum extent possible.

Bhabhatron is a cobalt-60 teletherapy machine developed in BARC. In this machine high-energy gamma radiation emitting from the cobalt-60 isotope is collimated to the desired size and directed to the cancerous areas. This machine is used for treating localized solid tumors, such as cancers of the skin, tongue, larynx, brain, breast, or uterine cervix. About 60 per cent of cancer incidents can be treated effectively with the cobalt-60 teletherapy machine.

All operations of Bhabhatron are completely computer controlled to facilitate easy operation, complete control over all operating parameters and improved radiation safety. Patient details and treatment details are displayed on screen for close monitoring during treatment. Fully closable collimator for improved radiation safety is a unique feature of the machine. Automatic source withdrawal during emergency, lower penumbra for better beam quality, on-screen status of AC power, battery, door, wedge, key and air supply and position of radiation source displayed: safe/ transit/ treatment, are some of the operator friendly features of Bhabhatron machine. The machine conforms to the safety requirements as per International Electromechanical Commission (IEC), and is certified accordingly.

Bhabhatron has many superior features compared to its imported counterparts comes at a significantly lower cost. Bhabhatron has the potential to address the acute shortage of such facilities in India mainly caused by high cost of imported machines. The technology of this indigenous machine has been transferred to private industry for commercialization.

Bhabhatron is an advanced low cost tool for fighting cancer in the developing world. Recently, the IAEA expressed keen interest in outsourcing this machine for the Agency's Programme of Action for Cancer Therapy (PACT) in the developing member states. One Bhabhatron machine will be installed in Vietnam under PACT. Eight machines are already operational at different sites in India.

Domestic Water Purifier DWP: This device is based on poly-sulfone type of ultrafiltration membrane and used to purify the domestic

water with respect to microorganism, colour, odour, suspended solids and organics. It is basically a dip coating on a cylindrical porous cartridge using solvent exchange cum immersion precipitation technique. It is very effective as it removes bacteria to the extent of > 99.99 per cent (4 log scale) and removes complete turbidity and produces crystal clear water. This device does not need electricity or addition of any chemical. Unlike most of the other devices available in the market which only deactivates the micro-organisms, this device physically eliminates them. It is almost maintenance free except for occasional cleaning of membrane on which suspended solids get deposited and this does not take more than a few minutes. The know-how is licensed to several companies and the range of products developed by them are available under different brands with the names like DOLPHIN UF, JALAJ, PURE FLOW, INSTA-PURE, JALTARA, NIRMAL and B.nova.

Private entrepreneurs came out with innovative products based on the basic dip coating technology. Some enhanced the aesthetics, some incorporated activated carbon filters/pre-filters and some catered to the fluoride/arsenic contamination also. The basic know-how was customized into a fine user-friendly product by our industry and is well received by public. This has demonstrated that public-private partnership can bring about synergistic results and help in successful deployment of R&D in industry for public benefit.

Sludge Hygienisation Research Irradiator SHRI: The sewage sludge after conventional treatment processing in municipal Sewage Treatment Plants (STPs) contains a heavy pathogenic microbial load and needs to be hygienised before application in the agricultural processes. The SHRI plant situated at Vadodara, Gujarat next to the STP treats sewage sludge by radiation processing and reduces this pathogenic population by a factor of ten thousand and raises sludge quality to class 'A' as per requirement of United States Environmental Protection Agency (USEPA compliant). The SHRI plant treats up to 110 cubic meter per day in three shifts, of liquid sewage sludge emanating from 27 MLD (million litres per day) conventional STPs serving domestic population of 0.3 million of Baroda. On drying, 110 m3 liquid sludge with 4 per cent

solid yields ~4 tonnes/day of dry hygienised sludge which is high quality manure.

Successful operation and utilization of SHRI Facility for over five years has shown very good results on all aspects. About 3 kGy of absorbed dose in sewage sludge removes 99.99 per cent of pathogenic bacteria. The continuous operation of SHRI has been very smooth. It produces high value manure containing plant nutrients and soil conditioners for immediate reuse. The technology is easy to integrate with the existing STPs and the hygienized sludge has been found to be an effective natural fertilizer in the large field scale trials and it enhances crop quality and productivity. It is also an excellent clean medium to produce bio-fertilizers.

In the field trials for use of hygienised sludge as a soil conditioner, it has been observed that soil treated with the sludge has better water holding capacity as compared to the normal soil. Thus, utilization of sewage sludge in agricultural practices reduces the demand for water and provides valuable resource for other applications.

The hygienised dry sludge, being free from pathogenic microbes, will eliminate or greatly reduce risk, improve the quality of life and reduce the potential pressure on the country's health care system. Further wider use of this hygienised dry sludge will arrest the problem of top soil erosion due to excess use of water and chemical fertilizers. Finally, increase use of SHRI plants with more and more STPs will reduce the pollution of water sources such as rivers, sea and big lakes, caused by effluents from these STPs.

Super Computer System Anupam-Ajeya: The ANUPAM computers have been extensively used to compute intensive applications such as Molecular Dynamics, Monte Carlo simulations, Finite Element Analysis, particle tracing in BARC and other DAE units. In addition, 37 super computers of Anupam series have been installed at leading R&D and educational institutions in the country including the National Centre for Medium Weather Forecasting and Aeronautics Development Authority, Bangalore.

BARC has been actively engaged in the development of super computers based on parallel processing technology since 1991. Supercomputers developed in the initial period were based on specially designed hardware. Since then a series of Anupam Super computers have been developed. The Anupam systems developed since 1997 have been based on common off-the-shelf hardware components, and free and open source software (FOSS). A complete software development and execution environment along with management system has been developed to fully harness the capabilities of the Anupam systems.

The latest in the series of supercomputers Anupam-Ajeya, designed and developed at BARC has attained a sustained speed of 8.73 Tera Flops, more than five times the speed of the system developed in 2005. The Anupam-Ajeya has 288 dual-core, dual CPU computing nodes (1152 CPU-cores) with High-Speed Infiniband and Gigabit interconnects. Each processor is running at 2.66 GHZ with 4 Giga Byte of main memory.

Biodegradable Waste based Bio-Gas plant

Nisargruna: It uses biodegradable waste as input and produces energy and high quality organic manure (OM) without producing any kind of effluent in a very eco-friendly manner. Nisargruna is a money-breeder with zeroing garbage, energy and high quality OM producer, no effluent, pollution reducer, hygienic environment creator, degraded agricultural-land recoverer and highly eco-friendly plant with a potential of earning carbon credits. Twenty such plants are in operation in different states of India with a varying processing capacity of 1 to 5 tonnes of waste per day.

This plant can process biodegradable waste such as kitchen waste, paper, grass, gobar and dry leaves and produces high quality weed free manure and methane gas. Weed free manure obtained from such waste has high nitrogen contents and acts as an excellent soil conditioner. This plant could be set up for eco-friendly disposal of wet-waste generated in kitchens, canteens of big hospitals, hotels, factories, residential complexes and can avoid health hazards due to dump sites.

The waste in Nisargruna gets biodegraded by two processes viz. aerobic and anaerobic in a cascaded manner. In the first aerobic phase it is largely converted to butyric, fumaric, acetic and other organic acids with the help of thermophillic bacteria. This acidic waste in the second anaerobic phase with the help of methanogenic bacteria gets further degraded and generates high purity methane and what is left over is high quality organic manure, leaving no effluent whatsoever.

Nisargruna is a pioneering effort for urban and rural waste management. It offers an excellent alternative for decentralized processing of solid biodegradable waste. So far this technology is being successfully implemented at 20 different sites in India with a total processing capacity of ~90 tonnes per day. All the waste generated in these areas would have been otherwise dumped in open landfills creating shortage of landfill sites and leading to methane emission to the atmosphere. Implementation of these twenty plants has resulted in reduction of Green House Gas (GHG) emission and has potential to earn CERs (Certificate of Emission Reduction) worth ~Rs 1 crore/yr. Effectively, 1 tonne/day capacity NISARGRUNA plant has a potential to earn CERs worth Rs 1.25 lakhs/yr if operated co-operatively under the consortium. This technology has been transferred to more than forty entrepreneurs all over India. This technology assists in achieving sustainable development by improving economic, social and environmental conditions in the region.

For the rural heartland

In a country as vast in size as ours, technology innovations have to be evolved indigenously and in greater measure to enhance the quality of life. Help from outside, through collaborations and joint ventures can be good for development to some extent if found to be locally appropriate, provided it does not perpetuate dependence on such outside help. BARC-DAE has gone through a learning process the hard way, a steady accumulation of experience built up through facing and overcoming technological problems and errors and has become at pursuing self-reliance. Building this innovation capability within the country is essential if technology is to be applied quickly in the interest of the larger community, particularly since such technology has to fit with varied local conditions.

Considering the wealth of technology and innovative capability generated in BARC-DAE, as an off-shoot of nuclear applications in the areas of water, land, agriculture, food processing and urban-rural waste management, a detailed formatted functional programme for advancement of rural sector is being implemented under DAE societal initiative. This programme is called AKRUTI-KRUTIK-FORCE.

AKRUTI-KRUTIK-FORCE

AKRUTI is an acronym for 'Advance Knowledge and RUral Technology Implementation' programme. Through this programme, the technology node is set up in a village and called

AKRUTI node. This is done under the guidance of BARC, through technically oriented NGOs. The AKRUTI node will park number of BARC developed technologies for use by villagers. These technologies are demonstrated and taken to different villages around the node via working centres established in different villages around it. These working centres are called KRUTI Kendras or KRUTIK. It stands for 'Knowledge and RUral Technology Implementation Kendra, which works with villagers and farmers' groups in their own villages and in the fields. These groups are known as FORCE meaning Farmers' Organised group for Rural Creative Entrepreneurship. Each member of FORCE is made familiar with technologies of AKRUTI through KRUTIK.

Three AKRUTI nodes are set up in Maharashtra State (MS) in collaboration with three NGOs as follows:

AKRUTI-NIRMITEE (NIRMITEE at Uddhar, Dist. Raigad, MS)

AKRUTI-PARIVARTAN (PARIVARTAN at Chiplun, Dist. Ratnagiri, MS)

AKRUTI-CARD (CARD—Community Action for Rural Development Society at Khirala village, Dist. Amravati, MS)

Rajiv Gandhi Science and Technology Commission of the Maharashtra Government has financed the above AKRUTI nodes.

Two more AKRUTI nodes are in operation in Andhra Pradesh (AP) and Madhya Pradesh (MP) as follows:

• NAYUDAMMA's AKRUTI (Kaviti Mandal, Srikakulam Dist, AP)

• AKRUTI (Fresh-O-Veg Krishak Club at Indore, MP).

PRESENT ACTIVITIES: Various technology deployment and demonstration activities— such as setting up of NISARGRUNA plants, demonstration experiments with Foldable Solar Dryer, Domestic Water Purifier, Soil Organic Carbon Testing Kit, SHRI sludge utilization and sowing of new seed varieties of BARC—have started in more than 100 locations around these AKRUTI nodes through KRUTIKs amongst the villagers and farmers in the surrounding villages. Laboratory training of village farmers as AKRUTI Trainee in BARC has also been initiated in the field of tissue culture technology.

The Federation of Farmers Associations (FFAs), Andhra Pradesh is in the final stage of a project proposal called 'SAMARPAN' to set up six AKRUTIs in Andhra State to begin with, for deployment of

BARC-DAE and Department of Space (DoS) technologies.

A number of technically oriented NGOs from all over India are in contact with BARC to set up AKRUTI nodes in their respective areas. Many banks such as SBI, ICICI Bank, Bank of India, NBHC/MCX are in discussion with BARC to create channels of participation in the AKRUTI programme.

This programme complements, supplements and augments the efforts of all existing programmes of different organizations, departments and ministries to facilitate large scale deployment of several BARC-DAE technologies in rural areas. AKRUTI-KRUTIK-FORCE will enable the villages to deploy and make these technologies with local adaptation for them under BARC guidance to create 'People Centred Research & Extension for Assured Livelihood & Enhancement'. This in turn will generate village entrepreneurship and make this activity self-sustaining and wide spread. It aims to create a strong, well spread network to embed of S&T culture in the rural sectors.

The AKRUTI initiative and technology transfer to industry demonstrate the approach of how an organization working in hi-tech area can use its knowledge base for the benefit of industry and larger community base and promote an environment of entrepreneurship, creating more job opportunities with innovation for both rural and urban sectors.

Future Scope

The first stage of the nuclear programme, already in the commercial domain, and the second stage just entering the commercial stage, have generated a huge wealth of advanced technologies in various fields. The completion of the three-stage nuclear power programme, will serve as a big catalyst for technology development across an incredibly wide range of fields.

We expect advances in nano technology, advanced materials, desk-top super computers, stand-alone power packs, waste recycling, pollution reduction systems, ultra fast secured networks providing jam-free communication, advanced smart sensors, automation and robotics, predictive/precession farming and host of other technologies that may pay dividends higher than the main activity in long run. BARC-DAE while working with Indian industries to meet technological challenges of the second and third stage of nuclear power programme, will generate a new wave of beneficial NPAs and spin-offs. This will spark the imagination of industry and generate new ideas for improved commercial products.

The Indian market has become a global market. Products and services have to be competitive in cost and performance. The NPAs and spinoff technologies described earlier have stood the test of time in facing up to the challenges of liberalization/globalization of economy and embargoes on the transfer of advanced technologies imposed by the developed world.

BARC-DAE has created an extremely confident community. No matter how easy the access may be to ready-made know-how from abroad, BARC-DAE will devote itself to the quest for technological development with the same dedication, curiosity and thoroughness that its founders encouraged. BARC-DAE has a tradition of setting high standards in dealing with new situations successfully. New methods of technology deployment, interactions with private industry and public participation will evolve at BARC-DAE units, to improve the speed of utilizing indigenous R&D for solving our unique problems. □

M Srinivasan
Former Associate Director
Physics Group, BARC

A third route to nuclear energy?

Every now and then the citadel of Science is rocked by the discovery of a new phenomenon that the scientific community refuses to accept. 'The Theory of Relativity' and 'Quantum Physics' were two such paradigm shifts that shook the very foundations of Physics in the 20th century but which, when first propounded, had many detractors. The phenomenon initially called "Cold Fusion" but now more commonly referred to as "Low Energy Nuclear Reactions (LENR)" which came to light in March 1989 is yet another example of a paradigm shift in science that has not yet been fully comprehended by the majority of mainstream scientists.

The story of Cold Fusion began with the announcement of two electro-chemists, Martin Fleischmann and Stanley Pons of the University of Utah, who claimed that they had invented a very simple "battery and bottle" tabletop device for producing nuclear fusion reactions at "room temperature". Their device was basically an electrolytic cell where the cathode was a rod of palladium, the anode was a coil of platinum wire surrounding it, and the electrolyte was lithium deuteroxide dissolved in heavy water. To put it simply, the claim was that during electrolysis the palladium absorbs part of the released deuterium gas to form palladium deuteride (PdD) and that a special type of fusion reaction takes place between the deuterons inside (or on the surface of) the Pd cathode.

Fleischmann & Pons reported that they were measuring massive amounts of "excess heat", way beyond what they were putting into the cell for causing the electrolysis! These authors postulated that in the near surface region of the palladium metal, the repulsive coulomb barrier for fusion is somehow suppressed. This was the crucial part of the claim, one that the physics community vehemently opposed and criticized as being against all that has been learnt in nuclear physics over the last half a century! But is it not possible that the Utah chemists had stumbled upon a revolutionary new phenomenon?

The two pioneers became instant celebrities, at least for a few months! They unleashed shock waves in the scientific world at a time when the technologically advanced countries were building complex and expensive magnetically confined plasma machines (costing billions of dollars) to create working models of Thermonuclear Fusion Reactors such as the ITER, currently under construction in France. Under these circumstances the claim that fusion reactions can be made to happen in a simple tabletop device was one that the physics community found difficult to digest. Further, when the majority of those who attempted replication did not succeed, the field fell into disrepute. The official report of the committee appointed by the US Department of Energy in 1989 came to the "unfortunate" conclusion that the claims of Fleischmann and Pons are not supported by the experimental evidence available and this essentially killed the field.

The main objections and criticisms of the skeptics were (a) very poor reproducibility of the experiments; (b) no experimental evidence of nuclear products or other signatures of the occurrence of nuclear fusion reactions, and (c) no valid theoretical explanation as to how the coulomb barrier (repulsion between positively charged deuterons) is overcome at normal temperatures.

However, 19 years and 13 international conferences later, we see that the proponents of the new field of "Condensed Matter Nuclear Science (CMNS)" comprising several hundred researchers the world over have painstakingly toiled to unravel the science behind the phenomenon of "Low Energy Nuclear Reactions" and kept it alive. Patient research has answered, at least partially, some of the skeptics' questions.

Michael McKubre and others at SRI International have done commendable work to point out why most people who tried to replicate the original Fleischmann-Pons experiments failed. They have shown that for "excess heat" to be generated in Pd-D2O electrolysis cells at least three conditions need to be satisfied. First, the deuterium to Pd loading ratio in the cathode has to exceed a threshold value of about 0.93; second, the current density needs to be more than 0.6 amps per cm2 of the cathode surface area; and third, the system needs to be triggered appropriately after the initial loading so that an adequate deuteron flux is established across the cathode surface boundary. All these conditions are not easy to achieve, but even if achieved, are still insufficient. There seem to be additional factors that the special "Nuclear Active Environment" needs for initiating the mysterious nuclear reactions formed on the cathode surface. It is obvious that most people who attempted replication were unaware of these vital facts!

Excess heat

As for the question regarding the end product of the nuclear reactions taking place in these cells, careful measurements in excess heat producing deuterated palladium devices have shown that Helium-4 gas is the primary "nuclear ash". However, other nuclear signatures such as neutrons, tritium and, sometimes, even energetic charged particles have also been detected.

But a very important new observation is that in a variety of LENR devices such as electrolytic cells, glow discharge devices and even simple gas absorption systems, all kinds of nuclear transmutation reactions involving the host metal atoms such as palladium (or nickel or titanium) seem to be taking place. In other words, slowly but steadily, over the years the whole complexion of the nature of cold fusion has been transformed and hence the new name LENR or even CMNS!

In a clean and stunning experiment, Iwamura and others of Mitsubishi Research

Laboratories in Japan have reported the occurrence of transmutation reactions during the simple
process of diffusion or permeation of D2 gas through a Pd complex on the front surface of which a layer of Cesium was deposited. During the diffusion process, a single Cs nucleus is found to absorb simultaneously four deuterons resulting in Praseodymium (charge number up by 4 and mass number up by 8). Occurrence of such multi-body "heavy ion fusion reactions" has not heretofore been demonstrated even in the most advanced nuclear research laboratories of the world! This is indeed a fundamental and important discovery representing a significant paradigm shift in science.

As of today a number of theoretical models have been put forward to explain how the coulomb barrier can be overcome and how all these various nuclear reactions are enabled inside a metallic lattice. But as yet no single theory by itself seems to be able to explain the plethora of experimental observations.

Review

The American Physical Society (APS) and American Chemical Society (ACS) have been holding separate sessions in the last two years on Low Energy Nuclear Reactions (LENR) at their annual meetings. In fact the ACS has just completed publication of a collection of review articles, "ACS Sourcebook of Low Energy Nuclear Reactions". Many of the mainstream scientific journals have also slowly started accepting papers pertaining to this field.

When the phenomenon first became public in 1989 many groups of scientists at the Bhabha Atomic Research Centre (BARC), the Indira Gandhi Centre for Atomic Research and the Tata Institute of Fundamental Research jumped into the fray by quickly setting up experiments to verify the claims. Some Indian scientists reported positive results. But soon interest in India waned as scepticism about cold fusion became widespread in the world. and a negative report came out from the US Department of Energy.

After a gap of over 15 years, in early 2008, it appeared that the field was being resurrected. Renowned LENR researcher Michael McKubre and science journalist Steven Krivit apprised the Indian scientific community of the new results during their tour of India. Several senior scientists took stock of the status of 'cold fusion' research. They discussed for a day the theme "Emerging New Energy Concepts for the 21st Century: Low Energy Nuclear Reactions" at the National Institute of Advanced Studies (NIAS) in Bangalore. That meeting has been instrumental in opening up the field again. Experiments are currently being set up in several laboratories and universities in India to replicate some of the results, especially on the occurrence of nuclear transmutation reactions in simple experimental configurations such as the carbon arc experiment.

The importance to India of this emerging new field of science has to be seen in the context of the rapid rise of the global crude oil prices. The push towards bio-fuel option can cause a food crisis. The effects of the use of fossil fuel on global warming continue to haunt the world. Nuclear power generation in India is constrained by inadequate fuel supplies and insufficient natural uranium reserves. The import of Light Water reactors along with their lifetime requirements of enriched uranium fuel will depend on a favourable international supply regime. Power from "hot fusion" reactors, at this stage, remains somewhat elusive.

Humankind has obviously accidentally stumbled onto a new route to extract the energy of the atom. This "third nuclear option" stems from the new science of Low Energy Nuclear Reactions. LENR offers the prospects of developing small (20 to 100 Kw range) captive power generating units, promising an era of "gridless electricity".

It is heartening to note that several groups in India have already come forward to pursue the science behind this "emerging third option" of generating power for our future! At least one private company with financial backing from venture capitalists is committed to promoting research in the field of LENR! Clearly, to make a dent in the overall power scenario of the country such plants need to be mass-produced and in this the private sector has a grand opportunity to play a crucial role.

It is my fond dream that the message of the waiting bonanza will trigger one or more of the doyens of Indian industry to grab the window of opportunity and propel India towards becoming the world leader in this exciting new technology of the future! □

DEFENCE
RESEARCH

बलस्य मूलं विज्ञानम् बलस्य मूलं विज्ञानम् बलस्य मूलं विज्ञानम्

Heat shield

M Natarajan
Scientific Adviser to Raksha Mantri
Secretary, Dept. of Defence R&D
Director General, DRDO

Defending nation through knowledge

A key factor driving the power of nations is their ability to operate on the frontiers of scientific and technological knowledge...

— Prime Minister of India, July 2007

With foresight, India's leadership quite early on established a very extensive defence research and development organization. It is one of the largest S&T and R&D organizations and covers a wide technology spectrum. Its developmental activity falls under eight major disciplines spread over 50 laboratories—from Leh in the north to Cochin in the south, Jodhpur and Pune in the west to Tezpur in the east.

The Defence Research and Development Organisation (DRDO) is responsible for the development of all major weapon systems for the Indian Armed Forces. It has a human resource strength of 30,000, of whom 7000 scientists and 11000 technical staff contribute directly to the development of systems, products and technologies in key areas of Aeronautics, Armaments, Combat vehicles, Missile systems, Naval systems, Electronics, Materials and Life Sciences. Perhaps no other single organisation in the world has the responsibility for developing and managing so many diverse systems under one umbrella.

The early '80s gave birth to a number of landmark systems that helped immensely in propelling India to the technological forefront. The launchings of the Integrated Guided Missile Development Programme, Main Battle Tank Arjun, and Light Combat Aircraft programmes were the catalysts that led, in the '90s, to taking up challenges in the strategic arena. By the mid-'90s, DRDO had established its credentials with the successful development efforts in Agni, Prithvi, and MBT Arjun, and the unmanned aerial vehicles Lakshya and Nishant. It then went on to consolidate its position in the newly challenging field of electronic warfare, modular avionics, missile defence, communication security, control command and communication systems and other fields. Here is a broad overview of developmental challenges taken up in the mid and late '90s.

Aeronautics: In the field of aeronautics, LCA Tejas is our signature in the sky. This highly agile aircraft, with state-of-the-art composite structure and modular avionics, is today the most cost effective multi-role fighter aircraft in its class. Taken up for full scale engineering development in 1993, the LCA achieved technological success with the very first flight of Technology Demonstrator-1 in Jan 2001. This was followed by a speedy flight test programme, which saw the development of two TDs, and four PVs in a span of five years. This entails over 700 flight tests, clocking over 300 hrs and meeting specified milestones on supersonic flights and maneouvres. The Air force has placed an initial production order for 20 aircraft, the first of which completed its maiden flight in 2007. In addition, the LCA-Navy and Trainer are well into development. Today, the programme is poised at the start of the final haul towards weaponisation, slated for 2010. Utilising the combined efforts of over 30 DRDO establishments, ordnance factories, defence public sector undertakings, CSIR laboratories and over 300 private industries, the LCA programme has established a strong technology base in the field of avionics, composites, airframe etc and provided a massive fillip to our industry.

DRDO has sought to consolidate its burgeoning expertise in surveillance and reconnaissance by taking up the development of AWACS on an existing platform, with a state-of-the-art AESA antenna, using indigenously developed TR modules, for its primary radar. This is expected to be ready by 2012.

The success of our efforts in aeronautics has put India firmly on the aviation map of the world, and given a boost to our aviation/ aerospace industry, which is confirmed by the advent in recent years of aerospace majors setting up their R&D and Service centres in India.

Missiles: The early success of indigenously developed Agni and Prithvi missiles and their subsequent deployment have boosted the strategic status of our country. The Integrated Guided Missile Development Programme, taken up in the early '80s, comprises the Akash, Agni, Nag, Trishul and Prithvi missile systems. Akash and Nag have completed development trials and are awaiting user acceptance.

In line with the requirement of the LCA programme, DRDO also took up for the first time the development of a Beyond Visual range Air-to-air missile Astra, which has entered its preliminary testing stage and is expected to be ready by 2012. This has resulted in the establishment of an indigenous technology base in the areas of missile propulsion, command and guidance, navigation systems, telemetry, data links and warheads. All of this has helped immensely in the first ever Indo-Russian Joint venture—Brahmos is the one-of-a kind supersonic cruise missile, capable of being launched from land as well as sea, with speeds of 2.8 Mach and a range of 290 km. It has been a successful indicator of joint development with foreign partners.

The unsuccessful first flight test of Agni-3 in 2006 was certainly a setback, but DRDO bounced back in just nine months, locating the deficiencies in design. Such resilience culminated in the successful test of April 2007, which propelled India into an elite league of technologically advanced countries. The 16m long IRBM, with a range of over 3000 km established many 'firsts'—flex nozzle control, specially developed composite propellants, autonomous guidance and control. In essence,

Agni-3 confirmed India's strategic capability for 'minimum credible deterrence', corroborated by the first successful test of the Interceptor missile.

The technology base of the IGMDP and Brahmos also led to DRDO trying out newer business models, while taking up the development, in collaboration with Israel, of a Long Range SAM, for the Indian Navy. The LRSAM will combine the core competencies of both countries to provide defence against multiple threats at sea. It is expected to be ready for user trials by 2010.

The missile development programmes have given to India a dual benefit—the strategic missile family has propelled us into an elite club of advanced nations, while the tactical missiles have brought into the country much needed precision technology, especially in navigation and guidance.

Armaments and Combat Engineering: The successful development of the Main Battle Tank Arjun, leading to user acceptance in 1996, resulted in production orders for 124 pieces in March 2000; this is now underway at the HVF, Avadi. With literally no knowledge base at the inception of the programme, the Arjun, with its state-of-the-art features including an indigenous hydro-pneumatic suspension, hydrostatic steering, composite armour and armament, fire-on-the-move capability etc, has helped in the development of a number of variants, namely, Tank Ex (a hybrid tank with Arjun turret and T72 hull), CI Ajeya, and a number of engineering, reconnaissance and support combat vehicles.

In the area of mechanical and engineering systems, DRDO has achieved a steady success with the development of bridging systems like Sarvatra, engineering recovery vehicles, amphibious dozers and mobile launchers for the missile projects.

The success of projects in the combat vehicles and engineering discipline has given India standing as one of the few countries in the world with the capability to develop its own battle tank, uniquely configured to suit its customized requirements. This has helped to establish a technology base for future requirements.

Electronic Warfare (EW): This programme comprising the Samyukta (for the Army) and Sangraha (for the Navy) was taken up in the mid '90s and achieved remarkable success in a relatively short timeframe, with user acceptance of most systems of Samyukta and Sangraha. Through this programme, DRDO gained expertise in the hi-tech and dynamically varying field of EW. Technological advances in antennas, microwave and millimetric wave components and supercomponents, and signal processing have gone into the realization of these systems. This led to the development of capability in ESM, ECM & ECCM, covering the frequency spectrum right from HF to mmw (Mhz to 40 Ghz).

Electronics disciplines: DRDO achieved major successes in radar development, which included acquisition, tracking and weapon-locating radars, most of which have resulted in production orders. Special efforts were also initiated in providing C4I and networking capability to the Armed Forces.

DRDO's efforts in the development of Electronics & EW systems have established indigenous capability in this highly classified and security sensitive field. These systems, which no country would have risked sharing with others, are today an integral part of land, air and naval systems, thanks to the extensive development efforts over the last decade.

Naval Systems: Yet another of our key successes has been in the area of naval systems. With a group of laboratories focusing on the Indian Navy's requirements and a strong commitment on the part of the customer to use our services, we have gone on to develop and establish an indigenous technology base in the area of sonars, sensors and signal processing, torpedoes, naval materials and paints, naval electronic warfare systems and ship-based missiles. The decision of the Indian Navy to stop the use of imported sonars and use only indigenous systems is a strong commendation of the technology achievements in this field.

Infrastructure: A major facet of technology development is the infrastructure that needs to be developed and installed for customized requirements. Every major weapon system development has included the concurrent development of test and evaluation facilities. As a result, DRDO can lay claim to building up a sophisticated set of world class test facilities, which have been utilized for its development programmes. These include:
- Integrated Test Range at Balasore—a state-of-the-art, world class range facility for the

flight test of rockets, missiles and airborne weapons systems, with appropriate infrastructure for tracking, acquisition and data processing
- Structural dynamics and ground vibration test facility—which enables integrated test of complete airframes
- Real time simulators for Tanks and combat Aircraft
- ELSEC EW test range at Hyderabad—enables integration, testing and evaluation of EW systems, simulating field conditions
- Gas turbine test rigs—for testing of military engines with sophisticated controls & data instrumentation
- Rocket propulsion test facilities
- Gun Firing range for warhead testing
- Rail Track Rocket Sled Facility for testing of armament sub-systems
- Test tracks/rigs for wheeled and tracked vehicles & sub-systems
- Antenna test rigs
- EMI/EMC test facilities for complete platforms
- Underwater weapon test ranges.

The cost of these facilities is a significant component of the development cost of the project and an invaluable part of successful development.

All these achievements could not have been possible, without DRDO's extensive inter-linkages with academia and industry. With a well developed framework for interactions with academic institutions, DRDO uses CARS (contracts for acquisition of research services) and the directorate of extra mural research at DRDO headquarters to inculcate basic research as technology seeding for our development programmes. Recognising the need for filling up technology gaps, DRDO has set up Centres of Excellence—one each in High Energy Materials at University of Hyderabad, in mmWave Devices at the University of Calcutta, and in Life Sciences at Bharathiar University. Over 75 institutions have contributed either directly or indirectly to our programmers and DRDO relies on enhanced participation from academia, keeping in view the long term, long gestation programmers of weapon system development.

Interaction with S&T agencies: DRDO also understands the importance of networking with other S&T agencies in the country such as DOS, CSIR, DST, and the Department of Earth Sciences and Ocean Development. It has set up mechanisms for working at S&T level with these agencies for research in basic sciences for some common applications.

Interaction with industry: In the development of all our major systems, we have had the opportunity to interact with all types of industries, including the defence public sector units, ordnance factories, public and private industries, with the result that DRDO today has created a strong industrial base, with over 800 industries being involved in its programmes. This has not only led to an enhanced learning curve for industrial units but has also improved their export potential. DRDO has also established strong links with industries through CII, Assocham, and FICCI in the pursuit of technological goals.

In its constant bid to maintain a cutting edge advantage, DRDO has taken up the development of a number of systems dealing with the technology requirements of tomorrow. The key areas for future development include:

- Propulsion systems
- Sensors and multi-sensor data fusion
- Robotics and Unmanned systems
- Stealth and specialized Materials
- Network-centric systems.

In today's world of globalization and cross border linkages, DRDO is looking for new development partners and newer business models. It constantly endeavours to provide timely and best possible technological support to the armed forces of our country. □

M Somasekhar
Science Journalist

India's emergence as a missile power

It has been a journey spanning exactly 25 years. India's trajectory to emerging as a player in the exclusive club of nations with expertise in missile technology. The journey has been tough, with a fair measure of success and failure.

By the end of 2007, India could boast of a missile arsenal that constituted the capability to hit targets as far away as 3,500 km (Agni-3), a cruise missile strength in the form of Brahmos and defend its skies and important installations from enemy aggression, with the first major success of a Ballistic Missile Defence (BMD) system.

The country's big success has been in inducting the shorter range, surface-to-surface Agni-1 (700–800 km) and medium range Agni-2 (1500–2000 km), into the Indian Army and the medium range, surface to surface Prithvi missile system, which also has a naval version called Dhanush.

It has made strides in developing the medium range, surface-to-air missile Akash, multiple role, quick reaction, short range Trishul, and the third generation, anti-battle tank Nag missiles.

In the supersonic class, cruise missile, the country's long and trusted partnership with Russia yielded good dividend in the form of Brahmos missile. BrahMos, the corporate entity that makes the missiles also exhibits a good example of collaboration between not just two nations, but among a large number of companies and institutes from both sides which are participating in the development of the missile, giving India tactical advantage. In future, there is scope for exporting it to countries interested as well.

Encouraged by these developments, the missile scientists in the Defence Research and Development Organisation (DRDO), have unveiled their preparedness to even build Agni-4, which could be a real long range missile with over 3,500 km range and reach up to 5000 km, depending on the threat perception of the country.

Giving an overview of the implications of these developments, Dr V.K. Saraswat, Chief Controller, R&D (Missiles and Strategic systems), at DRDO said "The big achievements in the missile field clearly demonstrate the synergy between the Indian industry, especially the aerospace and the defence scientific community. Today we can boast of having broken the barrier, migrating from medium range to long range ballistic missiles, with proven accuracy and precision of delivery to hit the intended targets".

With the ability to deliver both conventional and nuclear warheads, the missile delivery systems give India the necessary deterrence and strike power. In addition, the ballistic missile defence shield, which is expected to be in place in the next couple of years, will give the country the necessary safety cushion, from the perceived threat at present.

These developments, no mean achievement for a developing country, especially with investments which are way below the missile powers, and under trying circumstances, have firmly propelled India into the exclusive club of less than half a dozen nations, with advanced missile technology.

These include, the US, Russia, China, France and Israel. To continue the country's path to further advances, an impressive base has been created with Hyderabad emerging as the missile complex with a string of national facilities. These include, the mother lab- Defence Research and Development Laboratory (DRDL), Research Centre Imarat (RCI), which is focused on Prithvi and a range of key technologies to be developed; Advanced Systems Laboratory (ASL), piloting Agni and composite development programme; Defence Electronics and Defence Metallurtical labs DLRL & DMRL providing the critical material and component support.

For the trials and validation of the technologies and missile systems developed here, DRDO has established the Integrated Test Range (ITR) at Balasore in Orissa and the Wheeler Island off the coast. There, both the flight tests and user trials with the Indian Army, Air Force and Navy are carried out.

In addition to these, around 60 small and medium enterprises (SMEs), mostly in the private sector, a handful of public sector units like Midhani have made wide ranging contributions into the missile programme. The production company, Bharat Dynamics Limited (BDL), is also located there. For BrahMos, the Indo-Russian joint venture also in Hyderabad has a massive complex in place.

Information technology

Bolstered by an impressive infrastructure and manpower skills and successes, Indian scientists have ventured into a whole new range of futuristic technologies that will be the bedrock for the next generation weapon applications. With information technology, playing a major role in the entire development of weapon systems as well as battlefield scenarios, there is a huge emphasis on the sector as well.

The ambitious multi-million dollar IGMDP, has come a long way and entered into an exciting phase which includes the development of the beyond the visual range (BVR) missiles like ASTRA, latest technologies which will give rise to precision missiles with 'hit to kill' capabilities and carry multi-munitions to home in on several targets, says Dr V K Saraswat.

Astra would be a new class of missile with the capability of dodging radars and striking enemy targets in ranges up to 80 km. At present only the US, Russia, France and Israel possess such missiles. A consortia, led by DRDL and including the missile labs, public sector units such as HAL, ECIL and a good number of private companies, would be involved in the fabrication of important components and

systems integration, explained Mr Prahlada, who initiated the programme.

Astra will weigh 150 kg, making it the lightest in its class. It can be integrated with the Light Combat Aircraft (Tejas). The US has a similar missile but heavier, while Israel has a BVR, but the range is comparatively shorter.

It was in 1982–83, under the leadership of the then Prime Minister, Indira Gandhi that the country embarked on the Integrated Guided Missile Development Project (IGMDP). The project leader, was Mr A P J Abdul Kalam, who is today known as India's 'missile man', and was the President of the country during 2002–07.

Five missiles

The vision and initial goal of the IGMDP was to develop five missiles. Named by Mr Kalam and his close team in an open exercise carried out at the DRDL in the initial days as Agni, Prithvi, Trishul, Akash and Nag, the 'panch missiles', the programme got a big boost only in 1989, when the first significant success was achieved with Agni (May 22, 1989), which continues to be the workhorse.

The Agni Mission Director, Dr R N Agarwal, and team successfully tested the unique re-entry technology for Agni as well as the all carbon composite nose tip, which withstood the high temperatures at re-entry stage of the missile into the earth's atmosphere. It gave the the scientists the confidence to use the new light-weight composite material in the missile body.

Today, more than 75 per cent of the material constituting the Agni missile is made of this composite and is among the lightest in its class. The Advanced Systems Laboratory (ASL), which was carved out of the Defence Research and Development Laboratory (DRDL) around 2001–02, to exclusively drive the Agni programme, has today established a separate production centre for composites.

The present Programme Director, Mr Avinash Chander, who led the mixed performance of Agni-3 in the last two years (failure in July 2006 and success in April, 2007), has added a major feather to the missile programme by demonstrating the success of the complicated all-composite rocket motor casings used in the missile.

In addition, ASL has launched a large programme on the development of technologies in the area of carbon nanotechnology. It is bringing into the fold several national laboratories and private industries to explore applications in medical, super conductors, key components for strategic use.

The success of will BMD in its first attempt has given a big boost to the missile community. The reason being the complexity of the task, which requires a network of command, computer, control, communication and intelligence network. Though, it will take a few more trials, they are confident of converting it into a deployable system in the next couple of years.

In a few years export of tactical missile systems is also a possibility. India will be able to offer missiles at a very competitive cost in the global market as the development and production costs are one-fifth when compared to the US or European models.

On the technology front, the defence scientists have clearly proved their expertise, in areas like re-entry, the two-stage solid propellant, strap on boosters, inertial guidance and propulsion systems, electronics, on board computers, simulation, Infra red and Radio frequency etc. The series of successes of Agni, Prithvi, the Akash, and the BMD have also validated several key components, systems and materials developed both by the labs and industry in trying conditions in real time situations. For example the flex nozzles, which are critical in helping the missile change its trajectory have been proved in the Agni launches.

Spin-offs

While IGMDP has come a long way, with its share of ups and downs it has given the country's defence forces confidence that there is indigenous capability to deliver strategic weapon systems. A welcome spin off has been availability of interesting material, products and technologies with potential civilian applications.

Realising the potential, a separate entity called the Indian Society for Biomedical Technology, was floated in 1992, by Mr Kalam and Dr P Rama Rao, then Secretary, Department of Science and Technology, in collaboration with ministries concerned to harness the missile technologies for civilian use.

The trigger for the programme was the all-carbon composite material that formed the nose tip of Agni missile. It proved its credentials as a light weight, rugged material that could withstand high temperatures and difficult conditions. Defence scientists exploited these

characteristics to fabricate light weight calipers for polio affected people.

Thereafter, a series of projects were launched and titanium-based biocompatible materials that could be implanted were developed. Artificial pace makers, heart valves, laser systems, stents, bone and teeth implants etc. were demonstrated at the laboratory level by the defence laboratories.

While some of these technologies and materials have been taken up by the private sector companies or hospitals, a good number have also ended up languishing for want of entrepreneurs.

Industrial base

When IGMDP was launched in 1982–83, the industrial infrastructure to support cutting edge technology development was rudimentary. DRDO had to struggle to get industry support even for small components, forget about larger systems. In the international arena, there were regimes like the MTCR (missile technology control regime), which prohibited imports.

The Central Government's decision to extend necessary push to help the willing industry to put in place infrastructure and also production facilities, resulted in a steady flow of funds. Industries such as Walchandnagar, Godrej, HAL, L&T, Tatas were among some of the early companies which lent solid support to the indigenous programme. These included BHEL, BEL, HAL, ECIL, Midhani, Sameer and private companies like Kerala Hitech, MTAR, Zetatek, and SEC Industries.

In retrospect, missile scientists claim with a sense of pride that the programme has nurtured the domestic industry in a big way. Prithvi has more than 35 industries involved, while Agni has over 60 and the total number of all sizes of industries involved with the missile development programme is estimated to be around 250. From components to critical systems like missile launchers and mobile control systems, all are today made by the industry.

The maturing of the Indian industry in the programme has been clearly visible in the recent successes of Agni-3 or the BMD, where a large number of them are participating from the beginning of the project itself. The sound infrastructure base and the highly skilled, young manpower that has been created is allowing the luxury to take on complex and difficult projects.

The synergy with the industry has brought down the development and production costs.

For example if the cost of production of a Prithvi missile was Rs 4–5 crore in the early phase, after six-seven years it is only Rs 7 crore now. If one had to compare with any of the ones developed abroad the costs would be atleast five times, though at present, the scope to import does not exist.

Another plus has been reduction in time lags and delays in large projects, which was the bane of most of the ambitious projects in the strategic sector. To name a few the Light Combat Aircraft (LCA), Main Battle Tank (MBT), Arjun, the Kaveri engine for the Cryogenic rocket etc.

The overall time lags have come down in this sector, where technology curbs and India's stated positions make it tough to get anything imported easily. The strategy that seems to have worked in the concurrent technology and component development and production with the participation of the industry.

Concurrent development and production is the new mantra in the DRDO. This has helped in reducing the time between development to production. A measure of the mutual confidence between DRDO-industry can be gauged from the meeting with the Confederation of Indian Industry (CII) a few years ago where nearly 150 industries took active part. Further, by a conscious decision, the DRDO, which has a network of 52 national laboratories across the country, also threw open nearly 10 of its laboratories to the industry, especially to identify and go in for technology transfer or to jointly develop initiatives.

Technology denials

Sanctions, especially after the first successful launch of Agni in 1989, have undoubtedly posed problems to the IGMDP. There have been delays and in some cases cost overruns in projects. However, the optimists and protagonists of the missile development programme argue that it has given a shot in the arm to indigenous efforts and talent.

Today, the country can boast of expertise to fabricate from the simplest to the most complicated system. How did it do this? It was a well thought out strategy. In the beginning, the challenge was taken to public sector. The

development of all critical systems in DRDO was the responsibility of these organisations with huge manpower. Thereafter, the private industry was also roped in. As a result the dependence on foreign countries has come down dramatically. In contrast, the country has benefited with new capabilities in avionics, aerospace, systems engineering and building of large systems.

The other offshoot of this huge exercise has been the continuous demand and churning out of skilled manpower. DRDO has been recruiting a large number of bright young people into its large national mission programmes. In the ongoing IT boom, however it has been a victim of high attrition rates. On an average, more than 450 engineers and scientists have been recruited across the network of the laboratories.

Even as the IGMDP was closing with significant successes, defence scientists finally removed the lid off one of its top secret projects called 'Sagarika', which was test fired. The success of the submarine launched ballistic missile (SLBM) Sagarika will enhance the capacity for nuclear deterrence.

The defence scientists also gave some insights into the future initiatives with large projects like the Precision Guided Munitions (PGMs) and hypersonic cruise missile technology. The PGMs, to fly onboard missiles (like Prithvi), will have the capability to precisely hit targets with least collateral damage. The project has been technically cleared by the Government and the necessary funds are expected to be allocated for their development. The PGM programme would be open to collaborations. An array of technologies would be required to develop these missile launched PGMs. Israel, for example has PGMs, laser guided and has proposed co-development.

India is also pursuing efforts to gain ground in hypersonic cruise missile technology. The Hypersonic Technology Demonstrator Vehicle (HSTDV), with speeds of Mach 6.5 is under development at the DRDL, Hyderabad.

The project is expected to validate the scramjet engine, air-breathing technology and give a direction to the future cruise missile technology, re-usable launch vehicles and civilian aircraft applications. □

B R Gandhe
Director Armaments, DRDO

Modern armaments developed

The Armament Group of Laboratories, now in existence for more than four decades, has made valuable contributions towards the nation's quest for self-reliance in conventional armaments for the Defence Services. A high percentage of the production value of the Defence Ordnance Factories of the government originates from weapons and munitions developed by the Armament Group of Labs of DRDO. In recent years these laboratories have contributed significantly to the development of technologies pertaining to small arms, mines, guns, rockets and allied systems.

Years of experience have led the Armament Group of Laboratories to develop core competence in designing state-of-the art small arms, grenades, mines, guns, mortars, artillery rocket systems, as well as explosive components for these systems. DRDO ranges have state-of-the art facilities for the dynamic evaluation of the ballistic performances of these systems. This article highlights some of the significant technological advances in weapon development made by DRDO in the course of the last decade.

Multi-barrel rocket system—Pinaka: The Pinaka multi-barrel rocket system designed and developed by DRDO is an all-weather, indirect fire-free flight artillery rocket system. It delivers accurate and massive firepower at a high rate over extended ranges. A battery of six launchers can fire a salvo of 72 rockets in 44 seconds. Over 7.2 tonnes of payload in the form of lethal warheads can be delivered up to a range of 38 km and can effectively neutralize a target area of 1000 m by 800 m.

The Pinaka weapon system consists of the following: rocket, multi-barrel rocket launcher, command post, loader vehicle, replenishment vehicle and Digicora MET radar.

The Pinaka launcher system has been built with the most sophisticated technologies available, such as

- A hydraulic vehicle stabilization system with auto-levelling facility
- A user-friendly launcher computer as a man-machine interface
- A microprocessor-based all electric servo-drive system for fast and accurate laying of the launcher
- A secure radio communication for automatic data transfer between Launcher and FCC
- An Automatic Gun Alignment and Pointing System (AGAPS) for autonomous navigation and orientation capability
- A helmet mounted passive night vision device for effective night navigation in blackout conditions.

The Pinaka launcher has both capabilities—rapid coming into action, and ability to deliver massive fire at a high rate.

84 mm light weight launcher: DRDO has successfully designed and developed the 84 mm Light Weight Launcher (LWL), with state-of-the-art composite technology established for the first time in gun barrel design. It lightens by almost half the weight of the existing in-service 84 mm RCL Mk-2 weapon, thus substantially enhancing the mobility, ammunition-carrying capacity and combat efficiency of the troops, especially in high altitude mountain warfare.

The 84 mm LWL is a multi-purpose, close support weapon system capable of firing all the existing HEAT, HE, TPT, smoke and illuminating ammunition. It also meets the firing requirements of advanced ammunition like High Explosive Dual Purpose (HEDP) and High Explosive Anti-Tank (HEAT) with Rocket Assisted Projectile (RAP). For effective target engagements, the weapon has been provided with telescopic, flare and open sights.

Canopy severance system for fighter aircraft: The canopy severance system (CSS) of a fighter aircraft is a life-saving device to help a pilot in distress to eject safely. Two critical components required for the CSS to function effectively are: MDC for cutting canopy bubble and Explosive Transfer Line (ETL) for transmission of explosive shock from one point to another without affecting surroundings.

These were developed and their production established. MDC and ETL function at a detonating velocity of 6000 m/s, ensuring that the cutting action of the Canopy occurs in less than 5 m sec from the time of initiation. An upgraded system developed for HJT-36, a trainer aircraft in flight since February 2003, has, after successful evaluation, been assembled for the first prototype of HJT-36.

FSAPDS ammunition: Technology for developing Fin Stabilised Armour Piercing Discarding Sabot (FSAPDS) ammunition was developed in the country by undertaking *ab initio* R&D activities in DRDO. This technology, once acquired, led to substantial enhancement of the firepower of in-service main battle tanks as well as those under development. The 125 mm FSAPDS Ammunition consists of Penetrator, Sabot, Tail Unit and Combustible cartridge. FSAPDS components are intricate and sophisticated and call for high standards of precision and accuracy during manufacture. These have been indigenously and successfully established in ordnance factories (HAPP, Trichy), an indication of self-reliance in this area.

Under barrel grenade launcher: The Under Barrel Grenade Launcher has been developed to bridge the gap between the hand grenade's maximum range and the mortar's minimum range. In other words, the equipment can be deployed for distances ranging from 50 m to 400 m. This equipment is an add-on attachment to the INSAS Rifle 1B and the AK-47 Rifle, and converts the weapons into dual calibre

weapons, allowing the soldier to fire KE Ammunition or launch 40mm grenades from the shoulder. Attaching this UBGL in no way affects the normal functioning of the rifle. UBGL fires a variety of in-service Multiple Grenade Launcher (MGL) ammunition, for example, HE, HEDP, RP, smoke etc. UBGL consists of two major assemblies in which all other components are housed.

A majority of the components such as barrel, body and sight-assembly are made of aerospace grade aluminium alloy to reduce the overall mass of the weapon without compromising its strength. It is thus a simple design from the point of view of assembly, dis-assembly and maintenance. Integrated Iron Sight as well as Beta Light Sight (BLS) are provided for firing by day and low light conditions.

Modern sub-machine carbine: MSMC is a compact, light sub-machine carbine that is easy to carry and operate. With an effective range of 200 m for close quarter battle, it is meant for the infantry and other arms and services. The MSMC is in the calibre of 5.56 × 30 mm; the length of the weapon is 700 mm with butt extended and 50 0mm with butt retracted. The configuration adopted is a semi bull-pup type. The principle of operation is the same as INSAS, that is, gas operated with rotating bolt. The cyclic rate of fire is 600 to 650 rounds per minute, while the capacity of the metallic box type magazine is 30 rounds. It has single and auto mode provisions. This carbine can effectively penetrate 24 layers of Kevlar Soft Body Armour (SBA) at 200 m range. The carbine has furniture made of lightweight, high strength plastics; it is provided with Iron Sight, Reflex, Laser, PNS and Beta Light Sight (BLS) for firing in all weather and light conditions.

Adrushy Mk II influence mine: Adrushy, the intelligent anti-tank mine is India's answer to the increasing threat posed by modern MBTs. With the introduction of the charge and magnetic influence fuze in the mine, a new dimension has been added to mine warfare. Sophistication, simplicity in handling and an indomitable killing capability make the mine invincible and easy to use.

Anti thermal—anti laser smoke grenade: An 81 mm calibre, the anti thermal—anti laser smoke grenade, based on red phosphorus has been developed by DRDO. The grenade is mounted on either side of the tank's turret and electrically actuated from the MBT grenade launcher. On bursting above the ground, the grenade forms a smoke screen at a distance of about 90m within 4.0 to 5.4 sec. A single grenade forms a white dense smoke screen approximately 10m wide and 8m high, obscuring sight in the visible and infra red range from 0.4 to 14µ. The smoke screen is capable of defeating the thermal imagers and Nd–YAG laser range finder.

Non-lethal sensory irritant hand grenade: A lachrymetric agent, popularly called teargas, is traditionally used in riot situations for mob control. These grenades have limitations; approaching a terrorist hideout is a danger they cannot handle. The newly developed grenade is based on the concentrated extract of a natural red pepper in lower concentrations; this is dispersed in the atmosphere, instantaneously causing irritation in the throat and mucus membrane and also to the skin. This hand grenade is potential ammunition for effectively combating insurgency operations, and useful to the armed forces as well as the civil police.

Within a few seconds it creates a useful smoke screen, which does not allow anyone to hide once it has been dispersed. The exposed mob or terrorist has to either vacate the location or be incapacitated by coughing and irritation to the eyes.

Warheads for missiles: Dual Purpose Improved Conventional (DPIC) bomblets, incendiary and Runway Denial Penetrating Submunition (RDPS) warheads, designed for the Army, Air Force and Navy, are versions of the PRITHVI missile system. Technologies have been developed for submunition, cutting, removal and dispensation mechanisms, safety arming and sequencing unit, and RF altitude switch.

A Tandem warhead for NAG (ATM-3) has been designed and developed. Pre-fragmented (PF) type missile warheads have been developed for PINAKA, AKASH and PRITHVI missiles.

Explosive reactive armour: ERA effectively disrupts and defeats the shaped charge jet of anti-tank missile warheads, thereby reducing its penetrating capability. DRDO developed an ERA capable of defeating the latest anti-tank missile warheads. The ERA developed is lightweight, cost-effective and can be mounted on various different parts of the tank to increase levels of

protection. The total weight penalty on account of mounting of ERA panels on T-72 tank is less than 1.5 tonne.

PBX technology: An aluminized case PBX composition with 85 per cent solid loading has been developed for underwater applications as filling for the 250 kg warhead of a heavy weight torpedo.

Gun propellant for low vulnerability ammunition: Conventional gun propellants are highly vulnerable to accidental initiation during combat operations. After extensive experimentation and evaluation trials, a low vulnerable propellant (LOVA) based on RDX and CA was developed for gun application. The propellant is comparatively less sensitive to impact, friction and accidental ignition and meets all the ballistics requirements of 120 mm FSAPDS ammunition.

Combustible cartridge case: Brass cartridge cases used in gun ammunition are not only costly but also pose logistic problems, and the copper required for making them is imported. These drawbacks are overcome by the use of combustible cartridge cases (CCCs). An indigenous technology for the manufacture of CCCs for tank gun ammunition of various calibres has been established at DRDO. The CCCs exhibit excellent burning characteristics and do not leave any debris in the gun chamber, at the breach or in the fighting compartment. In addition to other advantages, these cases also exude an additional energy to the extent of 600 calories per case. Resin-based CCC with higher strength also has been developed by DRDO for gun ammunition.

Case bonded technology: The processing of large size case bonded motors up to 1000 mm in diameter, up to 5000 mm in length and total weight up to four tons has now been established. Technology for processing a case bounded motor, with a high length-to-diameter ratio, is also available. Propellant grains are cast by conventional vacuum or pressure casting techniques with a high degree of interface integrity. The technology has been established and proved in both large diameter and small diameter grains. Burning rates achieved are between 4.5 mm/sec to 40 mm/sec at 70 KSC. Motors have been processed with very complicated web geometry, for instance, the 26 petal fin-o-cyl configuration.

Cyclotetramethylenetetranitramine: DRDO has established a synthetic procedure for largescale manufacture of this powerful solid explosive. A Pilot Plant of 6 TPA capacity, based on the continuous nitrolysis of hexamine was established. The process for preparing the fine HMX that needs to be incorporated in explosive and propellant formulations has been developed on pilot plant scale.

PZT-based electroceramics: Modified Lead Zirconate Titanate (PZT) Piezoelectric Ceramics, a class of polycrystalline oxide materials, exhibit excellent piezoelectric properties and find wide-ranging applications in electro-mechanical/ mechano-electrical energy conversion transducers. DRDO has done pioneering R&D and production work on these materials and offers various grades of high quality PZT based ceramics for strategic defence and commercial applications.

This is a strategic energy-converting material that finds applications in:
- Impact initiation of Hollow Charge (HC) warheads
- Electro-acoustic transducers for SONAR systems
- Sensors for sea mines, torpedoes and imaging arrays.

Over the next decades, the Army will be interested in a number of new complex weapon systems such as Guided Gun and rocket munition, smart mines, countermine systems, indirect fire systems that are lighter in weight and MLRS. The developments in the field of micro-sensors and nano-materials are bound to influence the development of a new range of weapons. The Armament Group of Laboratories of DRDO are now preparing to undertake the development of these weapons/munitions and related technologies in a bid to keep pace with advances in the field of armaments. □

Sudarshan Kumar
Director, Materials, DRDO

New materials technologies

All major systems needed by the Services require material having the capability to perform under various stress conditions for extended periods. New materials, which are lighter but meet the required performance specifications, are critical: particularly those in aerospace, missiles, and naval systems.

DRDO materials laboratories are entrusted with the development of advanced and specialized materials and to pursue technologies in the areas of metals and alloys; ceramics, polymers and composites; rubbers, fluids and lubricants; textiles, explosives, paints, etc., to function under critical and hostile environments. The current areas in focus include specialized nano and smart materials and technologies for specific applications in systems and devices. Some of the materials technologies developed by DRDO and the infrastructures created during the last ten years are presented here.

Modern turbojet aerofoil castings: Extremely complex thin walled aerofoil castings of directionally solidified and single crystal super alloys for modern turbojet engines have been developed. The state-of-the-art facility of vacuum precision casting, finishing and testing in this area established. The castings meet extremely tight visual, FPI and radiographic specifications.

Super alloy integral castings: Super alloy integral castings with grain size below M5.5 in hub portion, aerofoil profile within ±0.2 mm from the nominal and micro-porosity below 0.5 per cent have been developed. These conform to Class-I standard, stringent visual and DP specifications and have the capability to perform under high stresses at metal temperatures of about 900°C.

Titanium sponge extraction: Production of titanium from indigenous raw material ($TiCl_4$) at an industrial scale of 3000 kg per batch by modular type 'Combined Process Technology' and with good consistency and repeatability was demonstrated. It involves electro extraction of Mg from $MgCl_2$, a by-product of titanium production. Sponge product satisfies international standards recommended for raw material for production of high quality cold rolled products in the areas of aerospace, petrochemical, chemical, power, medical, biomedical implants, oil exploration, armour, automotive, ordnance, sports goods, jewellery and architecture.

Titanium aluminide: The metallurgy, melting, processing and heat treatment of Ti_3Al base alloys have been established and optimized and the role of alloying elements investigated. Scale-up up to 250 kg level has been established. It has room temperature and 650°C strength equivalent to INCO 718; adequate tensile ductility and fracture toughness and stress rupture equivalent to INCO 718. Its applications are potential replacements for higher density Ni base alloys in compressor stages of aero engines.

High strength aluminium alloys for aerospace applications: High strength Al-Zn-Mg-Cu-Zr alloys are widely used for aerospace applications. Two such alloys: 7010-T7451 (plates: 20 mm) and 7449–7751 (sheets: 5 mm) indigenized and produced in DMRL at laboratory scale. These alloys containing Ag and Sc have good weldability.

Ultrahigh strength, high fracture toughness low-alloy steel: Steels of ultrahigh strength (yield strength > 1400 MPa) coupled with high fracture toughness developed to meet requirement of minimum weight, while ensuring high reliability. In such applications, cost and availability make low-alloy steels an attractive option. New Ni-Si-Cr-Co-Mo containing low-alloy steel (DMR-1700), has strength-toughness combination, attainable in commonly used hardened (air cooled) and tempered condition better than hitherto best reported values for low-alloy steels 300M and D6ac and falls in upper-bound range for 18Ni (250) maraging steel, that has total alloying content in excess of 30 wt per cent.

The reproducibility of attractive strength and fracture toughness properties has been established in tonnage scale melts. With base steel as filler, near 100 per cent weld efficiency can be achieved in weld+heat treat condition. It provides cost effective replacement of maraging steels for Booster Motor Casings and Lighter version of Mortar Base Plates. DMRL has successfully demonstrated technology for smaller diameter motor casings.

AB class steel: Technology for AB class of steel has been developed. Based on DRDO technology, the special steel in the form of sheets and plates and the bulb bars bulk orders of the Navy have been executed through SAIL to meet entire requirement of high quality steel for construction of the very first aircraft carrier to be built in the country.

High performance samarium cobalt magnets: Permanent magnets of Samarium Cobalt ($SmCo_5$) with hardness: 450–500 VHN, density: 8.2–8.4 g/cc, residual induction: 8.4±0.2 kG, maximum energy product: 17–18 MGOe, coercivity: 8.0±0.2 kOe, intrinsic coercivity: >16 kOe, reversible temperature coefficient: 450 ppm/°C and maximum service temperature: 200°C were developed. With excellent combination of remenance coercivity and energy product, these offer additional advantage for their use in miniaturization of devices. VSSC has provided quality assurance and is their potential user.

Silver nanoparticles: Optically clear and stable colloidal solutions of silver nanoparticles of variable sizes and shapes showing different colours depending on their plasmonic absorption frequencies were synthesized at room temperature by chemical reduction of silver ions ($AgNO_3$). There were coordinated with dendrigraft polymer-polyethyleneimine (PEI) with formaldehyde in aqueous medium. The process of reduction could be completed within 5 minutes with very good control on particle size and shape by varying $AgNO_3$/PEI ratio.

Carbon nano tubes and polymer nanocomposites: The lab scale production of Multi Walled Carbon Nano Tubes (MWCNT) at 30 g per batch and micro coils, nano coils at 15 g per batch level with desired micro structure and purity was established. Based on CNT, chiral and high permittivity materials synthesized in lab and the electromagnetic radiation absorption coatings with reflection loss over 10 dB in 2–18 GHz region developed. The CNT-based structural composites were also prepared.

A room temperature curable polymer nanocomposite prepared by incorporating functionalised MWNT into polyurethane resin for damping applications. The damping in frequency range 1–1000 Hz was 10–15 dB for 2 per cent of MWNT incorporation. It finds application in low frequency vibration damping.

Fibres from CNT in PP composite and silver nano particles in PAN composite: DMSRDE designed, fabricated and established unique facility to draw fibres from composites. Using this facility, fibres from CNT in PP composite and silver nano particles in PAN composite were drawn. CNT based fibre showed an improved tensile strength. The fibres based on silver nano particles exhibited different colours depending upon conditions of processing. These also showed excellent anti microbial characteristics.

Conducting polymers and nanomaterials: Conducting polyaniline synthesized by DLJ at room temperature in aqueous medium and doped with specific metal complex ions. It has good environmental stability and stable dc conductivity over a wide temperature range of 200–400 K. It was used to develop a number of strategic products including camouflage paints in visible, near infrared and microwave regions of electromagnetic spectrum. The technology for production in 25 kg batch scale has been established.

Nanofibers of polyaniline and its copolymers through electrochemical route by template method and also through chemical route were synthesized by NPOL. Conductivity was in the range of 1–10 S/cm. UV curable conducting polymers of polyaniline synthesized had conductivity ranging from 3 to 10^{-5} S/cm.

Conducting fabrics: A process to convert any textile fabric into highly electrically conducting material using electroless process of *in-situ* reduction of metal from metal ion containing solution The product reveals electrical resistance in the range of 1 ohm/cm^2 and microwave reflection of 40–60 dB. The product has been converted into easy to apply adhesive tapes. It can find wide range applications to provide EMI shielding and microwave signature simulation on complex geometries.

Nanocomposites of metal oxides:
Nanocomposites of pure and mixed metal oxides in copolymer matrix of aniline formaldehyde were synthesized in single step in aqueous medium. The polymeric a matrix contained uniform distribution of nano-particles of binary and ternary metal oxides, including spinel- and hexa-ferrites. Formation of single domain particles, observed in case of nanocomposites of spinel ferrites, showed phenomena of super para-magnetism. Some of these nanocomposites showed diffuse reflectance properties, useful for camouflaging in visible and near infrared regions. Coatings of paints developed by using these materials have reflectance, which highly match with corresponding terrain elements viz. sand, vegetation, etc.

Nanophosphors: Luminescent ZnS based nanophoshpor materials, synthesized through a highly versatile wet chemical route, showed wide range of emission colours from blue to orange. The synthesis of ZnS and its doping was a single step process at room temperature. The optimization of reaction parameters enabled incorporation of wide range of dopants viz. Cu, Cu-halogen, Cu-Al-halogen, Cu-Al-Mn, etc., in ZnS matrix. The size of ZnS nanoparticles range in 2–4 nm.

There is high quantum efficiency of product, easy control of particle size and tunability of colour (Blue to red). Three categories of nanophosphors synthesized are: PVP-capped nanocrystals (highly luniscent); Doped nanorods (2d-extended doped ZnS nanorods) and Nano-micro core-shell structures (highly luminescent ZnS nanoparticles, *in-situ* doped with Cu-Al pairs and encapsulated with ZnO shells).

ZnO nanostructures: A simple surfactant and catalyst-free wet chemical method has been established to grow highly oriented bi-pyramidal ZnO nanorods into hexagonal shape with c-axis preferred orientation perpendicular to substrate surface, with tip size of ~20–40 nm in diameter and aspect ratio upto 10. Different tip morphologies of these rods are also synthesized by changing the chemical conditions. Further, successful doping of different dopant ions such as Sn, Cd, Zn and Co etc. into these rods has also been achieved at room temperature. The cobalt doped ZnO nanorods have been found to show ferromagnetic character at room temperature. Such materials may find applications in the area of spintronics.

Coolants and fluids: A variety of coolants for use in engines, radar systems, laser range finders etc. to function at high altitudes areas and extremely low temperatures (–40 to –60°C) have been developed. These protect metal parts from corrosion without any adverse effects on rubber materials. Recoil fluids for Bofors gun for operation up to –60°C and hydraulic fluids for Sindhughosh class of submarines developed are in service. Based on technologies developed by DMSRDE, the requirements of all these fluids for Services are being met from trade.

Structural adhesives: A structural adhesive, SA-8, has been developed for bonding of optical components of Ring Laser Gyro. It has excellent toughness and low/high temperature performance properties and successfully used in gyro-assembly of missiles. SA-6, another structural adhesive is for use as binder between copper cone and explosive mixture (HMX/TNT) in warhead assembly of NAG missile.

Anticorrosive paints: Two grades of solvent-free anticorrosive paints developed at NMRL for corrosion protection of interior compartments of naval ships/submarines. One Grade (EP-1) is for general interior compartments and the other Grade (EP-2) for areas susceptible to damage by chemical spillage (acid). The composition is epoxy resin cured with polyamide, pigmented with suitable pigments and extenders (two-pack system). It can be applied through brush to produce dry film thickness of 250±25 microns/coat, and the pot life is 2hrs (min). The areas of applications are interior compartments of ships, storage tanks for petroleum products and the areas prone to spillage of acids.

Heavy duty non-skid paint: A heavy-duty non-skid paint composition has been developed to prevent skidding of personnel and aircraft on flight, helo and weather decks of naval ships. It also possesses resistance to thermal stresses due to intermittent heating up to 250°C. Its composition is epoxy resins cured with polyamide hardener, pigmented with titanium dioxide, suitable extenders and coarse aggregates (two-pack system). It can be applied through brush to produce dry film thickness of 250±25 microns/coat. The pot life is 4hrs (min). The areas of applications are deck surface, engine room floors and surfaces requiring anti-slip properties.

Fire retardant intumescent paint: A fire retardant paint possessing intumescent characteristics has been developed. It produces char of about 100 times of original thickness, protecting the underneath substrate by thermal insulation. It has composition of polymer emulsion pigmented with titanium dioxide and intumescent materials (one pack) and can be applied through brush to produce dry film thickness of 250±25 microns/coat. It produces non-toxic smoke. Its applications include electrical installations, interiors of high-rise buildings, railway compartments and interior compartments of ships.

Polycarbosilane: Process for bulk synthesis of polydimethyl silane and poly carbo silane suitable for preparation of polycarbosilane fibre leading to SiC fibre or for preparation of polycarbosilane based composites has been established.

Carbographite materials for seals: Carbographites, the advanced composite materials, based on graphite filler dispersed in carbon matrix produced by DMSRDE. These contain specific reinforcing fillers with silicates of Al, Mg,

Ca; silica as reinforcing fillers and P salts as additive. These materials combine strength, hardness and wear resistance properties of carbon and the natural lubricity, good conductivity and machinability of graphite. The seals meet requirements in gearbox assembly of Kaveri engine.

Submarine seals: This is a critical component for sealing of underwater objects and has been designed for very low compression set, retention of sealing force, retention of mechanical and physical properties in severe environment involving temperature extremes, pressure variations and salinity. Material functions effectively under transient and dynamic loading unloading conditions.

Activated carbon spheres: Activated Carbon Spheres (ACS) beads developed by DMSRDE possess large adsorption capacity. ACS based fabrics in NBC Permeable suits Mk IV provide them a high protection level and a breakthrough time of more than 22 hrs.

NBC pads: NBC pads based on polyethylene and specific fillers lead or ferro boron powder with matching performance in terms of physical, mechanical and radiation shielding characteristics compared to imported Russian pads for BMP-2 vehicle and T-72.

Summer cool materials: Multiple phase change materials containing hypo and hyper eutectoid solid solutions of binary systems of fatty acids have been prepared. Owing to their multiple phase changes in 30-60°C range and easy phase reversal in tropical nights, these are highly suitable in passive heating/cooling applications in extreme climates and more effective than conventional single phase change materials.

These materials can be filled in metallic or FRP cavities to make panels for passive cooling/heating applications in permanent/temporary buildings and structures. These can also be incorporated in heat exchangers to make low power incentive air cooling/heating devices. After macro/micro encapsulation, these materials can be utilized for heat sink applications in electrical/electronic devices for increasing their reliability in hot tropical (desert) regions.

Cation and anion exchange membranes: Cation and anion exchange membranes are capable of exchanging cations and anions, respectively, through them and are used in fabrication of Electrodialysis Desalination plant for conversion of brackish water into potable water. The ion-exchange capacity of these membranes has marked increase in capacity from 1.5 to about 3.0meq/g (cation exchange membrane) and from 1.2 to about 2.4 meq/gm (anion exchange membrane) on dry basis. Ion-exchange membranes consist of support cloth (nylon/polyester), PVC resin as binder and exchange resin powder (divinylbenzene-styrene copolymer based cation and anion exchange resin). These improved membranes were used for development of ED plant for highly brackish water treatment.

Metal oxide coated titanium electrode: A stable mixed oxide coated titanium electrode for polarity reversal ED plant developed by coating mixed oxides of ruthenium, iridium and platinum on titanium sheet using thermo chemical glazing process (pyrolysis). Prototype electrodes of different sizes prepared and trial tested in 15 m^3/day capacity ED module, which gave more than 100 hrs trouble free operation with 80–85 per cent desalination capacity. The technology has been upgraded to make 2 m x 0.5 m electrode.

Rubber encapsulants: Rubber encapsulant developed at NPOL, functions as barrier material for protection of electro-acoustic transducer against seawater and marine corrosion and provides window for acoustic wave transmission. It also provides the electrical insulation for piezoceramic materials and the required structural integrity against various mechanical stresses encountered in service and handling. Its special characteristics include low water absorption and permeation, low dynamic damping, optimum processability, acoustic impedance and amenability to bonding with various substrates.

Low-temperature vulcanizable rubber: This material and the process developed enable encapsulation of transducers at temperature as low as 60°C. Curable at low temperature (60–80°C) with property levels of normal cure rubber (150°C), optimal combination of physical, mechanical, electrical and processing characteristics.

Acoustic wedges: Wedge shaped linings are familiar for common use in area of room acoustics and microwave anechoic chambers. The wedge shape geometry of lining reduces criticality of

impedance matching, since the gradual transition of impedance is made possible. Two types of composites have been used for the fabrication of acoustic wedges. The core is a light weight composite of glass microspheres embedded epoxy resin which acts as sound reflector and material system for clad is a heavy composite with low sound velocity and acoustic impedance close to that of water to facilitate capturing of incident acoustic energy.

Acoustic baffle: Rubber is an important functional member of acoustic baffle, which is a critical acoustic component of advanced sonar passive surveillance array. The viscoelastic layer has a multi role function. The material is tailor made for durable adhesive bonding. This is a rubber based viscoelastic layer, custom designed for specific acoustic and damping properties.

Anti shock and vibration mount: These mounts are meant primarily for isolating machinery onboard against the damaging effects of underwater explosions and for preventing or minimizing machinery vibrations from transmitting to the platform base-structures and vice versa. Importance of anti-vibration treatments has increased many fold recently on account of the initiatives for stealth. Reduction in radiated noise from structure-borne vibration has been actively pursued. Shock and vibration mount technology is an important area for meeting this challenge.

Vibration isolation module jelly: This is a modified polydiemthylsiloxane jelly material. The raw materials, ethoxy terminated silicone resin, catalysts and silicone oil, are mixed in predetermined ratios for *in situ* curing to form the final jelly material. The material is elastomeric and flexible, therefore winding on the winch is facilitated. It is inert and non-corrosive and therefore does not affect the components in contact with it. Viscoelastic properties remained stable within temperature range –20 to + 80°C. The material is a critical component of vibration isolation module of towed array sonar, due to which the acoustic modules are isolated from ship borne vibrations transmitted through the tow cables and rear end vibrations, to the tune of 10 to 13 dB/m in the frequency range 20–4000 Hz.

Passive underwater acoustic absorbers: Passive underwater acoustic absorbers were developed using modified polyurethanes. An echo reduction of 8–16 dB was achieved for various compositions. Minimum sample thickness required was 20mm. Acoustic panel of 0.5×0.5m was fabricated and was found to have 12–18dB echo reduction from 5–15 kHz. Results indicate that the panels can act as a good anechoic lining material in underwater calibration tanks. The samples were found to have good aging resistance and moisture resistance. These panels will have applications as acoustic lining material for anechoic tanks and underwater towed bodies.

Thermoplastic elastomers encapsulants: A series of Thermoplastic Elastomers (TPE) for encapsulation and damping applications has been developed. TPE combine the functional performance and properties of conventional thermoset rubber with the processability of thermoplastics to enhance the design freedom, improve functionality and reduces part costs. Compared to thermoset rubber, TPE compounds simplify processing and shorten cycle times by eliminating mixing or vulcanization steps, eliminate flash, increase consumer appeal with unlimited colors or fragrances and bond easily with themselves or with numerous other materials to allow soft touch-over molding.

Syntactic foams: Syntactic foams are a class of low density high strength materials which contain a continuous polymer matrix with embedded hollow micro-spheres to achieve high strengths and low densities. Syntactic foam developed is a material with densities as low as 0.3 g/cm^3 with very high strength and is acoustically transparent. The applications include acoustic reflector, buoyancy module for NAGAN, float for LCA fuel gauge, end-cap for MEMS vector sensor, etc.

Thermal insulation materials: A coating material to solve thermal insulation problem associated with front cover of bearing of Kaveri engine as per requirement of GTRE has been developed. The material composition is room temperature curable silicon resin filled with suitable fillers and silane-based adhesion promoting agent incorporated for improved thermal and adhesion characteristics. Prototype of K-4 engine component was coated with the material and evaluated at GTRE.

Tetragonal zirconia polycrystalline (TZP) ceramic: Nanocrystalline, pure and homogeneous yttria and ceria doped TZP powders, developed at NMRL, using spray-drying technique. These TZP ceramics have superior mechanical properties with high melting point: 2680°C, high hardness: 13 GPa, high mechanical strength: 700–1200 MPa at elevated temperatures, high fracture toughness, negligible creep and low coefficient of friction, compatible thermal expansion with cast iron and steel, high resistance to thermal shock, corrosion, oxidation and wear. The major application areas are high temperature structural dies crumbles and ball melting.

Zirconia toughened alumina (ZTA) ceramic: NMRL developed powders of ZTA, using a semi-wet process, and technologies for producing ZTA ceramic tiles. The Material is TZP dispersed alumina with hardness: 15.5 GPa, strength: 550 MPa and fracture toughness: 8 MPa√m. Application areas include body and vehicle armours, wear resistant coating, high temperature structure and cutting tools. The tiles exhibit excellent performance as armour material. Full body armour plates have also been developed.

PMN-PT ceramics: Piezoelectric, electrostrictive compositions of PMN-PT powders developed at NMRL using an innovative technique to avoid formation of pyrochlore phase. It is cost effective processing route and the PMN-PT ceramic components developed exhibit improved properties. Ceramic compositions have excellent piezoelectric and electrostrictive properties with performance superior to commercially available ceramics. These have applications in hydrophones, multi layer actuators and structural health monitoring.

Polymeric rubbing fenders: NMRL developed polymeric rubbing fenders are a better substitute for wood. The material is not damaged by impact with concrete or steel or by seawater and is resilient enough to damp impact force. The material is a combination of high strength polymers and has long life (>10 years) in marine atmosphere.

Composite for dock-blocks: A composite metallic lightweight structure embedded in high strength polymeric blend system has been developed as a better substitute for teak wood. The material is not damaged by impact or by seawater and is resilient enough to take up the contour of ship in repeated dry docking operations. It is a unique invention in the field of high load bearing lightweight structures and has long life (>10 years) in marine atmosphere. Maintenance during service life is not required.

The areas of applications include dock-blocks for ships, railway sleepers and blast proof containers.

Sacrificial anodes for naval ships: Ships and structures submerged in seawater are protected from corrosion attack by indium activated aluminium based sacrificial anodes. Optimised composition of these anodes has led to considerable increase in efficiency. It has efficiency of 90 per cent, provides cathodic protection of ships, submarines, offshore structures and subsystems and available in various dimensions and shapes.

Low potential anodes for cathodic protection of high strength steels: High strength steels can undergo hydrogen embrittlement at more negative (–870 mV) cathodic protection potential. This anode can protect high strength steels from corrosion and also reduces structural failure due to hydrogen embrittlement in seawater. Its application area is cathodic protection of high strength steels used for submarine hull and its subsystem. The salient features include

efficiency of 70 per cent, OCP and CCP are –900 and –850 mV vs SCE and it can be shaped into various dimensions and shapes.

ICCP anodes for naval ships: Corrosion protection of ships is also achieved by using non-consumable inert electrodes in Impressed Current Cathodic Protection (ICCP) systems. In the majority of the Naval ships lead-silver alloy anode has been used whereas platinised titanium anode is used in Naval ships requiring higher current density. It is dimensionally stable and cost effective.

Ferrocene polyglycol oligomer (FPGO): Process for synthesis of FPGO successfully developed at HEMRL. It is a potential ballistic modifier, which has tremendous advantages over currently used high burn rate modifier, n-butyl ferrocene.

Amorphous boron powder: Facility created at HEMRL to produce Amorphous Boron Powder (ABP) Grade-II (85–88 percent purity) at 10kg/ month with a particle size of 3–4 mm and the enrichment of ABP Grade-II to Grade-I (purity>92 percent). □

Light Combat Aircraft

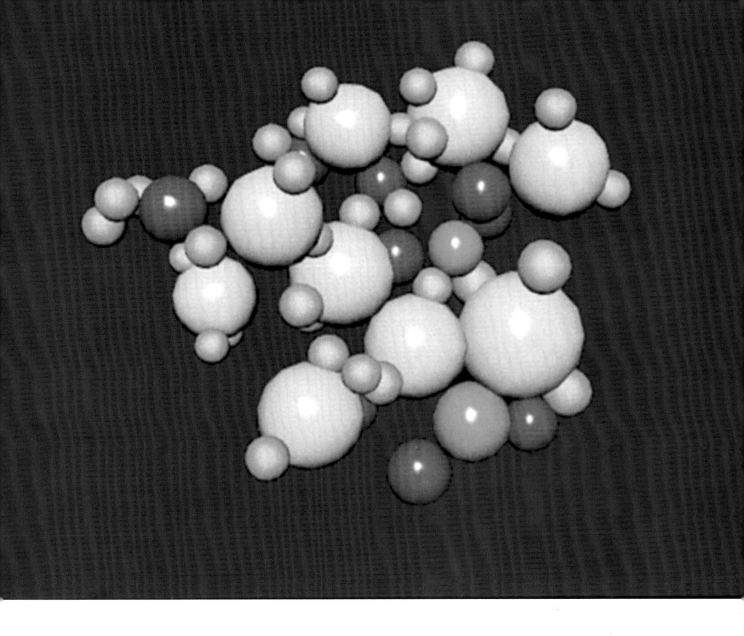

BIOTECHNOLOGY

Samir K Brahmachari
Institute of Genomics and
Integrative Biology &
Director General, CSIR

Human Genome research in global context

Biology has undergone a transformation in recent years. High-end technology, large volumes of data and a multi-disciplinary approach are the corner stones of this revolution. Ten years back, when the world was racing to finish the sequencing of the human genome, I used to wonder if we Indians, with our unique gene pool and ethnic diversity, will be just watching from the sidelines the world leaping forward into the post-sequencing era that promised new drugs, personalized medicines and biomarkers. Of course, it promised to enrich fundamental knowledge.

Fortunately, our genomics research over the past decade has aimed at harnessing science of international standards to create economically viable solutions for India. The scientific endeavour has been technologically challenging and intellectually stimulating.

India is a melting pot of human genetic diversity. It has over a billion people encompassing a few hundred ethnic groups, over four thousand communities, several thousand endogamous groups with about 325 languages and 25 scripts and separated by extensive social, cultural and biological assortment. Such richness of genetic diversity is not observed anywhere in the world with the exception of the African continent.

This genetically rich resource presents a template for analyzing exciting questions related to ethnic diversity, migration, founder populations and history of diseases. Additionally, the large family sizes, social structures which govern marriages amongst the diverse ethnic groups and sheer size of the population provides an excellent opportunity for mapping genes associated with common and complex diseases and for understanding the genetic predisposition to complex disorders.

Complex disorders such as epilepsy, schizophrenia, bipolar disorder, diabetes and cardio vascular disorder among several others, each affects about 1 to 5 per cent of the Indian population. These disorders have emerged as a major public health problem and a national concern in terms of person-days lost. The management of the disease through conventional methods requires expensive interventions. In addition to this, most of the complex disorders require long-term medication that amplifies the disease management problems. In such a scenario, availability and affordability of the drugs and accessibility of services for combating these complex disorders will be the prime determinants in the control of the disease.

The availability of human genome sequence has heralded a new era of predictive medicine wherein it is anticipated each individual can have a personalized health regime based on his or her genetic make-up. However, this is an expensive proposition and is likely to benefit affluent individuals only. Can India that has a sizable economically marginalized population afford it? Can innovations within the purview of existing resources in genomics be able to provide a sustainable health care affordable to all? In this regard, pharmacogenomics, originally conceived to provide a genotype-based individualized medication predominantly for the developed countries, could be successfully adapted for application amongst marginalized populations of the developing countries as well as to the large section of the developed world that lack health insurance.

Pharmacogenomics, which has the potential to reveal the underlying genetic basis of adverse drug reaction and limited drug efficacies that might limit market size in order to avoid 'one size fits all' is expected to play a critical role in clinical medicine in the near future. Pharmacogenomics-based-drug and dosage management is very expensive and unaffordable to millions in India.

However, a recent breakthrough in the field of pharmacogenomics shows that it has a potential for making drugs affordable by keeping old and cheap drugs in the market and reviving drugs withdrawn from the market because of side effects. For example, the choice of antiepileptic drugs (AEDs) (the drugs given for lifelong medications) in patients with epilepsy is mainly based on efficacy and safety of each drug, both of which are highly variable from patient to patient. To reach everyone who needs AEDs, economic issues are a major determining factor. In countries like India, the annual cost of first-line AEDs (generic version) for one patient varies from $20 for phenobarbitone, $30 for phenytoin, $45 for carbamazepine, and $90 for valproate. In contrast the cost of the newer AEDs is much higher, varying from $150 to $400. Therefore, the anticipated total annual savings for about one million patients (a much lower estimate than the actual incidence) under the public health care system, by retaining low-cost drugs, will be several hundred million dollars.

However, one also needs to take into account the higher incidence of adverse effects from the older AEDs compared to the newer ones. Therefore, a balance has to be exercised in the choice of drugs. Not all Indians can tolerate the same amount of a given AED. For example, a section of Indian sub-population do not tolerate high dose of phenytoin, 300 mg and beyond per day, while Caucasians seem to tolerate a higher doses. Therefore, for fine-tuning of dose adjustment and to minimize the side effect, in addition to absorption, transport, and metabolism of drugs, pharmacogenomics needs to be examined for commonly used AEDs.

In this regard, development of drug response biomarkers will enable low-cost drugs to be retained in the market for therapeutic use. Once this is done, only a small percentage of patients that do not respond or show low-tolerance to existing low cost drugs need to be prescribed the more expensive new generation drugs, thereby reducing the overall public health care cost without compromising the quality of treatment.

Another example is the treatment of schizophrenia by typical antipsychotic drugs wherein 20 to 30 per cent of the patients develop side effects characterized by involuntary movements (tardive dyskinesia). Newer drugs reduce the risk of tardive dyskinesia but have increased risk of weight gain. In this case also, identification of potential drug response biomarkers would permit fine-tuning of the risk vs. benefit profile and lead to individualized medicines.

Thus, the discovery of potential drug response biomarkers suitable for a large fraction of the Indian population would be a key to effective disease and drug dosage management. This would also need extensive validation and replication across India. Some critical issues are: how do we define a prototype Indian population? Would there be one or many? Could we identify units of genetic homogeneity amidst the diversity of populations wherein a potential biomarker is likely to behave similarly across all the members of the population? This therefore necessitates the need for building a map that would define the genetic structure of the Indian population and also enable comparison with other populations of the world. This novel thought led the Council of Scientific and Industrial Research (CSIR) to initiate a unique scientific endeavour that generated the Indian Genome Variation database.

Indian Genetic Map
The Indian Genome Variation initiative is a network programme, the first of its kind in the country in the field of genomics undertaken by over 150 participants from diverse disciplines of life sciences, anthropology, statistics and computational biology. Initiated in 2003 and tenured for five years, the project was undertaken as a consortium effort by six constituent laboratories of the Council of Scientific and Industrial Research (CSIR) and ISI Kolkata with funding from the Government of India. In addition to the institutional facilities, the project also involved participation by the Anthropological Survey of India that has helped in the identification of the various Indian subpopulations.

The collaboration involves The Centre for Genomic Application (TCGA), established through the support of the Department of Science and Technology and CSIR with The

Chatterjee Group (TCG) for high throughput sequencing and genotyping; and SilicoGene Informatics Private Limited along with LabVantage, India, for development of a comprehensive platform for IGV database management, analysis and portal development. The project would not have been successful but for the voluntary participation of thousands of individuals from diverse ethnic groups spread across the regions of India.

The Indian Genome Variation database (http://igvdb.res.in/) houses information on variations of over a thousand genes which have been implicated in disease like asthma, diabetes, neuropsychiatric disorders, cancer, coronary artery disease, clotting disorders, high altitude disorders, retinitis pigmentosa, predisposition to malaria, as well as other infectious diseases and drug metabolism. The populations selected in the study have been taken from contrasting ethnic populations (classified on the basis of size) derived from four major linguistic lineages viz Indo-European, Dravidian, Austro-Asiatic and Tibeto-Burman. The number of populations selected and their sizes, as estimated from various surveys, represent nearly a quarter of the Indian population.

This huge amount of basal variation data would allow one to address fundamental questions related to predictive marker discovery and pharmacogenomic studies. For instance, a pilot pharmacogenomic study on response to salbutamol, a beta2-adrenergic agonist used to treat asthma, identified polymorphisms in the beta2 adrenoceptor gene that predicted response to this drug. Individuals could be classified into poor and good responders based on this marker. This biomarker was found to have frequency differences across different populations in the country with pockets of populations having respectively extremely high frequency of the responder or non-responder genotypes. A follow-up study using this basal data would be extremely useful, not only for pharmaceutical companies, but also for devising therapeutic regimens for different populations.

The efforts of the international and Indian scientific communities via the HapMap project and the Indian Genome Variation database project respectively have made available the genome-wide SNP variation data on selected populations across the globe and for India in particular. These rich resources are likely to yield several potential biomarkers that might be associated with complex diseases. Extensive data mining and laboratory based experimental efforts in conjunction with clinical data from hospitals would be required to pinpoint the biomarkers that have a tight association with the disease.

To transfer the beneficial effects of these findings to potential patients, one needs to have an active pharmacogenomics programme in the country, the output of which would be the incorporation of pharmacogenomics data into medical prescriptions. This will usher in a major transformation in health care system of the country. However there is one reservation – will the price-conscious pharmaceutical companies support development of therapies that will help only a small section of the population, or the majority who would belong to the economically weaker section of the society?

Open source

We need global initiatives to develop rational means for optimized drug therapy to ensure maximum efficacy with minimal side effects. In conjunction with the above approach there is a need for developing an open source biomarker programme that will strive to keep the low-cost drugs in market. This could involve voluntary participants from government and private sector research laboratories, universities, institutes, and corporations working together with appropriate credit sharing/distribution mechanisms.

This will provide an opportunity for scientists, doctors and technocrats with diverse expertise to work for a common cause. The output of this would be a open-source platform: computational, experimental and clinical for developing a pharmacogenomic approach for ensuring the availability of cost-effective drugs to the economically marginalized people of the developing world. Examples of successful open source systems can be found, among others, in information technology and the Human Genome project. Thus, the open source approach towards pharmacogenomics is the logical next step towards providing personalized medicine at an affordable cost for the developing world. □

C R Bhatia
Former Secretary
Deaprtment of Biotechnology

Biotechnology for crop improvement

Advances in understanding the metabolic processes in plants at molecular level are leading to their applications for genetic enhancement of crop plants. Genomics—structural, functional, transcriptome (expressed genome in a cell at a defined time) analysis, proteomics, metabolomics and other omic sciences are rapidly moving forward, providing conceptually new opportunities for the improvement of crop plants. Plant tissue culture (PTC), marker assisted selection (MAS) and genetic engineering (GE or application of recombinant DNA techniques to move genes across species) are the three main areas of modern biotechnology that contribute towards the improvement of cultivated plants. The process for delivering agronomically useful new genotypes to farmers for cultivation, however, is a long process even in conventional plant breeding. Biotechnology applications reduce the development time but require larger team efforts and higher investment. When GE is used, bio-safety, food safety and environmental concerns further increase the time and cost.

The trend in the USA—the current leader in crop biotechnology—is for basic research to be supported by public funds while the product development for commercialization is done by private companies. Even there, the high technology basic research on plants is supported by the Department of Energy and the National Science Foundation and not by the Department of Agriculture. However, as happened in the human genome project, private funding pushed the research efforts ahead of the Government funded laboratories. Many private companies have either initiated plant genomics or are supporting such efforts in public-private partnerships. Development of new cultivars/hybrids is with the seed industry. Recent global developments in genomics and GE are described for a better appreciation of the progress in India.

Global scenario

Genomes of the model plant *Arabidopsis* (a dicot Crucifer species) and the crop plant rice (a monocot) have been sequenced. The current efforts in these plants focus on functional genomics involving identification of specific genes for their functions. A few plant pathogen genomes have also been sequenced and functionally important genes in host-pathogen interactions have been identified. It emerges that resistance or susceptibility is determined by interactions between specific host and pathogen proteins. Such studies are giving further insights into the functioning of resistance and resistance genes in the host and respective virulence genes in the pathogen.

Crop improvement has moved into the post-genomic era. Rice also serves as a model for the genomics initiatives in other cereal crops such as sorghum, maize, barley, wheat and pearl millet, making use of chromosomal synteny. Thanks to the pioneering programme supported by the Rockefeller Foundation for rice biotechnology, a number of molecular biologists in the developed world applied their knowledge, skills and tools to the rice. Japan and China also made large investments to promote rice molecular biology. Scientists from the developing countries, including India, where rice is the staple crop, were supported to work in the advanced laboratories. This led to rapid advances in rice biotechnology. Hybrid rice, haploids, and breeding for insect and disease resistance are now extensively practised in many developing countries. MAS is increasingly used in the breeding programmes, while gene expression studies using micro-array systems are under way in advanced laboratories. A large number of genes that express under different abiotic stresses like salinity and water have been identified and cloned. Nutritionally improved rice strains with higher amount of pro-vitamin A (Golden rice) have been developed. Human milk proteins that provide protection from infections have been expressed in rice. A US company claims to have developed a genetic system that improves the nitrogen uptake, thereby reducing significantly the amount of nitrogenous fertilizer needed for a given yield level. This also works for rapeseed and wheat.

Second generation biotechnology that aims at metabolic engineering is growing rapidly. Chloroplast transformation provides high expression of the transferred genes and is particularly suitable for producing proteins of pharmaceutical use in plants. Metabolic pathways are being altered for the production of desired alkaloids, terpenoids in medicinal and aromatic plants and biopolymers in others. In oil-yielding plants, fatty acid composition has been altered to produce the right proportion of the desired fatty acids. Production of Omega-3, a long chain polyunsaturated fatty acids, and plant-based substitutes for fish oil are being attempted.

Globally, GE cotton, soybean, rapeseed, maize and papaya are under commercial production, to the point where the area with GE crops reached 102 million hectares in 2006. Out of a global cotton area of 35 million ha in 2006, 13.4 grew GE cotton either for Bt or herbicide resistance (HR) or both. The trend is to incorporate more than one gene for insect resistance or to combine it with HR. Drought tolerant maize, high oil soybean and maize, and high stearate soyabean are in the pipeline for commercial release. MAS and PTC are routinely used in breeding programmes abroad.

Plant tissue culture: Propagation of the planting material through PTC (micropropagation) moved out of the research laboratories to commercial activity about fifteen years ago. It provides rapid, large-scale multiplication of elite stocks, new crop cultivars in vegetatively propagated species, and produces disease-free clones. Approximately fifty commercial units with capacities ranging

from 1 to 5 million plants per annum are now operational, while the total production capacity is estimated at about 200 million plants. Some of the units, working as export oriented units, cater exclusively to the needs of overseas clients from USA, Europe and Australia. Micropropagation is a labour intensive activity, and hence, the country offers tremendous cost advantage for the companies abroad to outsource production of planting material from India.

The domestic needs for elite, disease-free planting material is very large and the demand for banana, sugarcane, potato, ornamentals, horticultural plants, spices, medicinal and aromatic plants is rapidly increasing. The Department of Biotechnology plans to set up a national programme to certify the tissue culture propagated planting material for quality assurance to the farmers in a manner similar to the seed certification system. The National Horticulture Mission has identified micropropagation as a means of rapid multiplication of fruit trees and grape vines, and the research efforts continue in a number of laboratories to develop protocols that will lower production costs by reducing energy inputs and using less expensive chemicals in the growth media. Micropropagation can have a huge impact on social and agro-forestry, reforestation, horticulture and replacement of old bushes in tea plantations. A comprehensive programme for the development of wastelands and planting elite tree clones has been taken up by few organizations. The area covered by one of the companies exceeds 29,000 ha. There is increasing interest in such plantations as they serve as carbon sinks, and can earn carbon credits. Tree-based bio-fuel crops can further enhance returns.

Genetically engineered crops: GE cotton with the entomotoxin gene from *Bacillus thurringiensis* (Bt) was approved for commercial cultivation in 2002. Bt cotton has been widely accepted by the farmers, and the area under cultivation increased to 3.8 million ha in 2006. One of the studies showed a 31 per cent increase in yield, a 39 per cent reduction in the number of pesticide sprays and an 88 per cent increase in farmer's profit even though the seed cost is considerably higher compared to non-Bt. Besides the original four hybrids approved for cultivation in 2002, Bt gene has been incorporated in a range of hybrids marketed by various seed companies. Two different Bt genes have been stacked in the new hybrids. Two genes provide wider protection for the boll worm complex and are expected to delay breakdown of resistance. Another Bt gene different from the one presently in use has been imported from China. Bt cotton developed through local research efforts is at an advanced stage of development. Besides cotton, research through local efforts in a variety of crops, including mustard hybrids, nutritionally enhanced potato, insect resistant rice and castor, disease resistant sorghum, potato and groundnut, is at a fairly advanced stage. Some laboratories developed GE stocks, by using gene constructs obtained from abroad under material transfer agreement, have shown excellent expression of the desired trait.

Further efforts towards commercialization have, however, been hampered by issues related to intellectual property rights. Bio-safety and food safety evaluations are expensive, and in the absence of clarity on IPR, funding of such experiments remains uncertain. Network programmes involving several national research institutes are operational for developing GE rice for drought and salinity tolerance, and improved nutritional qualities. Another programme is under way for developing late blight-tolerant potato.

A Task Force on Agricultural Biotechnology constituted by the Ministry of Agriculture, Government of India, recommended high priority for developing GE crops; priorities for all major crops were identified.

An excellent model for public-private partnership has emerged where the private company has made an IPR protected Bt gene freely available to public institutions for incorporation in the open pollinated varieties of egg plant (*Brinjal*), while retaining its right of using the same gene in the hybrids. This has led to the incorporation of this Bt gene into several locally adapted and preferred varieties. Currently both the hybrids and open pollinated varieties are under multi-location evaluation trials. At the basic level, prospecting for new genes and new alleles of the known genes from a diverse ecosystem continues for possible use in the future.

Marker-assisted selection: MAS provides for indirect selection of the desired traits by laboratory screening of the segregating

populations for closely linked DNA marker. A large number of markers suitable for MAS, both for qualitative and quantitative traits (QTLs), with low heritability, have been identified in major crops. The main advantage of MAS is that the desired selections can be made even in the absence of specific biotic or abiotic stress. It is the only option for pyramiding more than one resistance gene from different sources in a genotype. In back cross breeding programmes, selections based on MAS considerably reduces the time involved. The use of MAS in public funded breeding programmes has been slow due to limited interaction between plant breeders and molecular biologists. Wherever the cooperation between the two is good, MAS is becoming a part of the breeding procedure. In many private seed companies, with urgency to bring new hybrids, MAS is extensively used. The International Crop Research Institute for Semi-Arid Tropics (ICRISAT) released a pearl millet hybrid with improved level of downy mildew resistance in 2005. This is the first public-bred hybrid developed using MAS in the country. In 2007 this hybrid was grown in an area of about 30,000 ha.

High productivity

This brief summary of Indian achievements in this field shows that the farmers who raised crops from the new planting materials have benefited. Plant biotechnology has a large potential for increasing productivity, improving quality of the produce, and reducing both the production cost and the environmental impact of the production systems. As evident from excellent publications in plant molecular biology and genetics in last few years, highly competent human resources and reasonably well equipped laboratory infrastructure are now available at a number of places in the country. To fully realize the potential benefits however, acceleration in the pace of research, and change in the mindset to develop products that benefit the farmers are both needed. Crop biotechnology can create wealth and bring social justice for the poor only when they can freely access the new biotechnology products. Even the farmers at the Bottom of the Pyramid can benefit from the enhanced genetic potential embedded in the seed using high science. Such seeds/planting materials offer them a ladder to climb out of the poverty trap. □

Lalji Singh
Director, Centre for Cellular &
Molecular Biology (CCMB)
Hyderabad

Improving health care through genetics

Virtually all human diseases result from the interaction of genes with environment. Studying and understanding this interaction will make possible the development of medicines to treat such diseases and improve the quality of life.

What makes India unique? Many assets and resources, one of which is the country's enviable natural wealth, its rich biodiversity—plant, microbial, animal or human. This wealth ought to be tapped not merely to create knowledge but also to improve the quality of life. Take Ayurveda: It taps the traditional knowledge of medicinal plants to develop medicines for the people of the world at affordable prices.

India, with one-sixth of the world's population, is the best treasure house of human biodiversity. The subcontinent has 4635 anthropologically well-defined endogamous groups, of which 532 are tribal communities (including sub-tribes), 72 are 'primitive' tribes and 36 are hunters and gatherers. Four tribes in Andaman and Nicobar islands with small population sizes are on the verge of extinction. They still live as hunters and gatherers, totally untouched by 'civilization' and without any access to modern medicine. They are products of natural selection and the fittest to survive in the environment they live in. They also have large families with a high degree of consanguinity.

Such rich treasure could potentially be used to map new genes (particularly recessive traits) and to trace the origin and history of mankind.

Gene-variants in populations

Over the past two years, McLeod and his colleagues at Washington University in St. Louis, Missouri, have developed a database of gene variants that affect the efficacy or toxicity of drugs on the WHO's essential medicines list. This data is associated with information on the frequency of such variants in populations throughout the world.

As a result, indications are emerging about which drugs are likely to be most effective in those populations.

Though many of the populations are not covered under this scheme, we think that McLeod's idea of targeting treatment at specific populations can be relevant to developing countries such as India. The broad-spectrum treatment approach based on population responses is determined not only by an individual's genetic fingerprint, but also by his interaction with the environment or lifestyle. As India is unique in studying gene-environment interactions in the manifestation of disease, why can't we use this situation to develop personalized medicine?

Gene-environment interaction

Why do different individuals respond differently to environmental conditions? Virtually all human diseases result from the interaction of genetic susceptibility factors and modifiable environmental factors, including infectious, chemical, physical, nutritional, and behavioral factors. This is perhaps the most important fact in understanding the role of genetics and environment in the development of disease.

While it is clear that common diseases such as diabetes or cancer result from the complex interplay of genes and the environment, our understanding of the 'gene-environment interaction' is only beginning to emerge. It has been established that numerous factors—age, sex, body weight, nutrition, organ function, infections, co-medications and genetic factors—contribute to drug response.

All of us carry genetic variants that increase our susceptibility to some diseases. By identifying and characterizing gene-environment interactions, we have more opportunities to effectively target intervention strategies. Many of the genetic risk factors for diseases have not been identified. The complex interaction of genes with other genes and that of genes with environmental factors has not yet been understood.

Clinical and epidemiological studies are necessary to further identify these factors and their interactions. As our understanding of genetic variations increases, so should our knowledge of environmental factors, so that ultimately, genetic information can be used to plan appropriate intervention strategies for high-risk individuals.

Let me cite two examples of the importance of environmental influences. Little is known about the effects of environmental stresses on stem cell function—and in particular, on the memory mechanisms in stem cells. Investigations in this direction will shed light on the global dynamics of chromatin modifications in response to environmental stress. A dramatic example of gene-environmental interaction is the use of temperature as a sex-determining clue in crocodiles. It would be worthwhile to carry out global gene expression profiling to establish the genetic factors that respond to temperature and implement alternative sex-determining pathways.

Human evolution in progress

Genetic variations do not cause disease but influence a person's susceptibility to the environment. We do not inherit a disease state *per se*. Instead, we inherit a set of a susceptibility factors to certain effects of the environment. Thereby, we inherit a higher risk for certain diseases. This explains why individuals are differently affected by the same environmental factors. However, this will be a continuing study.

There has been increasing evidence that the human population is evolving. It is not immune to natural selection despite modern civilization and the adoption of technology-driven life styles. For example, two genes involved in brain development emerged recently in the human species. Microcephalin arose between 14,000 to 60,000 years ago, while a variant of ASMP emerged between 500 and 14,000 years ago. They have quickly affected the human population. More recently, African populations have shown an increase in the CCR5-Δ32 variant, which confers resistance against HIV-1 infection. It would be worthwhile to track and characterize, the slowly but certainly, evolving human populations.

Curse of genetic disorders

The problem of genetic disorders in India is enormous. Millions of people are suffering from inherited diseases like thalassemia, muscular dystrophy, diabetes mellitus, coronary heart diseases etc. One-sixth of the world population living in India has never been systematically studied for the prevalence of inherited genetic disorders. Several diseases prevalent in India are yet to be identified and reported. Examples: there are families with four generations of women who do not have fingers and toes; in many families, several individuals have been affected by muscular dystrophy; there are families with generation after generation of disabled children. This may well be the tip of the proverbial iceberg.

Such phenomena cannot be explained on the basis of current knowledge. Hence, genetic factors must be studied. Unfortunately, there is a huge gap between the pace at which new discoveries and technologies are being developed, and the pace at which they get utilized by clinicians for the benefit of the common man. It is to reduce this gap that we have established the Genome Foundation. This is a non-profit organization that will help deliver health-care services to rural India by networking the voluntary services of doctors, pensioners, students, NGOs etc.

Extensive collaboration among clinicians, epidemiologists, geneticists, mathematicians and computer experts will be required to solve the puzzle of the genetic underpinning of complex diseases that affect the lives of millions.

Completion of the human genome sequencing has stirred the scientific world in more than one way. Apart from deciphering the biological meaning of the sequence-language written in three billion letters which may itself take a century, scientists face many other challenges. Overcoming these challenges will not only revolutionize genetics in terms of knowing ourselves better but also help us tremendously to identify genetic diseases, prevent them, modify the risk and find a cure for them.

It is predicted that due to genetic screening for about 40 generations, people in developed countries will be much more beautiful, intelligent, symmetrical, healthy and emotionally stable. What about a developing country like ours where genetic screening of our population has not even begun? It has to be done, particularly in our rural populations. It will become possible to prevent a large number of genetic disorders in the population by genetic counselling and prenatal diagnosis.

Recent breakthroughs in genomics and proteomics research have provided an opportunity to change the way medicine is practised today. This modern technology is waiting to be fully exploited. The Centre for Cellular and Molecular Biology (CCMB) has proposed to set up a state-of-the-art institute of translational research and a medical school in mission mode.

Personalised medicine

This endeavour will help physicians to explore the optimal management of disease with high quality genomic and proteomic data that permit the design of tests for early accurate diagnosis and better treatment. In addition, the information on susceptibility/predisposition and predictable drug response will ultimately lead to personalized medicine. The long-term goal would be to develop innovative and

socially validated treatment approaches based on the science of regenerative medicine that would improve the quality of life for afflicted individuals, populations and their families.

Pharmacogenomics is a harbinger of personalized medicine. Toxicogenomics, SNP maps, and rapidly expanding data on functional polymorphisms, have generated high expectations for applying pharmacogenomics to optimize therapies for individual patients. A paradigm shift from a 'one-drug-fits-all' to 'the right direction for the right patient at the right dose and time' is on the horizon.

Social outreach

India is a country on the fast track. It is now knocking at the doors of select clubs of developed countries. Setting up milestones and timelines of progress is easy; however, these have to be both ambitious and realistic. We need to reach the unreached—particularly the rural masses. We Indians are known to be susceptible to diabetes mellitus and coronary heart diseases because of genetic reasons. Therefore, identifying the genetic variants that underly complex diseases would be hugely beneficial. A systematic scientific approach is essential. A few generations from now, market-based genetic technology may surpass socio-sexual selection as the driving force of human evolution. India ought to be at the forefront of such technology.

Jawaharlal Nehru was prescient when he said, "It is science alone that can solve the problems of hunger and poverty, of insanitation and illiteracy, of superstition and deadening customs and traditions, of vast resources running to waste...Even more than the present, the future belongs to science and those who make friends with science."□

Narayanan Suresh
Group Editor
BioSpectrum

Innovations spur Indian biotech

On a quiet September evening in 1997, an unassuming electrical engineer in Hyderabad, Varaprasad Reddy, 49, launched India's first home-made recombinant DNA vaccine, Shanvac. It was a small function, but it laid the foundation for building the superstructure of India's fast-growing Rs 10,000 crore (US $ 2.5 billion) biotechnology business.

Reddy did not set out to be a biotech entrepreneur. Once he visited a cousin in California after facing the trauma from the break-up of his earlier business venture manufacturing high tech batteries in early 1990s for India's missile programme. Just to kill time, he attended a vaccine conference where the adverse effects of the infection caused by the Hepatitis B virus, affecting over 400 million people worldwide were discussed. India had one of the highest prevalence of Hepatitis B in the world. It struck a chord in him and Reddy wanted to do something to alleviate the suffering of the people affected by the infection.

He explored a technology transfer agreement with the company that had developed the Hepatitis B vaccine. Reddy was ridiculed in public by the company officials who doubted the capabilities of Indians to manufacture a high end vaccine. Reddy swore to develop another version of the Hepatitis B vaccine within three years. He returned to India, sought the help of scientists at the Centre for Cellular and Molecular Biology (CCMB), an autonomous laboratory funded by the Government of India, founded a company, Shantha Biotechnics, named after his mother from whom he borrowed some capital, selling her ancestral property. The company developed India's own Hepatitis B vaccine in four years. It was launched at one-tenth the price of the imported vaccine, and then marketed by multinational GlaxoSmithKline (GSK). Today, the Hepatitis B vaccine is available at the lowest cost in the world in India. Shantha Biotechnics supplies nearly half the world's Hepatitis B vaccine, distributed by various United Nations agencies, to immunize the world's most vulnerable populations.

Buoyed by Shantha's success, five other companies started making the Hepatitis B vaccine in India. And the Indian biotech industry was born. Though two other now well known biotech companies, Serum Institute of India, founded by Dr Cyrus S Poonawalla in Pune in 1966, and Biocon, founded by Mrs Kiran Mazumdar-Shaw in a Bangalore suburb in 1979, had been in existence, it is this Hepatitis B vaccine that marked the beginning of India's biotech industry, now thriving with over 275 exciting companies, developing a wide range of innovative products and services, using the cutting edge tools of biotechnology.

Innovation club

One of the latest entrants to the biotech Innovator's Club is Dr Naveen Kulkarni, a scientist trained in Australia and the USA. His company, Polyclone Bioservices, incubated at Dharwad University in North Karnataka, has set up a high-tech Nucleic Acid testing facility. Polyclone will offer various diagnostic services to researchers and companies which are now done abroad. Kulkarni now plans to set up an end-to-end support system for stem cell research. His team is developing Stem Cell validation and quality and assurance assays using the polymerase chain reaction (PCR) technology. It is this PCR technology platform that revolutionized the genetic research segment.

The new breed of India's biotech innovators is best exemplified by Dr K R Rajyashri and Vinay Konaje, who left their cushy jobs at another Bangalore-based biotech company, Avesthagen, and founded Navya Biologicals in early 2006. This company is also based in Dharwad and is developing a large number of biopharmaceutical and neutrceuticals. Navya has been given a handsome grant under a government scheme and plans to file at least six international patents in 12 to 18 months. In less than three years, the company has reported a nominal profit in revenue terms.

Industry's birth

Companies like Navya Biologicals and Polyclone are the trend-setters in India's biotech quest for affordable healthcare products and services. Spurred by the Shantha Biotech success story, the first wave of entrepreneurship came between 1998 and 2001. This was also aided by the excitement created by the unveiling of the Human Genome Map in the USA in June 2000. Nearly a 100 biotech companies were set up in this period, many by first time entrepreneurs. Prominent among them are Avesthagen, founded by Dr Villoo Morawala-Patell, a Belgium-trained scientist away slogging in a public laboratory in Bangalore. Villoo's Avesthagen has focused on developing top class intellectual property in biopharmaceuticals, bio agriculture and nutraceuticals. Within a short time of seven years, Avesthagen has filed over 150 international patents, developed a testing service to identify genetically modified seeds, genetic markets and launched nearly a dozen nutraceutical products. This privately held company has raised millions of dollars from some of the top venture capitalists and preparing for its first public offering of shares in 2009.

Two other Bangalore-based companies, Metahelix Life Sciences and XCyton Diagnostics, were founded during this entrepreneurship boom. Dr K K Narayanan, an agriculture scientist with Monsanto founded Metahelix with 3 other colleagues and an angel investment of Rs 7 crore from N S Raghavan, one of the co-founders of IT software giant, Infosys Technologies. Metahelix is now seeking regulatory approval for its own set of

genetically modified products using different types of bacteria. Dr B V Ravi Kumar left the AstraZenca Research team to found Xcyton and among the cutting edge diagnostic tools developed by the company are the detection kits against the Japanese Encephalitis which plagues Gangetic plains during the monsoon months. A host of other DNA-based diagnostic kits are on the anvil from the company's newly-built research center in a Bangalore suburb.

The leader among this pack of first timers is Dr Vijay Chandru. This professor of computer science at Indian Institute of Science (IISc), Bangalore, was not satisfied with the hand-held computer, Simputer, developed and popularized by his team. With another set of colleagues, Chandru founded Strand Genomics (now renamed Strand Life Sciences) to develop the software tools that can speed up the drug discovery process. The Strand team built the Avadis platform of computational tools by 2003, and its products are now licensed to a large number of drug discovery companies around the world. Stratagene, the global leader in this space, which initially distributed Strand's products, has now replaced some of its own product lines with that from Strand. And Stratagene has also entered into a strategic relationship with Strand to further develop these products using the Indian team's expertise.

In Delhi, during the same period, Dr Jitendra Verma founded Lifecare Innovations. Lifecare has carved a niche for itself in the anti-fungal market with its portfolio of products that are world leaders in their own right. Ever since the launch of the Fungisome-Liposomal Amphotericin B (fungisome IV) in 2003, the product has been the company's star performer. It has a success rate of 90 per cent and a toxicity of near zero owing to its unique suspension medium and lipid composition.

Second wave

As the first timers attracted attention and won acclaim for their efforts, they also spurred further innovations. A second wave of biotech entrepreneurship came in 2005 and 2006. Over two dozen companies were founded in these two years across India.

Premas Biotech, located in Manesar in Haryana is one such company. Dr Rajiv Soni has set up a world class biotech laboratory to develop technologies that can quickly diagnose many infectious diseases, proprietary vectors for protein expression in bacterial, yeast and

The biotech business is booming. A sample list of biotech products developed and released in the market from mid-2006 to end-2007 illustrates the complexity of the product pipelines coming out of India.

BioMAb EGFR, Biocon: BIOMAb EGFR, a monoclonal antibody which has been specifically engineered to target and block the epidermal growth factor receptor (EGFR) which causes a variety of cancer.

BioMab EGFR targets the human EGFR, a protein found on the surface of normal and cancer-hit cells. The drug is reported to work well in combination with chemo and radio therapies.

Biocon had invested over $32 million to develop this drug.

BioMab EGFR has made a very good debut in the Indian market and Biocon has been able to license this molecule for the Pakistani market. Biocon is looking at doing similar licensing arrangements with Sri Lanka, Bangladesh, the GCC region and South Africa.

Redituxa, Dr Reddy's Lab: Redituxa is a monoclonal antibody (MAb) used in the treatment of Non-Hodgkin's Lymphoma.

Reditux is approximately priced at half the originator's price. Product availability is planned at company's C&F agents and at all major hospitals in the country.

Nanoxel, Dabur Pharma: Nanoxel is a novel drug delivery system for the widely used anti-cancer drug Paclitaxel. This nanoscale drug delivery system is India's first indigenously developed nanotechnology based chemotherapy agent. Owing to its water insolubility, the chemotherapy agent paclitaxel is now currently used with a castor oil based solvent, cremophor which has life threatening side effects.

The anticancer drug Nanoxel, based on the principles of nanotechnology, is a cremophor free water soluble formulation—and is indicated as an effective and safe therapy for advanced breast, non-small-cell lung, and ovarian carcinomas.

Nanoxel is available to all specialist cancer therapy providers and healthcare institutes for cancer treatment from 2007.

The price of this nanoparticle drug delivery system for paclitaxel has been pegged at $361 for one cycle of chemotherapy administration.

Sii HibPro, Serum Institute of India: Serum Institute has a capacity to produce over 100 million doses of the vaccine.

Serum Institute will supply this new age vaccine to Global Alliance for Vaccines and Immunisation (GAVI), Pan American Health Organization (PAHO) and UNICEF.

The HIB vaccine is fully manufactured in India, and Serum Institute has invested heavily in R&D, which has yielded significant results.

BioHib, Bharat Biotech: BioHib is Haemophilus Influenza type b (Hib) vaccine.

The scientific, manufacturing and product development teams at Bharat Biotech have completely developed all the processes required to manufacture BioHib in-house at Bharat Biotech.

Bharat has made significant investments to the tune of several million of dollars over the past 4 years, into its R&D capabilities.

Rabirix, Bharat Biotech: Rabirix is an anti-rabies vaccine, indicated for both prophylactic (pre-bite) and therapeutic (post-bite) treatments.

Rabirix is a lyophilized cell-based rabies vaccine (PVRV), which is chromatographically purified to reduce cellular DNA content and foreign protein content. The vaccine has proven to be well tolerated with minimal or no side effects.

Sarchitecht, Strand Lifesciences: Sarchitect is a SAR modelling and deployment platform. Sarchitect addresses the challenge of taking the model building prowess of computational chemists through to decision support in medicinal chemistry. Two editions of the Sarchitect product have been launched, Designer, for use by computational scientists, and Miner, for in silico lead optimization by medicinal chemists. Strand lifesciences also offer high-end custom solutions and technology-based consulting in predictive modeling for lead optimization.

Cytoscreen, Xcyton Diagnostics: 'XCyto-Screen' is the first DNA Macro Array chip developed in the country for diagnosing 15-20 pathogens.

It can identify infections like Keratoconjunctivitis, Uveitis, Retinitis and endophthalmitis, providing simultaneous identification of 15 different pathogens causing eye infections. The cost of diagnostics with the DNA chip will be Rs 2,500 for each infection.

Human Papilloma Virus (HPV) Chip is meant for genotyping the dreaded cervical cancer. The unique features of the HPV screen is that it is highly sensitive to detect many different genes of HPV. Right now, the kit is used to test the samples taken from a cervical brush through cervical biopsy.

Eprime and eOligo, Polyclone Bioservices: eOligo is a online tool for the design of Oligonucleotides for Hybridization reactions, PCR, Real time PCR and siRNA.

Eprime is desktop application to design primers for qualitative PCR studies. It designs qPCR primers and probes for SYBR green, Taqman and Molecular Beacon studies. The salient feature is that it designs Taqman probes for a given SNP position.

mammalian cells. Premas also plans to manufacture several specialized enzymes for research and make some of the proteins required in drug discovery research.

During this wave, US-returned P Sudhakera Naidu founded Biovel Life Science in Bangalore to make therapeutic proteins and manufacture them on contract for global pharma companies. Its first product, made for US-based Dow Pharma, was a human growth hormone. Biovel is now developing a more cost-effective process using the Pfenex Expression Technology to improve the yields. of endocrinology products from a US major. In association with a European company, Biovel will be developing a first-of-its-kind DDS to control infection in wounds and cuts.

As the new entrepreneurs make their mark, the two giants, Serum Institute and Biocon are also actively pursuing innovations. Biocon developed the country's first monoclonal anti body based drug, BioMab EFGR to treat head and neck cancer. Biocon improvised on the discovery made by a Cuban laboratory and brought it to the market after extensive trials. The drug is now being tested against other forms of cancer too. Biocon introduced recombinant insulin in 2005 and is trying out new delivery systems to eliminate the use of injectable doses of insulin. Serum Institute has gone from strength to strength with its vaccines portfolio of DPT, Hepatitis B and Human Influenza and is already one of the world's largest makers of paedetriatic vaccines in world. Half the world's children get their first shot of vaccination using the vaccines made in Serum's manufacturing facility in Pune, Maharashtra.

India's biotechnology journey is on course. According to the fifth BioSpectrum-ABLE Industry survey, the industry revenues surpassed the 2 billion-dollar mark in March 2007 and the industry grew at 31 per cent. Nearly 60 per cent of these revenues came from exports and the balance from domestic market sales. The sales cover nearly 60 biotech products, most of which are made in the

country and the rest imported. The industry is expected to continue to grow between 25 and 40 per cent for the next seven to eight years and reach revenues of 5 billion dollars by 2010 and 25 billion dollars by 2015.

Meanwhile, in Hyderabad, Varaprasad Reddy, now 60, is not resting on his laurels. France's BioMerieux bought over 60 per cent of the shares of the company held by the initial investors from Oman and others who helped out Reddy in the mid-1990s. BioMerieux has inducted Reddy on to its Board of Directors and plans to make Shantha's Hyderabad facilities as its manufacturing hub for Asia-Pacific. Reddy's scientists are now developing an alternative to the cervical cancer vaccine. Over 3 million middle-aged and young women suffer from a cancer of the cervix caused by the Human Papilloma Virus (HPV) globally and over 10 per cent of them die every year. Merck has started marketing a cervical cancer vaccine, Gardasil, developed originally by Nobel Laureate, Dr Ian Fraser for CSL. Three doses of it costs approximately 480 dollars or 60 dollars per shot. This makes it unaffordable for majority of women who are most likely to suffer from the viral attack in the developing countries. Countries like Australia have made the vaccination part of its immunization programme and heavily subsidize it for its citizens.

Reddy's team will start clinical trials of their cervical cancer vaccine in late 2008 or early 2009. They are hopeful of good results and after the necessary regulatory approval plan to sell each shot of the vaccine for just about 15 dollars or 45 dollars for the treatment course. This will be less than a tenth of the current vaccine price.

Going by his track record, Reddy is bound to succeed and make sure that by 2010, millions of girls and women in India and other developing countries who need it the most get their vaccination at affordable prices. And he may also launch the third wave of biotech entrepreneurship in India. □

M Somasekhar
Science Journalist

Indigenous vaccines

The story of indigenous vaccine development, especially through the recombinant route, is just over a decade old in India. In 1997, the successful launch of the recombinant Hepatitis B vaccine by the Hyderabad-based Shantha Biotechnics may be seen as a significant milestone in this direction.

The vaccine named Shanvac B was unveiled in August, 1997, which happened to be the 50th year of India's Independence. It demonstrated that India was capable of deploying recombinant technology, and secondly, of manufacturing recombinant vaccines at affordable costs.

An engineer, Varaprasad Reddy, with high entrepreneurial skills, saw the potential of biotechnology in vaccine production rather early. He got initial support from the Molecular Biology Department of the Osmania University, Hyderabad. Then, he moved on to the Centre for Cellular and Molecular Biology (CCMB) with sharpened ideas for developing the Hepatitis B vaccine. The incubation and the infrastructural support from CCMB helped Shantha Biotechnics to firm up the development and manufacture of the cost-effective Shanvac B.

This development represented many things. For instance, a good public-private partnership in research, boldness to take on global challenges and first generation entrepreneurship through start-up efforts in the emerging scientific areas. It helped change the rules of the game in the Indian vaccine market forever.

The indigenous effort not only challenged big multinationals on efficacy and costs of the vaccine, but offered the people, perhaps for the first time, an affordable vaccine from the country's stable. Till then, most vaccine makers had had to depend on the Government or WHO programmes to push their products.

The pioneering move by Shantha Biotechnics triggered a sudden rush of Indian corporates, start-ups and institutes to plunge into the vaccine world, in the next few years or just at the turn of the millennium. By 2001, nearly a dozen makers of the Hep B vaccines emerged in the Indian market, five of them indigenous.

Bharat Biotech, Serum Institute of India, Panacea Biotec, Biological E and Wockhardt, Indian Immunologicals (animal vaccines) and a host of other companies are now into vaccine manufacture. More importantly, money is also being put into research and development (R&D) for vaccines.

The fact that today India has emerged as a big supplier of recombinant vaccines to the UNICEF immunisation programmes in developing countries clearly demonstrates the country's capabilities, says Mr Varaprasad Reddy.

In the global vaccine arena, India has capabilities in recombinants and is equipping itself in the monoclonal antibody space. "We have caught up with the few Western nations with the technology edge. It has also given confidence to the scientific community to undertake research and develop vaccines on the technology platform," he added.

Shantha Biotechnics, which now has majority ownership by the French major Alliance Merieux, has brought out the hepatitis B and combination vaccines—Quadrivalent or four-in-one (DPT-hep B) and Pentavalent or five-in-one (DPT-hep B and Hib) to the market. It has in the pipeline vaccines for dengue fever, typhoid, cholera, HPV (human papilloma virus) and rotavirus. It has created vaccine production facilities, research capabilities and trained manpower near Hyderabad. Greater still, it has acquired all the global accreditations for vaccine manufacture and can deliver the products at affordable costs.

The Pune-based Serum Institute of India, which is one of the leading vaccine makers in the country is another major contributor to the development of the Hepatitis B vaccine market. It has also started developing quadrevalent vaccines (combination of Hep B, diphtheria, pertussis and tetanus). Serum exports its vaccines to more than 140 different countries worldwide and has established sound facilities for production and testing.

The Hyderabad-based Bharat Biotech has emerged as another major player in the vaccine sector. It launched the Hepatitis B vaccine named Revac B in 1999. Thereafter, it has hit the market with a slew of products such as the Typhoid vaccine in 2003, the Rabies vaccine (IndiRap) in 2006, the Bio Hib vaccine for influenza and the tetravalent DPT-HepB in recent times.

Ms Suchitra Ella, who together with Dr Krishna Ella started the company, said Bharat Biotech is also involved in a global project for the development of Rotavirus. Under the Indo-US Vaccine Action Programme, with the Department of Biotechnology (DBT), All India Institute of Medical Sciences and Bharat Biotech from India, and the National Institutes of Health, CDC, and Atlanta and Stanford Universities in the US are involved in the project. The vaccine is in trials now.

The company is also in collaboration with the International Centre for Genetic Engineering & Biotech (ICGEB), New Delhi, for a malaria vaccine. It has established separate and dedicated vaccine production facilities from recombinant, viral and bacterial routes.

The fast growing Wockhardt is another important player in the vaccines market, with its own version of the Hepatitis B. Elsewhere, the New Delhi-based, Panacea Biotec has a slew of vaccines, including Hepatitis B. It has tied up with Chiron Corporation of the US and the Cuban Institute for vaccine manufacture. It is also developing a vaccine against Anthrax.

Despite all these efforts experts believe that India's presence in global vaccine research is very small. There are not many research projects going on at present and there is shortage of

funds. Just about 20 centres are conducting research. The interest shown by corporates and the insistence by paediatricians on results from indigenous studies when a new vaccine is introduced in India, holds out promise of increased activity on this much needed front.

As in the case of the drug manufacturing sector, so too in the vaccine area, sophisticated manufacturing units have come up. This helps in easy and fast absorption of technology. But there are not many top class R&D facilities, which suggests that while manufacturing vaccines is passé, indigenous invention of a new vaccine is still a far cry.

The challenge ahead for Indian companies and research institutes is to invest in discovering and developing vaccines which are desperately needed by the country, for example to fight dengue fever, cholera, malaria and typhoid. This is imperative. Multinational Companies from the West would not be interested in investing in these vaccines for which they might not find a lucrative market in the West at present.

Combination vaccines

One of the routes for developing countries to meet both the vaccine demands and patient compliance is through combination vaccines. It must be said, however, that the issue has its pros and cons at present. Combination vaccines, which are used in single slot instead of giving separate pricks, offer advantages like fewer injections, fewer visits to doctors, fewer side effects such as pain or swelling. Hence, the compliance from children and acceptance from parents is better. Indirectly, it also helps to reduce the number of syringes required, which means huge cost savings.

Industry forecast put the global market for vaccines at around $12 billion last year and project about $20 billion in 2012. The share of the domestic Indian market in turnover terms would be less than one per cent. Vaccines and recombinant therapeutics are the leading sectors driving the growth of the biotechnology industry in India.

Till recently, the domestic market was the victim of cost competition with manufacturers trying hard to grab a chunk of the small market. This discouraging trend has been partly corrected by the Central and State Governments as well as organisations like UNICEF and WHO, with their proactive roles in encouraging vaccine makers. Accordingly, Shantha Biotechnics, Serum Institute of India, Panacea

Biotec and similar units have been given the tag of pre-qualified vaccine manufacturers, which gets them to supply vaccines at highly competitive prices.

The excitement in modern biology, especially molecular biology, about newer ways of drug development is expected to lead the way for several vaccine makers to find new and cost effective products in the future. In the recombinant vaccines segment, the era of combination vaccines is emerging.

There is already considerable movement in the erythropoietin, G-CSF and insulin segments. Interestingly, here giants like Ranbaxy and Dr Reddy's, as well as smaller companies like Zenotech have made impressive progress.

Traditionally, big MNCs dominated the recombinant market in India. Names like GlaxoSmithKline, Aventis and Wyeth had a huge share of the market. In the past decade, the scenario is changing with the entry of several homegrown companies like Shantha Biotechnics, Biological E, Cadilla Pharmaceuticals, Haffkine Bio Pharmaceuticals, Bharat Biotech, Panacea Biotec, Serum Institute and Wockhardt.

The other big opportunity that seems to be lurking around is in the area of monoclonal antibodies. Discovered way back in the early 1980s by Dr Caesar Milstein and Dr Georges Kohler, monoclonal antibodies remained dormant for more than a decade before making their impact in the last few years. Indian biotech leader, Biocon for example, has brought

a monoclonal antibody based product to the market called BioMAb.

Bolstered by the successes of start-ups like Shantha Biotech and Bharat and bigger biotech companies like Biocon and Avesthagen, there is a welcome trend in the offing. Venture capital funds have started flowing in the country, including a few home grown ones to boost the vaccine and biotech sectors.

Interestingly, the Government, which continues to be the largest investor in R&D in the country, did play a critical role in the growth of the indigenous vaccine development. Through the Technology Development Board (TDB), which is a fund to promote commercially viable technologies created out of R&D cess, the efforts of Shantha Biotechnics and Bharat Biotech as well as several technologies in agri, medical biotechnology have been funded.

In the life sciences area itself, the TDB has funded more than 10 projects in a single year. Some of the beneficiaries include Genotech Labs, Celestial Labs and Vimta Labs of Hyderabad, BioVet of Bangalore and Haryana Biotech.

Given the expanded base for manufacturing, manpower and the growing domestic market, India promises to emerge as a hub for vaccine making in the near future. Some of the Indian companies have already realised this potential. While Hyderabad-based Shantha and Bharat have readied a manufacturing and research base, another one, Biological E, is investing more than Rs 100 crore in exclusive facilities in the Genome Valley area on the outskirts of Hyderabad. ☐

Sadhna Joglekar
Vice President
Jeroze Dalal, Senior Manger
GSK Pharmaceutical Ltd.

Growing footprint of clinical research

Clinical research sponsored by the pharmaceutical industry has traditionally been carried out in highly regulated countries in North America and Western Europe. In recent years however there has been a shift in the location of these clinical trials to the so-called 'emerging' regions, especially in the Eastern European, Latin American and Asian countries. A quick look at the global R&D landscape suggests that the pharma industry spends close to 60 billion dollars on R&D, of which expenditure on clinical trials is in excess of 20 billion dollars. Approximately, 90,000 clinical trials were performed globally in 2003, involving nearly nine million patients. Of these, about 4000 studies are of new drug applications. It is estimated that 20–30 per cent of global clinical research activities are being conducted in developing countries.

Outsourcing to new countries

Over the last decade or so, the regulators, analysts, consumers, media and the public at large have come down heavily on the pharmaceutical industry. On the one hand, the drug-pricing model of the pharma companies is being questioned, while on the other hand the economics of the entire R&D process is being critically dissected. It is a well-known fact that the cost of drug devPelopment has gone up significantly in the last few decades. The 2003 report of the Tufts Center for the Study of Drug Development has pegged the fully loaded cost (inclusive of molecules which failed to reach the market) of bringing a new drug to patients at more than 800 million dollars. Coupled to that is the equally disquieting fact that the R&D pipeline of many of the leading research based companies is at an all-time low. In the past five years, at least six or seven products a year, each with peak sales potential exceeding one billion dollars annually, have been terminated in late stage (Phase III) development or when just about to be filed with the National Drug Administration, resulting in an opportunity loss of tens of billion dollars. Added to this are at least 11 drugs which were withdrawn from the market in the same time period due to safety concerns.

How has the industry responded to the challenge of cost containment? Most companies have taken a hard look at their operational efficiencies on the commercial side and the R&D side, downsized to the extent possible and embraced the use of modern technology such as the use of recombinant DNA or bioinformatics during the discovery phase, or robust technology-enabled data management tools. Importantly, these companies have also shifted many of their activities to countries that could provide some cost arbitrage without compromising the quality. This has paved the way for several Latin American, Eastern European and Asian countries coming into prominence in the field of clinical development.

Why India?

As mentioned earlier, offshoring clinical development has now become a strategic imperative for most global pharmaceutical companies. India has already emerged as one of the favoured global destinations for clinical research. The clinical trial industry in

India is estimated to be worth approximately 170 million dollars. At what rate it will grow is, of course, a million dollar question. While some estimates suggest that it will grow to between 500 million and 1 billion dollars by 2010, others anticipate a size of around 250–300 million dollars, assuming that India captures about 10 per cent of the global Clinical Research market. Admittedly, the pace of change has been rather slow. India's journey into clinical research started in the 1990s when just a few pharmacy companies ventured into using India as a rescue country (i.e., bringing in those studies which were not doing well globally).

It was a very cautious approach, with the rest of the companies watching how the situation would unfold. While the early entrants did face several challenges including regulatory issues as well as poor awareness of ICH GCP, it is these companies that have, in the long run, benefited from the relationships they have painstakingly built with all stakeholders. Encouraged by the promise of their early initiatives, many of them have increased their investments aggressively by setting up dedicated clinical research teams to operationalize even pivotal studies. India has moved from an 'acceptable' destination to an 'attractive' destination. Some of the key factors that weigh in favour of India are described below.

The push factors
The global need to enhance the R&D productivity, coupled with pharma industry globalization, and has been the single most powerful trigger driving clinical research activities into the emerging markets. The number of patients required per new drug approval has gone up from 2500 in the1970s to 6500 in this millennium. Commensurately, the cost of R&D has moved up from 250 million dollars to more than 800 million dollars in the same period (inclusive of molecules which failed to reach market) The number of new molecular approval by the US Federal Drug Adminsitration went down from 53 in 1996 to 14 in 2005 and as low as nine in November 2006. Given that the effective patent life of a drug left by the time that drug reaches the market is a handful of years, time-to-market is another critical matrix.

The pull factors
India offers several enabling factors for accelerated activity of high quality in the clinical research domain. A nation with more

than one billion people, India has the second largest population in the world; availability and easy access to large population with a diverse gene pool is a very attractive feature for clinical research. The diseases of developing countries such as diarrhoeas, acute respiratory infections, malaria, HIV and peri-natal and maternal conditions prominently plague the healthcare system today in India. Added to that, urbanization, a change in lifestyle to one that is sedentary, and unhealthy nutritional intake has invited diseases of the developed countries to our society, diseases such as diabetes, depression and other psychiatric disorders. Try these numbers. Forty million asthmatics, 34 million diabetics, 15 million hypertensives, 3 million patients with cancer, 1.5 million with Alzheimer's and 1 million with schizophrenia! Who would not find it appealing to do clinical research in India? An immensely improved medical infrastructure, increased awareness and training in ICH GCP requirements of investigators compared with what prevailed a decade ago and the use of English as the primary business and medical language have also contributed their bit towards making India an attractive destination.

Recent changes in India's healthcare policies, including the much-discussed Third amendment to the Indian Patents Act, and a maturing regulatory environment have significantly brought down the anxiety of multinational pharma companies. Recent regulatory reforms and initiatives have made significant changes in the regulatory processes for clinical trial approval. These amendments have resulted in improved confidence amongst the global pharmaceutical community. Since the release of Schedule Y in 2005, there has been a tremendous increase in the number of trial applications to the Indian regulators (Schedule Y of the Drugs & Cosmetics Act controls the conduct of clinical trials in India). Recent regulatory initiatives, like categorization of clinical trial applications to speed up approval, have brought in more predictability to the approval process and timelines. The new plans of the Indian government to create a Central Drug Authority (CDA) will go still further to make the Indian regulatory system competent, transparent and responsive.

And then there is the cost advantage. If the average cost of doing Phase I/II/III clinical trials in the US are approximately 20/50/100 million dollars respectively, the same can be done at a saving of up to 50–60 per cent in

India. This cost benefit is mainly due to lower wages and infrastructural cost as well as lower recruitment cost. At 5.43, the PPP (purchasing power parity) multiplier for India is the highest across all countries of significance in the context of clinical research outsourcing. This indicates that one is able to get 500 per cent more value for a dollar in India as compared to what one could get for the same dollar in the US.

Benefits to India

With a growing number of clinical studies being conducted in the developing countries, the pharma industry is coming in for a fair degree of criticism for using the poorest of the world's populations as guinea pigs and acting in an unethical manner that fails to reflect the standards applied in the developed world. The reality, in most instances, is far from this accusation. Global studies, which are conducted in India in tandem with the rest of the world, follow the same fundamental ethical principles, including the ICH (International Conference on Harmonization) Good Clinical Practices (GCP) guidelines. All such studies are necessarily approved by the Ethics Committees of the institution where plans are underway for conducting studies the studies. Further, clinical trials are only conducted in those countries where the medicines are likely to be suitable to a wider section of the population. Often, in the developing countries, an agreement is reached beforehand on issues such as responsibilities for standard of care and post-trial treatment. No trial should begin without taking a patient's voluntarily given 'informed' consent.

Why should Indian patients participate in these studies? How do the patients and the country as a whole stand to benefit? Some of the key benefits include early access to medications that may otherwise take several years to become commercially available. This is especially true in all those settings where a patient has run out of therapeutic options in life-threatening conditions, or in all those disease areas where the medicine being tested is likely to provide better efficacy or safety than the existing medicines. One should also not overlook the importance of the close supervision and monitoring that a patient receives during the trial period. Such monitoring could result in tangible benefits such as better healthcare provision as well as intangible benefits such as the psychological satisfaction of feeling cared for by the treating physician. In a clinical trial setting, the medication (and often the investigations) are provided free of cost, resulting in a material benefit.

The societal benefits of doing clinical studies are unique: from the progress of science to the creation of several high-value jobs. A boost to biological sciences is likely to arrest the brain drain from India, which is primarily due to lack of opportunities within the country. In addition, attracting global R&D to India offers immense societal benefits as a result of higher revenue earnings for the government through taxes. These taxes ought to be ploughed back to improve healthcare services to the poorest sections of the society. All of this is in line with the government's public interest objectives. If, one day, India hopes to discover and develop its own medicines for diseases relevant to our country, it is imperative that we harness all the requisite skills through these opportunities.

The future

By 2010, India is expected to capture about 10 per cent of the total global clinical research market. A quick back-of-the-envelope calculation suggests that if India is to attract the predicted quantum of clinical studies and the resultant fiscal inflows, we will need to recruit at least about 50,000 patients per year, assuming an average per patient cost of 5000 dollars. At an estimated 20 patients per investigator, we would need about 2500 GCP trained investigators, which translates into at least 500 medical hospitals (based on 5 investigators per hospital). If we compare this with the current estimated numbers of 500 investigators (of whom only about 150 are registered with the US FDA) and about 80 hospitals participating in global clinical studies, it certainly seems to be a tall order to achieve!

At present, the development of necessary infrastructure required for clinical trials is scanty in most medical institutions and is mainly restricted to institutions such as AIIMS (Delhi), PGIMER (Chandigarh), NIMS (Hyderabad), NIMHANS (Bangalore) and CMC (Vellore), to name a few. Consequently, most companies are vying for a limited number of clinical research facilities and a relatively small pool of trained and experienced personnel. This has already started to result in erosion of the so-called cost arbitrage. While several institutions in the country have started collaboration with the industry, or taking support

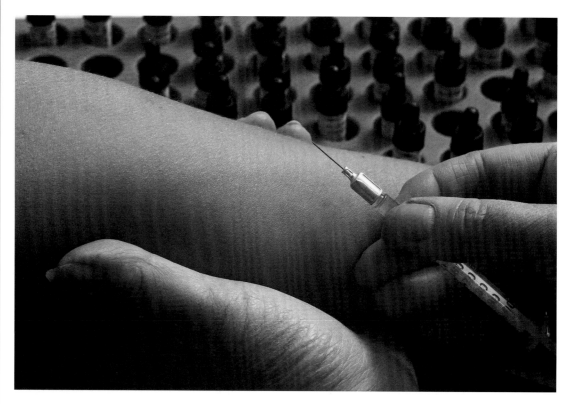

from state and central governments or funding agencies to upgrade the existing infrastructure so as to cope up with the growing demand for generating valid and acceptable clinical trial data, the pace seems to be at best sluggish.

In India most institutions lack organized patient databases, which results in marked variations in the numbers estimated at the study feasibility level vis-à-vis actual enrollments. Lack of nation-wide epidemiological data makes it difficult to obtain real estimates for diseases of global interest. Retention of patients in today's long and complex trial process depends on the investigator teams, communication skills and relationship with the subject. Account also needs to be taken of the strong impact made by patient literacy, society's attitude and bad media publicity on recruitment and retention of patients in trials.

If India is to really emerge as a global hub for pharmaceutical research, the country must take active steps to capitalize on her competitive advantages. These include undertaking measures for capacity building, continuing regulatory reforms and initiatives aimed at technical training and education in clinical research. We believe that the last is perhaps the most crucial since it is only on the back of this initiative that India can truly boast of leaping forward becoming a research hub with both, data integrity, the safety and well being of the patient at the centre. □

Ananda M Chakrabarty
Department of Microbiology &
Immunology
University of Illinois College of
Medicine, USA

Biotech research: Challenges and opportunities

The surge in science and technology in India has led to great expectations and some hype. Advances in biotechnology have been part of this surge. The intellectual property laws have been changed, with product patents having been recognised in 2005. New and clinically useful candidate drugs have been developed by the pharmaceutical and biotechnology companies. The Indian Government has generously increased the funding for the science and technological infrastructure. This has provided momentum to the endeavour for meeting the challenges of the future and for being globally competitive. Much remains to be done though. There are two areas of weaknesses that India must address and rectify if it wants to be a major player in the knowledge economy.

A major strength in the US biotechnology, starting from the promising days in the seventies, is the role of the academic sector in creating intellectual property and new businesses. Pioneering researchers at the universities like, UC-Berkeley, Stanford, UC-San Francisco, Harvard, etc, started up companies like Cetus, Genentech, Chiron, Biogen, etc, that developed products from academic research for global markets and quickly became targets of acquisition by multinational corporations creating enormous wealth for the nation, the institutions and the investors. The Bayh-Dole act of 1980, enabling ownership of the Government-funded research by the academic sector and small businesses, fueled this surge of academic activity. This in turn allowed many university professors to develop new businesses and bring new technologies or products to the market. Sadly, this enterprising activity from the Indian academic sector, particularly the highly-funded elite national laboratories, is sorely missing.

The Indian Government is trying to introduce a Bayh-Dole type of Act in India, and the CSIR, DBT and other government agencies are actively promoting new inventions or filing patents applications. However, these activities in India are nowhere comparable to similar activities in the US or Europe with regard to globally-marketable products. Indian academics are more interested in publishing their scientific findings in open literature for gaining recognition and credibility among their foreign peers. They have little genuine interest in using their research to develop new marketable products for the amelioration of human suffering or for economic gain.

While the Indian industrial sectors, particularly the biotechnology/pharmaceutical industry led by Ranbaxy, Dr Reddy's Laboratory, Biocon, Nicholas Piramal, Sun Pharma, Wockhardt and others, have made major efforts for generating and marketing new products, diagnostics, devices or for providing important services, the Indian academics largely remains isolated and depend heavily on Government handouts to maintain their status as public-service educators. Entrepreneurship is a word that they do not seem to like.

This needs to be changed through incentives provided to members of the academic sector, including the elite national laboratories, for scientific and technological innovations. The Government of India should consider establishing an Office of Technology Management (OTM) to support the filing of patent applications and their licensing, as well as some form of conflict management within the academic sector. This is the normal custom in US universities. The OTM should expose the academic scientist to

Photo credit L K Sharma

interested industrial sectors, venture capitalists and outside entrepreneurs for effective dialogue and interaction for generating new ideas, raising funds and new business development.

A second need of the hour is to have a streamlined system of encouraging innovations and conducting human clinical trials in India. Having recognised the product patents to encourage young Indian innovators to develop new products, including life-saving drugs for global markets, the Indian Government must establish regulatory guidelines and appropriate laws for protection of clinical data supplied to regulatory agencies including the Drug Controller General of India (DCGI) for marketing approval. It is widely accepted that India is an ideal place for human clinical trials not only because there are thousands of patients with every conceivable disease who need access to therapeutic intervention and drugs. India also has more than half a million doctors, nearly 40,000 hospitals and reasonably trained nurses.

However, most Indian doctors are not trained to analytically evaluate performance of drugs in a clinical setting and there is a need for setting up new medical centers and clinics/hospitals for drug evaluation purposes, the way NIH has set up General Clinical Research Centres in the United States. If young Indian inventors need to produce candidate drugs for clinical evaluations, there must be good laboratory practice, good manufacturing practice and good

clinical practice facilities available for facilitated production and evaluation of candidate drugs. While India has a large number of FDA-approved facilities, more are needed and should be upgraded if the potential drugs are to be designed and manufactured in India for regulatory approval, both in India and abroad.

An encouraging sign in this respect is the positive attitude of the Indian Government, particularly the Ministry of Finance, which recently abolished the 12.2 per cent service tax levied on human clinical trials. This will certainly make human clinical trials in India competitive with the rest of the world, particularly with countries such as Taiwan or Singapore. Another positive sign is the emergence of the Contract Research Organizations (CRO) with trained information technologists or biostatistics specialists who can evaluate and manage clinical data for human phase I, II and III trials.

There is a need for more such facilities for conducting both preclinical animal toxicity studies and managing human clinical trials. Given the huge market for clinical trials and the potential availability of many hospitals, trained doctors and a wide range of patient groups in India, as well as the Government's very positive attitude for addressing Data Exclusivity issues with category A and category B applications, the potential for human clinical trial facilities in India looks encouraging. The

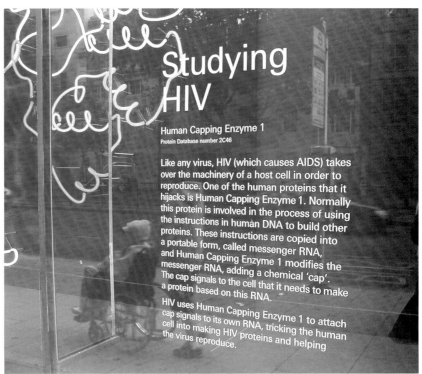

Studying
HIV

Human Capping Enzyme 1
Protein Database number 2C46

Like any virus, HIV (which causes AIDS) takes over the machinery of a host cell in order to reproduce. One of the human proteins that it hijacks is Human Capping Enzyme 1. Normally this protein is involved in the process of using the instructions in human DNA to build other proteins. These instructions are copied into a portable form, called messenger RNA, and Human Capping Enzyme 1 modifies the messenger RNA, adding a chemical 'cap'. The cap signals to the cell that it needs to make a protein based on this RNA.

HIV uses Human Capping Enzyme 1 to attach cap signals to its own RNA, tricking the human cell into making HIV proteins and helping the virus reproduce.

Photo credit L K Sharma

offices of DCGI and other regulatory agencies need to be strengthened to allow them to evaluate candidate drugs or diagnostics/vaccines in a fair, speedy and timely way. The judiciary needs to be strengthened to decide contentious cases involving patent infringements or regulatory approvals.

Way forward

The development of biotechnology in the United States is believed to have been greatly accelerated because of two major government policies: the US Supreme Court decision of the patentability of life forms that allows patents on anything under then sun that is made by man. In contrast, Indian patent laws allow patentability of lower forms of life, but not higher forms, although the lines of demarcation between higher and lower forms of life remain blurred and fuzzy! The second government policy, namely, the Bayh-Dole Act of 1980, to allow academic and business sectors to own government-funded research is getting better reception in India and a law similar to the Bayh-Dole Act is likely to be passed in India.

While the Indian Government and the Indian industrial sector are moving forward, hopefully to recognize data protection and to grant patents on alternative uses of known drugs, the universities and national laboratories in India, long used to receiving unconditional handouts from the government without providing any material or economic return to the government's investment, appear to be much more resistant to the changes on the horizon, particularly with regard to industrial capacity buildup and human resource development. India needs to upgrade the universities, not just build more, and ensure that the students and faculty are exposed to an ever-changing S&T curriculum that includes innovations and new ideas, both theoretical and practical. Such educational activity must also include not only liberal arts, sciences and technologies, but also ethics and law.

The patent attorneys and even judges need to be educated in writing and filing solid and legally acceptable claims, as well as enforcing their legal status fairly and in a timely manner. The recent establishment of the Rajiv Gandhi School of Intellectual Property Law at a technology-oriented academic institution such as IIT-Kharagpur, or the development of a curriculum of intellectual property laws in the Centre for Biotechnology at the M.S. University of Baroda, is an excellent example that other Indian institutions may like to follow. □

C N R Rao
Jawaharlal Nehru Centre for
Advanced Scientific Research
Bangalore

Nanoscience and nanotechnology plan

Nanoscience and Nanotechnology have become flavours of the day. Every country is trying to carry out work in this area not only because it promises many potential applications related to development, but also because the subject itself is fascinating. Children and grown-ups alike have been fascinated by the small size of objects one deals with in nanoscience and nanotechnology. Nanoscience deals with materials which have nanometric dimensions in at least one direction. Remember that human hair has a diameter of ~200,000 nm. Nanomaterials include nanoparticles, nanowires and nanotubes, nanofilms and nanowalls. Nanoparticles are generally spherical and are therefore zero-dimensional materials. Nanowires and nanotubes are one-dimensional materials. Carbon nanotubes are the most well known one-dimensional materials. Nanofilms and nanowalls are two-dimensional materials. Today, we have the ability to make any given material in any nanoform with the required dimensions. We can prepare nanoparticles of semiconductors, metal oxides, metals and other materials. Similarly, we can make nanowires and nanotubes of most materials. New methods of generating nanomaterials are being discovered all the time, and new nanomaterials are being described regularly. In addition to making nanomaterials, one has to find ways to assemble these materials.

With our ability to make nanomaterials of desired dimensions, size and shape, many applications have become possible. Nanomaterials were used as early as the Roman period. Let us not forget that we in India made the famous Damascus sword using a steel which had carbon nanotubes in it. However, we did not know at that time the science behind the strength of Damascus steel just as the Romans did not know why they got those beautiful colours in the glass vases. The recent history of nanoscience is, however, traced to the famous 1960 lecture of Richard Feynman entitled *There is plenty of room at the bottom*. The main driving force for nanotechnology is miniaturization. Note that everything in the electronic world is becoming smaller. This is particularly true of computers. Today, small computers that one can hold in one's hand can perform the same calculations as those done by huge machines in the 1950s. The tendency for miniaturization is often expressed in terms of Moore's law which refers to the decrease in the size of a device or the increase in the number of transistors in a chip with time.

Most of the applications of nanotechnology today, have been in medical diagnostics, sensors, cosmetics, textiles and chemical industry. While some applications have already been found possible in electronics and related areas, they have not yet become commercial. For example, carbon nanotubes are supposed to be good for flat-bed displays because of their excellent field emission properties but the displays are yet to come in the market. One of the problems has to do with the difficulty in producing nanomaterials in large quantities. For example, we would need carbon nanotubes in tonnage quantities. Most of us make them in milligram quantities. This problem will certainly be solved in the near future and the production of nanomaterials will not be an impediment for the progress of technology. The difficulty with nanoelectronics will be our ability to do integration. At present, we have transistors made of nanomaterials such as carbon nanotubes or oxide nanowires. However, integrating them into real devices will take some effort.

Translucent medical nanobots fixing blood cells

Countries like the US and Japan are investing a few billion dollars every year for research and development in nanoscience and technology. China has become a major competitor in this area and it is supporting this area in a big way. South Korea and Taiwan are also emerging as major players. In the last few years, the number of research papers in nanoscience and technology has increased enormously and in this, the contribution of China is particularly noteworthy. China today publishes more than most countries and contributes to research and development at a fairly high level both in terms of quantity and quality.

India started supporting nanoscience and technology research about four years ago. Till now, it has spent around Rs 120 crores to support research projects in various laboratories and to invest in some facilities such as electron microscopes. For the first time, we now at least have one transmission electron microscope in each region of India.

We should note that there have been individuals in India who have worked in nanoscience much before the subject became popular. The Indian Government has recently decided to have a nano mission with an investment of Rs 1000 crore for five years. We are hoping to establish three institutes of nanoscience and technology in different parts of the country. In addition to this, we will be supporting a number of educational projects to enable universities and other educational institutions to train young people in nanoscience and technology. Research projects will continue to be supported with some emphasis on technology and product development.

India was not part of the industrial revolution. Neither was it part of the semiconductor revolution. We missed the silicon boat long ago. At least in the area of nanotechnology, we can be as good as others. We should be able to develop new ideas and technologies and also commercialize some of them. I do hope that this will indeed be possible. □

Photo credit Shutterstock/Bio Spectrum

Aditya Mittal
Department of Biochemical
Engineering and Biotechnology
Indian Institute of Technology, Delhi

Nanotechnology in biological sciences

The emergence of nanotechnology as an independent multi-disciplinary and inter-disciplinary field has opened up a two-way exchange route for fascinating physics and chemistry (material sciences included) to be coupled with biology. On the one hand we are able to obtain mechanistic insights into a variety of events occurring in living systems on small length and time scales. On the other hand we are striving to mimic the efficiency of biological nano-systems in the form of nano-fabrications inspired by biological machines. This kind of fascinating work is being accomplished with the development of new tools, both in terms of instrumentation and discovery or synthesis of novel entities with specific physico-chemical characteristics.

Events taking place on the surface of and inside living cells, from the smallest known life forms to those identified as the largest occur at nano-meter to sub-micrometer scales by default. Thus, a large body of biological research falls under the umbrella of nanosciences by default. This has created a globally recognized interface between biological sciences and nanotechnology that is revolutionizing the ideas that drive several areas of scientific and technological innovation.

There are basically five major categories that are having a major impact on the direction of the evolving nano-bio interface: (1) Bio-derived template design, (2) Bio-inspired machines, both in terms of the small sizes and the efficiency of operations, (3) Molecular diagnostics, both in terms of applied medical research and basic biological applications, (4) Research and development of drug delivery systems, more commonly referred to as nanomedicine and, (5) Instrumentation research and development for pushing the measurement limits required in the nano-bio interface.

Work being done in India in all these categories has thrown up promising examples. However, we cannot be among the leaders in the field unless we address some issues, both at the scientific/technological and bureaucratic levels.

Bio-derived template design & bio-inspired machines

Biological systems comprise excellent patterns created from nano-scale assemblies. Utilizing entities that constitute biological systems for generating nano-patterns for a variety of applications including templates for microfluidic flows and electrical conduction are a few specific areas of global interest. While still in its infancy in India, some remarkable contributions are emerging from our national research scene.

The research groups spearheading a wide array of fascinating discoveries and developments in the area of bio-derived template design belong to several institutions. These include the Indian Institutes of Technologies (IITs), Indian Institute of Sciences, the Tata Institute of Fundamental Research group of institutions (NCBS in Karnataka and TIFR in Maharashtra), Central Scientific Instrumentation Organization in Chandigarh, University of Delhi, National Chemical Laboratory in Pune and the Indian Association of Cultivation of Science in Kolkata.

The developments range from utilizing DNA polymer structures for construction of nano-scale materials (e.g. nano-wires for sensors and actuators), to protein assembly based patterns for the creation of 'smart' textiles, to formation of thin film patterns and nano-shells inspired by or utilizing the self assembly principles of a variety of biomolecules. Recently, a collaborative venture aimed at training specialized scientists on the theme of biodesign has been initiated between IIT-Delhi and Stanford University. Some international collaboration is taking place at the level of individual Indian scientists.

In terms of bio-inspired machines, the Indian research system has been somewhat short-handed by a lack of proper personnel in the area of development or even procurement of the specialized instrumentation required for such work. This shortcoming is magnified by the neglect of the manufacturing sector by Indian businesses.

Molecular diagnostics

These are the most productive areas of work in the nano-bio interface in India. Academic research is being well complemented by some industrial interest. Identification and development of India-centric applications are being carried out at institutions like All India Institute of Medical Sciences (AIIMS, New Delhi), National Institute of Pharmaceutical Education and Research (NIPER, Mohali) and several others. From early detection of tuberculosis, to oral delivery of a variety of drugs including insulin, academic research is being carried out in continuous collaboration with industry.

The Confederation of Indian Industry (CII) and Associated Chambers of Commerce and Industry of India (ASSOCHAM) bring together Indian scientists engaged in academic research in these areas with industrial interests. Dabur, Nicholas Piramal, Ranbaxy, Dr Reddy's Laboratories are some of the leading companies, amongst others, who have taken a strong interest in identifying specific areas in both nano-diagnostics and nano-drug delivery systems. The acceptance of nano-bio interface in these areas has led to the industry shaking off its closed-door policies and approaching the academic scientists to develop not only nano-based products but also the right kind of expertise for the immediate future.

Indian research projects are directed towards developing nano-centric solutions for better utilization of already existing drugs (e.g. increased bioavailability, targeted delivery etc.). While Indian research (both academic and industrial) lags substantially in the field of new drug molecule development, the advent of nanotechnology in these areas of medical

applications globally has seen a somewhat parallel growth. Regardless of the parameters for measuring success (e.g. number of quality publications, patents filed, patents granted etc.), India is certainly quite competent at this point. India can claim a legacy since its ancient medical system has used, for thousand of years, products like *swarna-bhasma* (translates to gold-aerosol) comprising of therapeutic gold nano- and micro-particles. Based on such examples, the Indian Academy of Sciences (Bangalore) recently produced a well compiled document on ayurvedic medicines. This should enable a scientific exploration of pharmaceutical products that have been accepted by the Indian culture for many years but are yet to gain a global acceptance due to lack of proper scientific data on how these products work.

Instrumentation

When it comes to the nano-bio interface, India does face a challenge. At this point of time, India has a complete lack of any expertise in instrumentation required for working on the nano-bio interface. It is the services sector rather than manufacturing that attracts the business interests. Not a single instrument required for conducting research/development in nanoscience and nanotechnology is being manufactured in India. Research organizations (academic as well as industrial) have to rely on imported equipment. Not surprisingly, there is a large sector of industry that qualifies as dealers or agents of manufacturers spread across the globe (including USA, Japan, Korea, China and Europe). This lack of expertise in manufacturing will widen the gap between global progress in the nano-bio interface and the Indian research scene.

Instrumentation manufacturing requires not just financial investment but also trained manpower which we do not have. We need to learn from the history of technological advancement, starting right from the industrial revolution in England, to the rise and establishment of Japan as a hub of innovative instrumentation. Without developing the required human resources, India cannot even dream of competing with the countries advancing the area of nano-bio interface. Our scientific ambitions can be frustrated and scientific talent can be wasted by the want of a nail!

How many manufacturers of polymeric membranes are there in India (these are essential to bioprocesses and downstream processing)? Or how many trained personnel are there in high resolution electron microscopy who can actually prepare/process biological samples.... The list can go on and on.

Even imported instrumentation is of no use in the absence of trained manpower to keep it going. It is not enough to sanction posts in an institution. One has to actually hire the person and also run a training programme. Science planners and administrators must remedy the situation.

Learning from mistakes

India identified, some three decades ago Biotechnology as a key future growth area. Despite promises and investments in the sector, India seems to have missed the bus. While the number of biotechnology educational programs have mushroomed all over India in numbers that are simply mind boggling, most of the graduates from these programmes (ranging from BSc and MSc and, BTech to MTech) are actually un-employable. Three decades ago, the students were told that biotechnology is the future. But because of certain mistakes in planning, that future still remains in future. Today political leaders and science administrators project the nano-bio interface as the future. It is a multi- and inter-disciplinary area that requires a huge impetus in developing the right kind of human resources.

We must accept the failure of both language and strategies that were used for approaching biotechnology and not repeating the same for nanotechnology in biological sciences. As an example, the word 'innovation' has become commonly utilized by a variety of agencies to describe the need of stressing on specific research areas. It must be realized that one cannot create innovative individuals by forcing specific areas of work on scientists. India cannot innovate on the basis of approaches taken by 'developed' countries. India will innovate in the nano-bio interface by allowing the freedom to explore. An increase in trained human resources will increase the chances to innovate and lead. Innovation cannot be forced on or out of individuals.

We need to speed-up the bureaucratic process that forms a part of the research and innovation infrastructure. In any fast moving field of growth, to be competent globally, one has to ensure a well oiled bureaucratic machine that does not slow down the pace of progress. Today when an idea is conceived for exploration, if the pace of execution is even slightly slow, there is very little chance that it will remain an innovative idea tomorrow.

Human resources

We must take steps on the basis of the past experience in the field of biotechnology. For example, it is well realized that working on the nano-bio interface is very capital intensive. Our institutions have funds to buy expensive instrumentation but they do not have the trained manpower to maintain and operate these. There is no point in providing funds for procuring special techniques that are required, without actually creating specialized positions to ensure sustainability of such techniques after the normal three to five years of the funding period is over. Training programs need to be developed and conducted to create specialists in the techniques of the present to allow for innovation and development in future. More capital is needed to create such human resources.

A recent venture in nanotechnology has set an example. Formed by former graduates of the IIT system, Appin Knowledge Solutions (based in New Delhi) has initiated programmes for creating strong human resources in nanotechnology. The most important aspect of this venture is the fact that even certification programs offered come with an assurance of employability in core nanotechnology related work.

This comes in the form of a tie-up as knowledge partners with educational institutions and companies that are working in nanotechnology. The opening of the Tata Chemicals Innovation Center in Pune will help create good human resources to work at the nano-bio interface. Without such initiatives, nanotechnology research in biological sciences will always remain the future in India.

India is moving in the right direction in the context of this critical research field. It has learned from its experience with another 'field of the future', biotechnology. Therefore, it should be easier to approach this 'field of the future' called nanotechnology and its important interface with biological sciences. In a few aspects it is indeed a field of the present already on the Indian scene. □

Priyanka Bhogani
Journalist

Knowledge Park as incubator

The ICICI Knowledge Park is now known as an incubator for life sciences research and development. It is a unique institution which provides space for research facilities and attracts scientific workers who have marketable products in mind. The Park is situated in Genome Valley cluster near Hyderabad. While the current focus of IKP is in Life Sciences, innovation in any knowledge-based sector that requires wet labs is encouraged.

IKP lies in a 140,000 sq ft Innovation Corridor. IKP has allotted around 45 acres of land on long lease to six anchor companies to build their own facilities. The facilities created by the Park are now fully occupied by a wide spectrum of companies from technology startups to SMEs to very large companies. There have so far been 31 R&D companies at ICICI Knowledge Park. Of these companies, 11 have graduated and currently there are 20 companies (13 Indian, 5 American, 1 German and 1 Japanese company) in the Park working in the areas of pharmaceuticals, biotechnology and chemistry. Seventy per cent of these are into technology/product development while the rest are engaged in contract research. About 1,400 people work on the campus. So far 20 patents have been filed by the Park residents; but the number is expected to grow exponentially in the near future. The companies have in turn invested over Rs 300 crores in the Park.

The Project was made possible by ICICI Bank providing management support and initial funding of around Rs 39.5 crores and the State Government of Andhra Pradesh giving 200 acres of land free of cost for establishing the Park. IKP also received around Rs 3 crores as grant from the Union Government for establishing a Virtual Information Centre, a Life Science Incubator and the Garden of Life (a medicinal plant garden) at the Park.

Mr N Vaghul, chairman of ICICI Bank, proposed the idea for a science park for use by researchers, entrepreneurs and small companies. The idea was to see how Indian industry would do in a globally competitive atmosphere, says Deepanwita Chattopadhyay, the chief executive officer of the Park. Established companies came to Knowledge Park for the state-of-the-art facilities, whereas the startup companies needed equipment, and guidance in capital-raising, networking and marketing. IKP has IKP also has a mentoring role. The Park's tenants include Matrix labs, Krebs Biochemicals, GVK Biosciences, Anu's Laboratories, Sai Life Sciences, Bioserve Biotechnologies, Indigene Pharmaceuticals, Helvetica Industries, EPR Pharmaceuticals, Daewoong Pharmaceuticals and Mithros Chemicals. The United State Pharmacopeia serves pharmaceutical companies around Hyderabad and elsewhere in the country. Du Pont is setting up its Knowledge Centre (DKC), with over Rs 300-crore investment. These companies do R&D mainly in the fields of pharmaceuticals, chemistry and biotechnology. Ms Chattopadhyay says it was a conscious decision to focus on life sciences rather than on information technology.

The Knowledge Park at the beginning tried to attract small Indian companies. Then it reached out to the NRI-owned companies. Finally, it started hosting the branches of companies from Japan, Germany and the US. The laboratory space is leased out for three years, and some of the larger companies have the option to buy land to have their own buildings. One of the first units to be incubated at IKP was Laurus Labs. Mr. Satyanarayana originally worked for Matrix Labs, also a member of IKP, but wanted to conduct independent research. Laurus Labs was started in March 2006, and in June 2007 received a substantial funding. It shares land with Aptuit labs and without the timely support of IKP, such an opportunity would have been missed.

IKP houses two new research centres, the Centre for Technologies in Public Health and the Centre for Advancement in Agricultural Practice. A Virtual Information Centre was launched in 2001 with a grant from the Department of Scientific and Industrial Research for researchers to access databases and share information easily. The next step to innovation is to set up a Seed Fund which would allow start up companies to raise capital, filling the gap in venture capital.

Contract research services provider, Laxai Avanti Life Sciences Pvt Ltd, is in the process of setting up a 100-seat clinical data management centre on a four-acre plot in the Park. It would also focus on bio-equivalence studies to cater to the needs of mid-sized pharma companies.

The CII and the Andhra Pradesh Technology Development & Promotion Centre have set up the Intellectual Property Rights Facilitation Cell at ICICI Knowledge Park, in association with the State Government to assist industries and MNCs intending to invest in biotech and pharma projects. The cell would be the hub of IPR services in South India. An interesting initiative that is coming up at the IKP is a partnership model between an Indian biosciences company and a global drug discovery firm to establish facilities and carry out research, clinical trials and drug discovery services.

GVK bioSciences Pvt Ltd, of the Hyderabad-based GVK group, has entered into a three-year partnership with Ricerca LLC, based in the US. It is a $50-million drug discovery company belonging to the SG (Societe Generale) bank.

The tie-up is for setting up medicinal chemistry and discovery biology facility at the IKP, the GVK bio Chief Executive Officer, Mr G.V. Sanjay Reddy said. The partnership would help small molecule drug discovery and development. It would also undertake medicinal chemistry and discovery services for Ricerca's clients and also take up jointly owned proprietary discovery programmes.

In turn, Ricerca would guarantee GVK Bio a minimum number of medicinal chemistry contract research projects and provide it with some of its proprietary drug targets or early hits towards the joint drug discovery and development programmes, Mr Reddy said. The company proposes to increase the strength of its professionals to 250 by the year-end and consider pumping in funds of Rs 50 core to Rs 100 core in the next three years depending on the evolving opportunities.

NASSCOM-ICICI Knowledge Park Fund (NIIF) is the most recent initiative that has come to IKP. In January, 2008 the NIIF, with a corpus of Rest 100 core was announced. TCS, ICICI Knowledge Park and Bharti Airtel are anchor investors. The fund would be fully operational in three months. It has been created with the intent of providing seed stage investments in order to promote Intellectual Property driven innovations in emerging technologies.

At present, the focus areas identified for investment by the fund are wireless technologies, automotive infotronics, life sciences, energy conservation technologies and devices and medical devices.

Moving up innovation chain

A Life Sciences Incubation Centre has been set up in the park with an investment of Rs 3 core with eight labs, of which four will be exclusively for biotech and the remaining labs will be for chemistry. The LSI not only provides fully furnished dedicated lab space and shared equipment but more importantly, a mentoring program for start-up companies and scientist entrepreneurs. The idea is to incubate companies/technology entrepreneurs and make them "VC ready" in three-years. The LSI model is a little different from that of a university-led incubator where technologies come primarily from the university and are pursued with the help of faculty/students. So far LSI has received proposals mainly from entrepreneurs who have a track record of working with the industry and have decided to pursue ideas/technologies on their own. It was a real proud moment for the Life Science Incubator when its first incubatee Laurus Laboratories received a valuation of USD 100 million from Aptuit Inc. within two years. Aptuit-Laurus is now an anchor company at IKP.

The Park is now working on a strategy to promote and incubate companies in the areas of clean technologies, especially those that border life sciences, materials and energy. ICICI Knowledge Park's goal is to be a hub of innovation in India. □

INFORMATION
TECHNOLOGY

TATA's supercomputer EKA

Rajdeep Sahrawat
Vice President
NASSCOM

From techno-coolie to creative

Few words are more ubiquitous in business or society today than 'innovation'. It would be an extremely rare publication or a business channel or conference which did not dwell upon innovation today. As a strategic lever for enhancing competitiveness, innovation is perhaps the most sought after as business and government leaders attempt to survive and grow in an increasingly competitive and flat world.

But what does innovation mean? As with anything which acquires a gospel status, innovation implies different things to different people often based on individual experiences and is analogous to the parable of the five blind men who came up with their versions of the elephant based on what part of the elephant's body they touched. While it may sound overtly simplistic and offend the purists, innovation is simply about solving an existing problem using new ways and means. Successful innovations are not only about making existing solutions cheaper and better but are also about understanding untapped user needs that need to be addressed in an ingenious and path-breaking manner.

Contrary to the common perception that the Indian IT industry does not innovate enough, the Indian IT industry is no stranger to innovation (IT is being used here holistically and refers to both IT and the BPO segments of the industry). While cost and infrastructure arbitrage are often attributed as the key factors behind its stupendous success, it is often forgotten that the offshore outsourcing model pioneered by the Indian IT industry has been one of the most disruptive innovations in the global IT services industry. Through a concatenation of tools, processes and infrastructure which enabled it to deliver large volumes of high quality work from India, the Indian IT industry changed the rules of the game in the global IT services industry.

From humble beginnings, the Indian IT industry has grown ten times over the last decade into a $ 60 billion behemoth which today contributes over 5 per cent to the Indian GDP and constitutes nearly 25 per cent of Indian exports. It employs 2 million people directly and by creating four jobs in allied sectors for every direct job in the IT industry, the Indian IT industry is responsible for creating nearly 10 million jobs. With India forming a core component in any global IT sourcing strategy, 'Why India' has been replaced by 'Why not India'.

The Indian IT industry has evolved through three distinct phases (1 Figure 1). Phase was an export led growth driven by factor arbitrage for relatively commoditised services like application development and management. The Indian IT firms invested little in R&D and consequently created little intellectual property assets. During phase 2, the Indian IT firms gained domain experience and developed a reputation for superior delivery and hence were able to capture value in the market in some market segments and domains. During Phase 3 (current phase), the Indian IT industry is seamlessly transforming the India centric offshore outsourcing model into a Global Delivery model which enables it to not only operate on a 24/7 basis but also overcome language, cultural and regulatory barriers. Through continuous innovations to the basic offshore outsourcing paradigm, the industry has evolved new service lines including BPO, engineering services, outsourced R&D etc with each of them becoming multi-billion

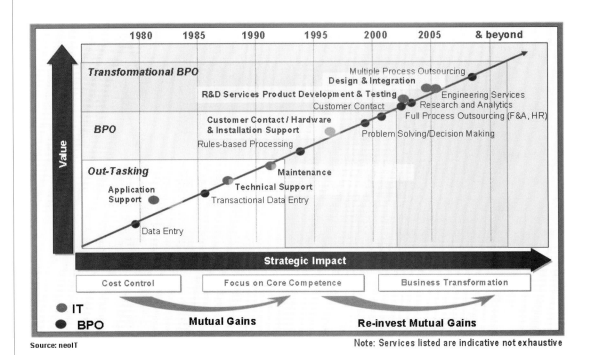

Source: neoIT

Note: Services listed are indicative not exhaustive

Fig. 1: Evolution of the Indian IT industry

dollar opportunities. Two other important features of the current phase are that firstly the domestic IT market is increasingly becoming a focus area for the Indian IT industry and secondly there has been a substantial increase in the average size of the contacts awarded to Indian IT firms with USD 100 million plus deals now being considered passé.

However, the traditionally successful business model of the Indian IT industry is increasingly coming under strain and the traditional competitive advantages are weakening. Geographical and cultural affinity, growing concerns in the key western markets over outsourcing to India, similar time zones and active local government support have resulted in Latin America, East Europe and China emerging as alternative offshore destinations. MNC firms are increasingly making India a core part of their global delivery operations and are ramping up their delivery capabilities in India. Rising factor costs in India coupled with macro trends like the rupee appreciation and wage inflation are nullifying productivity improvement efforts. The structure of the Indian IT industry is currently skewed towards a small number of large firms which dominate the industry and the vast majority of the firms in the middle and small segments are struggling to address the twin challenges of top-line and bottom-line growth. Not only will manpower supply constraints prohibit a linear

expansion of the current model beyond a certain threshold, this high rate of employee growth is also likely to put tremendous strain on a IT firm's governance and management capabilities. Customers are becoming more knowledgeable and demanding and want to move from pure factor arbitrage predicated vendor services to partnerships which deliver business value and productivity gains beyond mere operational efficiencies. While a strong and vibrant domestic IT market is critical to anchor the growth for the Indian IT industry beyond the short-term horizon, several challenges continue to impede the growth of the domestic IT market including, high tariffs and import duties, poor rate of commercialisation of domestic R&D, lack of IT adoption in key sectors including agriculture, healthcare, education and in the SME segment etc.

Therefore the Indian IT industry is at an inflection point today and needs to reenergise by creating new sources of competitive advantage. Delivering 'more' or 'better' can be done by increasing efficiency, but beyond a point the value curve begins to flatten and it becomes increasingly difficult to keep providing ever increasing value-for-money. Commoditisation of IT services, advent of new disruptive technologies and the blurring of the distinction between hardware, software and services indicate the need for the Indian IT industry to develop more market-facing

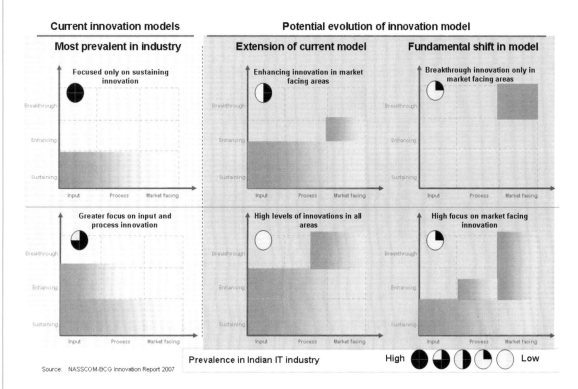

Fig. 2: Innovation Portfolio of the Indian IT Industry

capabilities and domain expertise and move towards a more consumer-centric business model. The only way for the Indian IT industry to achieve a transformational change is therefore through innovation: not just executing the same series of steps more efficiently, but by doing new things in different ways to achieve new levels of output.

However, innovation does not occur at the level of the industry or nation. Ultimately it is the firm which is the atomic unit of competition and it the firm who brings products and services to the customer. As a result, innovation ultimately has to occur in the context of the firm and the markets it targets, irrespective of whether it is a start-up or a large firm.

Unfortunately the innovation aspirations of the Indian IT firms today tend to focus on the easily attainable resulting in an innovation intensity which focuses on achieving operational efficiencies. As shown in figure 2, the current innovation portfolio of a majority of Indian IT firms is heavily skewed away from market facing and breakthrough innovation efforts and is focussed predominantly on sustaining and incremental innovations on inputs and internal business processes. While sustaining innovations are important, only a significant shift towards more market-facing breakthrough and enhancing innovations will

lead to increased competitiveness and provide the necessary revenue impetus in the medium to long-term.

There are several areas of innovation which can effect this transformation in the innovation portfolio of the Indian IT firms, for instance:

• Penetrating new customer segments in intellectual asset-intensive service lines like engineering and R&D services
• Creating Intellectual Property (IP) in frontier technology areas
• Developing and codifying specific domain expertise
• Technical innovations to own standards for next generation of technologies.

The target or aspirational innovation portfolio for the Indian IT firms needs to be overweight on the market facing and breakthrough aspects. The gap between the current innovation portfolio and the target portfolio will point to the extent of change an IT firm will have to embrace. Assessing the capabilities and success-criteria of the current versus the target portfolio will shape the actions that firms will need to take to bridge the gap successfully. This change in portfolio will require a well thought out transformation roadmap, i.e. a pathway to innovation.

The pathway to innovation for any firm can be defined in terms of two broad dimensions: the motivation for innovation and discipline for innovation. Discipline is achieved through policies and practices and also importantly requires the commitment of the firm's senior leadership. Motivation is achieved through working together and changing attitudes and comes more from a pull across the firm. Actions taken by a firm for developing innovation capabilities will have an impact on both the motivation and discipline dimensions.

Irrespective of the approach adopted by individual firms in constructing an optimal innovation portfolio, Indian IT firms will have to go through three core steps:

- Creating the foundation: This includes putting in place a defined process to aid in innovation management and also enhancing motivation through specific and directed incentives.
- Walking the talk: This includes designing the appropriate organisation structure with permeable boundaries that is aligned for enabling innovation. It also requires investing visibly in emphasizing the culture of innovation including implementing incentive models which encourage risk taking and innovation.
- Working with other stakeholders: Creating the organisational enablers for encouraging 'open innovation' and developing well defined collaboration models for working with other innovation partners.

However innovation does not thrive in isolation or silos. An enabling environment at the national/region/industry level is required to foster innovation at the firm level. A typical innovation ecosystem provides linkages among the various innovation stakeholders including firms and entrepreneurs, investors, government and governmental bodies, industry bodies and educational and research institutions. These linkages encourage collaboration for idea generation and transformation of these ideas into successful innovations. The degree of participation of the different stakeholders, and the nature and strength of their interactions gives the ecosystem its vibrancy and its raison-d'etre. For innovation ecosystems to thrive, ecosystem stakeholders need to successfully play myriad roles and poor performance on any of these roles by the stakeholders often renders the ecosystem sterile.

A relative comparison of the various global innovation ecosystems based on the contribution and impact of stakeholders, highlights that the Indian innovation ecosystem is in a relatively nascent stage.

While all important stakeholders of an innovation ecosystem are present in India with sufficient maturity, the Indian ecosystem suffers from the twin structural weaknesses of insufficient participation in terms of roles being played by different stakeholders and also weak linkages between them. These structural weaknesses are preventing India from becoming a global hub for IT innovations.

As the key delivery mechanism for commercializing innovations, and as probably biggest beneficiaries of innovation, the Indian IT firms have a crucial role in the development of the Indian innovation ecosystem. They need to take the lead in nurturing linkages among other ecosystem constituents and driving collaboration.

Linkages

As Figure 3 shows, the linkages need to be formed and nurtured at both upstream and downstream stages of the invention to innovation continuum. Strong upstream linkages will require the Indian IT firms to collaborate with the R&D and academic institutions and will not only enable the Indian IT firms to guide the technology development efforts but also give them an early view of disruptive technologies being germinated in the R&D institutes. For these linkages to result in the desired outcomes, the IT firms will need to incorporate these linkages as part of the firm's core strategy instead of treating them as corporate social responsibility or 'feel-good' activities. On the other hand, creating strong downstream linkages with the customer organizations will enable the IT firms to partner in creating market facing innovations based on actual customer needs and thus increasing the success probability of these innovations. The IT firms will need to adopt an entrepreneurial mindset and invest in these partnerships with customers.

The domestic or home market is another critical lever available to the Indian IT industry for driving breakthrough innovations. Today, India promises more opportunities for innovation than any other country perhaps. There is a huge unfulfilled market in India for many products and services, including healthcare, education, financial services, retail, e-governance etc. IT and telecom technologies will play a critical role towards addressing these market needs at the scale required in India and hence these hitherto untapped markets

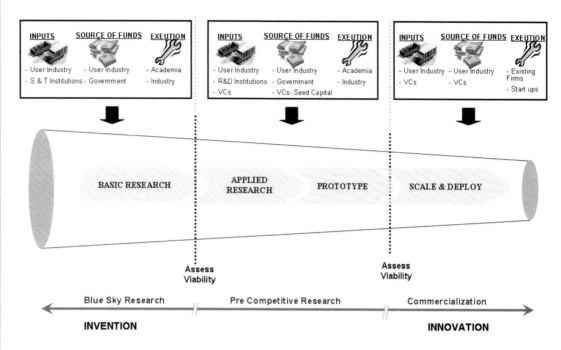

Fig. 3: Invention to Innovation Supply Chain

present significant opportunities for innovative IT solutions that can enable lean, cost effective and value-creating business outcomes. The billion problems of India are a billion opportunities for innovation and India has the potential to be a crucible for global innovations which are applicable not only in the emerging markets but also in the developed markets.

Over the last decade, the Indian IT industry has been the poster child of the young, confident and resurgent new India and its achievements have had a galvanising effect on other sectors. However, with each success come greater expectations. High innovation aspirations resulting in bold initiatives created through 'out-of-the-box' thinking can enable the Indian IT industry to maintain its leadership in face of growing global competition. A successful innovation wave will not only strengthen the Indian IT industry but will also give rise to products and services that will benefit a wider cross section of society in both India and other parts of the world and greatly help in addressing the digital divide in India. The Indian IT industry stands on the cusp of a unique moment and failure to innovate now will be an unfortunate case of lost opportunity. □

S Ramadorai
MD & CEO
TATA Consultancy Services

TCS innovates along multiple dimensions

Productivity and profitability in the software industry are driven by the nature of the software beast: According to Brooks (1987), software can be thought to comprise the *accidental* (or *incidental*) and the *essential*. Most of what is done in programming, or by hardware infrastructure and technical software is actually incidental, i.e. it can, in principle, be automated. The essential consists of the *'what'*: creating the conceptual structures that bring real benefits to enterprises, which software merely implements.

Innovation in reducing the incidental continues, starting from automated migration of legacy systems to new technologies, to code generation from specifications and, now, moving towards code interpretation in which programs need not be written for each new functionality. Rather the software itself can be configured and extended by analysts or users.

Coming to the essential, there are two dimensions—strategy and re-use. Take re-use: if you already have software that meets a large part of a customer's needs, you can deliver a solution faster and with much better productivity (and therefore margin). This is the 'product' space, but focused on high-value, fairly complex functionality: banking, manufacturing etc. Such 'asset' or product based solutions—sometimes also called 'frameworks'—are the natural extension of the industries' learning from all the implementation work we do.

The software industry traditionally, and the Indian IT services industry in particular, sought to elicit strategy and requirements from customers. In the recent years however, the role of technology and IT within the enterprise has changed: from an enabler to being able to lead change. Leading IT companies participate with the end-user organization to *define* how technology can be exploited and thereby drive business strategy. To achieve this, there is a need for a deep understanding of vertical domains. The most important change that we need to engender is a culture of focusing on understanding the domain and leveraging technology—both which is available today and that which is emerging—to deliver expected business outcomes. In the Indian context, we have seen major initiatives in which the Tata Consultancy Services (TCS) has participated in defining, designing and implementing transformational business changes through technology. Examples are the National Stock Exchange, the National Depository and, recently, the MCA project that have, through technology, changed the way financial systems in India operate.

To lead and define the future in this environment, we need to continuously track technology—especially potential disruptive innovations—which could change the nature of the industry. TCS has a systematic approach to innovation and research built on the right governance model, talented people and close partnerships.

Innovation in TCS is built on four fundamental axioms:

- First, that innovation is not just invention of new technologies and processes; it is also the market positioning and business impact of the invention.
- Second, innovation may happen by 'happy accident' but, at an organizational level, we need to have an enabling process and an active culture for finding, executing and rewarding new ideas.

- Third, in today's world, no single organization can do it all. While we continue to invest in our own capacity to innovate— we have established 19 Innovation Labs across the world—we have also established an open, co-innovation model where multiple stakeholders come together, pool their intellectual property and create an innovation outcome where the collective whole is more than the sum of its parts. Our co-innovation partners include venture capital funds, startup companies, academic institutions, our strategic partners and our own clients.
- Finally, there are multiple types of innovation that an organization needs to take through the lifecycle of idea through implementation and, each type of innovation needs a different process, culture and implementation methodology.
  - ☐ Derivative innovation is based on delivery excellence and delivers continuous improvement of current products and services in terms of measurable cost, time and efficiency benefits. It is best executed by existing business units—in the case of TCS, this would mean delivery, sales and relationship management. The ideas for improvement come from the people in the field and this requires an enabling culture of 'creative dissatisfaction with the status quo'. Teams typically ask the question—how can we be better, faster, cheaper, more effective than what we were yesterday? Tools, new processes and methods, measurement, benchmarking and systematic improvement are typical methods for derivative innovation. This is a core premise of our 'certainty' promise and is the basis for other types of innovation.
  - ☐ Platform innovations extend our own products, services and capabilities and offer transformational capabilities to the businesses of our clients. These are conceptualized and delivered by our industry and service practices, R&D teams, co-innovation partners and our clients. Typically, we will evolve next generation technologies, new business processes and business models in this category of innovation. These innovations are incubated in our Innovation Labs, and are demonstrated through our showcases, where customers can come and experience the application of technology within their

business context. This kind of innovation 'pushes the envelope' of current work and process, and needs to be 'sold' through a 'business advisor' channel rather than a 'business as usual' channel.
  - ☐ Breakthrough or 'disruptive innovations' create new markets based on dramatically different costs, capabilities or technologies. These are enabled through our Innovation Labs which anchor the TCS Co-Innovation Network. Our innovation ecosystem catalyses disruptive thought and creates a framework for the lifecycle from thought to implementation. The open innovation model embodied in TCS Co-Innovation Network includes channels such as the TCS Innovation Forum, TCS Customer Innovation Days and the Technology Sponsor Programs among others to deliver on this promise.

The classification helps us appreciate and create innovations that may fit into various stages of an organization's strategic roadmap—our clients and our own. Thus the 'client centric' view of our innovation portfolio would have the same three dimensions, now from a 'what does TCS Innovation mean to our clients' perspective:

- **Delivery excellence or 'derivative innovation' needs.** These are delivered in terms of measurable cost, time and efficiency benefits within our and/or our customers' current businesses.
- **Business model or 'product line' innovations or 'platform innovation' needs.** This set of needs requires transformational services, assets and business models, which TCS delivers by aligning our practices and R&D teams to our customer needs. These innovations are also demonstrated through our showcase Labs, where customers can come and experience the application of technology within their context, e.g. transport & hospitality and retail smart store.
- **Breakthrough or 'disruptive innovation' aspirations.** These are enabled through our Co-Innovation Network—an ecosystem that catalyses disruptive thought through synergies drawn from open innovation. It uses channels such as the TCS Innovation Forum, TCS Customer Innovation Days and Tech Sponsor Programs among others to deliver on this promise.

The innovation portfolio in TCS is owned by our global network of Innovation Labs, and the work is catalysed and amplified by an entire ecosystem through the TCS Co-Innovation Network (COIN).

1. **Innovation Labs:** We have a global network of 19 Innovation Labs. These Labs attract the best of R&D talent, are equipped with state-of-the-art infrastructural resources, and have continuously evolved new standards of technology, business, and domain innovations. These Labs are continuously innovating and evolving next generation solutions such as:

   - New standards for software development,
   - Next generation processes in specific domains, or

   - Developing and demystifying new technologies such as grid computing, web 2.0, bio-informatics and so on.

2. **Co-Innovation Network (COIN):** Over the years, our Labs have collaborated with many external entities including academia, industry thought leaders, other research labs and, more recently, various start ups and venture funds. These collaborations were established in pursuit of an intuitive felt need of bringing a diversity of perspective in our research. Having established this conduit over the years—and today being more convinced than ever before that 'Open and collaborative innovation' is the order of

---

Box 1. Supercomputing & the Paradigm Shift in Engineering

Supercomputing has traditionally been driven by strategic—read 'military'—imperatives. Spooks trying to tap encrypted enemy communications or defence scientists trying to simulate their nuclear arsenal readily come to mind.

Of late, however, there is a growing emphasis on the usage of supercomputers for peaceful purposes, for engineering. In fact, the usage—or, more correctly, the potential usage—of supercomputers promises to usher in a paradigm-shift in the way we do engineering design. This trend is underlined by a report by the US Council of Competitiveness which emphasizes the need to develop a petaFLOPS-grade supercomputer to keep American industry globally competitive (1 petaFLOPS is 10^{15} floating point operations per second).

To participate in—or even to drive—this paradigm shift, the Tata Group, in its well-known pioneering tradition, set up the Computational Research Laboratories (CRL) in Pune with a mandate to achieve a position of global leadership in supercomputing. As a first step to achieving this goal, CRL has built the supercomputer Eka—in Sanskrit, literally 'One', figuratively 'One of a Kind'. Eka has a sustained computing power of 120 teraFLOPS (1 teraFLOPS is 10^{12} floating point operations per second) and has been ranked the fourth fastest in the world and the fastest in Asia (http://www.top500.org). CRL has indeed done India proud.

With a unique architecture, layout, cooling system and innovative software stack, Eka provides excellent application efficiency. Since it uses standard—but state-of-the-art—hardware, it is very cost-effective and application developer friendly.

The one word that describes the paradigm-shift supercomputing can cause is 'simulation'. The idea is to build a (mathematical) model of what is being designed and evaluate its properties before it is even prototyped. This saves cost of prototyping and, in some cases, of destructive testing. Some representative paradigm-shifting applications of supercomputing are:

1. Aerospace: Modelling the behaviour of an aircraft as it moves through the air and simulating it to estimate its performance and stability. Technically known as Computational Fluid Dynamics (CFD), such simulation can reduce expensive wind-tunnel experiments. More interestingly, with sufficient (100 teraflops or more) computing power, we can get better and more accurate results than from wind-tunnel experiments.

2. Automotive: Structural modelling and crash simulation of cars to evaluate their safety. Result: fewer cars need actually be crashed!

3. Natural phenomena: Modelling and simulation to predict weather, global climate change and natural disasters such as earthquake and tsunami.

4. Drug design: Modelling the potential drug molecule and the relevant human biochemical processes to simulate the behaviour of the drug in terms of its efficacy and side-effects. This will reduce the ethical dilemmas of animal and human testing.

5. Thermonuclear energy: India is a member of the International Thermonuclear Experimental Reactor (ITER) Consortium which plans to harness thermonuclear energy to provide a sustained, clean solution to the energy demands of humankind. The essential requirement for building such a reactor is to simulate micro-turbulence effects in plasma (the stuff of which most of our Sun is made). This needs a supercomputer with a rating of 1 petaFLOPS or more.

The team at CRL will drive all these paradigm shifts using Eka and its successors. The possibilities are limitless; indeed, the real paradigm shifts will occur in ways as yet unimagined. With Tata's CRL as its vanguard, India is poised to pioneer this new industrial revolution.

Box 2. Instant apps for enhanced productivity in software development

The MIT's Centre for Bits and Atoms has developed the 'Fab Lab', a 'personal fabricator', that potentially allows an ordinary person to rapidly build almost anything. Using the Fab Lab, individuals, SMEs can rapidly design and actually fabricate the innovative gadgets or devices they require. Traditional manufacturing industries can use the Fab Lab as a rapid prototyping engine to improve industrial design, enable far more cost-effective user testing, and thereby reduce new product cycle times—all critical elements of the 'lean manufacturing' vision.

How does this analogy work in the arena of software development? Software development requires technical skills; is it possible for individuals to rapidly 'put together' simple applications without technical skills? In the enterprise context, can the software development process be made leaner and faster?

Researchers at TCS's i-labs believe that such software flexibility ideas have the potential to change the software development in an analogous manner to which the Fab Lab can enable 'lean manufacturing'. With these goals, TCS's Innovation Lab has been exploring the concept of 'software flexibility' and has developed InstantApps, which implements such a concept.

The typical IT department includes analysts who prepare business requirements that are handed over to developers who write programs (creating new applications or modifying old ones) which are tested by business users and then implemented and maintained by administrators.

Getting a new user requirement into production involves a development team, which is assigned the task of first designing and then programming the new application or enhancement. Meanwhile the operations team plans where and how to deploy the software once it has been created.

This turn-around time could be reduced significantly using computing appliances that act as 'application players'. An application player executes (or 'plays') a specification (possibly XML) for an application. The specification includes a UI model, object model (UML), operations (scripts), and workflow (XPDL or BPEL4WF). The player interprets this specification at run-time to render application functionality over the network (via a browser interface or a similar thin client program). Most importantly the player includes intuitive tools which enable analysts to dynamically modify the application specification as well as search for and assemble units of functionality in the form of components, i.e. the player appliance appears as a highly configurable application, with built in tools allowing an analyst to dynamically modify its functionality.

Using such appliances, an IT department could (ideally) look very different, with analysts directly configuring application players deployed in the data centre—thus reducing turn-around time to get new functionality into production and also reducing (ideally even eliminating) software development costs linked to each functional enhancement. Instead, some programmer-architects and analysts would maintain and enhance the 'application player' internals and provide major functional updates in the form of new pre-packaged components, either freshly developed or harvested from different application specification 'playing' in the data center—but this would be a background activity outside the critical chain of getting requirements into production, changing the way software is developed and maintained.

InstantApps developed in TCS's Innovation Labs implements these ideas and is now being used in practice, and significant productivity improvements have been observed using the technology, which in principle could potentially change the economics of software development and maintenance.

---

the day—we formally launched the TCS Co-Innovation Network (COIN) in January 2007, to create a structured ecosystem where such collaborations would work.

We are convinced that in times to come, this new order will establish a paradigm shift, not just with the innovators but also the consumers of innovation and will expedite the removal of distinction between the two categories. Collaborative innovation brings with it its own new set of challenges around the development and management of IP, engagement models, and partnering strategies. COIN has pre-empted these challenges and has established scalable models of engagement for 'open innovation' to help our customers stay ahead of the curve in this new order.

3. **Innovation management process:** While to many, the words 'process' and 'innovation' present an inherent dichotomy of sorts, at TCS we believe we have successfully established a systematic approach to innovation—be it innovation in our Labs or through COIN. This will enable us to 'make innovation happen' rather than 'waiting for innovation to happen'.

The following case studies provide an insight into TCS's initiatives that reflect the innovations along each of the dimensions defined above. Importantly, each of these brings value to different stakeholders in the ecosystem. The first addresses a truly disruptive innovation extending across industries and possibly having global ramifications on the way we conduct our lives

Box 3. The Role of In Silico Methods in Drug Discovery and Development

The cost of discovering new drugs keeps skyrocketing and the cost per new drug has increased from $ 318 million in 1987 to $ 1,200 million in 2006. While the R&D budget of the global pharmaceutical industry has been growing at 15 per cent annually to reach $ 55 billion during 2006, the number of new drugs approved by the FDA has remained constant at around 20 per year. Moreover, the time needed for a drug molecule to obtain all the requisite regulatory approvals has remained constant at around ten to twelve years and since the lifetime of the patent on a potential drug molecule is only twenty years, every day lost in bringing a drug to market results in a loss of revenue.

Against this background, the pharmaceutical community is finally, and perhaps reluctantly, turning to 'in silico' methods for drug development. In silico approaches refer to the use of computer simulation to model the various processes involved in drug discovery and development, with the aim of eliminating drug molecules that are likely to fail without undertaking expensive laboratory or clinical work. The expression in silico is a fake Latin phrase, to contrast with the proper Latin phrases in vitro (in glass, that is, in a laboratory environment) and in vivo (in a living animal).

The schematic below shows the various steps involved in discovering a new drug, from target identification through regulatory approval and the likelihood of a particular candidate drug (or molecule advancing to the next stage. While the probabilities of success at each individual stage appear to be reasonable, the cumulative likelihood of success is a paltry 1.5 per cent resulting in the cost of all the failed drugs to be piled on top of the few successful drugs, thereby resulting in the very high notional cost per successful drug.

At TCS we have undertaken to develop end to end capabilities for in silico drug discovery. Our first step was the development of the software package Bio-Suite™ in collaboration with CSIR laboratories in an innovation partnership. Subsequently we have developed versions of Bio-Suite™ that work on clusters and also grids of heterogeneous computer platforms. Recently we have developed tools for 'reading' journal articles in electronic form and automatically constructing signal transduction databases. As most candidate drugs are rejected not because they are ineffective, but because of side effects, we are currently working on mathematical models for predicting toxicity effects.

As time goes by, we anticipate that the in silico methods proposed by us and other groups will gain greater acceptance and begin to reduce the cost of drug discovery and development.

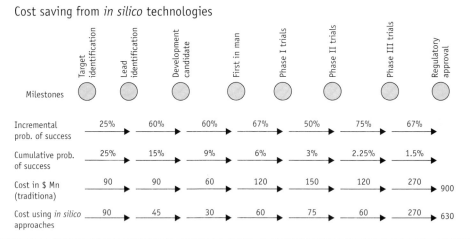

Cost saving from *in silico* technologies

in the future. The second is an innovative solution with an impact on software companies. The third is a framework that redefines processes in a vertical user industry.

Innovation and R&D in TCS are key parts of our strategies for the future. They enable continued delivery excellence across TCS offerings. Collaborating with our Co-Innovation Network partners, we continually explore new capabilities and platforms for markets and technologies adjacent to our current businesses and invest in radically new technologies which could give us breakthroughs for the future. In the words of a respected IT industry analyst, "The TCS Co-Innovation Network has set the bar high for global IT providers". □

Ashish Arora
The Heinz School of Public
Policy and Management
Carnegie Mellon University

Moving up the value chain

India's emergence as a major exporter of software services has excited debate about the causes of its success and ignited hopes for similar success in other industries. The subsequent growth of exports of other business services appears to validate the belief of some observers (including myself) that India's software success will have broader benefits for the Indian economy.

Despite this, there is a perennial undercurrent of concern about the prospects of the Indian software industry. The causes for concern are not difficult to find. Wages for software professionals have consistently risen year on year and employee attrition remains a persistent problem for companies. Indian exports continue to be mostly services with modest technology content and there is little evidence of successful product development. Add to these the ever present possibility of China (or Eastern Europe or the Philippines) emerging as potent rivals, and there is much to be concerned about.

I have studied the growth and evolution of the Indian IT industry and identified major factors that contributed to its success, and some possible ones that were not important. However, here I focus only on the prospects of the industry in this context. I shall summarise the available evidence on the extent to which India and Indian firms are participating in software innovation. This will lead to an assessment of whether the industry has and can provide higher value added products and services.

In 1996, the time when I first became interested in the Indian software sector, this seemed fantastic, in the original sense of the word. But then observers began to note the shortage of skilled workers ('software professionals'), the terribly deficient physical infrastructure, potential competition from China and the Philippines, the development of automated tools that would substitute for the lower end of software services provided by India, and the apparent unwillingness or inability of Indian software firms to move beyond leveraging access to lower cost workers. Together, this potent mix of forces was seen as threatening the future of the industry. The prescription for the malaise was clear: firms had to 'move up the value chain' by developing proprietary products, and by providing more technology-intensive services. Innovation was the watchword, and implicitly, most understood this to refer to new technologies or new products.

For the most part, the prescriptions have not been followed. The shortage of workers is said to loom as large as ever, the infrastructure has improved only modestly and there are few Indian software products on the world markets. And yet, exports have increased dramatically and an entirely new sector of related business services has emerged. The domestic software market has also grown. This growth has enabled the industry to overtake Brazil.

To understand this astonishing story, we need to take a detour to understand the software sector itself. Contrary to popular belief, software products such as word-processing software, accounting software or email software are not the dominant part of the industry. Rather, the bulk of the value added, and the bulk of employment, in software is generated in customizing these products, maintaining them, adding functionality, and making these products work with existing products already in use. Some, but not all, of this activity is performed by firms classified as software firms.

Software using firms, which include the vast preponderance of all firms of any size in advanced economies, are responsible for a substantial part as well.

One can distinguish three sets of value adding activities in software. First, there are design and development activities, which encompass all of what one would traditionally define as software products, such as word processors, operating systems, enterprise software such as Enterprise Resource Planning (ERP) and business intelligence software, as well as middleware software products, such as some transaction processing middleware and enterprise application integration.

Firms that operate in this value chain include all of the well-recognized names that are traditionally regarded as 'software' firms, including Microsoft, Adobe, Oracle and SAS.

Quantitatively more significant is the set of firms involved in custom programming and software analysis and design for clients, including the custom development of software products (also called 'bespoke software products').

Users

The third set of actors involved in software is the users themselves. Even if one confines oneself to the activity of professional programmers and software designers employed by IT-using firms, (and ignores programming activities performed by others in IT-using organizations), the monetary value of this user based activity, though difficult to estimate precisely, is very significant. Occupation data from the US indicates that over two thirds of software professionals do not work for IT firms but instead work for IT-using industries.

The bulk of the software exports are accounted for by software services. These are a mixture of different types of activities. Indian software exports started as Indian firms 'rented out' programmers to the American clients, by sending them to work for the client, typically in America itself. In addition to these firms that focused on software exports, there were others that served domestic users, most notably Computer Maintenance Corporation, or CMC. Responsible for maintaining computer systems after IBM left India, CMC developed the ability to develop and implement large and complex projects, especially for infrastructure systems. CMC also proved to be a good training ground for managers that would later be employed by other, private sector firms.

Early export projects involved jobs such as rewriting code to migrate applications from mainframes to the then newly emerging client-server platforms. Coincidently, Indian programmers had acquired a degree of expertise in this due to IBM's departure from Indian in the late 1970s. In the early stages, most of the clients were user firms, and most of the jobs involved systems that these firms needed to run their businesses. Software firms, especially firms developing software products, outsourced more sparingly, and were more likely to simply 'rent' Indian programmers for tasks such as testing.

The success of the serendipitously discovered business strategy of sending small teams of programmers overseas to service the client is not surprising, at least in hindsight. Indian firms were short of capital, infrastructure and management. But far more important was that even in the early 1990s, 'Brand India' was anything but that. Clients in America had to be cajoled to entrust their technology systems to a country which was until recently among the poorest in the world. It took time and initial successful projects before American firms would be comfortable having the projects performed in India, managed by the Indian supplier.

Lead time

Texas Instruments and COSL (part of Citibank) played an important role in pioneering the other part of the business strategy, namely using India as a place to develop software, not merely to hire temporary programmers. Though infrastructure constraints imposed large fixed costs on outsourced software projects, there were offsetting factors. The 12-hour lead time difference meant that investing in dedicated satellite links would enable the use of hardware facilities lying idle in the US. Combined with the cost advantage in software salaries, this conferred enormous cost advantages to locating in India. The experience of COSL and TI demonstrated that an Indian subsidiary could be a low cost way for a large corporation to develop software for sale, or to provide for its in-house software needs. Software was developed at the Indian subsidiary and then installed on-site by teams of Indian software professionals. Even so, the projects were small, and rarely mission critical or on the bleeding edge of the technology. With time, firms such as Oracle were able to move responsibility for much more significant tasks to its Indian subsidiary. Rafiq Dossani describes a similar evolution, but for a later date and on more compressed time scale, for business services, which once again was pioneered by American multinationals such as GE and Agilent.

Though multinationals pioneered the offshore model, their ability to leverage it was limited by their internal market and organizational exigencies. It was left to the domestic firms to develop and exploit more fully what was to become the offshore model—developing software for clients in India, managed by the Indian firm. The process was slow. But even at that stage, at least one leading US computer manufacturer started outsourcing mission critical device-driver software that was shipped directly from the Indian vendor for distribution.

Managing skills

Offshore development was substantially cheaper, although few American firms were willing to say so openly amidst concerns about alienating their own workers and to facilitate their lobbying for more work permits for Indian programmers. But if cheap programmers was all that mattered, the Indian software would have not seen quite as many domestic firms, for many customers were large enough to profitably set up Indian subsidiaries. Instead, they outsourced to Indian suppliers because it appears that the latter were better at recruiting and managing Indian programmers, and in particular, appear to have become more skilled at 'ramping up and ramping down'—putting together large teams at relatively short notice, and redeploying them when the project was done. They were also better able to cope with the high levels of turnover that the frothy IT markets of the late 1990s created. Simply put, Indian firms were better at managing software projects executed in India for overseas clients, using low cost and inexperienced developers and managers.

India's success can be attributed to its comparative advantage: India was relatively abundant in the factor in which software is relatively abundant, or in plain English, software depends heavily on software developers, and Indian had many people willing and able to develop software for less.

But this is not enough of an explanation. How did a poor country like India become so well endowed with human capital? What of other countries, with similar endowments, that perhaps ought also to have succeeded but did not? Why was this latent advantage not adequately exploited by established software firms or large users in America and elsewhere?

India is not well endowed with human capital by most measures. It is merely that India is (or more precisely, was during the relevant period) well endowed with human capital relative to its economic needs. Or, more provocatively, during the 1970s and 1980s, India found itself with more engineers than its stagnant domestic economy could employ on attractive terms. Many of them emigrated to America, where they rose to middle management positions in large firms.

When the big surge in IT demand came in the early 1990s, these emigrants were well positioned to broker the small initial contracts with Indian software firms, or act as 'reputational intermediaries'. Some became entrepreneurs, leading the on-site model of software service exports. In more recent years, there has been a greater return flow to India, chiefly to pursue more niche, technology intensive activities.

Initial software exports from India relied upon software developers, who had gained experience in the domestic market or by working on overseas projects. Also talented developers and managers were hired away from other domestic sectors. However, experienced managers and developers were often snared by multinationals in India or employers overseas.

Rising exports

The surge in exports has been fuelled by young and inexperienced engineering graduates. Over the last decade and a half, Indian engineering baccalaureate capacity has increased dramatically. This expansion has sustained the growth of Indian software exports. Sharply rising wages would have choked the growth in the industry but for the remarkable expansion in engineering education. Though the fruits of this expansion are frequently touted in discussions of the number of engineers India graduates, the fuller account is worthwhile for what it teaches us about the process of economic growth and development. Much of what Indian software exports consist of does not require an engineering background, yet software exports from India rely very heavily on engineering graduates.

If simple comparative advantage is not enough, what are the missing pieces of the puzzle? The first potential one, which can be readily disposed of, is a protected domestic market, which enabled firms to develop expertise that they could leverage for. It is true that IBM's departure and some fortuitous decisions to invest in Unix platforms provided useful experience to Indian programmers. But Indian software exports, particularly early on, did not require deep technical skills. Rather, they relied upon a 'reserve army of underemployed engineers' with the knowledge of software tools and a willingness to undertake tedious tasks.

Protection undoubtedly helped produce the miserable economic performance which led to the 'reserve army of underemployed engineers', but the irony here is self evident. More to the point, the growth of software exports depended upon firm capabilities in recruiting, organizing teams and maintaining service in the face of high rates of employee turnover.

Balakrishnan (2006) makes the clearest case for targeted public policy. He notes that Bangalore was unusually well supplied with public sector R&D institutions, including nine defence related labs, which made it an attractive location for software firms, especially multinationals. Thus, he argues that India's software success testifies to the success of the government's 'strategic intent'.

Bangalore

Almost all private entrants, whether Indian or foreign, had started out in Bangalore as this was seen as the locale most conducive, at least initially, to the success of an IT enterprise in India. Bangalore was India's science city, a deliberate construction of the policy of trying to establish an independent, world-class scientific foundation on Indian soil. By locating here, private entrepreneurs had access to scientists, engineers and management professionals who had honed their skills in the best technological environment in India, almost exclusively created by the government (Balakrishnan, 2006).

Balakrishnan concludes the success of the software industry required a two pronged effort. "First, via long-term investment by the state in technical education and science and technology, with neither necessarily directed at the production of software. Subsequently, an incipient software industry with recognizably high export potential has been targeted via fiscal incentives and the provision of export-enabling infrastructure. The emergence of a globally competitive Indian software industry serves as an interesting example of successful

state intervention at a time when the model is largely out of fashion."(Balkrishnan, 2006).

Although the presence of public sector R&D labs may explain why Bangalore has emerged as an IT hub, it is not the only IT hub in India: there are five, roughly equally-sized software clusters. Though Bangalore has attracted most of the hype, it has not been the only source of exports. The second reason for doubting the claim that government science and technology investments explain why Bangalore emerged as a leading IT hub has to do with the nature of software exports. As I have stressed repeatedly, software exports, especially at the start, consisted of relatively simple activities or of programmers sent to America and elsewhere.

Entrepreneurship

Undoubtedly, some of them were hired away from the many public sector labs, which proved to be a useful reservoir of skilled human capital. But that is it. The sophisticated capabilities resident in the public sector labs were, for the most part, irrelevant to software success, with the exception of attracting firms such as TI and Motorola to locate there. Ironically enough, these capabilities and the multinational labs they attracted may explain why Bangalore is now acquiring a reputation for being the place to do product development and other R&D intensive software activities.

Underlying this remarkable export success story is a perhaps even more remarkable story of Indian entrepreneurship. Even though the details of the entrepreneurial process are poorly understood one may tentatively induce two explanations for India's export success: entrepreneurship and openness.

What precise product lines and activities that will eventually succeed are hard to predict. An early, but unsuccessful, attempt to exploit India's comparative advantage in labour intensive activities is illustrative. Patni Computer Systems, through its US affiliate, Data Conversion launched a project in the late 1970s for the data entry as well as code embedding for commercial databases (now Lexus-Nexus). However, steep import duties on computer equipment imports, as well as union regulations caused much of data conversion work to be shifted to China and Taiwan and the project failed (Athreye, 2005).

The importance of the 'foreign connection' is evident in the Indian software industry as well. A number of successful software entrepreneurs in India had substantial overseas experience.

Much ink has been spilled on whether Indian software exports are low-end or not. For instance, many observers of the Indian software industry believed the growth of the Indian software industry was unsustainable unless firms began to invest in R&D to undertake sophisticated product development, because rising wages would surely deplete their revenue.

Onsite working increases the opportunities for a 'brain drain' of talent, while offering programming services can become self-reinforcing with little skill being built up, so that the higher skills necessary for software innovation remain the preserve of developed countries.

Indian software entrepreneurs would need to focus more on innovation of new IT products rather than on services or outsourcing if India had to be at the forefront of the IT revolution and transform itself into a software powerhouse, according to founder of Hotmail, Sabeer Bhatia.

Such views are sometimes part of a broader mindset wherein progress in technology intensive industries must necessarily take the form of moving up the technology ladder, to parallel (if not imitate) the activities undertaken in the rich countries. Indeed, policy makers in developing countries often point with pride to the technological accomplishments achieved in their countries, treating them as indicators of success. Considerable pride is staked on the formation of national champions and the ability to undertake high-tech projects and produce technically sophisticated products, regardless of their commercial feasibility.

No sophisticated products

India has not produced technically sophisticated products and services, although there certainly are exceptions to which one can point. On the other hand, Indian software growth appears none the worse for being behind the technological frontier, though a sceptic may contend that it is surely only a matter of time before wage growth exacts its revenge.

What then are the prospects for the Indian software and for Indian software firms? It is helpful to distinguish between two distinct ways in which one can move up the value chain. First, one could produce software products. Products allow one to write once and sell many times, the ultimate source of

economies of scale. The reality is of course more complicated. Products, once written, have to be patched to take care of bugs and security flaws that inevitably creep in, and have to be upgraded to remain interoperable with other products, and have to have new functionality added on to keep up with the competition. Moreover, products have to be marketed, and once sold, have to be installed and integrated with existing products. All of this takes software services.

Despite this, many of the leading Indian firms have tried to develop products, with limited success. The lack of success ought not to surprise anyone. Penny pinching and risk-averse management habits ingrained while growing in an infrastructure and capital scarce and labor abundant environment are unlikely to make for successful technology innovators. Development organizations geared to fulfil requirements laid down by clients are unlikely to be able to divine the needs of as yet unknown buyers of their product, and nor are sales organizations used to answering RFQs best suited to sell a product that the customer has not yet felt a need for.

Innovation, particularly technical innovation, will have to come from start-ups and other entrants. Some smaller incumbents, forced by the success of the market leaders, may also specialize and choose technology intensive software services as their niche. In unpublished research, Athreye reports on a survey of 205 Indian software firms. Of these, only 52 firms, about a quarter, reported any revenues from product and technical licensing and 39 of those 52 firms also earned some revenues in customized services.

Indian firms are not alone in their failure to develop software products. The US dominates the software product market to an astonishing degree and probably produces about a third of all software exports. Other than SAP, the German ERP producer, all the leading software product companies are American. An important reason for American dominance is the importance of user-producer interactions, which are particularly salient for successful software product design. For example, the well known SABRE airline reservation system was an outgrowth of a chance encounter between R Blair Smith of IBM's Santa Monica sales office with C R Smith, American Airlines' president, on a flight. This led to the two companies to collaborate on developing SABRE. As long as the lead users, particularly for enterprise software, are American, America is likely to remain the centre for product innovation in software.

Firms in other countries have succeeded typically when their products were targeted to niches where incumbent American firms had not entered, or where the products are deeply technical, such as design of chip components. Such was the case for security software, where Israeli firms such as Checkpoint, seized the opening. But even when firms from outside America successfully develop a product, the typical pattern is for those firms to move their commercial activities to America. This is certainly true of the Israeli and Irish firms, which have tended to retain only research activities in their home countries. For instance, Checkpoint, an Israeli firm that pioneered software security products such as firewalls, is now an American company with mostly research activities located in Israel.

Business software

This suggests a more nuanced approach to thinking about the issue of software products. Software products are typically used by firms to run their business processes such as accounting, sales and marketing, purchasing, and supply chains. For the most part, such software cannot be successfully developed and sold without a deep understanding of how these users run their businesses, and without the users having some ongoing relationships with the software vendor. Business software often is bundled with a set of business rules and assumptions about business processes that must be integrated with the existing business organization, its activities and its processes.

Proximity between software developers and users is particularly important for this co-inventive activity to occur. At the very least, large users are unlikely to adopt a product that will become enmeshed in their business processes without considerable assurances the support and maintenance of the products for the foreseeable future. Since America accounts for a substantial share of the software market and since most of the lead users, who play a very important role in a product's success, are American, it is difficult for a firm not substantially based in America to succeed in software product exports.

In turn, this raises two possibilities. First, firms outside America could develop products aimed at firms whose needs are different from American firms, as i-flex apparently did, or

develop products that are not embedded in the business processes of users, as is the case for firewalls and anti-virus software. A second possibility is that firms could use India (or Israel or Ireland) as a base for doing product development.

India could host technology intensive software development by the subsidiaries of large multinationals, by Indian firms developing technology that is not dependent on close proximity to customers, or by Indian firms doing contract research for overseas clients. The evidence suggests that all are going on.

Domian expertise

There is anecdotal evidence that even small firms are beginning to locate product development activities with a view to increasing the pace and reduce the cost of product development. There is also some anecdotal evidence that Indian firms may be increasingly performing R&D-intensive activities, especially in the semiconductor sector. Sasken and Mindtree are the prime examples of two Indian firms that are trying to develop proprietary technology, leveraging domain expertise and profits obtained by providing R&D services to clients.

The exports of R&D services in the global market are increasing. Some Indian firms are filing for US patents as well. Overall, the evidence suggests that in recent years, R&D and software related innovation activities in India have grown, albeit from a small base. However, the quantitative significance of such activities is still small. Using India to develop software for sale in distant markets poses significant challenges. One major challenge to offshoring software product development work will result from the difficulty of coordinating software development activity across a globally distributed team.

Supplying technology intensive products and services is not the only way of moving up the value chain; providing organization capability intensive services is another, and this is the route the leading Indian software firms will likely take. They may try to diversify into emerging niches without entrenched incumbents, as for instance TCS's forays into bio-informatics show.

A select few may attempt to acquire the required hardware capability to become systems integrators, though that remains to be seen. For the most part, however, the leading Indian software firms shall strive, quite sensibly so, to become capable of executing large, complex, multi-year software development, implementation and maintenance projects.

In so doing, they will build upon their existing business units which focus upon serving selected industries. Indeed, this sort of 'vertical' focus is more prominently visible among Indian firms which entered later, and hence, are smaller, and also less successful at competing for large multi-year projects. Examples include Cognizant in healthcare, Polaris in banking, RMSI in geographical mapping and GIS, and Geometric Software in CAD software and services.

In bidding for large scale projects, the established Indian firms will run up against established incumbents such as the global services division of IBM, Accenture and EDS. The outcome of this impending class is unclear, although the advantage must lie with the incumbents.

Whereas the Indian firms perhaps have an advantage in terms of superior access to the Indian labour market, the latter have much greater demonstrated expertise in large projects in a wider range of end-user sectors, established relationships with customers, and global presence. The latter also appear to have realized the seriousness of the challenge and have begun to recruit heavily in India, for the software to be developed in India itself. For instance, IBM Global Services is believed to have over 40,000 employees in India. By themselves developing software in India, American (for they are almost all American) software service and solution providers hope to lower their costs, and thereby undercut the only significant advantage that Indian software firms are thought to enjoy.

Global delivery

Even so, Indian firms have become experts at a 'global delivery' model of software services, wherein some of the work is done offshore and some done on-site, using the large number of talented but often poorly trained and inexperienced engineering graduates, a substantial fraction of whom will stay with the firm for a couple of years before moving on. As already noted, operating under these conditions, Indian firms were forced to develop management practices to cope.

This business model, which Indian firms stumbled into, is something that their foreign competitors have to learn. There is no reason why they should not be able to do so, but the Indian firms have a head start. The Indian firms, on the other hand, will have to learn how to operate as global companies, with a

multinational workforce, a task they have only recently embarked upon.

As the Indian market grows, MNCs will start aggressively going after 'local' business. For example, the 10 year deal between Accenture and Dabur for management of Dabur's IT needs, the Bank of India-HP deal for branch office computertisation, $750m Bharti-IBM deal and the mega Reliance Infocomm telecom network & Reliance retail petrol pump projects with IBM are clear indicators of what can happen in the Indian landscape. The lack of hardware and systems integration capability is clearly a weak area. On the other hand, this is the flip side of the coin of comparative advantage. Indian firms have certain relative strengths which imply corresponding relative weaknesses. Contrast this with the Chinese case where local business is almost exclusively the preserve of local firms, all of which are incredibly diversified and none are internationally competitive.

Moreover, one should distinguish between the prospects of Indian firms and prospects for India as a location for software and IT. The latter is surely brighter. Leading multinationals such as IBM, Accenture and HP employ over 70,000 in India. If Indian firms are indeed deficient in certain aspects of management, the multinationals could be the training ground for new managers and the seedbed for new start-ups.

Threats

A greater threat may perhaps come from the technology itself. Evangelists for service oriented architectures, software components, utility computing and so on, paint a picture of a world where users will no longer have to invest in large in-house IT infrastructures. Instead, computing will be like a utility—a menu of services that organizations can use, varying the scope and scale according to need. More importantly, the tedious business of maintaining and upgrading applications, and keeping up with changes in underlying computing platforms will become much less tedious: Information infrastructure providers, such as IBM, HP, EMC and others will take on this task for them. The market for third parties, such as TCS, Wipro and Infosys to customize, enhance, and maintain the existing software infrastructure will shrink quite dramatically.

Much like old soldiers, old code never dies but fades away, often very slowly. Prognosticating about technology is best left to experts, but a reasonable guess is that for the next decade or so, demand for software services will keep growing. The growth in emerging markets and especially the Indian economy may provide an additional source of demand, which will surely be satisfied by Indian programmers, albeit perhaps working for a foreign company.

Our optimism about the beneficial impact of the Indian software industry on the Indian economy in the long run is not based entirely on the quantitative importance of the relatively smaller number of successes among software service exporters. Prominent software services firms are developing a variety of new software products, components and technologies. Software service firms are exemplars of organisational forms and practices that are relatively new to India. A large number of software firms are de novo start-ups, indicating that the supply of entrepreneurial talent appears to be forthcoming when the opportunity arises, even in new and technology intensive sectors.

New heroes

Top managers of the leading software firms have been profiled in the popular press in India and are viewed favourably by many Indians, particularly in comparison to traditional Indian business leaders. Further, this industry has pioneered equity stakes and stock options for employees in India, and many of these companies are star performers on the Indian stock market. Thus, unlike in the past, the fruits of the success of the industry have been shared far more broadly. The implications of the success of this industry, at a time of changes in the Indian economy, can be far-reaching.

Athreye argues that the organizational capabilities, developed by the Indian software firms are generic in the sense of being applicable to sectors other than software. This is true in areas such as engineering services, where leading software firms such as HCL and TCS have a substantial presence. This is also true in the more rapidly growing area of business process services. Indeed, some of the entrants into the BPO sector have been IT firms. Some of the top BPO firms in India are also leading software firms. The diverse sources of entry mirror the sources of firm entry into software—start-ups, spinoffs, business houses and multinationals.

Information kiosk

Software made 'Brand India' a respected one, paving the way for other sectors. For instance, there is a small but growing set of firms that develop semiconductor technology and provide affiliated services. More than 200 semiconductor companies currently operate a facility in India, and of these, about sixty percent are involved in chip design (the remainder do software development). The membership of the ISA itself consists of over a hundred firms, most of which are American firms in semiconductor design, manufacturing and design tools and services. Of these, about half are American firms. A fifth are firms headquartered in America with CEOs of Indian origin, and another fifth are Indian firms, including HCL, Wipro and TCS.

The success of software exports surely played a role in signalling the potential of India as a location for such activities. The software industry also led the fight for regulatory reforms, in areas such as liberalizing access to the stock market and listing requirements. It also led the way in corporate governance, with emphasis on transparency and ethical management.

But perhaps the most important of all is that software showed potential entrepreneurs what is possible with talent, luck and hard work, that success is not reserved for those with connections or for those born to wealth (Kapur). Hitherto, wealth was acquired by breaking laws or at least bending them to one's convenience. Software was the first instance where wealth was created honestly and legally, and more important, visibly so. Hitherto commercial success had invited envy, cynicism and even outright hostility, and only rarely, admiration. While envy and hostility are by no means gone, there is much more of admiration, and more importantly, a desire for imitation. □

Rafiq Dossani
Stanford University, USA

Murali Patibandla
Indian Institute of Management, Bangalore

IT education for global services

Even a decade ago, the idea that India would in less than five years compete in the global services economy would have seemed far-fetched. Although it had by then a recognized and rising (though small) presence in software exports, the Indian services sector was, overall, no different from services in countries at similar stages of development. In such countries, services are largely provided by small, low-technology enterprises catering to the local economy. India was no different as of the late 1990s. Now in India, the services sector is driving economic growth and posing to be a formidable global competitor. It is the IT-enabled services sector in which India has made its mark as a global provider.

The term 'IT-enabled services' might not convey to the reader the range of services that are exported from India. They potentially include any service that can be delivered electronically using digital technologies. While initially the exports were confined to software programming and, later, call-centres, over the past few years, the range and depth of work has changed dramatically. The list now includes scientific research and development, financial services, market research, data-mining and a host of other services. Largely, the services are located in the vertical termed 'professional, scientific and technical services'.

Brand names

The Indian success with remote services provision disproves a widespread belief that Asia is better at manufacturing than services. This shibboleth is based on the evidence that even the advanced economies of Asia, i.e., Japan, Singapore, Taiwan, Hong Kong and Korea, have failed to create globally competitive service industries. In a range of other key services, such as software, retailing, telecommunications, logistics and insurance, there are no Asian global brand names. The common understanding behind this belief is that acquiring advanced services skills is not an easy or short-term task.

Yet, this is not true of India. Further, Indian firms such as TCS in software services and the Taj group in hotels are beginning to be recognized as brand names. Along with this, the provision of global services is growing in scale, scope and depth at rates that are increasing India's lead over potential competition.

We highlight the contribution of higher education to this success but there are other factors that enabled the success of India's global services sector. The first is the way that the world economy has developed. The previous paradigm of services spatially tied to core nationally-based manufacturing activities has been replaced by one based on the provision of globally tradable services. This advantages countries with advanced services skills. India's turn towards services, in part because of policies that restricted manufacturing, preceded other low-cost countries that were still intensely involved in harvesting manufacturing. This gave India a first-mover advantage that it has continued to capitalize on.

Second, some attribute India's success in providing technical services to technology itself. The technology for the remote provision of services has changed dramatically in the past decade. The Internet and lower digital storage costs have combined to reduce the capital costs associated with remote service provision; while modularization of software preparation and other services have reduced the operating costs of remote provision. The impact of the first mover advantage should not be overstated. India was not the first mover in global service provision from a low cost country. Many Asian countries entered global service provision much earlier than India, such as Japanese and Korean banks in the 1980s, with limited success.

Likewise, on the enabling power of technology, many other countries—in East Asia and Southeast Asia, for instance, had similar or better access to the latest technologies earlier than India. Their infrastructure, capital access and scale of global trade were far superior to India. Had technological change been the only enabler of services, these would have captured the business a long time before India was even an entrant.

The explanation for India's success is, therefore, unlikely to be a simple one. It is likely to lie in some dimension of human capital rather than physical or financial capital. Unlike manufacturing, where it is possible to produce high technology products by applying relatively unskilled labour to sophisticated machinery, skilled services, by contrast, cannot be provided by combining unskilled labour with physical and financial capital. By definition, the providers of 'just-in-time' skilled services such as IT help desks need to be as skilled as the service provided. Even many 'storable' services such as software code require skilled labour.

English, an asset

There are several skills that appear to be relevant. Indians' most obvious advantage over other low-cost providers is that a relatively large number of people, perhaps as many as 50 million speak fluent English. Once India opened up its economy in the 1990s, it has been argued, this became an asset.

However, this English speaking advantage is unlikely to be the only or even the main reason for India's success. There are many countries whose citizens speak equally fluent English, where wage rates are comparable, which globalized earlier than India, and have failed to become global service providers. The Philippines, which opened its economy to global trade two decades before India, is an example.

On the other hand, although it is hard to come by examples in the developing world, there are examples of firms operating in developed countries where English is not widely spoken and yet have succeeded widely in other

western markets. SAP of Germany is one example, but there are several others in services such as IT, retailing and logistics.

A second aspect is higher education including technical education is important. The need for such an education is no longer doubted by development analysts and policymakers. There have been several reports of late that show that India and China are producing a large number of students that are skilled in particular vocations, particularly engineering. Some of these reports also question the quality of the students.

Even if the number is high and the quality is good, it is not obvious that this 'scale-and-depth' factor is sufficient for success. Neither size nor stage of development is sufficient to explain a country's success. There are countries such as Japan, with a large and high quality software labourforce, which have been unsuccessful at global software provision; there are countries, such as Brazil and China, with a large software labourforce, and a more uncertain quality of engineer, which have also been unsuccessful. On the other hand, Ireland and Israel have small labourforces, presumably produce a high quality of engineer and are successful.

Social sciences

A third dimension is that the type of human capital needed is changing rapidly. In the field of engineering, for instance, the social science aspects of engineering education, such as business and entrepreneurial courses for engineers, may be as important as teaching engineering skills. Merely developing a large number of traditional engineers has much less relevance than in earlier industrial development. Perhaps India has succeeded in a transformation of the nature of engineering and science education so that engineers have 'scope' in addition to depth. India's success is possibly due to some combination of first mover advantages, English-language skills, scale, depth and scope.

Our study showed that India's greatest success was in establishing certain elite institutions, such as the IITs. The elite institutions like the IITs are managed and funded under a different organizational model than the overwhelming majority of state-owned institutions. They are run by the federal government with levels of funding that would be unaffordable were these to be generally applicable to all state-owned institutions. This means that, under the present environment, the 'IIT-model' is not widely replicable within the country.

Nevertheless, elite institutions like the IITs offer some important lessons. The first is that the policy goal of achieving excellence for a small cohort of students chosen entirely on a rules-based criterion of merit and funded primarily by the state can achieve the strategic target of attracting the country's best students and faculty into a small number of institutions. This sets the conditions for a rapid establishment of high quality. Certain minimal other conditions need to be fulfilled, such as a hands-off approach by the state to the educational core of faculty selection, curriculum development and minimal infrastructure. But, beyond this, even an intrusive state that otherwise runs a bureaucratic, even a corrupt administration, can co-exist with a high quality education.

Faculty erosion

It is recognized that the elite institutions are under threat. The primary threat is to faculty retention. The state caps salaries at its institutions at levels significantly below what private institutions can afford. The recent proliferation of private provision with higher budgets has allowed them to poach the best faculty and has already led to considerable erosion in faculty quality across the board from leading to smaller state-owned institutions countrywide. The state has tried to be responsive, offering better infrastructure and research budgets, but it remains insufficient when the private providers can offer salaries that are several times what faculty in the state-owned institution currently earns.

The overwhelming majority of state-owned provision is by individual states. This is an outcome of India's constitution where the central government assumes responsibility for setting standards while the state governments take responsibility for funding and provision.

The institutions run by the individual states are generally of significantly lower quality than federally-run institutions. This is largely an outcome of funding and results in a serious quality gap. In software engineering, for instance, there are about a dozen institutions, mostly federally-run, that offer a high (1st-tier) quality education, then a large gap, followed by lower-tier (3rd-tier) state-run institutions. The absence of a quality continuum at the second-

tier disadvantages students who fail to enter the elite institutions and must settle for a third-tier institution.

The state began to recognize this problem in the 1990s and responded with encouraging private provision. The private providers have, in turn, responded energetically. Though they are required to be legally organized as non-profit trusts, private provision offers enough opportunities, given the immature environment, for personal gain. In engineering, over three fourths of the providers are now private, a dramatic turnaround from a decade ago, when their presence was negligible.

The private providers are key to the system's future. Although they currently occupy the lowest tiers of quality, over time, as they mature, they, more than state-owned providers, are going to provide the scale, depth and scope of the system. There are already signs that some private providers are maturing into high quality providers.

State's role

Nevertheless, the state remains a critical player. Its institutions set the current benchmarks for standards, of course (as well as providing fertile ground for recruiting faculty!). But its primary influence is through its role as the system's regulator. The system allows it to be as intrusive as it wants. This is because the law allows the state to set institution-specific admissions standards; standards for faculty recruitment; funding standards for research; and to shut down those institutions that fail to meet these standards.

Hence, there is now a complex environment that characterizes the higher education sector. The state as regulator, provider and financier must interact increasingly with the private sector as provider. What sort of outcomes has resulted? Do they meet the needs of the nation?

To assess this, we surveyed institutions that are important suppliers of software engineers to India's software capital, Bangalore. We considered the role of the state through the assessment of its influence on fundamental aspects of an institution, such as entrance requirements, teaching, research and faculty selection. The influence was evaluated through three layers: influence on institutional policy (such as the focus on teaching versus research, equity versus merit etc.), influence on governance structures (such as the rules for selecting or compensating faculty) and

The Importance of the IITs

Perhaps the best known Indian engineering institutions, both within and outside India, are the state-owned Indian Institutes of Technology (IIT). These were established by the federal government starting in the mid-1950s. Recruiters around the world recognize the IITs as a global-class brand.

The IIT-system is emblematic of not just the best but some of the worst aspects of the Indian education system. The best is that the seven IITs produce a quality of undergraduate student that is, as noted, of global class. They do this through a four-fold strategy: selective, merit-based recruitment (over two hundred and fifty thousand applicants vie for less than 5,000 seats each year), low tuition costs (tuition costs are less than $1,000 per year), commitment to teaching excellence and adequate infrastructure. The first two strategies lead to a high quality of student admitted, while the latter two strategies cause high value addition in undergraduate education.

These strategies represent a compromise between state and institutional interests. The admissions procedures, for instance, are based on rules that are common across the IITs. The student's prior academic performance and, most important, her performance in a common entrance examination administered jointly by all the IITs determine whether she will get in. The contents of the entrance examination are, however, determined by faculty.

The faculty selection procedures are more flexible, with considerable autonomy given to the departments, although final letters of appointment require the approval of the head of the institution. Departments also determine curricula and pursue linkages with the corporate sector.

In all other aspects, the IITs are under the state's control. This has resulted in an overly rules-based and often corrupt administration that stifles academic freedom to pursue research or design new courses.

The worst aspects of the IIT-system are, first, the absence of a second-tier of quality below the IITs. There are the IITs, then about a dozen other state-owned institutions of repute and then a vacuum. The mass of the state-run and private institutions are third-tier. A shortage of funds is the main reason for the quality vacuum. Second, the current dynamics of the higher education system threatens the quality of the IITs. The staff at the IITs and other state institutions is being cannibalized by private institutions due to salary caps, the IITs research output is meager to non-existent (matched by a minimal output of graduate students) due to a lack of academic freedom and incentives, and collaborations with industry for training students are minimal.

The IITs offer important lessons on how a country can provide a high standard of education for a small cohort chosen on merit. First, it can be done quickly. The IITs were begun in the 1950s and achieved excellence within a decade. This was partly due to overseas collaborations in the initial years for the purposes of curriculum and faculty development. The country's best faculty and student applicants turned to the IITs simply because it offered the best students, teachers and infrastructure. Over time, the four strategies noted above emerged.

One lesson from the IITs' success is that while a rules-based process of admissions might not be optimal in a more mature environment, it might make sense in a less mature environment. It protects the institution from misuse that might arise if more discretion is given to the institution. Of course, it raises the question of how an institution is to transition to a less rules-based system that might be desirable as the environment matures.

Another lesson is that so long as the state does not interfere in faculty selection, or in curriculum development, and finances equitable access and infrastructure, its other dimensions of control will not, at least for a time, be a fatal deterrent to the provision of a good undergraduate education.

influence on the administrative structures (how flexible are the rules for admission? Do policymakers influence admissions directly? Do they waive standards in return for higher fees?). These influences and quality outcomes such as the quality of research and the quality of curriculum were evaluated against the quality of the institutions as ranked by recruiters, both commercial and academic.

We found that the average quality of the institutions that supply Bangalore with software graduates is high and that the public sector is of better quality than private institutions. The state-owned institutions are superior in certain key variables: curriculum, students and faculty. Nevertheless, even the private providers score well in these respects and score better than the state-owned providers on infrastructure. At the operating level, the state-owned providers tend to be less influenced by policymakers. By contrast, the private providers are more politicized. In one key respect, research, the weakness of quality cuts across all types of institutions.

The unexpectedly high quality of the independent variables even among the private institutions (which are newer and less mature) suggests that quality for the system as a whole will improve further as the system matures.

English in India

India is a multilingual country in two senses of the word. First, many Indians speak more than one language, although only one will typically be spoken fluently (most city dwellers are fluent in two). Second, there is no single language that most Indians speak. The most widely spoken language in India is Hindi, spoken as a first language by 180 million persons. Probably no more than 50 million people speak fluent English, most as a second language. Several Indian languages other than Hindi rank above English in the number of speakers, including Bengali, Marathi, Tamil and Telugu.

How important is fluency in English? Indore provides some interesting examples. It has over 50 IT exporting firms, including service firms and software product firms. In my visits to three such firms, I found that the quality of English varied greatly. In most cases, a lead business developer or marketer spoke in sophisticated English while the rest of the staff, including the programmers spoke English in 'second-language' quality. This did not seem to hamper success. This suggests that the engineer of today still does not need to have 'scope', provided such scope exists within his firm. It all depends on who he interacts with.

As an example, consider the case of a successful Indore-based startup, Astute Systems, that produces religious software for mobile phones. It has a staff of 15 engineers and 13 other staff, including business developers, salespersons and support staff. The software allows the user to play video clips of the prayers of most Indian religions, complete with gender-specific rituals and regional variations. The development team does their work in Java 2ME, the industry standard language for mobile applications. Prior to commercialization, the prayers are vetted for both religious correctness by a religious scholar and for script by grammarians in English and several other languages.

The firm's marketing team speaks fluent English and travels to various export markets. The software is widely exported, primarily to the Middle East and the rest of Asia. However, the primary market is in India. The main clients are the telecom service providers, all of whom conduct transactions in English.

The programming team is different: their standard of English is well below the Queen's English; yet, this did not impair their capability to program in Java 2ME. As I observed their work, I noted that they converse with each other and with the business development and marketing teams in Hindi while all their work on the computer (programming, tech support, emails etc.) was either in Java 2ME or in English.

The success of firms like Astute Software raises questions about the importance of English for India's success. While the marketing and business development team of Astute would not have succeeded even in domestic markets without an adequate command over the English language, most of the team did not have to know any more English than is common among second-language English speakers in many countries around the world. India has several hundred million who speak English as a second-language.

Second, we found that influence of the state is generally high on teaching, entrance and faculty selection. The exception is the research function, where the state plays a hands-off role. These findings confirm our hypothesis that the state plays an important corrective role where it can, given the immaturity of the system, while staying out of functions which it cannot influence, such as research. In addition, the state plays a more intrusive role in setting teaching standards for private institutions than for state institutions. The former are the newer, more immature institutions, so this role appears to be appropriate.

The low quality of research, despite limited state interference, suggests that other factors might be at work, such as private incentives. In our interviews, we found that the research function at even the highest ranked institutions is generally neglected. This seems to reflect poor university-industry linkages for research, even though they appear to be satisfactory from a recruiter's viewpoint. Even the final year design project of the student is typically done within the university rather than at a commercial enterprise.

This weakness in research is despite relatively generous allowances for research. Even in the smaller state-run institutions, it was found that faculty can relatively simply obtain funds for domestic travel, materials and assistance. In some of the larger state schools, even international travel for conferences is funded. The might improve if the state instituted rules that required, for instance, that a certain proportion of research funding needs to come from industry or if rules of tenure included a research evaluation (this factor is mostly missing even in the highly-ranked institutions). The private sector ranks even more poorly than the state institutions on research.

In summary, the education environment we studied shows that the institutional structure seems to have the capacity to produce a quality of engineer that is suited for the present needs of the workplace. Interestingly, all institutions, from the lowest to the highest ranked, seem to aim to produce technically competent engineers rather than a creativity-driven quality continuum.

As the demands of the marketplace evolve, certain weaknesses, particularly in the research and project management functions, will need to be addressed. We have argued that the role of the state will be critical. So far, the state has demonstrated its capability of being an effective regulator. To address evolving demands, new capabilities will no doubt be needed by the state. In particular, the state needs to address the issue of the quality gap at the second-tier and the absence of research capabilities at the first tier. It also needs to increase autonomy to first-tier institutions, particularly in administrative structures. Towards private providers, the state

currently plays a more intrusive role than it would in a more mature system. This reflects the immaturity of the private provision system, as evidenced by politicization and generally lower quality outcomes. The state ought to fashion its regulatory role so that it can transition to a less rules-based system as the environment matures. This is a transition that has not been achieved even in the best state-owned institutions and remains, therefore, a challenge.

Institutional structure of software engineering education has the capacity to produce a quality of engineer suited to the current needs of the marketplace. This is a remarkable achievement considering the rapid change in both job requirements and the role of private provision in higher education. While it is too early to assess whether the emergent needs, particularly in research, project management and entrepreneurship, will be met by the current structure, the state's role as regulator will be critical. □

Vanguard of open source movement?

Last month, when Sun Microsystems announced a $1 million grant for innovative open source projects at the Free and Open Source Software conference in Bangalore, it wasn't the sort of news that makes major headlines. Larger amounts have been committed before. IBM, for instance, is spending $1.2 million to set up an open source Software Resource Center in partnership with the Center for Development of Advanced Computing in Pune and the Indian Institute of Technology in Mumbai. And this is only one of IBM's India projects. Sun has spent almost $2 billion supporting open source initiatives across the globe.

Simon Phipps, chief open source officer at Sun, notes, however, that "[India] is where so much innovation is happening." The award is meant to catalyze projects in six Sun-created environments—OpenSolaris, GlassFish, NetBeans, OpenJDK, OpenOffice and OpenSparc. While the competition is not limited to open-source programmers in India, Phipps said he was announcing the award in India "because that's where I expect the greatest open source community growth to come from in the near future."

The question that Sun's award raises is whether India can become the new vanguard of the open source movement and, if so, whether that is a desirable goal. Not everybody agrees that open source is the best step forward for India's software industry.

Ajay Shah, senior fellow of the New Delhi-based National Institute for Public Finance and Policy and former professor at the Mumbai-based Indira Gandhi Institute of Development Research, has been an advocate of open source for many years. Nearly a decade ago, he wrote in the daily newspaper *Business Standard*, "Open source is a profound idea.... The enduring puzzle of India's software companies is their persistent inability to grow from projects to products. Open source is a powerful answer to this problem. Open source reduces the importance of products and raises the importance of services."

Shah points out that with open source software, "Anyone can contribute by improving the code—adding new features, correcting errors etc. The open source universe avoids the waste involved in 'reinventing the wheel,' which takes place in all software companies. In the open source world, each programmer builds on the work of others before him. This brings down the cost of development."

Although progress has not been as rapid as he had initially hoped, Shah remains optimistic. "My perceptions have changed from concerns to confidence," he says. "Earlier it was 'open source is great, but will it work?' Today, it is 'open source is great *and* it works.'"

Open source has drawn advocates from across the spectrum. Eric S Maskin, one of the three winners of the 2007 Nobel Prize for Economics, asserts that patents work as a barrier to growth in the software world. Innovations tend to be sequential; open source ensures that no black boxes block the growth path.

Another believer is A P J Abdul Kalam, India's former President. At a speech at the International Institute of Information Technology in Pune, he spoke about an encounter he had with Microsoft chairman Bill Gates. While Kalam was advocating open source as the best solution for a developing country like India, Gates was unmoved in his belief in the superiority of proprietary software developed by a commercial company, such as Microsoft's Windows operating system and desktop software. "Our discussions became difficult, since our views were different," said Kalam. Which view prevails? "The unfortunate thing is that India still seems to believe in proprietary solutions," Kalam added.

Not everybody is as pessimistic. IBM has been one of the foremost advocates of the open source movement and has helped to promote the initiative in India. "The nature of innovation is changing—becoming open, collaborative, global and multidisciplinary," says Manojit Majumdar, IBM India country manager for academic initiatives. "Global adoption of the Internet—and pervasive technologies based on open standards—have stripped away traditional barriers to innovation such as proximity of natural resources, geographical constraints and access to both information and insight."

Flexibility

Majumdar claims that governments and businesses "across the globe and in emerging economies like India are showing increasing interest in open source alternatives to proprietary software. The reasons for this choice are the flexibility in IT decisions and the time and cost savings of open standards that are now becoming increasingly popular with businesses around the world."

Majumdar is confident that this is the future. "The days of the lone inventor in a garage are long gone," he says. "Today, the world is our lab. Business, academia and government must work together to embrace these changes and help change the culture and practices to achieve the benefits of innovation in the 21st century.

"Although the open source platform has been around for quite some time, its advantages over proprietary software are being noticed only now. There was hesitation on the part of institutions, due to reasons like lack of awareness, lack of a policy, and concerns over compliance, licensing and intellectual property or ownership. It is predicted that by 2012, 75 per cent of software products will have embedded open source software. In fact, according to our estimates, the growth of the [open source] Linux operating system is now more than 100 per cent a year."

Sun is not alone in giving awards for open source in India. IBM has instituted the Great Mind Challenge, a national contest for students from engineering colleges who are required to

develop solutions in a real-life scenario using IBM open source software. Through this contest, now in its second year, IBM has provided training on open standards-based technologies to more than 80,000 students across 745 colleges in India.

Although open source has been progressing in fits and starts, it has several landmark projects to its credit. "Are you aware of the PRISM [Parallel Risk Management System] project?" asks Shah. "PRISM does risk management in real time at [India's] National Stock Exchange (NSE). NSE is one of the world's biggest exchanges. PRISM was done using open source." PRISM cost NSE only around Rs 2 million (approximately $50,000). Had a proprietary software package been used, it could have cost NSE several times that amount.

Open source has made headway in e-governance projects where the scale of operations is large. Venkatesh Hariharan, co-founder of the Open Source Foundation of India and an evangelist for the cause, mentions the Maharashtra e-governance projects, where the preferred option was the open source Linux operating system.

Not all the states in India have opted for open source, however. Maharashtra has company in Madhya Pradesh and Goa, but Punjab, Rajasthan, Karnataka and Andhra Pradesh use both open source software along with products from Microsoft. So does the government of India. SWARAJ, a state-of-the-art solution for managing the *panchayati raj* (local government) system in the country, was launched in late November 2007. It was developed by Microsoft as a single, integrated application. Microsoft partners with 14 state governments, and more than 300 e-governance applications run on Microsoft's Windows platform.

Microsoft view

Ravi Venkatesan, chairman of Microsoft India, says it is no longer an either/or option. "We firmly believe that multiple platforms can and should co-exist and [we] recognize both the advantages of open source and the fact that platform heterogeneity is a reality in today's environment," he says. "Accordingly, we have taken several interoperability initiatives in the larger interest of our customers, and this is well reflected in Microsoft's 'shared source' philosophy. Our focus is on enabling our customers to connect to other platforms, applications and data easily."

Venkatesan adds that "Microsoft continues to focus on providing better value through lower total cost of ownership [TCO], higher reliability and better performance as well as better IP [intellectual property] indemnification than any other software provider." In his view, despite its greater initial cost, Microsoft software is a better value than the open source alternatives. "Versus Linux, we deliver a clear value proposition to our customers. The USP [unique selling proposition] of the Microsoft platform and our range of offerings is our end-to-end stack of offerings and our focus on integrated innovation. Customers, too, have matured in their view and there is almost universal recognition that Linux is not 'free', and that Linux today resembles more a commercially driven technology. Customers are beginning to look at Linux vendors like any other commercial software provider—focusing on the overall business advantage, value for money and the risk associated with making long-term technology investments."

Cost of ownership

Venkatesan claims that "in today's do-more-with-less IT environment, TCO is an acid metric that enables customers to make informed IT investment decisions. An India-specific TCO study conducted by Frost & Sullivan concluded that Windows offers 15.9 per cent lower TCO than Linux on an aggregate basis. Further, the number of security vulnerabilities is lower on Windows, Windows' responsiveness on security is better than Linux, and Microsoft provides uncapped IP indemnification of their products while no such comprehensive offering is available for Linux or open source."

But isn't open source better for a 'poor' country like India? Not at all, answers Venkatesan. "We should look at technology discussions in perspective, and when we do we will find that it has nothing to do with a country being poor or rich, but more to do with reliability of the framework, affordability and relevance. We should not confuse affordability with 'price' but should look at the TCO or lifecycle cost, including cost of access."

"Open source is a relatively new concept in India," says Hariharan of the Open Source Foundation. "While it is fast gaining popularity, it is too early to expect it to be all-pervasive. As more people become familiar with the concept of open source, it will become a mainstream phenomenon. For example, recently, Samir Brahmachari, the director general of the

Center for Scientific & Industrial Research, said that we must use the open source model for research in tuberculosis. On the software side, many government agencies are moving over to open source. Kerala is moving 12,500 high schools to open source. Many corporations are standardizing on the open source office suite OpenOffice. So, overall, open source is catching on and the future is bright."

In looking at the growth of open source software in economies like India, Kendall Whitehouse, Wharton's senior director of information technology, stresses that it is important to distinguish between two different aspects of its proliferation: how quickly India will become a hotbed for open source development and the rate at which Indian companies and governmental agencies will adopt the use of open source software. "Although these two issues are obviously interrelated, they differ in terms of their economic incentives" because open source software is freely distributed. Whitehouse believes it is likely that the adoption of open source software by large companies may initially advance more rapidly than development efforts by Indian programmers, although, he admits, "the one will follow the other."

Workable model

Rajesh Jain, managing director of Mumbai-based Netcore Solutions, says that "the open source model does work. Look at some of the biggest Internet companies. Many of them have some elements of their IT infrastructure built using open source, as do other organizations—big and small. From the perspective of developers, there is an altruistic approach to software here. But that has also not stopped commercial companies being created around open source. Examples include Red Hat and MySQL. IBM, too, has over the years committed resources in terms of money and people to open source software. In the end, it's a business model which is a win-win-win—for developers, for IT companies and enterprises. And that's why open source has emerged as a formidable business model."

Wharton's Whitehouse agrees, and points out that within the world of open source software, there are different licensing models with varying restrictions on how extensions to the original software code can be used. "Some open source licenses require all modifications of the software to be distributed freely under the original open source license. Others, however, allow the developer to use the open source code as the basis of commercial, proprietary software." Whitehouse concludes that while some open source advocates decry the option to use freely-distributed code as the basis of a commercial product, this model may help to facilitate open source development efforts in emerging economies such as India.

If open source is the future, even if integrated into commercial products, is India going to be (as Sun hopes) its biggest hub for developers? "It's possible," says Jain. "India has one of the largest concentrations of software developers, and today a significant portion of software development is around open source. So what Sun says may be true. I do not have actual estimates."

It's not just Jain. Nobody seems to have any estimates of the number of people involved in open source work. Estimates of the members of

the community in India vary from 2,000 to 200,000.

Most Indian companies are involved in handling outsourced projects. They deal in proprietary software; interest in open source seems to be peripheral. "Currently most of our software companies are oriented towards coding," says Hariharan. "But that could change as many start-ups emerge across India. For many of them, using open source is natural because it helps them minimize capital expenditure."

"India needs to contribute more aggressively to the process of open source development," says Jain. "We have an opportunity to establish leadership in this space." Hariharan adds, "India has a lot of creativity, and it is just a matter of time before that is reflected through open source software." In other words, the future of open source in India is still an open question. □

© Pallava Bagla

Project - Low cost wind mill
for lifting ground water

GRASSROOT
INNOVATIONS

Inexpensive "Tree-climber"

Anil K Gupta
Indian Institute of Management
Ahmedabad

Cross-pollination: Science and Society

In situations of resource abundance, innovations that stress frugality seldom emerge. So, do we remain or revert to a scarcity prone society? Obviously not. The challenge is to evolve an ethics which combines abundance with frugality, scarcity with simplicity, fluctuations with resilience, and utility with multi-functionality. Strange as it may sound, my argument rests on the real ability of the poor to bring forth frugal, creative and versatile innovations—something that can stimulate the imagination of designers, policy makers and development planners.

While 'big' science promises large shifts to benefit them, it is the 'little' science that sustains the marginalised people till the promises bear fruit. Therefore, people who produce grassroot innovations, using 'little' science and technology, are not the 'sink' for our advice, or clients of public relief or charity. They have something there which, given a chance, can be a powerhouse of solutions.

How do we understand the potential of 'little' science and link it with 'big' science so that the excellence in both sectors fuse, blend and synergize to create the larger social good? How do we conceptualize the inclusive process of development. At what stage does exclusion take place and how? Exclusion of people begins with devaluation of their work and, if left uncontested, proceeds to indifference. Then a stage comes when the people and their knowledge system become invisible. The knowledge, innovation and processes of the marginalized can either be ignored or be tapped into when convenient—free of cost or acknowledgement—and utilised to create innovation.

These were the perceptions that triggered the start of the Honey Bee concept some 20 years ago. When I returned from Bangladesh in 1986, after a year-long stay, I felt a sense of guilt in my heart. It appeared to me that while I was getting recognition and rewards for the work I was doing with the people, not much of the benefits had flowed back to them.

Around 1988–89, the idea of Honey Bee came to my mind, while walking home one day. As they say, there was a light afterwards! The honey bee does what we intellectuals seldom do: it connects flower to flower through pollination. And flowers don't complain when their nectar is taken away! Since we do not often write in local language, the people to people connectivity is not possible when we take their knowledge and we make them anonymous and usurp their authorship. Almost all of ethno biological work is illustrative of this attitude.

The Honey Bee Network evolved to counter these asymmetries in the knowledge economy. Whatever we learn from people must be sourced to them. They should not become anonymous. We must share our knowledge with any third party only after their Prior Informed Consent (PIC). People should have a right to know what we did with their knowledge. They should also be able to learn from what we learn from other people through local language communication. If we get any consultancy, award or any other income through exchange or dissemination of the knowledge, with or without value addition, a reasonable share should go back to them.

The Honey Bee Network, as it grew over the last two decades, began to bring in a large number of people into its fold, at the village level as well as at professional or institutional level. The major energy came through inclusion rather than exclusion.

Towards that end, the Honey Bee newsletter was brought out as a vital communication tool and it is published in different languages.

Inclusion or harmonious development is recognised as one of the most important goals for socio-economic development. Inclusion can take place by building the capacity of people to produce what they already know and do, or enable them to convert their innovations and traditional knowledge, either as such or by blending or bundling it with the knowledge of others, into products. This can begin to happen only when the elite in the S&T community starts interacting with knowledge-providers in the grassroots community on a basis of mutual respect.

However, there are several basic tensions in the pursuit of a local knowledge-based approach to development.

These tensions are between

- modern concepts of taxonomy vis-à-vis indigenous schemed of classification of things, thoughts and properties,
- validation of knowledge by formal scientific methods and local approaches,
- scientific and institutional context of knowledge vis-à-vis cultural and community context of knowledge,
- causality as a preferred attribute of functionality vis-à-vis functionality as more important even if for wrong reasons or causes,
- relevance of single or specialized explanation of things versus multiple and diversified explanations, including sometimes a purely ritualistic aspect for which scientific validity is difficult to claim or prove,
- individual contributions well recognised in the formal scientific system vis-à-vis less well established conventions for recognising such contributions,
- similar methods considered scientific when pursued by scientists, such as random selection of natural mutations for developing varieties, vis-à-vis such methods being attributed as trial and error in the case of farmers' varieties,
- ethical basis of extracting local knowledge by the formal sector as against the same by the informal sector, for different purposes, and
- the respect for intellectual property rights of the formal sector as against free access to the informal sector for contemporary as well as traditional knowledge of individuals and communities.

Keeping these tensions in mind, Honey Bee Network mobilised thousands of grassroot innovations and traditional knowledge examples from all over India and different parts of the world. Some of these provide useful heuristics for innovations in totally unrelated sectors.

What does it take to make the development process more inclusive? Minds on the margin are not marginal minds. Here I describe some user-driven innovations and the evolution of the Honey Bee Network. I keep asking why don't institutional scientists take interest in grassroots innovations? What lessons can we draw from our experience?

Bridging two cultures

Traditional knowledge enables Ram Nivas of Janjariawas village in Haryana to comprehend climatic uncertainty through ecological indicators. In a drought prone region, he takes recourse to using proxy variables for anticipating rain and crop performance. The flowering on the weeds such as *calotropis* was assumed to be correlated with the yield of millet and other crops. This triggered a longer investigation of ecological indicators.

During a field study in the same district of Haryana, we found a community practice of growing coriander around a chick pea field, ostensibly to repel the pests. Michele Pimbert did research at ICRISAT, Hyderabad, and found that coriander did help, not by repelling the pests but by attracting the predators. The outcome was the same, the causality was not. Often, farmers' functional knowledge has been discounted because of seemingly illogical or untenable explanations.

Bhohgilal Rajwadia and some other farmers from Bharuch found a unique way of repelling the pests by crushing a particular insect together with the leaves of a creeper. About ten labourers moved in the windward direction carrying this crushed material in hand, and the pests were repelled. Perhaps, some alarm pheromones were generated through this novel chemistry, not tried in any study on pest control.

A windmill costing about Rs 5000 was developed by Mehtar Hussain in Assam for irrigating small fields. It is now installed in western India through GIAN (west), Gujarat, by a cooperative of very poor salt workers, for pumping brine solutions for making salt. The vast arid region has no chance of getting a power line in the near future, being a sanctuary area for wild ass species. Windmills at this affordable cost have expanded choices and made the development process very inclusive.

The inexpensive 'tree climber' developed by Appachan in Kerala found application in Boston and Florida. A Boston professor uses it for doing research on insect diversity in tree tops for which she and her students previously had to build costly structures. An entrepreneur in Florida wants to use it to harvest coconuts.

Herbal pesticide

Under a CSIR-National Innovation Foundation research programme, 200 plant protection practices developed by farmers were taken up for screening and trial at IHBT, Palanpur, a leading laboratory for the Himalayan region. Most neem based pesticides suffer from degradation when exposed to air and daylight, and the solution offered by scientists makes the product unaffordable to a large section of farmers. The laboratory validated the claim of a farmer who made a neem compound that is storage stable. Jadubhai combines a few plants along with neem, making a multiple compound that is not affected by even 20 minutes of exposure to ozone. This is the first report of an herbal compound achieving what chemists have achieved in the lab through solvents or modification of molecular structure of neem compounds.

Thakershibhai developed a groundnut variety with a strong peg and smooth surface i.e., no ridges on the pod. The taste was sweeter than the existing varieties and its oil content was also very high. Like HMT and many other farmers' varieties, this was also rejected by institutional scientists. But farmers continued to grow it. They have developed several varieties of cardamom, pepper, wheat, chilly, cauliflower, sesame and many other crops. However, there is no mechanism to generate data through public institutions for protecting their intellectual property claims. Why is there so much institutional indifference towards such varieties?

The Enfield Company in England may have never imagined that the motorcycles manufactured by them would ever be used for performing farm operations. The motorcycle based multi-purpose tool bar provides very useful service for those farmers who could not afford bullocks or tractors. Why don't we focus on artisans who contribute so vitally to farmers' productivity?

The late Mr Savalya, a very creative small-scale entrepreneur, tried to improve the thermal efficiency of a cooking pan by making grooves or ridges on the bottom side of the aluminium plate. Studies at Indian Institute of Petroleum, Dehradun, and University Institute of Chemical Technology, Mumbai, demonstrated a gain of about 1.09 per cent in the thermal efficiency because of the ridges. The thermal efficiency of industrial boilers could be raised by having tubes with ridges all around.

Mansukh Bhai Prajpati has been painting earthen clay hot plates (*tava*) with non-stick *Azo Nobel* (liquid) which is similar to Teflon. UICT scientists found this affordable and accessible clay plate interesting. Because of the porosity of the clay plate, the paint gets embedded and does not come off as happens with metal surfaces. It consumes less gas while providing for low fat cooking.

Dada Khobargade, a dalit farmer from Maharashtra, has developed several paddy varieties and one of these is reported to have diffused over 0.1 million acres in five states. One of his varieties is included as a national reference for thinness of rice grain by the Protection of Plant Variety and Farmers Rights Authority.

Cycles of creativity

Kanak Das has designed a cycle which can harness the energy normally dissipated in the shock absorbing springs for propulsion, so that when cycling on an uneven road or a mountainous track, the bumps work for the rider. Saidullah and Chaurasia have developed slightly different designs of amphibious cycles which at very low cost provide entertainment, means of transport and exercise, as well as facilitating research in water bodies and aquatic photography.

Vikram Rathore has designed a cycle-based pump which works in shallow waters: Mansukhbhai has developed a cycle-based sprayer, 'Prem Singh has attached a switching device to a cell phone to switch on or off and home or farm appliance; Kamrudhin has converted the cycle into a small workshop for grinding, cutting and drilling. None of these innovations emerged in a large high-tech laboratory. It does not mean that we don't need high tech labs. It only shows that outstanding innovations can emerge at grassroots level.

If entrepreneurs in developed countries can find application for innovation by grassroots innovators in the Third World, then a poverty alleviation model will emerge which would look at the 'poor as providers' of solutions and not as problems in themselves.

Shodh Yatra

Every six months, we walk from village to village honouring local knowledge experts and grassroots innovators, young children who have extraordinary sensitivity about the biodiversity based knowledge systems and other change agents.

Having walked for about 4200 km, in twenty *Shodh Yatras* (learning walks) every summer and every winter for the last nine years, a great deal of cross pollination has taken place.

We have been inspired by the innovations we came across. During the 16th Shodh Yatra in Kerala, at one of the roadside meetings when we were presenting the innovations, a lot of people gathered around. After half an hour, we stopped the presentation and asked people to share their insights about local creative people. There was a lull. We were asked to continue our presentation, but we refused. After a while, several people came forward and told us about fascinating innovations involving, for example, a modification in car steering to make it possible for handicapped people to drive, improvement in vanilla processing technique to raise the level of vaniline extraction and the development of a cardamom variety.

During these journeys we discover a lot!

This interaction with the people with knowledge to offer has led to the identification of new products and processes. The National Innovation Foundation has helped file 140 patents including six filed by GIAN and SRISTI in the US. NIF has signed memoranda of understanding with official scientific agencies such as CSIR and ICMR.

About two dozen technologies have been licensed to small-scale entrepreneurs directly or through GIAN centres. What is remarkable about the licensing experience is that all the technologies have been transferred without having received a patent for any one of them. It is obvious that diffusion of technologies does take place through social as well as commercial channels. There is no doubt that diffusion through farmers and artisans' own networks has been most effective.

The formal scientific system does not take note of the solutions that come from outside its own programmes. We have to build bridges between formal and informal science. This can be done in some of the following ways:

- It can be done by recognising scientists who work with local innovators and traditional knowledge holders
- Funds should be earmarked for schemes that add value to local knowledge and creativity
- Every conference on natural or physical sciences should cover informal science
- Innovators should be enabled to hire scientists to work on their ideas
- Examples of outstanding blending of grassroots knowledge and modern science get incorporated in the curriculum of various science disciplines.

If we implement such suggestions, 'sink' will become 'source' and the poor will become

An innovator in Assam showing his bamboo teeth to R A Mashelkar

providers. Grassroots to Global may become the new mantra, with small farmers, artisans and labourers vying for space in global markets.

The need for blending formal and informal science remains. The process has started after the National Innovation Foundation after its signed agreements with CSIR and ICMR.

A small natural product lab (Sadbhav SRISTI Sanshodhan) has licensed and commericalised more than nine products including herbal pesticides, veterinary medicine and human medicine in the last two years. substantial benefits are flowing towards the knowledge providers and their communities. Shouldn't there be a large network of labs dedicated to the cause of people's knowledge?

I have no doubt that the Gandhian belief in building upon the local best practices could once again provide a way of revitalising the science and technology knowledge systems in formal and informal sectors. □

Devyani Srinivasan &
Paul Basil
Rural Innovation Network

Changing rural lives

From his home in Athanur village, Tamil Nadu, V K Palanivel's looks at the verdant surrounding hills. Palanivel speaks with pride about how his land is good for cultivating just about any crop–paddy, turmeric, groundnut. But as the availablity of water kept falling, Palanivel had to first abandon agriculture and then, poultry farming, and become a dairy farmer instead. The drudgery and painful stress that his wife, Amutha, had to go through to milk their cows almost led to their giving up of the dairy as well. But, with no other source of livelihood and two sons to educate, the couple had no option. A conventional power-driven milker would have relieved Amutha, but the cost was a prohibitive Rs 60,000.

In the midst of this difficult situation, Panivel chanced upon the JS Milker. The JS Milker is a manual milking device manufactured and marketed by J Support Industries, a Kerala based company headed by Joy John. The JS Milker is a simple vacuum driven device to milk cows. This portable machine has a vacuum handle, which is used to create the necessary suction power and draw milk out of the udder in the most hygienic and easy manner. The device is also fitted with a vacuum meter to monitor the vacuum built. This helps in preventing any damage to the milk nodes and makes the whole process absolutely safe for the cows.

JS Milker

Through its various initiatives Rural Innovation Network (RIN) offers innovators recognition through its annual Innovation Awards Programme, funding, networking, and mentoring. In addition, through its Samruddhi programme, RIN provides innovators the opportunity to make their products known among farmers through a direct retail chain.

For the JS Milker, RIN provided support and advice for sales personnel and other market development services. It was at a stall at the Codissia Trade Fair put up by RIN (for which the organization received first prize), that Palanivel first saw the JS Milker. RIN is currently tapping the market for manual milking machines not only in Tamil Nadu but in other southern and western Indian states as well. These machines are perfect examples of enterprises that RIN believes can have a macro impact. While other organizations take technologies into rural areas, RIN takes them out. RIN champions this 'technology outwards' approach because in many cases the same need that resulted in the innovation is the same in other rural areas.

RIN also conducted studies and field tests of the milker in various locations in Tamil Nadu and Karnataka both, to gain market feedback and to understand why it was difficult to persuade dairy farmers to change their normal milking practice. Based on the results, RIN supported refinement of the final product. For example, Palanivel and Amutha found that while securing one of the udders with a nipple from the milker, another would come loose and they would have to start the milking again. This problem was addressed.

The impact of the JS Milker on dairy farmers like Panivel and Amutha is clear. It now takes only one-third of the time to do to milk their cows than earlier, and because the milker reduces the bacterial content in the milk, they have been earning 10–15 paise more per litre of milk. They have been so happy with the milker that they have recommended it to many people, as a result of which nearly 20 JS Milkers have been sold.

With a production of nearly 85 million tonnes, India is the world's largest producer of milk. This production is achieved by more than 70 million dairy farmers. Within this 70 million are a diverse group of people. In Tamil Nadu, the average number of milch animals per farmer is 2.5. For farmers with fewer than four cows, the JS Milker, at Rs 7,500 to Rs 8,500, is unfortunately still out of reach. With RIN's focus on inclusion, the Samruddhi programme sells these farmers a cheaper version of the JS Milker, called Johny's. Samruddhi has also supported sale of the Johny's Milker through a promotional campaign.

Creativity

However, farmers who owned 4–10 cows, like Panivel and Amutha, could not only afford the JS Milker but willingly spent Rs 10,000 for a product that also had a higher quality can, nipples and electric assembly. They powered it with a 0.5 HP motor themselves. The Panivels emulated Joy John's creativity in modifying the milker themselves. One of the intangible and very valuable outcomes of innovations is that they create a pipeline for new ideas, and certainly contribute to towards a more innovative India.

Another such case is that of the Indian firm SERVALS Automation Pvt Ltd. SERVALS was approached by V Thiyagarajan, the inventor of the Venus burner, to help him manufacture and sell his product. The Venus burner can save upto 30 per cent of the quantity of the kerosene consumed by other burners in the Indian market, and is safer than its counterparts. SERVALS took charge of the operations of the Venus burner and realised that their first challenge was to secure funding for the project. Mainstream venture capitalists were unlikely to look favourably upon this venture, since although it could well be profitable, the funding requirements are relatively small and the return would not live up to their's expectations. At this juncture, RIN introduced SERVALS to Aavishkar, a new venture capital fund set up to focus on ventures that

were socially relevant and financially viable. In addition to financing, Aavishkar provides advisory services, hands-on help in terms of marketing and sales, and professionalizes the operations of SERVALS.

Currently the sales of the Venus burner stand at 20,000 per month. Buoyed by this success, SERVALS developed a stove that utilises plant based oils as fuel. This design is different from the conventional stove and has a vaporizer with intricate nozzles, where the plant-oil is preheated before it enters the combustion zone of the burner. Kerosene is burnt for some minutes and the flame heats the vaporizer upon which the flow of kerosene is stopped and that of plant oil is started. The L-RAMP programme of RIN, in collaboration with IIT-Madras has provided seed funding for incubation of this innovation. L-RAMP's incubation support is primarily targeted at product refinement and field testing.

Fuel needs

The poor do not have access to these modern fuels. Kerosene in the open market is priced at a whopping Rs 30 per litre! Traditional fuels such as wood, crop residues, and animal dung still provide for 80–90 per cent of the fuel needs of rural India. Therefore, the plant oil stove will be a valuable gain for the poor, particularly women as it will reduce the time spent on collecting firewood and the health hazards due to smoke.

Over the last seven years, RIN's work has benefitting around 3 lakh rural users, created Rs 20 crores worth of consumer surplus, generated business worth Rs 6 crores, and identified over 1000 innovators.

But in order to have a social impact, rural innovations must have business viability. RIN only selects innovations that can meet an existing market need and demonstrate the potential to become commercially viable. RIN focuses on innovations in agriculture, dairy, water and energy, as the rural economy revolves around these sectors. Innovations that are income enhancing, cost-effective, energy-efficient and eco-friendly are considered high impact. Combining environmental and social sustainability with commercial viability, RIN is proving that innovations can turn into wealth-creating enterprises in the rural heartland of India. □

Bosco M A Henriques
Chief Functionary
Natural Dye Resources

Turning a red industry into green

Pollution threatens our sustainable way of life in innumerable ways. Air pollution has led to acid rain and global warming. Water pollution has caused destruction of land and water bodies. In India the dye industry is listed as highly polluting in nature, and as a consequence of the Madras High Court Judgment of 2006, textile dyeing units have to adhere to Zero Liquid Discharge of trade effluents. The EU and USA require imported textiles to be made in accordance with the environment-related laws of the exporting nation. Large dyeing houses have made investments needed to comply with the court ruling but small dye houses have shut down. Rural artisans, of course, continue to pollute for the want of appropriate wastewater treatment technology. The coloured and saline pollution from dyeing units has made farmland uncultivable and subsurface water undrinkable. It will prevent the small rural dyer from export their products to the developed world. The new dyes being developed by multinationals to reduce the pollution load are expensive and usable only with expensive dyeing machinery and offer no solace to the rural artisan.

India was famous for millennia for her natural-dyed cotton textiles that caused no pollution in the artisan clusters. With the advent of artificial dyes this tradition was lost, as synthetic dyeing was price competitive and quick and easy to perform. The pollution it generated was tolerated. Many artisans used synthetic dyes with a natural mordant and sold their wares as natural-dyed products. They compromised on the process and created the general impression that natural dyes were available in a few dull shades that faded in sunlight and bled when washed in water. The hobbyists, while keeping the tradition alive, propagated the belief that different dye sources and separate processes were needed to obtain distinct colours.

Old dyes

With her strong interest in textile history my colleague, Ms Ann Shankar of Punjab Durrie Weavers (PDW), has been aware that Indian textiles were at the centre of the spice trade. The Persians and Europeans exchanged gold for India's coloured textiles and then bartered these for spices in the Malay and Indonesian islands. These natural dyed textiles had to be of superior quality. Ms Shankar had the prescience to realise that natural dyes could regain their glory if appropriate technology were developed using modern scientific knowledge.

After my work on a PhD thesis in molecular biology at TIFR, I opted to pursue a scientific career in an entrepreneurial mode. I founded a firm TechnoSource to manufacture equipment for electro-separation of bio-molecules. The constant need to invent equipment and develop new models to maintain a market share kept one's intellect occupied, but this activity was not adequate to make a lasting impression in the field. A scientist's career develops through first learning to use the tools (equipment, reagents, assays, models, equations, software) of a particular discipline and thereafter the art of using the tools in different protocols or processes. The knowledge and skill acquired is then utilized to gather, organize, analyse and interpret data and sometimes modify old tools or invent new ones to address the problem at hand.

Technology is the organization and production of these modified or invented tools in an economically viable manner.

I was introduced to Ms Shankar during her quest to revitalise the tradition of natural dyeing through scientific inputs. This required harnessing of the knowledge and skills of practitioners from different disciplines. We were able to implement a public financed project in a private-public-participatory mode that brought the core competency of different institutions together in a consortium to achieve the goal of upgrading natural dyeing technology.

We realised that in order to develop a technology to make natural dyeing competitive with synthetic dyeing, we had to tackle the major challenges of poor fastness and non-availability of a sustainable supply of raw material. Then there are problems of producing textiles of all shades, tints and hues, of desired brightness, of softness to the touch and of adequate fibre-strength. We have to develop a process that can be mechanised and establish the entire value-chain.

Plant records

During the period of colonial rule the British had painstakingly recorded the various plants and processes used by Indian craftsmen in natural dyeing, and supported a number of scientific investigations in indigo cultivation and pigment manufacture. PDW, the project implementing NGO, was responsible for collating this information. Over 450 plants were recorded as being used in textile dyeing. A herbarium identified the various dye-yielding plants recorded in literature and collected parts of those that grew in the biodiversity-rich Western Ghat region of southern Maharashtra. A home science college tested the various plants parts collected for their dye potential. An ICAR institution tested and certified the fastness of the dyed samples. We studied the recorded processes to understand the principles underlying natural dyeing and then developed an alum-and-myrobalan-based mordanting process that could be used to dye cotton in shades that had equal or better light- and wash-fastness properties than that of synthetic dyes. Parts from more than a hundred different plants could serve as dye source with this mordanting method. A farmer group grew *Indigofera tinctoria* and evaluated it to ascertain if it could serve as the rotation legume in organic cotton cultivation practices. In

conjunction with a college laboratory my firm developed improved processes to purify indigo from *I. tinctoria*. Finally, artisan groups were taught the newly developed mordant dyeing method.

In a little more than two years that the project lasted we were able to find solutions to the main challenges facing the adoption of natural dyeing *viz.*, fastness and raw material availability. We identified more than a 100 plants whose parts could be used to dye cotton with high light-and wash-fastness ratings. The method was field-tested and it was ascertained that artisans could use the process.

We helped establish an entire value chain for producing natural dyed textiles—from collecting leaves and fruits from marginal land to pulverizing the vegetal matter, dyeing the yarn, weaving the fabric, training artisans to paint and print the cloth, designing and stitching the apparel, and finally, displaying the products in a fashion show. This project was implemented in a private-public consortium mode.

Rural women

One of the criticisms levelled against the use of natural dyeing on a large-scale was that it would use large amounts of farmland and thus compete with food crops. We therefore chose to direct our efforts to using chromogen (colouring principle) from the leaves of perennial shrubs and trees that would grow unattended on marginal land and provide employment for rural women in plant propagation, seedling cultivation and leaf/fruit harvesting activities. By providing women with LPG cylinders in exchange for collected leaves, random firewood collection was reduced; their health improved from non-inhalation of smoke and time was saved through both faster cooking on gas-stoves and not needing to gather firewood. This scheme preserved trees and maintained bio-diversity.

To keep inventories low we short-listed only seven trees/shrubs (local names being manjistha, helu, harda, anjan, shevra, peru and kalindrin), neel (indigo) that is cultivated as green manure, waste tea leaves and an animal derived colour (lac) for our colour palette. To keep dyeing costs down the vegetal matter was finely powdered, stored in nitrogen to improve shelf life and the dye extracted from the powder *in-loco*. With these short-listed dye-sources, we could dye cotton and silk in the entire range of tints, hues and shades with

fastness properties that were market acceptable. The chromogen was found in parts that could be harvested in a sustainable manner i.e., leaves, fruits or ground-runners. The *lac* procured was purified from waste-water discarded by the shellac industry. The new dyeing technology was imparted to *ikat* and *kalamkari* artisans. The use of a single mordanting method for all shades other than blue made it easy for artisans to learn and use the process. Students of fashion design were also exposed to the new developments in natural dyeing. They organized a fashion show where yarn and fabric made of cotton, linen, different kind of silks and wool were dyed, the coloured yarn was woven and the cloth made into apparel and displayed.

Indigo

Efforts are in progress to improve the economic viability of natural dyeing by developing environment-friendly pre-processing and finishing methods. A novel cost-effective method to produce enzymes that could be used to scour cotton and destroy peroxide bleach has been developed. As the enzymes are produced by non-genetically modified organisms, the scouring and bleaching process can be organically certified. Method were formulated for blending different dyes so that the shades could be reproduced. Levelling techniques were modified so that uneven dyeing was minimised. Indigo is the only natural blue. It has a poor rub-fastness and is sensitive to ozone fading. We developed finishing processes to improve indigo rub fastness and reduce ozone fading. We devised methods to reduce dirt attraction. Finally, we adapted the dyeing machines so that the process could be mechanized. With all these innovations we have come within striking distance of competing with synthetic dyes at comparable dyeing volumes. One important criterion to be borne in mind while developing all these processes was that all ingredients used should be non-toxic, biodegradable and removable in simple effluent treatment tanks; if compounds are bio-eliminable they should be used in small amounts. On account of this approach our sludge can be used as manure and our treated wastewater can be used for irrigation.

We at Natural Dye Resources have developed a cradle-to-cradle technology for dyeing cotton and silk yarn and fabric with natural dyes with fastness ratings that are equal to, or better than, synthetic dyes, and when scaled up through mechanization, can be competitive in prince and quality with synthetic dyes. The chromogen is obtained in a sustainable manner from leaves,

fruits, ground-runners or factory waste. The trees from which the leaves and fruits are obtained can be used in marginal land cultivation schemes and to provide rural employment for women. Natural dyeing can also provide income opportunities to local women in textile craft.

The dyeing activity is non-hazardous and the solid waste and treated wastewater can be used for agricultural activities. Besides these environmental and social benefits, natural dyed textiles have benefits for the user. These textiles dissipate heat and feel cool to wear and rest upon. They absorb UV-light and protect the user from the scorching effects of solar radiation; they retard the growth of microbes on perspiration-soaked fabric and thereby significantly reduced body-odour. Lastly, on account of the earth undertones, the colours are soothing to the eye. Further, the colours do not clash with each other but combine well. We have erected a pilot plant to demonstrate that natural dyeing has the potential of competing with synthetic dyes in performance and price. In terms of social and environmental benefits, natural dyeing leaves its competitor far behind. □

CRADLE OF
RESEARCH

Nehru with Homi Bhabha

Mustansir Barma
Director
Tata Institute of
Fundamental Research

TIFR links basic science to development

With the dawning of independence, Nehru, one of the architects of the nation, set its course under the guiding star of science. Science was to take India into the modern world, its discoveries and technological advances would galvanize the country into achieving rapid development. He turned to already established institutes to help the country take the leap forward. Chief among these was the Tata Institute of Fundamental Research, founded in 1945 by the Trustees of the Sir Dorabji Tata Trust in cooperation with what was then called the Government of Bombay. An institution that symbolized the nation's hopes, it was already beginning to make a name for itself in the scientific world.

Homi Bhabha, Director of TIFR in the fifties, understood and underscored the importance of basic research in the new India. Speaking at the inauguration of the new buildings of his Institute in 1962, Bhabha made two points: first, engagement in basic research results in training and developing the youth of India as no other discipline can; and second, the history of science has demonstrated that all knowledge was ultimately useful to mankind.

In keeping with that faith, TIFR today has research programmes at the frontiers of Mathematics, Computer Science, Physics and Astronomy, Chemistry, Biology and Science Education. Besides research across all disciplines at the main TIFR campus in Colaba in South Mumbai, TIFR conducts subject-specific research in some areas at other centres and field stations. These include the National Centre for Radio Astronomy (NCRA) in Pune; the National Centre for Biological Sciences (NCBS) in Bangalore; the Homi Bhabha Centre for Science Education (HBCSE) in northern Mumbai; the Centre for Applicable Mathematics (CAM) in Bangalore. Finally, a new centre, the International Centre for Theoretical Sciences, has begun to operate over the last year. Besides, TIFR also runs research facilities at Ootacamund, Pachmari, Hyderabad, and Gauribidnur.

TIFR has obviously grown in scope and size over the sixty odd years of its existence. From the 1950s onwards, the Institute has been the National Centre of the Government of India for Nuclear Science and Mathematics, supported by the Department of Atomic Energy as an autonomous grant-in-aid institute. This short piece will focus on a few areas and discuss their development, highlighting research achievements and contributions to the nation.

Theoretical sciences
Mathematics: In Homi Bhabha's vision, pure mathematics had a natural and important role to play in an institute of fundamental research. The School of Mathematics quickly acquired a formidable international reputation, particularly in the areas of algebraic geometry, Lie theory and number theory. Over the decades, work done in the School has evolved with, and sometimes defined, the dynamic changes taking place in mathematics in the international arena. Over the last decade, for example, the work in number theory in the School has changed considerably in its character, with a greater input of methods from algebraic geometry and representation theory. In algebraic geometry too, while the work on moduli problems continued along traditional lines, there has been considerable interest in the subject of cycles and motives. Also, interesting developments in ergodic

theory and dynamical systems were initiated by members of the school. While mathematicians in Mumbai pursue largely pure mathematical areas, the TIFR Center for Applicable Mathematics (CAM) in Bangalore has been vigorously pursuing mathematics centered around partial differential equations and has established itself as a leading centre in this field.

Some of the traditions built in the initial phase continue even today, for instance the four-yearly TIFR international colloquium, which has ranged over diverse topics over the years. There have been strong links with the International Mathematical Union since the early days. TIFR mathematicians have also actively promoted mathematics throughout the country. They were involved in the founding of the National Board for Higher Mathematics (NBHM), which supports mathematics in the country in various ways. NBHM programmes include funding for mathematics research institutions and research proposals, region-wise support to libraries, and a nurture programme to spot and support students with a talent for the subject. Another important activity of the School of Mathematics has been the preparation and dissemination of lecture notes on research topics in mathematics, some of which have become classics in the field. These activities continue vigorously today.

Computer science: The history of computer science in TIFR goes back to the 1950s. The first full-scale, general purpose electronic digital computer designed and built in India was the Tata Institute of Fundamental Research Automatic Calculator (TIFRAC), which was commissioned in 1960. The TIFRAC used about 3000 vacuum tubes, 1700 germanium diodes and 12500 resistors, and initially a thousand word ferrite core memory. The machine was inaugurated by Pandit Nehru. It was used extensively, first by cosmic ray physicists and later by other groups, and remained the main workhorse for computational needs for not just TIFR but other academic and government institution as well until the mid 1960s.

In the late sixties and seventies, there was a focus on computer-based applications, two major developments being an indigenously developed air defence system and a digital mobile communication system for the army. The core team of engineers involved with this project later formed an important component of CDoT. TIFR computer scientists also played a formative role in the early stages of CMC, and in

developing computers at ECIL. TIFR scientists and engineers also seeded the National Centre for Software Technology (NCST), which later became a focal point of software development and education.

Other major activities during these years were theoretical computer science and speech processing, both of which continue today. The recent activity of the group spans diverse areas of computer and systems sciences, such as logic and logic programming; computational geometry and computer vision; verification tools; algorithms and complexity; mobile and grid computing; network security; wireless and sensor networks; simulation; statistical computing for finance; e-commerce; stochastic control and optimization; estimation and resource allocation problems in communications; quantum computation; speech synthesis and speaker recognition with a focus on Indian languages.

Theoretical physics: By the time he returned to India in 1939, Bhabha had already made significant contributions to theoretical physics, including the scattering mechanism that goes under his name. In the first decade of TIFR's existence, theoretical investigations of cosmic ray showers, meson production and nuclear forces constituted the largest component of work. The next decade (mid 1950s to mid 1960s) was a period of expansion and diversification; research programmes in theoretical nuclear physics and solid-state physics began at this time. The following decade saw a phenomenon which was to recur many times in the history of TIFR; a significant number of scientists working in a particular area left TIFR to seed an activity elsewhere (in this case, plasma physicists left to join the Physical Research Laboratory in Ahmedabad). The next twenty years (mid 1970s to mid 1990s) saw contributions at the frontiers of practically all areas of theoretical physics. This period saw research in diverse areas: gauge theories of strong and weak interactions in high energy physics; the foundations of quantum mechanics; the renormalization group in statistical physics; high temperature superconductivity; and string theory which emerged as the leading candidate for a unified theory of all particles and forces including gravity.

Over the past few years, research interests in theoretical high energy physics are mainly in two fields: first, electroweak interactions, collider phenomenology and physics beyond the standard model; second, quantum chromodynamics and the quark-gluon plasma. In string theory, research has focused on noncommutative field theory, which is a nonlocal deformation of quantum field theory, noncritical strings, the duality between field theory and gravity, black holes and quantum gravity, and flux compactifications and cosmology. In condensed matter and statistical physics, research areas include disorder effects on strongly correlated electron systems, the effects of frustration in quantum magnets, phase transitions involving polymers and long needles, self-organized criticality and the dynamics of driven nonequilibrium systems. In theoretical astrophysics, research topics include accretion disks around black holes and neutron stars, gravitational collapse in general relativity, gravitational lensing, neutron stars, pulsars, supernovae and the properties of the Sun.

The recent founding of the International Centre for Theoretical Sciences promises to give a boost to research programmes in theoretical sciences in the Institute, and in the country.

Experimental research

The ambit of experimental research at TIFR is very broad, and ranges across high energy physics, atomic and nuclear physics, condensed matter physics, astronomy and astrophysics, chemistry and biology. Increasingly, the problems being discussed are interdisciplinary in character and cannot always be categorized in one or the other of these fields. Below is a very brief sketch of some of the activities undertaken.

With the aim of discovering new particles and phenomena at the highest energy and smallest length scales, high energy physicists from the Institute have been participating in large collaborative experiments performed in the US, Europe and Japan, involving groups from several countries. They are also spearheading the design and development of a new centre of non accelerator physics, namely the India Neutrino Observatory (INO), which aims to uncover the properties of the usually elusive neutrinos.

Nuclear matter at high excitation energies and angular momenta has been studied with the aid of the pelletron, a heavy-ion accelerator which is run in collaboration with BARC, and is used by groups from institutes and universities across the country. A superconducting linear accelerator has recently been commissioned, which significantly increases the energy of particles from the pelletron.

Light-matter interactions at ultra high energies and small times have been investigated using very high intensity pulsed lasers to explosively ionize matter and study its behaviour under extreme conditions. High resolution instrumentation has been set up to probe the dissociative electron attachment process.

Areas of research in condensed matter physics include studies of strongly correlated systems, with a focus on their magnetic and superconducting properties. An important discovery was the occurrence of the coexistence of magnetism and superconductivity in borocarbides. In semiconductor physics, the focus is on optoelectronic devices, and on the properties of organic semiconductors. The study of materials at the nanoscale was pioneered at TIFR in the 1980s, and continues to be an area of intense research.

Researchers in chemistry have been working on the structures of nucleic acids and proteins, the dynamics of protein folding and misfolding, the chemical basis of neuronal communication, biochemical pathways in living cells and the role of metal atoms in biological structures. The formation of hydrogen bonds and free radicals in smaller molecules has also been studied. TIFR hosts the National Facility for High Field NMR, which is used also by other researchers and by the drug industry.

In biology, the underlying theme has been the use of genetics to shed light on complex cellular processes. Earlier the focus was on the mechanisms of recombination, gene regulation and protein structure. Currently, the research ranges from examining nanoscale interactions in cells, to systems biology and behaviour. Also, model organisms are used to study mechanisms which underlie brain function and development, and the principal determinants of parasitic infections.

Studies in astronomy cover a wide range of wavelengths in the electromagnetic spectrum. Infrared and optical wavelengths reveal the dynamics of galaxies and star-forming regions, while X-rays and gamma rays probe black hole and neutron star binaries and the nuclei of active galaxies. Recently, TIFR has planned to do X-ray and infra-red investigations using the Astrosat satellite which will be launched by ISRO.

Radio astronomy at TIFR was initiated in the early 1960s; within five years the group had launched a major innovative project, namely the Ooty Radio Telescope, designed to use the diffraction of radio waves by the edge of the moon to achieve an angular resolution of a few arcseconds at a wavelength of 90 cm. A unique innovation was building a long parabolic cylindrical radio telescope on a north south slope inclined at an angle equal to the latitude, allowing celestial sources to be tracked by uniform rotation about one axis. The angular size-flux relation for faint radio sources was determined by 1976, revealing clear cosmic evolution. Other highlights included mapping the turbulence and outflow speed of the interplanetary medium, observing spectral lines of highly excited hydrogen, and putting limits on deuterium, from the galactic plane.

By the mid-eighties, the group proposed and executed a major new facility, the Giant Metrewave Radio Telescope (GMRT) at Khodad, near Pune. A major scientific driver was the study of the 21 cm line of neutral atomic hydrogen from objects so distant that the wavelength could be stretched to as long as a meter or more by the expansion of the universe. Such a telescope did not exist at that time. This plan required a large number of large (45 m) lightweight low cost antennas, a challenge which was met by an innovative design. GMRT came online in 1999. The high sensitivity and high resolution at meter wavelengths has attracted an extensive national and international user community apart from NCRA faculty. Highlights include measurements of the temperatures of a class of clouds of hydrogen in intergalactic space, the best results on the kinematics of dwarf galaxies, the discovery of several new pulsars with unusual properties such as high eccentricity, very young age and long period, new features of pulsar radio emission that give information about the emission height at different frequencies and field line geometries, results on gamma ray bursts and other transient sources, spectral index mapping of radio galaxies, and deep surveys.

The Homi Bhabha Centre for Science Education (HBCSE) is involved with curriculum development and promotion of excellence in science and mathematics education and research on cognition. The centre has contributed to textbook writing at the national and state levels. Extensive fieldwork has been carried out in rural, semi-urban and urban areas to monitor the effectiveness of science teaching in primary schools. HBCSE also trains young students, chosen by the government, to participate in International Olympiads in mathematics, physics, astronomy, chemistry and biology.

Young scholars

Since inception, TIFR has recruited promising young scholars whose engagement in research has expanded the range and the depth of the Institute's activities. The training of these young scientists is an integral part of the academic activity in the Institute. As the numbers grew, it was felt necessary to institute a formal graduate school with a variety of courses, both at the foundational and advanced research level. Today there are students pursuing research in every field. Since 2003, TIFR has been granted deemed university status, and awards masters and doctoral degrees to graduating students.

Further, TIFR has been running a widely successful Visiting Students' Research Programme every summer for students still enrolled in bachelors or masters programmes elsewhere, to give them an exposure to research.

Students graduating from TIFR have enriched the talent pool in the country and across the world in many fields. Today, many of these students hold prominent positions in both academic and nonacademic organizations in the country, for instance in the Indian Institutes of Technology (IITs), the Indian Space Research Organization (ISRO) and the Oil and Natural Gas Commission (ONGC). Irrespective of their subsequent careers, the success of these students may be traced to their ability to solve complex problems by inventing innovative strategies, a skill they have picked up during their years in research. Thus in diverse ways the Institute vindicates the Founder's insight about the twin uses of basic research—as a discipline that trains young minds and as an activity that finally has its uses. □

The author wishes to thank Dr Indira Chowdhury, Consultant Archivist, TIFR for the historical material.

INTERNATIONAL COOPERATION

Norman Borlaug with an Indian farmer

John Marburger
Science Adviser to
US President

US and India get more ambitious

The United States and India have for 60 years enjoyed a long history of scientific and technical collaboration. In that time, collaborative scientific efforts facilitated India's Green Revolution, the establishment of the Satellite Instructional Television Experiment, and the creation of the Indian National Council of Educational Research and Training.

President Bush has remarked that "India's greatest assets are its human resources and intellectual capital." The importance that these assets play, have been exemplified by the joint US-India projects in energy, space, the environment, and medicine.

Early scientific collaboration between the two countries began with the signing of the US Public Law 480 (PL-480) in 1954. With a focus on cooperative agricultural development, the law facilitated international collaboration in education, infrastructure development, and food production, marketing, and distribution. Collaboration between universities in India and the United States made a headway under the various incarnations of the PL-480 programme. Around $900 million was allocated through the primary vehicles—the Joint Commission on Economics & Commerce, Science & Technology, Education & Culture, and Agriculture (1974–1983); the Science & Technology Initiative (1983–1991); and the US-India Fund (1987–1998)—establishing a vast number of personal connections and setting the stage for future S&T collaboration.

Between 1962 and 1972, the Kanpur Indio-American Programme initiated a new era of US-India collaboration in the academia. The programme linked the Indian Institute of Technology-Kanpur (IIT-Kanpur) and a consortium of nine US universities (MIT, Carnegie Mellon, Caltech, Princeton, UC-Berkeley, University of Michigan, Ohio State, Purdue, Case Institute of Technology). The programme provided US-based training for Indian faculty and contributions of books and equipment. In total, US faculty members collectively served over 200 teaching years at IIT-Kanpur between 1962 and 1972. Today the links between US and Indian academia is growing at a rapid pace.

Continued cooperation

The bilateral Science and Technology Cooperation agreement signed in 2005 expanded the scope of collaboration further. It covers a variety of fields involving science and technology, as well as various stages of scientific research and technological development. Recent cooperative activities fall under the direction of several bilateral cooperative bodies.

The Indo-US S&T Forum, established in 2000, is a private grant-making foundation in New Delhi that facilitates and promotes the interaction, of government, academia, and industry in science, technology and other related areas. The Smithsonian Institution–India Science and Technology Partnership, established in Washington, D.C. in 2004, promotes the interaction of government, academia and industry in science, technology and health. The High Technology Cooperation Group, established in 2003, enhances the flow of trade in high technologies between India and the US, and the Next Steps in Strategic Partnership, signed in 2004, expands cooperation in civilian nuclear activities, civilian space programmes, and high-technology trade.

A new dimension of the US-India scientific cooperation is its global implications. For example, the US Department of State's Bureau of Oceans and International Environmental and Scientific Affairs worked in conjunction with the Indian Space Research Organization, to establish satellite links to facilitate tele-medicine and remote patient observation which assist Afghan reconstruction efforts. Important collaborations abound in key technologies like energy, space, environment and medicine.

Energy

International collaboration spans the breadth of the energy sector, from basic research in renewable energies to fine-tuning existing technologies for more efficient civil nuclear, oil, gas, and coal programs. The US Department of Energy's National Renewable Energy Laboratory (NREL) is working with the Indian Solar Energy Center to evaluate the performance of various thin film photovoltaic technologies. NREL is also working in Hyderabad to complete an emissions inventory and identify public policies for energy conservation. The US also collaborates multilaterally through the Climate Technology Initiative, in which the US and India work alongside other partner countries to identify hydropower and water management projects.

Space

A Memorandum of Understanding for Scientific Cooperation in the Areas of Earth and Atmospheric Sciences has been in place since 1997. It unites the US Oceanic and Atmospheric Administration, US National Aeronautics and Space Administration (NASA), India's Department of Space, and India's Department of Science and Technology in a cooperative exchange of Earth and environmental science data.

NASA has two scientific instruments on *Chandrayaan-1*, the lunar orbiter. The Moon Mineralogy Mapper is for assessing mineral resources of the moon, and the Mini-SAR is to look for ice deposits in the Moon's polar regions.

Environment

The Agriculture Knowledge Initiative builds on investments in cooperation begun five decades ago by expanding US-India collaboration in agricultural education, teaching, and research. The US Department of Agriculture (USDA) works with the Forest Research and Wildlife Institutes

President Bush and Prime Minister Manmohan Singh

at Dehra Dun to study biodiversity in the Himalayas and other Indian ecosystems. The US Fish and Wildlife Service have collaborated with Indian scientists to study the Shola grasslands of the Western Ghats and the alpine grasslands in the Himalayas and to develop conservation strategies there. Similar collaborative observation and conservation efforts have targeted the elephant, great ape, rhinoceros, and tiger.

The Atmospheric Brown Cloud Project, which involves a consortium of over seventy institutions in more than a dozen countries, encompasses an extensive US-India collaboration. Our countries, in conjunction with others, work to characterize the impact of atmospheric brown clouds on monsoon change, water balance, agriculture and health.

Medicine

Cooperation in the health sciences focuses on HIV/AIDS, anti-retroviral drug development, joint clinical trial research, and basic R&D toward product development.

The US National Institutes of Health sponsors numerous bilateral public health programs, including the Indo-US Vaccine Action Programme, which was renewed in 2007 and targets the development of vaccines against high-priority diseases such as HIV/AIDS, tuberculosis, malaria and rotavirus. The Indo-US Disease Surveillance Programme aims to strengthen India's disease surveillance system. The Indo-US Brain Research Programme promotes neuroscience and mental health research through targeted workshops to stimulate joint proposals. The HIV/AIDS

Prevention Research Programme promotes a range of HIV/AIDS and sexually transmitted disease prevention research efforts. And the Maternal & Child Health Research Programme promotes research in areas related to maternal and child health and development.

The US Center for Disease Control works in partnership with the Indian Ministry of Health , the Indian Council of Medical Research, and others to improve the health of the Indian population through the Global Programme on AIDS, the Field Epidemiology Training Programme, Tuberculosis and Malaria Control, Polio Eradication and Measles Control, Development and Evaluation of a Rotavirus Vaccine, Safe Water Intervention in West Delhi and Orissa State, and Indo-US Collaboration in Environmental and Occupational Health.

The US and India hope that future generations will appreciate the benefits of collaboration and carry these efforts forward. Contemporary cooperative educational programming includes dozens of bilateral links between US and Indian universities. The Indo-US Inter-University Network for Higher Education and Research enhance distance learning in India's fastest-growing universities and facilitates university courses via Edusat, a satellite e-learning network linking 20 US universities, two Indian departments (S&T and ISRO), Amrita University; and three US corporate partners.

Just as the Kanpur Indo-American Programme forged personal and technical relationships 60 years ago, these cooperative agreements establish a framework for a shared future. President Bush and Prime Minister Singh clearly envisioned such a future in New York in 2004, when they agreed that "the best is yet to come." □

B S Prakash
India's Consul General in
San Francisco

Cloning silicon valley?

It is the conventional wisdom, almost a cliché, to say that Silicon Valley leads the world as a hub for 'innovation'. I have observed Silicon Valley for three years from an unusual perspective. Unlike thousands of Indians who live here or are temporary residents working on contacts with its famous technology companies, I am not an engineer, a scientist, a technocrat, an entrepreneur, or a venture capitalist. And yet my focus has been on Silicon Valley's evolution and inherent strengths and its growing links with India and more importantly, on the inferences that we can draw from its success.

This interest is from my vantage point as an Indian diplomat based in the heart of Silicon Valley and placed at the cross-section of the extensive and intensive engagement between it and India. I will try to share my thoughts based on my experiences and the perspective gained through my interaction with some of the players in the technology business.

Silicon Valley is a distinctive habitat or eco-system, to use a fashionable phrase. Other areas, in the US (Boston, San Diego, Seattle for example), and other countries (notably Israel, Ireland, Taiwan, China and India), have tried to replicate some of the elements of this 'habitat'. The first question then is: What is so special about the region, particularly as far as India is concerned?

A conversation with a leading Indian industrialist visiting Silicon Valley may be used to frame the issue. This individual, CEO of a major and dynamic Indian group, was looking for people to join his Group. I was intrigued. "Why do you need to look for them here; aren't there so many in India with the necessary qualifications and skills?" I asked him. "Sure," he said, "There are hundreds with both academic qualifications and experience. But I am looking for people who want to take risks, think outside the box, are innovative and not afraid of failure. And this they imbibe in Silicon Valley."

This was his impressionistic account, but over a period of time, I have seen a number of studies which map how and why Silicon Valley has evolved as a unique place. A simple summary would run something like this. In the beginning there were some major universities and laboratories, most notably Stanford University, which encouraged its students and professors to tinker around with the application of their ideas and discoveries. Close by were also some major companies—Hewlett Packard, Intel— interested in the cutting edge of technology. A loose but close link between scientists and academics on the one hand and engineers and managers on the other came to be developed. As this process gathered momentum, more and more entrepreneurs gravitated towards Silicon Valley as an environment conducive to try out their ideas and business plans.

Scholars and young students at places like Stanford also began to try implementing their bright ideas rather than be content with the pursuit of knowledge. They found mentors—seniors with experience but willing to listen and guide; venture capital folks, ready to invest but also with an understanding of what may work and what may not in new products or processes; lawyers to take care of intellectual property issues and other essentials of starting a business; and other kindred souls with similar ideas and aspirations. Over time, the Valley attained a critical mass wherein all these different skills and groups have come together to an extent that there are now well-established networks in each of these crucial areas. In the literature analyzing the attributes of the Silicon Valley two features stand out: the links between the scientists and the industry; and the networks that nurture these.

It may be noted that the evolution of other hubs has followed similar trajectories. A more recent example is Seattle, increasingly seen as an attractive destination for start-ups. In Seattle, the presence of Microsoft and Amazon side by side with a good computer engineering department in the University of Washington has acted as a catalyst. Analysts note the social networks including venture capitalists, gizmo-geeks and lawyers giving momentum to the process.

Turning now specifically to the Indian connection, it is happily true that Indians (whether Indian-Americans or Indian nationals) have come to be a sizable and successful presence in this environment. This phenomenon too has had its growth curve. Starting from the mid-sixties, large numbers from the IITs and other good engineering colleges came here, drawn by attractive career prospects, and hundreds found places as employees of tech companies. By the eighties, however, many of them imbibed the entrepreneurial spirit of the Valley and were not content to be employees, however highly placed. Many started their own businesses, ascended in the dotcom rise and survived the dotcom bust. Today the Indian-American community in these areas is over two hundred thousand people and the contribution of Indian talent and enterprise is well recognized, as employees and as successes in start-ups.

Trailblazers

The last decades have also seen many Indian companies (including but not limited to Infosys, Wipro, TCS) becoming trailblazers with a synergetic connection with the Valley. A newer but equally significant phenomenon is that major US technology companies ranging from Intel to Google and from Sun to Cisco have established large research and development facilities in India. With all this, Bangalore and Hyderabad are as familiar names in the Silicon Valley as the latter is in modern Indian cities.

All this is an outline of the developments hitherto. The more important question is: What lies ahead? Which is the next wave? And specifically: can India aspire to be a hub for innovation on a global scale in the coming decades? And from my perspective, can it benefit from its Silicon Valley connection?

There are a number of pointers which argue for a significant role for India in the innovation business and some of these aspects are considered below:

- To start with: What is innovation? For our purpose, we can regard innovation in terms commonly used in the Silicon Valley. By innovation is meant not invention, not pure research, not a bright idea by itself, but more, the application of an idea to a process or a product or a transaction to make it faster or better or cheaper. It is in that sense the application of mind to matter with the aim of greater efficacy.

- If innovation entails application of mind and skills, it is obvious that India has at least some attributes. The emphasis traditionally placed in India on education and knowledge acquisition is the starting point. The success in IT, the recent strides in bio-technology and our confidence and ability in other areas of advanced technology shows that there is enough brain-power and a large enough talent pool in India, the first requisite. The success of people of Indian origin globally also reinforces this point.

- At this stage, it would be natural to ask as to why India has not had notable successes with innovative products or processes, if indeed Indians have the necessary attributes. Where are the examples of Walkmans or PCs or I-phones or even less iconic game-changing innovations emanating from the Indian soil? My answer to this can only be speculative. To begin with, it must be recognized that the Indian tradition has focused more on mind (and the spirit) than matter, more on ideas than application. In the realms relating to the mind or the spirit, there indeed are notable Indian innovations, say the techniques for concentration or meditation or *Yoga* or *Dhyana*. In the material and the marketing realms, it is possible that we have not been greatly successful in innovation hitherto, for organizational or market related reasons rather than any inherent inability. A closed market, the sway of monopolies, an economy where the demand always outstrips the supply and lack of global competition may have hindered the incentives for better, faster and cheaper products or processes. It is also to be acknowledged that in recent years the character of the Indian economy has changed, heralding a change in mind sets. Open markets are also opening minds to business opportunities.

- However, for an attractive locale for innovation, it is not just the individual brilliance or capability that is relevant, but the numbers available for team effort and for multi-disciplinary work. Herein lies India's potential advantage. An example from the pharmaceutical industry or bio-technology area will make this clear. Work in these disciplines requires sufficient numbers of skilled scientists to pursue a specific track. Further, the development of, say, a new molecule in pharma necessarily requires pursuit of many tracks, of which only one may be productive and the others abandoned. Often you also require a pool of multi-disciplinary specialists: physicians, pharmaceutical scientists, pathologists, chemists—to take one example. The ready availability of professionals in such streams and that too at relatively lower levels of remuneration is a distinct advantage that India can offer. Further, the availability of laboratories and even patients for trials, if we are sufficiently organized, will be a contributing factor.

Globalization

- Globalization and the flattening of the work-world in Tom Friedman's sense should give India additional advantages. First, there may be cost cutting in terms of locale and remunerations. These are well known in terms of outsourcing business processes. But increasingly, more complex and sophisticated work elements such as investment analysis or legal research are being handled in India with cost and speed benefits. The next step is for chunks of work to be undertaken in India in an autonomous manner but as a part of a global enterprise.
- The large Indian market (even if we focus only on the Indian middle class) means that there is a certain basic viability to look at India in terms of its domestic market potential. An additional aspect is the growing consciousness of finding the markets at the 'Bottom of the Pyramid' i.e. to find ways in which millions are enabled to buy a new product at a low price point. It would appear that with imagination and innovation, newer business models can be found to tap the large and growing Indian market.

- The upshot of some of these factors is to make India an attractive destination in bringing down the cost of innovation. The quantitative and the qualitative aspects mentioned above taken together makes India a suitable locale and a partner in the global innovation chain.

Recent studies and examples do indeed suggest that the factors outlined above are in fact at work and that there is a potential for India to get at least a slice of the innovation market. In 2006, a study commissioned by NASSCOM and done by the professional consulting firm Booze Allen showed that Engineering Services Outsourcing (ESO) is a high growth area in the years to come, and that India can undertake $40 billion of ESO work by the year 2020. The study details how customized engineering and detailed product design and development can be located in India by global companies with significant cost reductions and value addition. It also has a number of examples from aero-space and the automotive components industry to illustrate work of this nature already being done.

KPO

An earlier study in 2004 by Evalueserve on *India's transformation to knowledge-based economy* stresses the potential in Knowledge Process Outsourcing (KPO), a concept broader than BPO or even ESO. Varied work of this nature in which India may have an advantage include medical diagnostics, financial analytics, legal back-office processes including the highly knowledge-based work relating to intellectual property laws and in digital media technologies. In recent years we have fascinating examples of India being a hub for animation or graphics. In the broad areas of Life sciences, there are many examples of laboratory work, clinical trials and specialized manufacturing being undertaken on a contractual basis.

But even knowledge outsourcing at its best is a form of outsourcing and the ownership of the product or process still stays with the corporate giants outside India. The next phase has to be ownership, executing the full innovation cycle and coming up with innovation models that are uniquely Indian. The large size of the market, the emphasis on low prices and the need for distinct delivery models may influence the innovations originating in India. An example is the Jaipur artificial foot that was developed taking into account the Indian climatic conditions, habits (sitting on the floor and not

Photo credit L K Sharma

The famous Silicon Valley restaurant where during the dot.com boom, venture capitalists committed millions of dollars on the basis of business plans written on paper napkins.

on chairs), style of footwear (chappals or sandals and not shoes), affordability and utility. A recent example on a large manufacturing scale is the Tata Nano car built with the Indian market in mind but with a number of patented innovations in design and engineering. It would appear that the car is also capable of capturing markets in other developing countries with some adaptations. In the area of services there are many more examples of innovation ranging from delivery models: for example, the fabled Bombay *dabbawalah* system for lunch delivery; educational i.e. tutorial services to the US using the webcam; customer care to clients all over the world; micro-credit programs to tap the rural consumer and many more.

The constraints in unleashing greater innovation are the familiar ones. We still lack a close connection between industry and academia, between laboratories and industrial applications. As was noted earlier, this is indeed one of the big strengths of the Silicon Valley, and is conspicuously absent in India. In the last year alone, there was an exploration of this aspect at the first ever meet of the venerable Indian Institute of Science (IISC) alumni and also at the Pan-IIT meet. Institutional exchanges with the US, both governmental and industry-specific, may provide some best practices in building such a nexus.

Another aspect mentioned as a constraint by the Silicon Valley professionals is the relative absence of mentors and networks. This may be a question of developing them over a period of time and attaining a critical mass. Organizations such as The Indus Entrepreneurs (TiE) with extensive experience in the Silicon Valley and with many branches in India can play a catalytic role along with Indian organizations such as the CII, FICCI, NASSCOM. The venture capital industry is currently focused on profitable opportunities in India and it is realistic to hope that this aspect may change in the years to come. There is the formidable obstacle of infrastructural constraints, but this is a challenge affecting all aspects of growth and transformation.

As the historian Ramachandra Guha says in his book *India after Gandhi* in another context, an evaluation of India's possibilities and potential makes one say that our record is always "fifty-fifty". There are aspects and attributes that give India a rich potential. There are known and familiar obstacles which makes one conclude that the potential is underutilized. It is to be hoped that we will see a gathering of the momentum and a garnering of the benefits from innovation in the coming years. In that endeavour, India's existing Silicon Valley connection can be a big advantage. □

Chidanand Rajghatta
Foreign Editor
The Times of India

Upswing in US-India relations

On an improbably warm winter afternoon in Washington DC in early 2008, G Madhavan Nair, Chairman of the Indian Space Research Organization (ISRO), looked down from a podium at an event hosted by the Center for Strategic and International Studies, a policy institution in the US Capital, which, it is said, has more think-tanks than Ethiopia has tanks. Arrayed before him was a group of distinguished scientists, policy wonks and government officials. There was nothing imposing about Nair, a chubby, avuncular man with a distinct Malayali accent. But there was something very striking and unusual at the luncheon tables. Each of the dozen tables bore an Indian name in a rather bold and assertive show of confidence.

Just how forceful this display was became even more apparent when the event's host, Teresina Schaffer, a retired diplomat who has served extensively in South Asia, recalled the decades-long frosty ties between the United States and India, especially in the realm of space sciences. "The fact that we are even having this event is really an excellent illustration of the revolution that has taken place in US-India relations in the past 15 years," Schaffer exulted. "When I was in the government, space was basically taboo, as was advanced technological cooperation in other areas. There were severe restrictions... anything that involved getting stuff off the Earth was strictly off limits."

Nair, anchored in terra firma, made no mention of the decade-plus long US sanctions that tried to crimp India's space programme or Washington's pressures on Moscow not to transfer cryogenic engine technology that would have boosted Indian efforts in the early 1990s. Instead, the ISRO chief mused about the early days of India's space programme in the sixties, when, as a young scientist involved in the fledging efforts, he was inspired by VOA broadcasts of Neil Armstrong's landing on the moon. "We were still launching pencil rockets when you were landing on the moon," he told the Americans, winning them with good-natured flattery.

Visibly stirred, the audience broke into warm applause. One participant declared that the US private sector was totally opposed to the sanctions against India. Gradually, without fuss, Nair revealed a new paradigm to those who believed that technology trade is a one-way traffic from the US to India and that he had come to ask for technology transfers. India, the ISRO chairman told the audience that hung on to his every accented word, was in a different league now. It launches satellites at arguably the lowest cost in the world. Indian rockets had carried payloads for Italy and Israel, and many other countries' payloads were in the pipeline. Much of the western world was still digesting the impact of the Tata's showcasing the $2500 Nano.

A day later, having won a key public relations battle and planted the little germ of an idea in Washington DC that the Indian space programmed could do a 'Nano,' on the world, Nair and his team flew down to Kennedy Space Center in Cape Canaveral, Florida, to meet NASA administrator Michael Griffin. There, the signing of a pact on space cooperation was a mere formality because the nuts and bolts were already in place, put together over a three year period starting 2004. Scientists were scuttling between NASA and ISRO, carting two American payloads for the *Chandrayaan-I* Moon mission—a Miniature Synthetic Aperture Radar to map ice deposits in the Moon's surface and a Moon

Mineralogy Mapper to assess mineral resources of the Moon. It was the first time US instruments were included aboard an Indian space vehicle.

What was remarkable about the development was not that it happened, but how long it took for it to happen. After all, the Indian space programme, as Nair himself acknowledged, was inspired by American advances. So profound was NASA's influence on the Indian programme, and the Indian involvement in NASA in the early days, that it eventually gave rise to an urban myth—to the effect that some 35 per cent of all NASA personnel in the US were Indians (some similar percentage was ascribed to the Indian presence in Microsoft). Indeed, a significant and disproportionately large percentage (in relation to their population in US) of engineers in both NASA and Microsoft are of Indian origin.

Influx of Indian talent

In part, this has to do with the steady influx of Indian scientific and engineering talent to the United States, going back to the 1960s. Those were the halcyon years of US-India cooperation in science and technology, when, recovering from the early Cold War stutter in the 1950s, Washington took a fancy to New Delhi in the days after the Indian drubbing at the hands of China in the 1962 border spat. Not only did the US help kick-start India's space and nuclear power programmes, but it helped India overcome its anaemic foodgrains production by deploying the peerless Dr Norman Borlaug to launch the Green Revolution.

Unfortunately, that period of goodwill dried up rather suddenly in the 1970s when the war for the liberation of Bangladesh pitted India against Richard Nixon who viewed India with deep suspicion. Political instability and Cold War afflictions in both the US and India through much of the seventies and into the mid-80s sapped the two sides and cooperation in science and technology was sporadic and spotty. A brief revival in the late 1980s under a forward-looking and ideologically unshackled Rajiv Gandhi was quickly cut short amid turmoil in India. By the time India conducted its Shakti series of nuclear tests in May 1998, government-to-government ties in technology cooperation were negligible, with the one signature item, a tie-up for the Light Combat Aircraft, also hamstrung by political inertia.

Remarkably, through all these years of drought in the political, diplomatic and military sphere, one thing did not change. In

fact, if anything, unencumbered by political masters, it got accelerated. For more than four decades after the United States relaxed its immigration policy in 1965 to allow more Asians into the country, Indian professionals, particularly physicians, engineers, and scientists had arrived in droves and spread far and wide across America. Many of them came as graduate students and spread out into academia, often taking up teaching and research jobs at great institutions such as MIT and Carnegie Mellon. Others moved into government institutions such as NASA and NIH, and still others into national labs such as Brookhaven, Sandia, and Oakridge. Many thrived in the private sector, including in such legendary tech crucibles such as Bell Labs, General Electric, IBM and a host of new, cutting edge companies in Silicon Valley.

By some estimates, the US has trained and absorbed more than half a million Indian professionals in medicine, science, engineering and technology, many of whom have begun to trickle back to India. More than the numbers, it is the social, economic and academic profile of Indians in the US—and increasingly elsewhere in the world—that is the envy of other nations. Indians have the highest educational qualifications of all ethnic groups in the US, native-born Americans included. Almost 60 per cent of all Indians have a bachelor's or higher degree (compared to 28 per cent nationally). Almost 40 per cent of all Indians have a master's, doctorate or other professional degree, which is five times the national average. Indians have the highest median household income ($68,771 in 2004 compared to a nationwide $46,326). They are the second largest pool of doctors (more than 50,000), engineers (more than 100,000), and academic/teaching professionals in the US after native born Americans.

A recent Duke University - UC Berkeley study revealed that Indian immigrants have founded more engineering and technology companies from 1995 to 2005 than immigrants from the UK, China, Taiwan and Japan combined. They accounted for 25 per cent of all immigrant-founded companies. The study also reported that one-third of the engineers in Silicon Valley are of Indian descent, while 7 per cent of valley hi-tech firms are led by Indian CEOs. Even as far back as 2000, an eon in today's tech economy-on-steroids, *Fortune* estimated the wealth generated by Indian Silicon Valley entrepreneurs at around $250 billion. A 2003

Merrill Lynch study reported that one in every nine Indians in the US is a millionaire, comprising 10 per cent of US millionaires.

It was a brain bank; an intellectual treasure trove that few other countries had developed.

At the turn of the century, a confluence of cataclysmic events and strategic inclinations brought about a dramatic change in US-India dynamics. The Cold War ended in the late 1980s and the so-called war on terror—essentially a battle against extremism—had begun. The 1999 Kargil clash showed India as a victim of state-sponsored terrorism, and it unexpectedly helped overcome US anger and dismay over India's overt 1998 nuclear test. It was also the time Indian-Americans attained critical mass in the US in terms of their impact in science and technology. Shortly before he left office, Bill Clinton visited India to signal not just a thawing, but a warming up of ties. He bowed out of office before the delirium caused by his visit to India (who responded enthusiastically to his overtures) had subsided. But the hysteria his smooth talk had induced was parlayed in to cold 21st century geo-strategic re-alignment by the Republican neo-cons who succeeded him.

Resumption

By 2004, the tentative resumption and acceleration of ties in the field of science and technology was being codified in the so-called Next Steps in Strategic Partnership (NSSP) announced by US President George W Bush and the then Prime Minister Atal Bihari Vajpayee. The NSSP Initiative called for cooperation between the United States and India in High Technology, in Civilian Nuclear Activities, and in Civilian Space programmes. Within months, even those steps were deemed inadequate, as Washington openly sought strategic re-alignment to rope India into its sphere of influence. While the US moves were still being deliberated and digested in New Delhi, the last of the technology regime embargo was being whittled down. Indian scientists, from Nair to his predecessor Kasturirangan to R Chidambaram, who once faced the ignominy of being denied an American visa in the days after the nuclear tests, were being welcomed in the US.

American scientists too, particularly those of Indian ethnicity, began to travel and engage more frequently with their Indian counterparts. "The difference between now and a decade back is that India is now seen as a happening place," explains Ananth Dodabalapur, a University of

Texas nanotechnology expert who has begun visiting India more often to interact with his Indian counterparts. "There is a lot of energy, a lot of dynamism. We are also getting to see a lot more Indian scientists at international conferences and meetings." Tom Kailath, a doyen among engineering studies teachers (and professor emeritus at Stanford), believes nearly half the residents at Stanford Medical College are of Indian origin—either immigrants from India or first generation Indian-Americans. There is not a conference that Kailath goes to where he is not struck by the sheer number of Indians (and Chinese).

Such interaction is what has led Dodabalapur, Kailath and others to increasingly accept teaching assignments in India. More recently, Dodabalapur has also been able to invite young Indian PhD students to UT, Austin, a far cry from the days immediately after the nuclear tests when exchanges in critical areas were frowned upon. Eventually, he says, such exchanges will morph into greater innovation and commercial activity—for e.g. "If Suzlon can become a world leader in wind energy, how long before an Indian company takes the lead in solar cells given the country's inherent advantage in cost and demographics?"

The idea that two countries with complementary strengths in science and technology are finally teaming up is something that is driving both industry and academia to transports of delight. Shortly after the space event at CSIS, Ron Somers, one of the most experienced India hands in Washington DC who now heads the US-India Business Council, gushed "That the United States and India are cooperating at this level of space exploration marks the beginning of a whole new era of trust and partnership. The *Chandrayaan* lunar mission will lead to exciting scientific advances. The strides that the US and India can make together as partners in space will advance tele-medicine, tele-education, and disaster preparedness/management." In part, this optimism was based not only on the vast pool of Indian scientists, engineers and technologists who had made the US their home and roamed the world, but also the death of distance and the breaking down of barriers.

US-India cooperation in science and technology goes back much further than is generally realized, in part because much of our national legacy is tied to Britain, our political forbears, rather than to America, our font of innovation. India's first large hydroelectric plant at Sivasamudram spanning the Cauvery owes its origins to the power plants around the Niagara Falls, the region where celebrated American companies such as General Electric and Westinghouse pioneered electricity in the late 19th century based on the work of brilliant inventors such as Thomas Edison and Nicholas Tesla.

In fact, both these scientists were known to Indians who travelled to the United States in those days. Swami Vivekananda met Tesla (in the eyes of many a greater genius but a lesser entrepreneur than Edison) at the Chicago World Fair on the sidelines of the World Religious Conference in 1893. Vivekananda's successor in the US, Swami Abhedananda, called on Edison in New York several years later. Not much is known about these meetings, but evidently Indians were quite aware of the magnificent feats and developments in the US in the field of engineering and technology.

In 1880, just a couple of years after Edison lit the first electric bulb and jigged the first electricity transmission lines in upstate New York, the British struck gold in Kolar, India. But the auriferous veins ran to great depths and the British needed something less expensive and more reliable than coal and steam powered equipment for the deep-shaft operations. Trust the Americans to market new technology even in those days. Such was the entrepreneurial spirit in the post-civil war United States that Edison himself registered more than a thousand patents.

And so it transpired that in 1902, after several years of negotiations, Edison's General Electric was commissioned by the then Mysore State to build the first hydroelectric installation at Cauvery Falls. Mysore retained one of General Electric's engineers, Harry Parker Gibbs, as the Chief Electrical Engineer of the State's new Electrical Department, and sent four Indian members of the departmental staff to GE's headquarters in Schnectady, New York for training. So GE's connection to India goes a long way back, predating both Scott Bayman (till recently the GE honcho in India) and the outsourcing flap.

While this was going on, Jamshedji Tata visited Pittsburg in 1901 and buttonholed Julian Kennedy, one of the foremost metallurgical engineers in the world and head of the Julian Kennedy, Sahlin and Co. Ltd. Engineers to discuss the prospect of setting up a steel factory in India. Tata gained much from Kennedy's advice and the firm was appointed

construction engineer to the Tata Iron and Steel Co. (TISCO) in 1907. All in all, it appears that tech transfer from the US to India was far easier in those days. Something for today's mandarins to ponder.

Power and steel were the drivers of US-India cooperation in those early days. Around the same time as Edison and his electricity frisson, the legendary Sir Mokshagundam Visvesvaraya visited the United States and travelled across the country to see some of the most awesome engineering marvels including the Tennessee Valley Authority (TVA). That multipurpose project inspired Mysore's Krishna Raja Sagar (KRS) dam and other works in the Cauvery basin, scene of much recent squabbling between Karnataka and Tamil Nadu.

American advances

American advances in science and technology captured the imagination of a whole generation of Indians, even as vast numbers joined the political movement for Independence from Britain. In fact, as far back as 1885, a young woman named Anandibai Joshee went to the US to earn a medical degree at a Pennsylvania medical school, becoming the first woman physician in India. Unfortunately, she died on her return to India and never practised.

In 1912, a young science graduate from the University of Punjab made his way to the University of California in Berkeley as a research fellow. He meant to go back to India after his academic stint, but the First World War broke out even as the first stirrings of India's independence movement swept down from the Pacific Northwest, fanned by Punjabi immigrants. In time, Gobind Behari Lal, who began a writing career by joining the San Francisco Examiner in 1925, became a leading voice in America for India's independence and a celebrated science correspondent. By the time he died of cancer in 1982 at the age of 92, his more than half-century of science journalism had produced interviews with a range of eminences such as Albert Einstein and Enrico Fermi, and the first ever Pulitzer Prize for a South Asian.

He was the first American journalist to use the term 'science writer' with his byline, among the first to write on cancer research, and in 1940, he became the founder-president of the National Association of Science Writers. "My interest is to create among the readers a lust for the knowledge of science, which destroys superstition and all kind of false assumption and raises the power of the human brain," he said in an interview shortly before his death. For his efforts, besides the Pulitzer, Lal won the 1946 George Westinghouse Award from the American Association for the Advancement of Science, a 1958 distinguished service award from the American Medical Association and a Guggenheim fellowship in 1956. The Indian government too honored him with a Padma Bhushan and a Tamra Patra.

Around the same time that Lal began blazing a trail in science writing, another young scientist was starting a career in medicine and pharmacology that would highlight early Indian work in the United States. Yellapragada Subba Rao flunked matriculation three times before he managed to enter Madras Medical College, where he incurred the displeasure of his British superiors by wearing a khadi surgical gown in response to Mahatma Gandhi's call.

Rao went to the United States, earned a diploma from the Harvard School of Tropical Medicine and joined Harvard as a junior faculty member. He made a series of rapid medical breakthroughs while working on his PhD. He was credited, along with Cyrus Fiske, with developing a method for estimation of phosphorus in body fluids and tissues and discovering the role of Phosphocreatine and Adenosine Triphosphate (ATP) in muscular activity.

Denied a regular faculty position at Harvard, he joined Lederle Laboratories and went on to develop a method to synthesize Folic Acid. He is also credited with developing the important anti-cancer drug Methotrexate, still in widespread clinical use today, and the drug Hetrazan which was used by WHO against filariasis. Together with Benjamin Duggar, Rao developed the world's first tetracycline antibiotic, Aureomycin, in 1945. This discovery was made as a result of the largest distributed scientific experiment ever performed until then, when American GIs who fought all over the world at the end of WWII were instructed to collect soil samples from wherever they were, and bring them back for screening at Lederle Laboratories for possible anti-bacterial agents from natural soil fungae.

Remarkably, Rao remained a non-resident alien in America and an Indian national, right up to his premature death in 1948 at the relatively young age of 53, even though he led some sensitive World War II related research. In fact, more recent re-assessment of his work

suggests that he was never really given full credit for his achievements, and he died largely unhonoured and unsung, while some of his peers went on to win the Nobel.

The Nobel did not elude S Chandrasekhar. Hans Bethe, a fellow Nobel Laureate and eminent physicist described Chandrasekhar as "one of the great astrophysicists of our time." His most famous discovery was that not all stars end up as white dwarf stars, but those retaining mass above a certain limit—today known as 'Chandrasekhar's Limit', undergo further collapse. His detailed mathematical papers and books on a wide variety of astrophysical subjects, including, for example, black holes, are classic references for research at every level. NASA honoured Chandrasekhar by naming its important orbiting X-ray observatory after him. Chandra X-ray Observatory, a satellite launched by NASA in 1999, continues to explore the invisible universe and send significant observations.

Nobel laureate

Hargobind Khorana, molecular biologist, won the Nobel Prize in 1968 for his work on the interpretation of the genetic code and its function in protein synthesis. Another eminent Indian scientist George Sudarshan is the distinguished former director of the Center for Particle Theory at the University of Texas, Austin. Among his discoveries was the first theory of the weak nuclear force.

Sudarshan, Khorana and a host of other scientists, engineers, researchers and physicians came to the US in the sixties, following the footsteps of Joshee, Lal and Rao. C Kumar Patel's name will be written in the history of laser development. This generation of Indian immigrants included Hal Iyengar and Narendar Kampany. It was a generation that had to struggle hard to overcome barriers, personal and professional. Not only were the United States and India geo-politically misaligned, but the chasm between them was as much geographical as ideological. The common strain of democracy was not sufficient to overcome the distance of hearts and minds.

The 1990s changed everything dramatically and rapidly. The ending of the Cold War segued with the start of the Internet, or more broadly, the telecom revolution. Distance died. Suddenly, India's disadvantage of being on the opposite side of the globe turned out to be a big plus, enabling a 24/7 working day. Long seen as a colonial burden or hangover that threatened Indian cultural and linguistic sensitivity and diversity, English suddenly became one of India's assets. As India liberalized and America sought new partners and allies, people, ideas, and innovations flowed back and forth. General Electric, the American legend that for decades understated its century old ties with India, opened the Jack Welch Technology Center in Bangalore, its first research centre outside the US, employing more than 5000 top-notch researchers. IBM, kicked out unceremoniously in 1977, today has its second highest work force outside the US in India—70,000 and climbing. Likewise, Cisco System, Microsoft, Google and a host of other companies. Today, there is hardly a major American technology company that does not have an India footprint. And increasingly, more and more Indian companies are now starting to have a Western, mostly American footprint.

Dividing time

Such traffic is what keeps P Anandan, Director of Microsoft Research in Bangalore, India, in airplanes and airports for about 40 days in a year. Anandan is one of the new breed of technology professionals who increasingly have one foot in India and the other in America, an occurrence so routine that is necessitated a non-stop service between the Silicon Valley hub of San Francisco with its formerly poor cousin in India, Bangalore, now regarded as a symbol of booming India. An IIT graduate who took the usual graduate school route to the US, Anandan maintains a home in the Pacific Northwest close to Microsoft's Redmond headquarters, and in Bangalore, where the famed US firm, often accused of predatory practices, does some innovative ground-level research and development.

Increasingly, US industry and academia is turning to India and China to advance innovation, not always with a philanthropic motive and clearly with an eye on the huge market in the two countries, which between them account for 40 per cent of the world's population. Much of this is being addressed in the US by researchers of Indian and Chinese origin, whose rising numbers provide a stark contrast to the decline of interest among native born Americans in mathematics and science.

Hardly a week goes by in the US without the announcement of a technological breakthrough or innovation by a US-based Indian researcher, often with applications in India. A typical example is when researchers at Massachusetts

Institute of Technology and Texas Instruments unveiled a new chip design for portable electronics that can be up to 10 times more energy-efficient than present technology, one of the lead researchers was an Indian, Anantha Chandrakasan, and among his collaborators were graduate students Yogesh Ramadass and Naveen Varma. The team's design could lead to battery power in cell phones, implantable medical devices and sensors lasting far longer.

In fact, MIT's annual list of tech innovators now routinely includes at least a half-dozen researchers of Indian origin in their Young Innovator list. Many of these innovations are not US-specific or trendy rocket science stuff, but related organically to the needs of the poor in developing countries such as India. Among the winners in 2007 was Tapan Parikh, a doctoral student in computer science at the University of Washington, who carried the idea of mobile telephony for small business a step further by developing what he terms a 'Cam' (so-called because the phone's camera plays a key role in the user interface), a toolkit that makes it simple to use phones to capture images and scan documents, enter and process data, and run interactive audio and video. Cam is aimed at taking advantage of modern phones' computing capabilities.

Microfinance

Parikh's Cam project has focused on perhaps the trendiest field in economic development: microfinance, in which lending groups grant tiny loans in developing countries, typically to fund small-business ventures. The best-publicized version of microfinance involves a solo entrepreneur getting a small loan from a well-financed bank. But Parikh is collaborating with organizations that are more representative of the way it usually works. A big chunk of the microfinance business in India, for example, is conducted by self-help groups, in which 15 to 20 people (usually women) pool their capital and then meet weekly or monthly to make collective decisions about loans to members of the group. They also use their collective borrowing power to obtain loans from nongovernmental aid organizations or from financial institutions, and then lend that money to their members.

Parikh has built a software system on top of Cam to assist self-help groups in managing their information and their operations. Unglamorously called SHGMIS (self-help group management and information system), it includes a Cam-based application for entering and processing data, a text-messaging tool for uploading data to online databases, and a package of web-based software for managing data and reporting it to any institution that has lent money to the self-help group. Such groups have traditionally relied on paper documentation. Because their members still trust paper, the software also includes a bar-code-based system. Loan applications, grants, receipts, and other documents are printed with identifying bar codes; the software enables the phone to scan the code, identify the document, photograph it, process the data it contains, and associate that data with the code. The result is a system that facilitates a quick and accurate flow of data from small villages to bigger cities, and vice versa.

Like Parikh, Chandrakasan and his team keep the unique needs and constraints of the developing world in view as they work on innovative new technology. For instance, in their work on the new chip, the key to the improvement in energy efficiency was to find ways of making the circuits on the chip work at a voltage level much lower than usual. While most current chips operate at around one volt, the new design works at just 0.3 volts. Reducing the operating voltage, however, is not as simple as it might sound, because existing microchips have been optimized for many years to operate at the higher standard voltage level. One of the biggest problems the team had to overcome was the variability that occurs in typical chip manufacturing. At lower voltage levels, variations and imperfections in the silicon chip become more problematic. Eventually, says Chandrakasan, the goal is to make the power requirements so low that they could be powered by 'ambient energy', in some applications, such as implantable medical devices where the body's own heat or movement could provide the needed power.

Defence research

Remarkably, despite the profound mistrust and disconnect that has dogged the political and strategic relationship between the United States and India, many of the Indian-inspired innovations have been funded by grants from the US Defense Advance Research Projects Agency (DARPA) and have military applications. Chandrakasan and his team's chip advances for instance can result in the production of tiny, self-contained sensor networks that could be dispersed in a battlefield. At Nextgen Aeronautics in Torrance, California, founder

Jayanth Kudva is working towards the design and fabrication of antenna arrays for military aircraft, while associate Akhilesh Jha is intent upon reducing the weight of weapon systems using genetic algorithms for a proposed software design. Also at Nextgen, Shiv Joshi has proposed the use of a self-powered, compact, light, wireless sensor that takes advantage of advances in fabrication technologies and inventive packaging to reduce system cost to the point that the sensor is disposable. Elsewhere, Ravi Vaidyanathan of BioRobots in Cleveland, Ohio, is partnering with Boeing and Case Western Reserve University to develop a biologically inspired morphing micro air-land vehicle (MMALV) to enhance military intelligence gathering capabilities in battlespace environments. Shyama Chakroborty of Microcosm Inc. in El Segundo, CA, is working with Lockheed Martin, the Air Force, and the California Space Authority to design and develop a low-cost liquid-fuelled rocket engine that will be used in various launch vehicles at Edwards Air Force Base.

A detailed analysis of awards from Small Business Innovation Research (SBIR) programmes announced for 2004, and funded by agencies such as the Army, Navy, Air Force, DARPA (Defense Advanced Research Projects Agency), and BMDO (Ballistic Missile Defense Office), conducted by researchers Francis Assisi and Elizabeth Pothen revealed that 75 out of 470 research projects, or 16 per cent of the total research effort, was by scientists and engineers of Indian origin. A similar survey of the Small Business Technology Transfer (STTR) programmes funded by the DoD for 2003 showed that Indian Americans were involved in 25 per cent, of the research programmes for the Missile Defense agency. Overall the study reveals that Indian American scientists are playing key roles in transforming the US military into a smarter force for the 21st century.

However, vestiges of suspicion and mistrust remain, often given life by spasmodic episodes of illegal high-tech transfers. At the height of the talks on the US-India nuclear deal, an Indian businessman Parthasarathy Sudarshan was charged with violating US export control laws to supply high-tech electronic items to India's defence programmes—among them, vintage microprocessors and commonplace items which anachronistically remain on the US export control list. Such episodes, which are said to violate various US export control laws and technical alert lists, cause paroxysms of anxiety among Washington DC's non-proliferation lobby while keeping them gainfully occupied, even as the two countries try and build bridges at the highest level.

Ironically, Assisi and Pothen in their analysis show that if the US Technical Alert List were in place, none of the scientists working in the defence space whose projects they examined would have received an American visa in the first place. That list, as it now stands, precludes students from pursuing advanced research in every one of the strategically important areas identified by the US Department of State as 'sensitive', including: missile technology, navigation and guidance control, remote imaging and reconnaissance, materials technology, information security, lasers and directed energy systems, sensors, robotics, advanced ceramics, and munitions—all technology areas where Indian American scientists have a strong presence.

Eventually, the sheer weight of the achievements and the demographic dividend that makes the Indian diaspora the largest pool of scientific and engineering workers in the US after native-born Americans is expected to shift attitudes and policies. In the last few years, Indians have been routinely honoured by the White House with the National Medal for Technology, the country's highest civilian honor in the field. Among the honorees—Arun Netravali, formerly of Bell Labs, for his many contributions including development of the High-Definition Television, Ford's Haren Gandhi for his work on catalytic convertors, and Padmasree Warrior, formerly of Motorola and currently Cisco Systems' CTO, for her work in telecommunication technology. Many such luminaries are now dual citizens, in practice at least, as they shuttle between the United States and India, building bridges between the two countries. □

Chidanand Rajghatta, based in Washington, is the author of *The Horse That Flew: How India's Silicon Gurus Spread Their Wings*.

Innovative Indians of America

Amar Bose honoured

Amar Bose, who made an Indian surname a global brand in the accoustics technology industry, has ben industed into America's National Inventors Hall of Fame. The only other Indian in this Hall of Fame is Rangaswamy Srinivasan, a former IBM scientist named for his pioneering work on excimer laser surgery.

IBM researcher is Brookhaven Director

Praveen Chaudhari, a scientist who has spent all 36 years of his career as a researcher and manager at IBM, has been named the new director of the Brookhaven National Laboratory, one of the world's foremost scientific organizations and home to five Nobel Prize laureates.

At IBM, Dr Chaudhari, 65, oversaw major laboratory operations in New York, California and Switzerland. Research under his supervision became the basis of the 2 billion-dollar-a-year optical disk industry and helped win two Nobel Prizes in physics, one in 1986 for developing the scanning tunneling microscope and another in 1987 for discovering high-temperature superconductivity in a new class of materials.

Dr Chaudhari has studied amorphous solids, defects in solids, and superconductivity. He has published over 160 technical papers and holds 22 patents. Dr Chaudhari was born in Ludhiana, and has degrees from the Indian Institute of Technology and the Massachusetts Institute of Technology.

National Academy member

R Paul Singh, distinguished professor of food engineering at the University of California, Davis, whose research has applications in areas ranging from food processing to space exploration, has been elected to the National Academy of Engineering. This is one of the highest professional distinctions for engineers in the US.

Singh holds a joint appointment in the departments of Biological and Agricultural Engineering and Food Science and Technology. A member of the UC Davis faculty since 1975, Singh has a distinguished portfolio of discoveries in energy conservation, post-harvest technology, freezing preservation, and mass transfer in food processing. His laboratory is currently working on the design and development of food processing equipment for NASA's manned mission to Mars. The research team is also conducting studies related to fluid flow and heat transfer during

thawing and freezing and is designing packaging systems that will allow more efficient cooling of strawberries.

Singh received in 2007 the Kishida International Award from the American Society of Agricultural and Biological Engineers. The award recognizes Singh's visionary leadership and outstanding contributions to teaching, research and technology transfer in food science and engineering worldwide. He was elected to the Food Engineering Hall of Fame in 2003, and in 2000 was selected as a fellow in both the Institute of Food Technologists and the American Society of Agricultural Engineers.

Singh earned his doctorate in engineering from Michigan State University in 1974. He also holds a master's degree from the University of Wisconsin-Madison, and a bachelor's degree from Punjab Agricultural University, India, both in agricultural engineering. He is editor-in-chief of the *Journal of Food Engineering*.

New Dean of MIT

Subra Suresh—an IIT Madras alumnus—has been appointed Dean of—arguably the world's most prestigious engineering school at Massachusetts Institute of Technology.

Of course, some of America's top business schools have also had Indians as deans.

Subra Suresh is the Ford Professor of Engineering in the Department of Materials Science and Engineering. A 1977 graduate of the IIT Madras, Suresh received a master's from Iowa State University in 1979 before pursuing doctoral studies at MIT, where he received the Sc.D. in 1981. After two years of postdoctoral research at the University of California at Berkeley, he joined the faculty at Brown University, where he rose to the rank of professor of engineering in 1989 before returning to MIT.

An MIT statement said Suresh's prior and ongoing work has led to seminal contributions in the area of nano-and micro-scale mechanical properties of engineered materials. Last year, he received the Acta Materialia Gold Medal for "pioneering research" into the mechanical properties of materials and was selected by MIT's Technology Review magazine as one of the ten scientists whose research will have "a significant impact on business, medicine or culture" in the years ahead.

Among its more famous Indian alumni is Har Gobind Khorana, who shared the Nobel Prize for

Medicine/ Physiology in 1968. Other well-known Indian alumni at MIT include Amar Bose, who founded Bose Corporation, Suhas Patil, who founded the company Cirrus Logic, the late Prof Brahm Prakash of ISRO, and Dr Dara Antia, who founded the Indian Institute of Metals.

Prof Suresh acknowledged his debt to the rich legacy of Indian culture. He recalled that his mother, who did not go to college, insisted that he qualify for IIT, even though she did not know much about it at that time. "It is something cultural...studying science and engineering is seen as a ticket to success," he said.

Harvard institution builder

Venkatesh Narayanamurti announced that he would relinquish his charge as Dean of the Harvard School of Engineering and Applied Sciences (SEAS). He directed for 10 years the renewal and expansion of this former division and its transition to a School. "Venky's leadership has had a genuinely transformative impact on engineering and applied sciences at Harvard," said Harvard President Drew Faust. "He has in many ways been both the architect and the chief engineer of Harvard's newest School, and his vision, energy, and instinct for collaboration have strengthened our capacity and elevated our sights in a vital academic domain."

As Dean, Narayanamurti guided remarkable gains in the recruitment of junior and senior faculty. Sponsored research has grown 60 percent over the 10 years of Narayanamurti's leadership. Narayanamurti was an early champion of interdisciplinary initiatives and collaboration.

An accomplished scientist and administrative leader who bridged private industry and academia, Narayanamurti maintained an active research group in nanoscience and technology throughout his deanship. Prior to coming to Harvard, he served as dean of the College of Engineering at the University of California, Santa Barbara, from 1992 to 1998. For five years before that, he was vice president of research and exploratory technology at Sandia National Laboratories. From 1968 to 1987, he was with AT&T Bell Laboratories as director of the Solid State Electronics Research Laboratory from 1981 to 1987.

Narayanamurti holds bachelor's and master's degrees in physics from the University of Delhi, and a PhD in physics from Cornell University. He

has served on numerous national and international advisory committees and is a member of the National Academy of Engineering and the Royal Swedish Academy of Engineering Sciences. He is a fellow of the American Academy of Arts and Sciences, the American Physical Society, the American Association for the Advancement of Science, the Institute of Electrical and Electronics Engineers, and the Indian Academy of Sciences.

NASA Center

Dr Meyya Meyyappan is the Director of the Center for Nanotechnology, Ames Research Center. The Center was started by NASA it with a small group in 1996 and expanded gradually become the largest in-house nanotechnology effort within the government, and it is also one of the largest in the world.

Dr Meyyappan's team is researching and developing carbon nanotubes. The Center has been working on nanoelectronics and computing. It has been developing nanotechnology-based sensors and detectors, and utilizing nano-technology in gene sequencing. "Our project focus is primarily material-driven and we are looking at a variety of nanoscale materials. The first and the major focus is on carbon nanotubes."

Scientist patents life-form

For the first time ever, in 1980, the US Patent and Trademark Office issued the patent to Ananda Chakrabarty on the genetically engineered pseudomonas. It set a precedent for patenting of life and life-forms, including seeds, plants, mice, sheep, cows and even parts of human beings.

As a young scientist at General Electric, Chakrabarty developed the pseudomonas bacterium in his laboratory. The bacterium has the ability to break down crude oil into simpler substances that can serve as food for aquatic life.

It inspired scientists worldwide to experiment with genes and nuclei to create newer species of life. Chakrabarty became a bio-policy maker legal adviser to Supreme Court judges in different countries about research goals of scientists striving to create newer forms of life. He advised the United Nations on these issues.

Chakrabarty had earned his PhD at the University of Calcutta in India in 1965 before coming to the US. □

Chidanand Rajghatta

Arthur Carty
National Science Advisor
Government of Canada

Indo-Canadian ties strengthened

Although Canada has a large Indian diaspora with close to 1 million people of Indian descent in cities and towns across Canada it has become clear to me from my several visits to India as Canada's National Science Advisor, that in general India's citizens know relatively little about Canada, our land, our people, our resources, our culture, the nature of our economy and especially our achievements in science and technology. Surveys have also consistently indicated that while Indians have a nice, fuzzy feeling about Canada and Canadians (mounties, moose and mountains!), few recognize that Canada is a technologically sophisticated country with one of the world's most robust and highly performing economies, a mix of enormous natural resources combined with competitive high tech industrial sectors such as aerospace, information and communications technologies and biotechnology. Indeed a number of Canadian companies are the world leaders in their domains. These companies are underpinned by a highly educated workforce which has the highest percentage of the working age population with post secondary education of any OECD country.

In this article, the intent is to try to portray a picture of Canada's strengths and achievements: in science and technology, economic prowess and in the potential for development. In particular we will focus on the opportunities that exist for cooperation and collaborations in science and technology with India—opportunities which build naturally on complementary strengths, interests and mutual benefit. The historic signing of a country to country Science & Technology Agreement between Canada and India in November 2005, provides a gateway to a partnership which will take the Canada-India relationship to new levels of trust and mutual achievement.

Canada is a big country—the second largest in the world after Russia; 7,000 kilometres from St Johns, Newfoundland in the east to Victoria, British Columbia in the west. With only 33 million people, the population density is very low compared to India—effectively 3.3 people per square kilometre. Canada is resource rich, almost beyond belief: an energy superpower with the second largest reserves of oil in the world after Saudi Arabia and by far the largest supplier of both oil and natural gas to the United States—a fact not well known or appreciated. But resource wealth goes far beyond this. Canada is the world's largest producer and exporter of uranium, the world's largest exporter of potash and zinc, the second largest producer of nickel and the third of aluminium and diamonds. Canada has one third of the earth's boreal forests, 10 per cent of its freshwater and is a major exporter of agri-food crops such as wheat, canola, pulses, flax and barley. With vast tracts of arable land to grow biomass and with new technologies developed by companies such as Iogen and Lignol to convert cellulose into ethanol, Canada is well positioned to become a world leader in converting agricultural and forestry wastes into biofuels, as alternate, low greenhouse gas energy sources. Indeed biofuels, particularly those produced from non-food sources and waste biomass, represent a significant opportunity for R&D collaboration with India.

Although natural resources have long underpinned the Canadian economy and current world demand for primary metals, fossil fuels and materials is driving an economic boom particularly in western Canada, Canadian industry is now highly diversified. In fact, the largest Canadian corporation by market valuation is no longer a bank or a resource company but Research in Motion (RIM), a high-tech giant and maker of the Blackberry wireless e-mail device, with a valuation of more than $60 bn. RIM, located in Waterloo, Ontario is a phenomenal Canadian success story which has grown from a small start-up 10 years ago to a company with annual revenues of $4 bn and growing fast. RIM is part of a very large $140 bn information and communications technology sector (ITC) in Canada which also boasts telecommunication giants Nortel Networks, Bell Canada Enterprises (BCE), Rogers and Telus as well as large software companies such as Open Text and other multinationals including Ericsson and Alcatel-Lucent. Another ITC sector of great strength is multi-media and animation technologies where entrepreneurial small and medium sized enterprises drive new innovations in the marketplace. In fact, the ITC sector is responsible for more than 40 per cent of the $13.16 bn private sector R&D investment in Canada.

Competitive

Canada also has a very competitive high technology manufacturing sector dominated by motor vehicles and parts ($131 bn revenues) and aerospace ($26 bn). In the latter, Canada has the third largest aerospace industry in the world after the USA and EU, with Bombardier being the world's largest manufacturer of regional and business jets.

Finally, the Canadian biotechnology industry ranks second in the world, after the USA, in terms of number of companies (500) and with $3.8 bn in revenues ranks third behind the US and the UK. Excellent scientific infrastructure, a world class health science research community with 30,000 investigators in 16 medical schools and 100 teaching hospitals and institutes provides a strong base for future growth.

In terms of scientific collaboration India and Canada have shared a longstanding relationship going back to the 1950s and 60s. The National Research Council, the Federal Government's principal research organization, hosted many Indian scientists and post-doctoral fellows at its laboratories and institutes across Canada. As an example, Dr Subramanyan Chandrasekhar, one of the foremost astrophysicists of the 20th Century and a Nobel Laureate was a close friend and colleague of Dr Gerhard Hertzberg of NRC, Canada's 1971 Nobel Laureate in Chemistry and Dr Har Gobind Khorana, born in Raipur, took up his first professional appointment at the British Columbia Research Council, winning the Nobel Prize in Medicine in 1968. Other Indian scientists, educated and trained in Canada, retuned to India and rose to high positions in research and administration in India. One very notable example of technological collaboration between India and Canada was the transfer of Candu nuclear reactor technology from Atomic Energy of Canada Limited to the Government of India, kick-starting India's nuclear programme. While this later led to significant tensions between the two countries, many strong scientific connections were cemented in physics, chemistry and engineering as a result of the cooperation and Canada was at that time a prime destination for some of the best young Indian minds.

Full spectrum

Today, the environment in both countries is particularly conducive to enhanced scientific and technological collaboration across the full spectrum of university, government and industrial research. Both countries are investing massively in R&D to foster knowledge creation, innovation and commercialization. For example, in Canada over the 10 years from 1997–98 more than $15 bn of incremental research funding has been invested in university research, producing the highest level of public sector R&D expenditures as a share of GDP in the G7 advanced countries. New programmes such as the Canada Research Chairs, Canada Foundation for Innovation, Genome Canada coupled with a more than doubling of funding for the granting councils and new resources for the Networks of Centres of Excellence has transformed the research environment into one of the most attractive in the world. Many rising young stars and outstanding established scholars have been attracted to Canadian institutions.

India has made dramatic progress, increasing investments in science and technology by 16 per cent in 2006 and 21 per cent in 2007. India has improved its infrastructure for research and is aggressively investing in nanotechnology, biotechnology and pharmaceuticals. The face and pace of science is changing rapidly as technological convergence and the need for interdisciplinary approaches forge new collaborations across international boundaries.

To leverage resources and tap into new knowledge, both India and Canada have been reaching out to build S&T cooperation. The Canada-India S&T Agreement signed in November 2005 between Foreign Affairs and International Trade Canada (DFAIT) and the Department of Science and Technology (DST) provides funding of $6.75 m on both sides for S&T collaboration with the funds administered by the International Science & Technology Partnerships Programme (ISTPP) on the Canadian side and DST in India. A Joint S&T Cooperation Committee is responsible for overseeing and implementing bilateral S&T activities under the Agreement. This committee, with input from missions, workshops and meetings including a high profile Canada-India Technology Summit in Delhi, identified five priority areas for focussed collaborations:

- Biotechnology/Health/Medical Devices
- Sustainable Environmental Technologies and Alternate Energies
- Nanoscience/Nanomedicine
- Information and Communications Technologies (wireless, rural connectivity, infotainment)
- Earth Sciences and Disaster Management.

Each of these areas has a designated coordinator on each side. In setting the stage for collaborative proposals, several joint workshops have been held on: Biofuels; Plants for Human Health; Health Biotechnology—Infectious Diseases and Vaccines, Nanotechnology. Canada's part of the joint programme is being delivered by ISTPCanada, an organization at arm's length from the Government of Canada. A joint call for Expressions of Interest by ISTPCanada and India's DST was released in October 2007.

The ISTPP is a seed fund, meaning that various other public and private sector participants are also bringing significant S&T expertise and funds of their own to the bilateral relationship. Some provincial partners have already come forward with funds and programmes of their own. Tapping into alternative sources of funding and expertise from across the country will bring greater support of Canadian S&T activity under the S&T Agreement.

Although the new Canada-India joint programme will be a catalyst and stimulus for collaboration, there is already a solid base of researcher to researcher, university to university and company to company interactions and cooperation in place. As examples, 47 Canadian universities have MOU's or agreements with Indian IIT's and universities and the Indo-Canadian Shastri Institute supports a number of research projects in such areas as economic reform and environmental management. There are hundreds of research and scholarly collaborations occurring through these mechanisms alone.

Agreement

As a direct result of recent visits and discussions between scientists and advisors, new agreements to cooperate and share expertise have been signed. The Canadian Light Source/University of Saskatchewan and the Office of the Principal Scientific Advisor to the Government of India have an agreement permitting Indian scientists access to the second generation CLS synchrotron. A major agreement to jointly invest $5 m on each side for plant biotechnology research on Brassicas (eg Canola) has been signed by the National Research Council of Canada (PBI) and the Department of Biotechnology. These are very positive signs of the ramping up of activity under the S&T Agreement.

With full proposals for joint initiatives, involving a private sector entity on each side and with universities as potential partners, due in January 2008, there will be a good indication of the extent of interest generated by the programme. The stage is set for a major boost in Canada-India science, technology and innovation. □

Guri I Marchuk
Director, Institute of Numerical
Mechanics, Moscow

Old friends and partners

The year 2007 marked 20 years of the Integrated Long-Term Programme (ILTP) of Cooperation in Science and Technology between India and Russia. It is a milestone event for both countries. The ILTP has gone from strength to strength throughout its existence. Themes have been identified and ever new forms of interaction introduced and tested. In a number of areas cooperation reached a level that required the creation of joint thematic centres to coordinate complicated programmes including many projects, and engage in applied development and training. The creation of four more centers, dealing respectively with lasers and accelerators, bio-medical technology, non-ferrous metallurgy, and plastics and composites are currently being considered.

On the whole, the 20 years of work under the ILTP has led to the creation of joint teams in which Indian and Russian participants feel and behave as members of the same team wherever they may be working, whether in Chennai, Moscow, Pune or Novosibirsk. Up until now joint efforts have focused on research and personnel training. The joint scientific results make it possible to tackle many more practical tasks in many areas of the economy in both countries. We can say that the establishment of the programme met the vital interests of our countries. In terms of scale and results, neither Russia nor India has ever had such cooperation programmes with other countries. Russia and India are ready to meet national needs and gain a worthy place in the world market. We are sure that the experience of the ILTP will be useful in tackling that strategic task and that the heads and members of the programme will meet the challenge of combining major research efforts with large-scale applications in the key areas of modern production.

As a young scientist in 1952, I saw for the first time in my life two foreign guests, who happened to be Jawaharlal Nehru, then Prime Minister, and his daughter Indira Gandhi, a young and graceful woman. I did not know then that life would bring me closer to Indira Gandhi and also her son Rajiv, future Prime Ministers of India.

Many years later I was assigned to meet and accompany Prime Minister Indira Gandhi during her visit to the then USSR. I was warned by an official that she was rather a reserved woman, who prefers sightseeing from a window. Fortunately, this stereotype happened to be wrong.

During our trip to Zvyozdny, the USSR space centre, she asked me questions about our life, science, my family, and shared her personal concerns. The same evening, in the Bol'shoy theatre, they had changed programme and Indian ballet was shown instead of 'Zhisel'; Indira Gandhi was greeted with a great ovation, which was repeated when she stood up to leave. During our flight to Tallin, I met Rajiv Gandhi for the first time. In the very beginning of his political career, Rajiv Gandhi had formulated a very difficult goal: by the end of this century, science and technology in India must be at the level of developed countries. It was a bold vision, and Rajiv Gandhi tried to implement this idea, strengthening his country's economy and developing international collaboration.

The collaboration between Russia and India in science and technology was given a great impulse when a bilateral agreement on Integrated Long-term Programme (ILTP) of

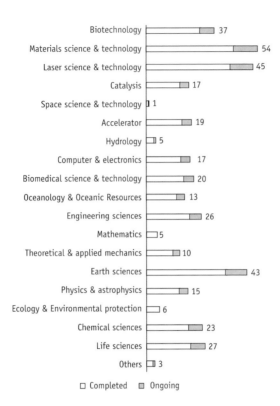

Biotechnology — 37
Materials science & technology — 54
Laser science & technology — 45
Catalysis — 17
Space science & technology — 1
Accelerator — 19
Hydrology — 5
Computer & electronics — 17
Biomedical science & technology — 20
Oceanology & Oceanic Resources — 13
Engineering sciences — 26
Mathematics — 5
Theoretical & applied mechanics — 10
Earth sciences — 43
Physics & astrophysics — 15
Ecology & Environmental protection — 6
Chemical sciences — 23
Life sciences — 27
Others — 3

□ Completed   ▣ Ongoing

Joint Projects

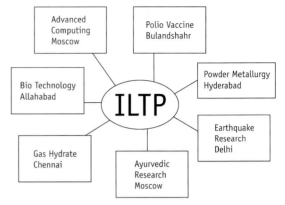

ILTP Centres of Excellence

Co-operation in Science and Technology was signed in 3 July 1987 by the President of USSR, Michail Gorbachov, and Prime Minister Rajiv Gandhi.

I had the honour to be the co-chairman of ILTP Joint Council from the Russian side. I interacted with my colleague and co-chairman Professor C N R Rao. Remarkable progress had been achieved under ILTP since its inception. Several projects became joint ventures.

The ILTP covers eight areas of science and technology: biotechnology and immunology, engineering and electronic materials, laser science and technology, catalysis, space science and technology, physics and technology of accelerators, computers and electronics. Joint research and development projects are carried out in six fundamental sciences: mathematics and applied mechanics, science on earth, radiophysics and astrophysics, ecology and environmental research, chemistry and biology.

The years of collaboration have proved to be very fruitful. The Programme acquired a momentum of its own. This makes us hope for future success. The ILTP Projects have demonstrated that development along the lines shown by Jawaharlal Nehru has brought about evident shifts in various spheres of life in India, science and technology included. □

Indo-Russian scientific and technological cooperation

ILTP in Science and Technology between India and the Russian Federation is one of the most exhaustive bilateral collaborative R&D programmes, covering all aspects of S&T. The two sides have agreed to extend it for another 10 years, to conclude in 2020. The contractual basis of the Indo-Russian S&T cooperation environment is an intergovernmental agreement going back to 1994. The working group on S&T of the Intergovernmental Russian-Indian Commission on Trade, Economic, Scientific, Technical and Cultural Cooperation co-ordinates the cooperation. It ensures the implementation of projects through the Long-Term Program for Scientific and Technological Cooperation. More than 300 projects have been implemented in such areas as mathematics, mechanics, chemistry, physics, materials science, laser beam and particle beam technology, electronics, ocean science and seismology. It comprises over 140 joint projects and covers a wide range of scientific disciplines.

Russia and India have been expanding cooperation in such areas of fundamental studies as mathematics, engineering and applied mechanics, geosciences, physics and physical astronomy, ecology and environmental protection, chemical sciences, natural sciences. They give a priority to industrial utilization of joint research results in their areas of expertise. These include biotechnology and immunology, materials science, laser beam science and technology, catalysis, space science and technology, launchers and their application, hydrology, computer science and electronics, biomedical science and technology, ocean science and resources, engineering sciences.

The Russian Academy of Science and the Indian National Academy of Science collaborate under a scientific cooperation and exchange agreement. The Russian Academy of Science and the Indian Department of Science and Technology have signed a memorandum of understanding on the establishment of joint centres on gas hydrates and earthquake research. The two have also signed a protocol of scientific cooperation.

Based on such cooperation, India began the commercial production of polio vaccine using the technology of the Institute of Poliomyelitis and Viral Encephalitis of the Russian Academy of Medical Sciences. There are plans to transfer to India on a commercial basis the technologies for the production of vaccines against rabies, measles, hepatitis-C, medicated products and food supplements, as well as foamed and iron concrete, polymeric roof and isolation materials and water purification systems of container type.

In Moscow, the Institute of Design Automation of the Russian Academy of Science set up a joint Centre of Advanced Computer Technologies equipped with the Indian supercomputer PARAM-10 000. It has been used for atmospheric processes simulation, research studies in the areas of microelectronics, medicine, seismology and ecology.

The Indo-Russian centres for biotechnology, oral polio vaccine production, and prospective studies of powder metallurgy and new materials have been opened in India. India became a member of the International Scientific and Technical Information Centre. This forum is used by the CIS states and some Eastern European and Asian countries.

The Indo-Russian working group on information technologies is involved in the creation and development of technological parks in Russia to support small and medium businesses in the area of information technologies. India's experience is very useful in this context.

A bilateral cooperation in software development and promotion, including emerging markets, has a large potential. Among other things, Indian partners might be interested in the Russian know-how in the area of information security that is recognized worldwide.

One of the key objectives today is to focus on a scientific and technical cooperation in such a way as to increase the share of high-tech products and services in bilateral trade and economic exchange.

Russian Embassy

José Manuel Silva Rodríguez
Director General for Research
European Commission

European-Indian cooperation

Louis Pasteur observed in the nineteenth century that "Science knows no country", an observation that could just as easily apply to recent and ongoing cooperation between the European Union and India in the field of scientific research.

In our rapidly globalising world, scientific challenges have become more complex in nature and often have a global impact, scientific research itself has grown to be highly international and technology is being developed in a global framework. Even if international science is always a mix of competition and cooperation, the answer to the new challenges have to be found jointly, which leads to the deepening of international cooperation in science and technology: more international cooperation boosts economic development, contributes to countering global challenges (climate change, energy scarcity, securing the provision of safe food) and gives access to knowledge to the underprivileged countries.

For quite some time now, neither India nor the EU have underestimated the importance of science and technology for economic and social development and whilst we have each recognised the critical role of independently building our respective knowledge based economies, we have also seen the benefits of extending and strengthening cooperation in areas of common interest. As we are both open to collaborative efforts with the potential to deliver mutual benefits, it is, therefore, hardly surprising that scientific cooperation between the EU and India has continued to grow steadily.

Research cooperation between us dates right back to the mid-1980s during the First European Framework Programme for Research and Technological Development, which is the main instrument of the European Union to support science and technology cooperation. Then, following a Cooperation Agreement on Partnership and Development in 1993, the first EU-India Science and Technology (S&T) Agreement was signed in 2001. This Agreement was based on the principles of mutual benefit, reciprocal opportunities for access to each others' programmes, the effective protection of intellectual property and the equitable sharing of individual property rights.

In terms of the practical application of these principles, in 2004 the first EU-India Joint Steering Committee under the S&T agreement, which I co-chair in my capacity as the European Commission's Director General for Research, identified five research themes as priorities for cooperation. These were information and communication technologies, surface transport, nanotechnologies and multifunctional materials, health, and climate change and natural disasters.

Then, arising from a Joint Action Plan drawn up at the sixth EU-India Summit in 2005 to implement the Strategic Partnership, several initiatives were launched in the areas of pharmaceuticals, biotechnology, information and communications technology, energy, environment, agriculture, marine products and food processing.

In total, over 80 projects have been funded through the 6th Framework Programme (FP6) for Research and Technological Development between 2003 and 2006 which involved Indian partners or were focussed on India. The total budget of those FP6 projects involving Indian partners exceeded 250m Euro with Indian participants receiving around 11m Euro.

In the same period seven EU-India workshops were organised within the framework of the Agreement. To date, some 35 Fellowships under the Marie Curie mobility programme have been granted to Indian researchers, enabling them to work in Europe. India has also signed up to participate in the Galileo satellite navigation system project and has become a full partner in the International Thermonuclear Experimental Reactor (ITER) nuclear fusion project.

The benefits of this cooperation can perhaps be best illustrated by reference to ITER. ITER is a joint international research and development project that aims to demonstrate the scientific and technical feasibility of fusion power, and is probably the most ambitious international cooperation project to date. This project is one in which not only the EU and India participate, but also the USA, China, Russia, Japan and South Korea. The project not only seeks to develop a new and clean energy source for the future, its ultimate success will have a great impact on political stability and peace worldwide.

Commitment

That we have an S&T Agreement at all underlines the importance of our cooperation in science and technology, in that India is one of only 16 countries with which the European Union has a formal agreement on science and technology. A further sign of the European Commission's commitment to strengthening science and technology cooperation with India was the decision in 2005 to establish a Science and Technology Section at the EC Delegation in India, making it one of only seven countries where a full time EU Science Counsellor is posted in the EC Delegation to that country.

Furthermore, India has had a fairly long-standing S&T cooperation with several of the Member States of the European Union. Some of the more noteworthy initiatives in these cooperation programmes are the Indo-French Centre for the Promotion of Advanced Research and the UK-India Education and Research Initiative. The German-Indian Science and Technology Centre is due to open in New Delhi in 2008. India has Science and Technology Agreements with 23 of its 27 Member States. The importance attached to scientific cooperation by EU Member States with India can be gauged by the fact that today nine of them have full time science counsellors in their embassies in India, up from four just two years ago.

There is also little doubt that this cooperation and the benefits which flow from it, will continue. In February 2007 the first India-EU Ministerial Science Conference was held in New Delhi. This was the first time ever that EU Member states and the European Commission met in Science Ministerial (or designate) level outside of the European Union. That India hosted the conference was both a recognition of how far scientific collaboration had progressed between the EU and India and at the same time a tangible vote of confidence that such collaboration would not only continue, but that both parties were committed to increasing the breadth and depth of future cooperation in our mutual interest and to our mutual benefit. A Communiqué issued at the close of the conference underlined that EU-India S&T cooperation should be based on the principles of symmetry, reciprocity and mutual benefit. There was also agreement on an EU-India strategic workshop series on key areas including climate change, clean energy, combustion, systems biology, infectious diseases and drugs development, including clinical trials. The Indian Government also indicated that they had set aside 5m Euro a year towards dedicated EU-India science and technology cooperation.

Mission

It was in this context that I undertook a follow-up mission to India in March 2007 where I held discussions with senior officials from the Government of India's Department of Science and Technology. These covered a wide range of topics of common interest, including an EU-India coordinated call for proposals to co-invest research projects on computational materials and importantly, the renewal of the 2001 EU-India S&T Agreement. This agreement, which expired in October 2007, was renewed at the EU-India Summit which took place on 30th November 2007.

During my visit I also chaired two workshops, which prompted vigorous discussions and much debate on how best to promote science and technology cooperation between the EU and India and I visited several institutes in Delhi, Bangalore and Mysore, such as the Jawaharlal Nehru University, the Jawaharlal Nehru Centre for Advanced Scientific Research and the Central Food Technological Research Institute All in all I am very impressed at the level of scientific expertise and ambitions but also with the positive experience in their cooperation with European institutes.

I subsequently visited India again in November 2007 to chair the latest Joint Steering Committee. Together with my co-chair, Dr T Ramasami, Secretary of the Department of Science and Technology, we discussed a number of S&T related issues and areas of common interest in which we expect strong EU-India collaboration in the near future (2008–2010). I believe there are ample opportunities to further strengthen our relationship in all main research areas and in particular water management, waste, solar photo voltaic, coal and carbon capture, fuel cells, hydrogen, biomass, new materials, health research, road and rail transport, software and security, audio-visual systems and infectious animal diseases etc. But let me immediately add that this list should probably be much longer. The cooperation in these areas could take many forms such as Indian participation in European projects, joint or coordinated projects with balanced EU-India participation, staff and researchers exchange etc. I also see opportunities to broaden the scope of our cooperation to research related areas such as innovation policy and transfer of technologies.

Current plan

In India's 11th and current five-year plan, the Government has set an objective for the country to become a "Global Innovation Leader" in the knowledge era of the 21st century. As a first step to achieving this goal, India has set a target of doubling public expenditure on research over the next five years.

Similarly, the EU has massively increased our research budget through allocating over 53 billion Euro to the Seventh Framework Programme (FP7) which represents an investment of over 7 billion Euro per year over the period of the Programme.

Importantly for EU-India cooperation however, as the European Union's external cooperation policy means that FP7 has been opened up to non EU participants, this should provide for increased cooperation efforts between the scientific, research and business sectors across a diverse range of areas including health, biotechnology, environment, energy, materials and nanotechnology and lead to even greater cooperation between us in the years to come. At the moment of writing this article the results of the first calls under FP7 have just been received. The steady rise of Indian participation in European research projects has continued and even grown. Based on the amount of submitted proposals including third country participation, Indian research organisations are our fourth largest international collaboration partner after Russia, China and the US.

India is the world's largest democracy. It also produces the world's highest number of science and engineering graduates each year. The Indian economy is booming, with economic growth having averaged around 8 per cent since 2003. In just a few years India has been transformed from an aid recipient to a global competitor and in the global knowledge economy, once peripheral zones such as India, are becoming central to emerging innovation networks.

In the context of the European Union's relationship with an open and outward facing 21st century India, there is little doubt that we both have much to gain from continuing to build on our cooperative relationship. That aside, given the cost and complexity of research in areas such as fusion energy, trans-national cooperation is becoming not only desirable but also necessary and Pasteur's words, whilst not intended to be prophetic, do seem particularly apt in the 21st century.

As India celebrates 60 years of independence in the same year that Europe marks 50 years of integration between our nation states, we can both look forward to realising the potential that a strengthened partnership will bring. □

Ranjan Mathai
India's Ambassador in Paris

Indo-French cooperation grows

Indian civilization has had an old and venerable tradition of scientific achievements and of contributions to global dissemination of knowledge. Jawaharlal Nehru, India's first Prime Minister, gave a high priority to development of science and technology in independent India, and our participation in the global march of science—"mankind's greatest enterprise today". His vision recalled the extraordinary achievements of Indian science from the 5th century BCE, the technological developments in pharmacology, metallurgy, dyes etc. that marked early Indian civilization, and the essentiality of science, technology and innovation for the revival of India after centuries of colonial subjugation and impoverishment. Over the six decades of independent India's existence, a network of scientific laboratories, industrial research organisations and advanced centres of excellence in universities have been set up, and cooperation with scientific establishments of other countries has become a feature of India's foreign policy.

Scientists from France and India have long had scientific and intellectual exchanges – both in fundamental research and technological applications. French achievements in science have been admired in India and Indian capabilities in scientific research have been recognized in the French intellectual tradition. French technology and expertise was involved in the setting up of the Rare Earths plant in Kerala, by the nascent atomic energy establishment in the early 1950s. Similarly, French scientists and engineers participated in setting up of the initial launches from the Thumba Equatorial Rocket Launching Station in the early '60s when India began using space technology for weather studies. This was later expanded to satellite communication experiments and today Indian and French agencies are developing satellites jointly for third parties. Over the years, the Indian National Science Academy and Indian universities have also established cooperative relationships with French counterparts.

The first bilateral agreement between the Governments of France and India for cultural and scientific cooperation dates back to 1966. This was strengthened by adding new areas for collaboration in successive agreements signed in 1978 and 1989. The implementation of the agreements is achieved through joint mechanisms, which work together with the aim of:
- identifying areas of cooperation;
- bringing together potential partners;
- supporting exploratory visits, exchanges and conference; and,
- nurturing cooperation projects till they become self-sustaining.

Fundamental sciences including mathematics, astronomy, physics and chemistry have been traditional areas of scientific cooperation. Today, the scope has been expanded to cover applications of relevance to industry (information technology, biotechnology, nano sciences etc.), medicine, and management of natural resources. Technology-oriented research programmes are also a priority in the agenda of cooperation. The cooperation is sustained through the institutional mechanism of the Indo-French Committee for Scientific and Technological Cooperation, which meets every year alternatively in France and India. Additionally, a number of specific institutional arrangements have been developed to manage the extensive and diversified programmes of collaboration.

The Indo-French Centre for Promotion of Advanced Research (IFCPAR), which was set up in 1987 as a joint and equally funded project, has ensured the adequacy of resources for funding projects. IFCPAR functions with a great degree of autonomy while under the aegis of the Department of Science & Technology in India and the French Ministry of Foreign Affairs. Since its creation, IFCPAR has received applications from more than 800 projects, and has provided support to over 350. These projects, whether for joint research, workshops or exchange of visits, have covered material sciences, pure and applied chemistry, pure and applied physics, life and health sciences, environmental sciences, computer and information sciences, biotechnology, water and a variety of critical subjects.

Biotechnology

The Indian Council for Medical Research and INSERM (Institut National de la Santé et de la Recherché Médicale) have institutionalized cooperative endeavours in medical research and public health, particularly tuberculosis and immunology. In the high priority field of biotechnology, cooperative research between the two countries is managed by leading agencies on both sides. The French National Institute for Agronomic Research and the Centre for International Cooperation and Agricultural Research work together with India's ICAR, while the CNRS (Centre Nationale de la Recherche Scientifique) and India's Department of Bio-Technology (DBT) have catalyzed progress in joint projects covering genomics, bio-medical research, and immunology. Recently, INSERM and DBT have reached agreement for setting up of laboratories for research in biotechnology.

Management of water resources will be a vital issue in world affairs in the 21st century and it is, thus, fitting that the Indo-French Cell on Water Sciences (IFCWS) has been created to advance bilateral cooperation in this field. It brings together the Institute of Research for Development (IRD – Institut de Recherche pour le Development) of France and the Indian Institute of Science (IISc), Bangalore, and the Indo-French Centre for Groundwater Research (IFCGR), which

has been jointly set up by the Agency for Geological and Mining Research BRGM (Bureau de Recherche Geologique et Miniere), in France and the National Geophysical Research Institute (NGRI), Hyderabad. There is also the advanced Indo-French Programme for Research on Weather and Climate (IFPREWEC) at the National Institute of Oceanography (NIO), Goa, a cooperative venture between CSIR and CNRS.

These are very significant programmes of cooperation, which will impact on the lives of our people as will ongoing projects in space and nuclear technology. The Megha Tropiques Satellite to study tropical climate is being worked on by the Centre National d'Etudes Spatiales (CNES) and Indian Space research Organisation (ISRO). Cooperation in nuclear sciences covers mainly studies relating to safety, waste management, reactor physics and life sciences.

Exchanges

The overall scope of cooperation is thus large and growing. As many as 112 French universities and institutions have programmes for exchanges of studies and research workers. As part of the genre of popularization of science, the French Science Today programme brings leading French scientists to India for lectures at Indian universities and scientific institutes. This endeavour provides the Indian public a comprehensive panorama of the contributions of the French scientific community and the impact of current research and discoveries.

This brief survey clearly points to S&T cooperation having emerged as one of the vital features of the burgeoning ties between India and France. We are both countries with a strong intellectual tradition, and a commitment to using technology for improvement of the quality of life. We share a belief that science and technology are vital to overcoming challenges of the 21st century (global warming, disease, and resource management). The quality and the range of work currently underway makes our cooperation a model worthy of emulation. Achieving the Millennium Development Goals worldwide would require greater international cooperation with particular emphasis on investments in S&T and development of indigenous technological capabilities. □

Kirsten Bond
Senior Researcher
DEMOS, UK

UK must strengthen S&T ties with India

A clear imperative to emerge from our DEMOS study is the need to scale up levels of collaboration and the skills and capabilities needed to coordinate it. New initiatives such as UKIERI are a positive development, which could supplement and enhance the UK's 'bottom up' approach to science partnerships. The UK and India should continue to experiment with different collaborative models, drawing lessons from the more strategic approaches taken by France and Germany. The UK should also learn from the US model of venture capital partnerships with Indian institutions and regional governments. The UK currently has one 'talent scout' in the form of the Global Entrepreneurs Programme Dealmaker: a good idea on far too small a scale.

Be a magnet for talent

Although the UK is home to a large Indian diaspora, the links that these bring are ageing and not as productive or creative as they could be. The UK must learn how to tap into these networks to support collaboration. New links should be activated, and stories of Indian success in the UK promoted. Indian researchers based in the UK should be provided with more support to collaborate in India. Universities also need to present a more coordinated approach to India that is about long-term research partnerships as well as prospecting for students. As a starting point, the UK and India could host a university summit to share knowledge and inform collective strategies. Investment in scholarships to the UK should be increased, and top universities in particular should step up their efforts to attract Indian students in order to multiply the number of future Indian science leaders that have close links with the UK. The new scholarship scheme recently announced by the Royal Society is a step in the right direction. It should be developed with Indian and Chinese researchers in mind.

Get UK story straight

Conservative Leader David Cameron suggested during a recent visit to Delhi, that Britain and India should forge a new special relationship. This relationship needs to be built not only on culture and history but on a shared understanding of how science can help to meet the most pressing global challenges. There is a need to improve the UK's visibility and promote its distinctive advantages as a collaborator. Crucial to this will be better promotion of the UK's scientific infrastructure, such as the Rutherford Appleton laboratory and diamond cyclotron. The OSI should assemble a scientific 'Doomsday Book', cataloguing the UK's science assets as part of a marketing strategy to encourage Indian scientists to work with the UK. The UK must also shed its reputation for 'talk and no action': too many networking efforts lack a clear sense of purpose. We need a more hard headed and rigorous evaluation of what has and hasn't worked, and a greater willingness to back small-scale projects and experiments. Above all, the UK needs to turn more of the ceremonial networking it does so well into genuine collaboration, no matter how small scale at first.

Build the knowledge banks

Despite our strong historical links, knowledge about how Indian science and innovation is changing is surprisingly limited in the UK. The knowledge gained from numerous scoping trips and networking activities is not collected centrally, so effort is duplicated, and wheels are endlessly reinvented. As more places in India become centres of innovation, the UK should look beyond the obvious and familiar locations. Pune and Kolkata should be significant targets for UK efforts. The Foreign and Commonwealth Office is ideally positioned to gather information through its science and innovation network, but these specialists need more time pounding the pavements, creating linkages with Indian organisations, and less time organising scoping visits for UK visitors. Other European countries combine their fact-finding trips to India into larger, less frequent delegations of 50 or 100 people. This can generate more interest from prospective collaborators, and greater recognition from the Indian government, so this is a model that the UK should consider adopting.

Lead global science

Collaborations will be more productive if they can help to address India's most pressing development needs, or tackle global issues like climate change. To this end, the UK should strengthen its science links not only with traditional institutions, but also with the powerful NGO community in India. As CK Prahalad has demonstrated in the context of corporate strategy, a focus on the market "at the bottom of the pyramid" can create new opportunities for innovation. There is exciting scope to apply this model to science and technology, and make it the focus of a fresh round of India-UK collaborations. □

Meera Shankar
India's Ambassador in Berlin

India and Germany join hands

Indo-German partnership in science and technology stretches back to the year 1920, when Indian Physicist Satyen Bose established contact with Albert Einstein, resulting in the ground-breaking Bose-Einstein theory of condensation. The doors opened by these two geniuses provided a pathway for future cooperation. Indo-German scientific contacts, disrupted by the World War, resumed after India's independence with strong support from Prime Minister Jawaharlal Nehru, who saw science and technology as critical for India's development and emergence as a modern nation. German assistance in setting up of IIT Chennai during 1958–59 was an important and visible symbol of this. Over the years, cooperation in science and technology has continued to flourish and has become one of the central pillars of the strategic partnership between India and Germany.

Our cooperation is wide ranging, embracing joint research, exchange of students and scholars, direct tie-ups between Indian and German Institutes and extending to frontier areas of research under the umbrella of the 1974 Inter-governmental Agreement on Scientific Research and Technical Development. Implementation is overseen by the Indo-German Joint Committee on Science & Technology (IGJCST) which defines the goals and helps identify new areas of research priority. At the last meeting of the committee in September 2006, several focus areas were identified for joint research including, biotechnology, health, space, information technology, materials and production technology. The scope for cooperation in these areas is seen as having high potential and there is keen interest in moving forward to shape concrete proposals.

Starting with 20 research projects in 1974, the number of bilateral research projects has grown rapidly over the years, with about 200 projects in 2007. Direct partnerships in various fields between universities and institutes in the two countries have now crossed 80. With 1700 joint scientific publications, Germans are at number two position in terms of joint authorship of papers with Indian scholars. Indian doctoral researchers are also the largest foreign group in the prestigious Max Planck Research Schools in Germany.

Academic exchanges

There has been an active and lively exchange of students, researchers, and scientists over the years. This has been instrumental in building relationships and intellectual connections between Indian and German institutions. Many of the hi-tech research projects which are on the anvil between India and Germany are a result of this rich human interaction.

The German Academic Exchange Programme (DAAD), the Humboldt Foundation (AvH), and the German Research Foundation (DFG) have been active in promoting academic exchanges with India. An interesting initiative has been the IIT/DAAD Masters Sandwich Programme for the exchange of around 70 MTech students every year for a period of 9 months between the IITs in India and six Technical Universities in Berlin, Karlsruhe, Stuttgart, Darmstadt, Aachen and Dresden. The programme has subsequently been

extended to include management students from the IIMs also. The DFG arrangement with the Indian National Science Academy (INSA) for exchange of scientists has also provided an opportunity to more than 300 Indian scientists to visit Germany for advance research over the years. Several distinguished Indians, including former President Dr Zakir Hussain, studied at Humboldt university.

Another initiative worth mentioning here is the annual meeting of Indian students/scholars with Nobel Laureates under the auspices of the Lindau Foundation. This unique gathering provides an opportunity to bright young Indian students/scholars at the Masters/PhD level in the field of the sciences to meet and interact with Nobel Laureates for one week on the picturesque island of Lindau in Germany. Recently the programme has been extended with a bi-annual meeting for senior students and young researchers in the field of economics to meet with Nobel Laureates in this field. The Department of Science & Technology on the Indian side, the Lindau Committee, and the German Research Foundation, support this excellent initiative to inspire and motivate the new generation.

In recent years, Indo-German cooperation in science and technology has gathered further momentum. In 2004, the Indo-German Science Circle, a high-profile series of lectures with an affiliated network and bilateral scientific website, was launched in New Delhi during the visit of former German Chancellor Gerhard Schröder. In that year, the Max Planck Society concluded an agreement with India's Department of Science and Technology (DST) providing for the promotion of partner groups and fellowships. In November 2006, the German Research Foundation (DFG) opened an office in New Delhi and a branch office in Hyderabad.

German Minister for Education and Research, Annette Schavan and EU Research Commissioner Janez Potocnik, attended the India-EU Ministerial conference which was held in New Delhi in February 2007. An initiative of the German-EU Presidency, the Conference was hosted by the Indian Science Minister, Kapil Sibal. This was the first time that EU Member States and the European Commission met at Science Ministerial level outside of the EU. It was also the first time that European Nobel Laureates and other icons of European science interacted in a forum with students outside of the EU. The Joint Declaration issued at the end of the conference recognized that there were opportunities for a significant increase in the breadth and depth of EU-India science and technology cooperation and stressed support for initiatives aimed at facilitating partnerships and generating benefits for both parties.

Science & Technology Minister Kapil Sibal and his German counterpart, Minister Annette Schavan, also signed a declaration on India's participation in the mega German project FAIR (Facility for anti-Proton and Ion Research) which will use accelerator technology to address basic questions relating to matter. In the field of space sciences, India's first Moon mission, Chandrayan-1 will carry a near IR Spectrometer developed by the Max Plank Institute. India launched the micro satellite LAPAN-TUBSAT built by Technical University, Berlin, in January 2007. India is also a participant in the EU futuristic fusion energy project ITER, which has recently been formally launched.

In April 2007, the President of Germany's largest research organization, the Helmholtz Association of National Research Centers, traveled to India with a view to stepping up cooperation, particularly in the medical and energy sectors.

Science and technology cooperation was the centre piece of German Chancellor Angela Merkel's recent visit to India in November 2007 with eight new agreements on science and technology collaboration, including an agreement for setting up of an Indo-German science and technology centre. This centre, to be jointly funded by India and Germany, would focus not just on fundamental research but also on research with practical applications with the ability to draw in industry sponsored projects and funding. We expect the centre to emerge as a catalyst for taking Indo-German science and technology cooperation to the next level.

The 'Science Express' was flagged off by Prime Minister Dr Manmohan Singh and Chancellor Merkel. This unique Indian train, carrying a science and technology exhibition mounted by Germany, is travelling to over 50 cities in India and helping to arouse the curiosity and interest of young minds across the country. More than a million Indian visitors have seen the Science Express, which has become a very effective instrument for bringing the wonders of modern science and technology to the people.

Prime Minister Dr Manmohan Singh and German Chancellor Angela Merkel share the vision of science and technology as an instrument of change and of development. An intensification of cooperation in this field is the fulcrum of the strategic partnership which the two countries are seeking to shape. We hope to carry forward the momentum generated and make the new initiatives launched operational at an early date. □

Rajiv Dogra
India's Ambassador in Rome

India & Italy: Partners in innovation

History is a great educator. And one principal lesson it conveys constantly is that culture makes all the difference; it is the basic raw material, the essential essence of civilization. In any such measure of civilization, Italy and India should have a claim to the top of the table. Sometimes it seems as if they have a monopoly of gifted people with a knack for the imaginative, people who stun the world almost continuously with marvellous achievements in arts, science and technology; in short everything that makes a great culture.

It is not just the spirit of innovation that finds us in consonance. There are so many similarities in social behavior that one often wonders as to what separates us. It is true that geographical distance separates us, but once you get over that handicap you are struck by the large number of similarities that provide the meeting points. The family values, the exuberance, the social structure and the constant quest for knowledge; all these suggest that Italy and India should be two natural partners.

Obviously a basis exists. Individually their record of achievements in science and technology is enough to do any civilization proud. Taken together their efforts would outshine many other comparable efforts. Such a natural partnership should prove that technology and science advance by sharing.

Yet, despite overwhelming evidence in favour of cooperation, something has kept us apart. It is odd that this should have been so despite mutual curiosity and a fascination almost from the beginning to know more about the other. It must have been this fascination that led Romans to build a temple during the reign of Augustus in India. Incidentally, this was the only temple that they had built outside the Roman Empire. And it must have been a similar quest that led St. Thomas to India. The Indian Emperors too sent missions to the Roman Empire. But compared to the immense possibilities in finding common ground, our contacts on a technical plane remained occasional. For long years curiosity remained restrained by inertia. Perhaps both were busy with themselves and in the immediate neighbourhood surrounding them. It is for this reason that we do not have any noticeable landmarks as signposts of shared scientific achievement.

There is therefore reason for some frustration that we were unable to write a more passionate chapter of innovation together. Still, ours is far from a blank sheet. As a matter of fact some striking contacts still shimmer through the long passage of history.

It is often said that there are only two civilizations that had made a fetish of cleanliness. The ancient Indus civilization was known for its building techniques for bathrooms and large basins. This ancient design was replicated and even surpassed by the Roman baths that were built 2500 years later. But it is not just the baths that establish a connection between India and Italy. There is another fascinating example that suggests a connection between our technical minds. Stupa, the hemispherical design for roofs, was first used in India in the centuries between 300 BC to 400 AD. Some experts claim that this inter-locking dome of stupa, that was so popular in ancient Indian architecture, became the prototype for the domes built by Romans. As with the baths, Romans innovated here too. Thanks to the Roman invention of concrete the construction of the dome was improved and it became capable of spanning enormous spaces like the Pantheon. But the basic inspiration, it is said, came from the design of Stupa.

The exchange of knowledge between two advanced and prosperous civilizations was natural. As trade partners there were constant innovations in the field of navigation too. Even if he didn't reach India, it should be remembered that Christopher Columbus was Italian. So trade and technical interchange in some form or the other must have continued throughout the centuries. In the field of mathematics Leonardo Pisano's celebrated work *Liber Abbaci* introduced to Europe and the latinized Arab world (AD 1202) not only the Indian numerals but also the notion of an algorithm, and the subject of algebra.

Nicolo dei Conti, an Italian traveller of 15th Century records that India built ships 'larger than ours'. He commented admiringly that some ships were built in double compartments in such a manner that should one part be shattered, the other may accomplish the voyage.

Old ties

The knowledge exchange may have been sporadic but the important point is that it had continued over the years. For instance, Pietro Tacchini went to India for spectroscopic observations of the transit of Venus in December 1874. His experience at Madhavpur was so rewarding scientifically that the Italian group eventually participated in setting up of a spectroscopic observatory in Kolkata.

If there are examples of learning from each other there are also instances from the pages of history that remind us of the missed chances or miscommunications. The scientific community still talks of the genius of Guglielmo Marconi and J C Bose in the development of communications technology. They were contemporaries, one was from Italy, the other from India. Even if they were working in two different continents, the subject was the same and the results intense. The scientific community remained enthralled for a long time by their achievements.

Moreover each instance was a landmark in a way; be it the fetish for cleanliness that resulted in baths or the quest for grandeur in dome design. It is a pity however that it took us an amazingly long time to establish institutional contacts. As a matter of fact it was only in 1978 that the scientific and technological relationship was formalized through an agreement between the two governments.

An Indo-Italian Joint Committee on Science and Technology now oversees the implementation of the programmes that range from material science, to energy, environment, medicine, health, robotics, agriculture, bio-technology, conservation and restoration of monuments. A unique new form of cooperation was begun through two centres in India and Italy which concentrate on advanced research and training in molecular biology and bio-technology. The 'International Centre for Genetic Engineering and Biotechnology' also does advanced research in bio-medicines, crop improvement, bio-pharmaceutical and other such frontier areas. Talking of frontier areas, scientists from India and Italy now visit each other on a regular basis. To give some other examples, the Indian Institute of Science, Bangalore is interacting with the Sincrotrone Trieste in the field of applied physics. The Indian Institute of Technology, Kharagpur and Mumbai and the Tata Institute of Fundamental Research, Mumbai are dealing with a number of Italian institutions, including Universities of Trento and Florence, in a range of projects pertaining to nanotechnology, multi-media and aerospace engineering, development of sensors, verification techniques in software development for business process analysis, material science etc.

Increasingly, there are examples of practical cooperation that go beyond a mere exchange of experience or discussion papers. For instance, ISRO launched on its Polar Satellite Launch Vehicle, the Italian Space Agency's astronomical satellite called AGILE from Sriharikota on 23 April, 2007. It was in fact ISRO's first commercial launch of a foreign payload.

The pace of cooperation in frontier areas of technology has picked up enormously. The genius of people is combining in brilliant new forms every day. Perhaps the mission statement of Indo-Italian cooperation and innovation can be seen on a daily basis at the factory where Ferrari cars are produced in Italy. Over 30 software engineers from Tata Consultancy Services are an integral part of this Ferrari team at its Maranello factory where they help in simulation, computer aided design, computer aided engineering and software. Together these young innovators from India and Italy produce the world beater in sports cars.

It is only natural that the results should be best when two imaginative and gifted people decide to work in tandem. After all if it is history's dictum that culture makes the difference, then the rich seam of Indo-Italian culture is the best augury for our quest in innovation. □

M Bandyopadhyay
Arun P Kulshreshtha
NAM S&T Centre

South-South cooperation in innovation

The increasing gap in science & technology capability between developed and developing countries has been a major source of concern for several years. Conventional North-to-South technology transfer has not helped the South. Developing countries have realized that they must work together to meet their own technology needs rather than depend on industrially advanced nations.

Through South-South cooperation, relatively strong countries in the developing world can cooperate with those less endowed. Multilateral cooperation and regional networks are a mechanism that can strengthen S&T capacities in weaker developing countries, stimulate interdisciplinary research and establish links between research and industry.

Since its inception in 1989, the NAM S&T Centre has promoted cooperation in science, technology and innovation in the developing world with the participation of 100 countries and support from several international developmental organizations. The Centre has provided opportunities for scientist-to-scientist and institution-to-institution contacts in developing countries. It has familiarized scientists with the latest developments and techniques. It has implemented collaborative projects and training courses and facilitated transfers of technology. These activities have helped the process of capacity-building in S&T and enabled experience-sharing and best practices in harnessing S&T for development.

With government encouragement and support, India has attained high S&T capability in diverse areas. As the host of the NAM S&T Centre, India has spurred some useful policy decisions on the Centre—which in turn have strengthened Indian science and technology through partnership. The participation of Indian scientists in the Centre's activities relating to capacity-building, human resource development and training, and to the generation and dissemination of information, has been invaluable both for the Centre and for Indian science and technology.

Developing countries share many commonalities relating to development and economic progress—both strengths and weaknesses. Countries of the South' are endowed with vast precious natural resources, flora, fauna, biodiversity, traditional knowledge and abundant cheap manpower. But they have to contend with many challenges—high population, poverty and unemployment, malnutrition and poor public health, unplanned management of natural resources and environmental degradation, high inflation, poor transport, communication and infrastructure facilities, and last but not the least, serious technological backwardness in the productive sector—resulting in low production efficiency, poor quality of products and lack of competitiveness.

Their natural resources remain largely unutilized or under-utilized. They are under constant threat of exploitation by industrially developed nations for export of raw materials without any value addition in the countries of their origin.

Resource-scarce developing countries are not in a position to invest adequately in science and technology. The Gross Expenditure on R&D (GERD) by most of these countries is often less than 1 per cent of GDP. The figures are 1 per cent for Brazil, India-0.8 per cent, South Africa-0.7 per cent, Argentina-0.4 per cent, Egypt-0.2 per cent. The GERD of China, however, is slightly higher at 1.2 per cent.

These figures are in stark contrast with those of advanced countries. Their GERD is usually greater than 2 per cent of GDP. For e.g. Israel-4.9per cent, Japan- 3.1 per cent, USA-2.8 per cent, Germany-2.5 per cent. The result is a sound infrastructure and rapid advancement in S&T. This has led to a huge gap in scientific output and technological innovations between the North and the South, which has been widening over the years because of increasing economic and knowledge disparities.

The gap has been further aggravated by rapid globalization, economic liberalization, free trade, increased competition and revolutionary advances in information and communication technology.

Knowledge divide

In order to bridge this knowledge divide, the countries of the North until recently provided scholarships and endowments for education and research in S&T and institutional and financial support to developing countries. They were also transferring technology to countries of the South—ostensibly as help; but this technology eventually bore a high price tag. Developing countries were being dumped with obsolete, inefficient and often environment-unfriendly technologies, for which they were being charged heavily.

It has therefore become imperative for developing nations to work together and cooperate amongst themselves rather than perpetually depend on assistance from the advanced countries to harness the benefits of science and technology for their own development. The Centre for Science and Technology of the Non-aligned and Other Developing Countries (NAM S&T Centre) is one of the most significant inter-governmental bodies that strives to promote South-South cooperation and collective self-reliance among developing countries. It accepts voluntary support from developed countries if that can accelerate capacity-building and economic growth in developing countries.

The NAM S&T Centre was established in 1989 as an inter-governmental organisation following the deliberations of the Conferences of the Heads of State or Governments of the NAM Countries and after adoption of its statute by consensus by a Meeting of the Plenipotentiaries of the Non-Aligned Countries in New York in February 1985. The Government of India offered to host the Centre, and the headquarters were located in New Delhi.

Besides the NAM S&T Centre, several other inter-governmental and non-governmental international organizations also strive to promote and support South-South Cooperation in science and technology. These include the Group of 77 Developing Countries (G-77); the Perez-Guerrero Trust Fund (PGTF), South Centre; the Special Unit for South-South Cooperation (SU/SSC) of UNDP; the Special Unit for Technical Cooperation among Developing Countries (TCDC); the Academy of Sciences for the Developing World (formerly, Third World Academy of Sciences—TWAS); the Consortium on Science, Technology and Innovation for the South (COSTIS) (formerly, Third World Network of Scientific Organizations—TWNSO); Third World Organization for Women in Science (TWOWS); and NAM Centre for South-South Technical Cooperation (NAM CSSTC).

These organizations predominantly finance scientific activities of other agencies—either through grants or through support for implementation by other agencies on the basis of contract or shared finance. In contrast, the NAM S&T Centre functions on the basis of collective self-reliance and partnership. It also draws on the strengths of developed countries whenever it is beneficial to the developing countries.

NAM S&T centre's role

The NAM S&T Centre seeks to promote mutually beneficial collaboration among scientists and scientific organisations of non-aligned and other developing countries; help establish links between national and regional centres; act as a clearing house of information on the technological capabilities of individual countries; maintain a registry of S&T experts of high caliber and stimulate and promote joint R&D projects etc.

Several priority areas of direct relevance and benefit to developing countries have been identified for the Centre. These include agricultural biotechnology, bio-safety and bio-ethical issues, environment and biodiversity, ecology, food processing, advanced materials in science & engineering, construction engineering, microelectronics, information & communication technology, non-conventional energy sources, natural disaster management, science popularisation in science centres & science museums, Intellectual Property Rights, science & technology policy, public-private partnership for technological innovation, technology transfer, S&T for society, S&T for women.

Since its inception, the NAM S&T Centre has been a facilitator in science-driven economic development in countries of the South by encouraging their governments to nurture S&T institutions and by formulating action plans and policy guidelines to integrate science and technology into national economic development plans. Over the years, the Centre has through its activities provided opportunities for scientist-to-scientist and institution-to-institution contacts among its 40 member countries and 55 other countries. It has enabled awareness with the latest developments and techniques. It has implemented collaborative projects and training courses and facilitated technology transfer.

The Centre's activities have helped member-countries in capacity-building in S&T. They have enabled sharing of experiences and best practices in harnessing S&T for development. The Centre has strengthened partnerships between academic and R&D institutions within the South. The Centre has so far trained some 700 scientists and professionals in various subjects and has organized 42 international workshops, seminars and roundtables. Some 1,800 scientists, experts and officials took part in these events to discuss S&T policy issues and topics.

The Centre has instituted three fellowship schemes. These enable scientists from developing countries to get affiliated with Centres of Excellence in other countries and upgrade their research skills. The Centre regularly brings out a quarterly newsletter highlighting S&T developments in the developing world. It has published more than 30 books, a compendium of status and needs of developing countries in S&T.

NAM S&T centre & India

As mentioned above, the NAM S&T Centre facilitates knowledge-sharing and collective reliance among almost 100 developing countries. But members of the Centre are at different levels of development. Brazil, China and India are almost at par with developed countries from the standpoint of progress in science and technology. Since India is the host country, the Centre banks heavily on the expertise available in India. Indian scientists and specialists serve as resource persons for training courses and workshops organised by the Centre, in areas like advanced materials, bio-

pesticides, disaster mitigation, earthquake-resistant housing, meteorology, DNA finger-printing etc. Indian scientists also serve as authors and editors of the Centre's publications.

India's tradition in science and technology dates back to about 2500 BC. Soon after independence, S&T was identified as a priority area for the country's development planning. Many national laboratories were set up by the government to pursue research in various fields. Concomitantly, an administrative support structure with a number of scientific departments and ministries was created to plan, evolve and administer S&T schemes and programmes. Higher education was strengthened by setting up a large number of universities and institutions of excellence like the Indian Institutes of Technology (IITs) and the Indian Institute of Science (IISc), also by introducing academic courses in modern disciplines of science, technology, engineering, medicine and management.

Manpower

A large contingent of S&T manpower, estimated to be around 17 million, the second largest in the world, was thus formed over the years. In recent years, government efforts on higher education and research have been supplemented by several industrial enterprises which have initiated R&D activities. The government has encouraged and promoted private sector investment in R&D, and implemented public-private partnership projects for technological innovation.

An important landmark in the history of S&T in India was the adoption of a Scientific Policy Resolution (SPR) in 1958, followed by a Technology Policy Statement (TPS) in 1983. These enunciated the principles on which the growth of science and technology in India is to be based. Further, a comprehensive S&T Policy was adopted in 2003, recognising the challenges and opportunities of globalisation and the need for an Intellectual Property Rights regime, high-speed access to information, freedom for academic and R&D institutions, and encouragement to research and innovation with greater participation from industry.

The main players in the present S&T system in India are the Central Government, State Governments, the higher education sector, the public sector, private industry, non-profit institutions, scientific and industrial research organisations. Nearly 4000 institutions under various sectors engage in S&T activities in India. These institutions vary in size, expenditure, manpower and infrastructure. The quality of research varies too. Encouraged and supported by political establishments and guided by policy decisions, India has attained impressive capability in diverse disciplines of science and technology—advanced materials, agriculture, astronomy and astrophysics; biotechnology, chemicals and pharmaceuticals; defence research, electronics, information and communication technology; medical research; nuclear energy; oceanography; space technology; remote sensing and its applications.

Though India's investment on S&T as a percentage of GDP is only 0.8 per cent, the Government of India over the years has progressively enhanced budgetary allocations for S&T in absolute terms through successive five-year Plans. Funds to support cutting-edge R&D and projects on public-private partnership and technological innovation have also been increased.

Initiatives

Some of India's initiatives in the recent past to promote S&T capabilities and technological innovation are Nanoscience and Technology Initiative, Funds for Improvement of S&T Infrastructure in Universities and Other Higher Educational Institutions, Intensification of Research in High Priority Areas, Drug Development Programme and Pharmaceuticals Research & Development Support Fund, Technology Development Board, Technology Business Incubators, Science & Technology Entrepreneurs Parks and National S&T Entrepreneurship Development Board; Home Grown Technology Programme of the Technology Information Forecasting and Assessment Council; Biotech Product and Process Development Programme and Biotech Infrastructure and Programme Support in Centres of Excellence of the Department of Biotechnology; New Millennium India Technology Leadership Initiative of the Council of Scientific & Industrial Research; Technology Development and Demonstration Programme of the Department of Scientific & Industrial Research; and Technopreneur Promotion Programme.

Being the host for the NAM S&T Centre, India has played a proactive role in the entire process to establish the Centre. This includes liberal funds for physical infrastructure. The Government of India through its Department of

Science & Technology has always maintained an umbilical cord relationship with the Centre and has provided policy directions to it from time to time through the Secretary, DST, who has been one of the two Vice-Presidents of the Centre from the very beginning.

India's Ministry of External Affairs, through its diplomatic missions located in various developing countries, has facilitated the flow of information and contacts between the Centre and other governments—both for the Centre's activities and for visits of dignitaries and delegations from those countries to the Centre. More importantly, the S&T institutions in India have been providing excellent technical support by hosting and co-organizing as many as 45 per cent of the international workshops, seminars and conferences and 77 per cent of the international training courses jointly with Centre. Hundreds of scientists and professionals from a very large number of developing countries have attended these events.

Data base

The Centre has carried out several networking initiatives among scientists, institutions and international agencies, as also between institutions and industry. It has spurred capacity building for R&D; capacity building through human resource development and training; collaborative projects; and dissemination of S&T information.

The Centre's database includes more than 4500 contacts across the globe. The Centre closely cooperates with some 30 UN agencies, other international bodies and NGOs engaged in South-South cooperation in S&T on global policy issues. Together, they formulate and implement multilateral collaborative projects. Indian institutions and scientists in their individual capacity benefit from this huge database and from the networking; they are able to share or tap into information and expertise.

The collaborative relationship between the Centre and India is demonstrated by the Centre's capacity-building efforts. The Centre has so far organized 22 training courses in various areas in partnership with institutions in India and three other countries. Of the 673 scientists trained in these programmes, 185 (27 per cent) were from India. Similarly, of the 1775 participants in 42 international seminars, workshops, roundtables and conferences held in partnership with institutions from 24 countries, almost 30 per cent were from India.

Indian scientists and institutions have significantly contributed to the multilateral projects implemented by the Centre with support from agencies like UNDP, PGTF and Commonwealth Science Council in low-cost housing, bio-pesticides, water supply etc.

The Centre has established an S&T-Industry network of academic, research and technical organizations. Members presently belong to six countries. India's members CSIR, VIT University, Vellore, and the International Advanced Research Centre for Powder Metallurgy and New Materials, Hyderabad. Prominent world agencies include the Botswana Technology Centre, the National Council for Research and Technology Development of Brazil and the Scientific and Technical Research Council of Turkey. By taking part in the Centre's workshops and conferences, India is in a position to showcase its strength and capability in relevant fields and explore the possibility of technology transfer to other countries associated with the Centre.

Conclusion

The end of the Cold War resulting from the disintegration of the USSR has brought to the fore the question of the relevance of the Non-Aligned Movement, which was formally launched during the Belgrade Conference of 1961. Some analysts have called for disbanding and closure of NAM which had successfully championed the cause of the third world at international forums.

But it has been reiterated at various forums that the NAM is still very relevant internationally today, in the era of globalisation and rapid advances in science and technology and ICT. It is pointed out that though the cold war is over, non-alignment as a foreign policy is still relevant to the 118 members of the NAM. In so far as India's position on NAM is concerned, the Foreign Minister of India has gone on record that 'India is a founding member of NAM and

believes that the movement has contributed substantially to the struggle against colonialism and apartheid in the post-Second World War period'.

The objectives of the NAM S&T Centre, however, go well beyond the NAM. It aims at benefiting all developing countries through scientific and technological interventions. Emerging economies in the developing world assist those less endowed to upgrade their S&T skills and capabilities, educate and train their scientific manpower, transfer technologies to industry, and carry out collaborative projects of mutual interest.

Such cooperation eventually helps in minimizing regional imbalances in the South and in reducing the dependence on developed nations. Through South-South cooperation, efforts are made to utilise the best of science from within the South itself for solving problems of the developing world. The S&T divide between the North and the South is minimized, with developing countries making full use of modern technological developments in various fields. They work together to develop skills and guidelines on the protection of Intellectual Property Rights and traditional knowledge. They evolve patent laws for negotiating WTO and other international agreements without any discrimination.

Among the member-countries of the NAM S&T Centre as well as among other developing countries, India has been the greatest beneficiary. It not only has the right to influence policy decisions on the functioning of the Centre, identify and implement scientific activities directly relevant to developing countries; but it has also benefited through the participation of scientists and professionals in the Centre's activities, and through the networking between its institutions and those of other countries. □

HERITAGE

आ नो भद्राः क्रतवो यन्तु विश्वतः

'Let noble thoughts come to us from all sides.'—Rigveda

THE PIONEERS

Asutosh Mookerjee	C V Raman	J N Mukherjee	Srinivasa Ramanujam	P C Ray
M L Sircar	M N Saha	J C Bose	K S Krishnan	S N Bose
S K Mitra	K R Ramanathan	P C Mahalanobis	S Chandrashekar	S S Bhatnagar
T R Seshadri	Homi J Bhabha	Vikram Sarabhai	Birbal Sahni	B P Pal

Men of Science in modern India

While the British government's policies on the scientific and technical education of Indians were designed to further its own interests, some Indian intellectuals and men of vision, themselves the products of such an education, provided a new leadership for the country's development. The last quarter of the nineteenth century witnessed eminent personalities like Mahendra Lal Sircar, Asutosh Mookerjee, Jagadish Chandra Bose and P C Ray, who were instrumental in heralding Western science teaching and research.

In 1876, Mahendra Lal Sircar, who had a brilliant academic record at the Calcutta Medical College and who was a firm believer in the rationality of science, founded the Indian Association for the Cultivation of Science on the model of the Royal Institution of London. Sircar was moved by the patriotic need to have an institution where Indian scholars were to be trained by Indian teachers in science and scientific methods in order to be able to carry on original researches in physical and biological sciences without European tutelage. During the first thirty years it functioned more or less as a science college. In the early part of the 20th century it developed into a research institution attracting young research workers from all over India including C V Raman and K S Krishnan. The Association sowed the seeds of a national effort for the promotion of a scientific movement based on self-reliance. Asutosh Mookerjee (1864–1924), a mathematician of high attainments, made significant contributions to the growth of scientific research. He played a pioneering role in converting universities into institutions of higher learning and research. This move was opposed by the government, so he successfully enlisted the munificence of private benefactors to achieve his objective. The recognition of a new generation of young scientists—Saha, Bose, Ghosh, Mukherjee, Agharkar, Mitra, Ray (P) and others came due to his vision.

Jagadish Chandra Bose (1858–1937) was the first Indian whose contribution to physics and plant physiology was of high order. His first scientific paper, based on experiments with instruments devised by himself, appeared in the May 1895 issue of the Journal of the Asiatic Society of Bengal, under the title: 'On Polarization of Electric Waves by Double Refracting Crystals'. He had succeeded in generating waves of much smaller wavelengths (from 25 mm to 5 mm). He investigated the quasioptical properties of these waves such as refraction, total reflection, polarisation and rotation of the plane of polarisation. In 1897, he delivered a lecture at the Royal Institution in London using a microwave spectrometer with a transmitter and a receiver constructed by himself. Later, he took up investigations which showed that not only animal but also plant tissues, under different kinds of stimuli, could display similar electric responses. In recognition of his outstanding scientific contributions, he was elected a Fellow of the Royal Society of London in 1920. Three years earlier, he had established a research institute, called Bose Institute in Calcutta through public donations, and was its Director till his death in 1937.

Prafulla Chandra Ray (1861–1944) was a pioneer in establishing a school of chemistry and chemical industries. In 1896 he presented a preliminary note on his discovery of mercurous nitrite to the Journal of the Royal Asiatic Society. He built up a centre of

'The problem of establishing science as a live and vital force in society is an inseparable part of the problem of transforming an industrially underdeveloped to a developing country'
—Homi J Bhabha

active chemical research in the Presidency College and later University College of Science, Calcutta. In 1900, he started the Bengal Chemical and Pharmaceutical Works.

The first half of the 20th century witnessed the spread of scientific education and research, and growing participation by enlightened Indians. A few of them rose to great heights and won international recognition. C V Raman (1888–1970), a brilliant student of the Madras University, first joined the Financial Civil Service but gave it up to work at the Indian Association for the Cultivation of Science, Calcutta, because of an inner urge. His investigations were in the fields of vibrations and sound, theory of musical instruments, optical studies such as diffraction and interference, colloids, molecular scattering of light, scattering of X-rays by liquids, magnetism and magneto-optics.

Indian journal

He started the Bulletin of the Indian Association which in 1917 became the Proceedings and much later the Indian Journal of Physics. He became the Palit Professor in the University College of Science in 1917 and was elected a Fellow of the Royal Society of London in 1924 and awarded the Nobel Prize in Physics in 1930 for his discovery of the Raman Effect in light scattering. With Raman were associated leading physicists like K R Ramanathan (1893–1984), K S Krishnan (1898–1961) and S Bhagavantam. A school of physics sprang up at Calcutta and later at the Indian Institute of Science, Bangalore which Raman joined in 1933. He founded the Raman Research Institute in 1948.

M N Saha (1893–1956), was a self-taught physicist, and a pioneer in researches in astrophysics. Saha's first papers were on the ionisation in the solar chromosphere and elements in the sun, published in the Philosophical Magazine, London (1920). His name is associated with the famous 'Ionization Formula' by means of which he could explain the ordered sequence of the spectra of stars. Saha was elected a Fellow of the Royal Society of London in 1927.

S N Bose (1894–1974) was an outstanding theoretical physicist who succeeded in deducting Planck's Law of black-body radiation by considering directly the statistics of an assembly of photons in a six-dimensional phase according to a method which was later extended by Einstein to an assembly of material particles. The method evolved by S N Bose resulted in Quantum—a new dimension of statistics—later known as Bose-Einstein Statistics which influenced the work of Fermi and Dirac. In his honour, particles following the Bose-Einstein Statistics are called Bosons. Bose was elected a Fellow of the Royal Society in 1958.

Srinivasa Ramanujam (1887–1920), a mathematical prodigy, had no formal university education but made remarkable contributions to mathematics. He was a clerk in the Madras Port Trust but won international recognition by his work on the Theory of Numbers. Ramanujan passed away at the young age of thirty three, only two years after his election as Fellow of the Royal Society of London in 1918.

Statistical institute

P C Mahalanobis (1893–1972) ushered in researches in theoretical and applied statistics in a systematic manner. As a result, increasing attention began to be paid to the application of statistics in the fields of agriculture, public health, economics. The important role of statistical methods became recognised. He founded the Indian Statistical Institute at Calcutta in 1931. Since 1920 extensive studies on the chemistry of coordination compounds were undertaken by P Ray (1888–1982) and his co-workers. These scientists addressed themselves in particular to the question of variable valency of metal ions and the structure of complex compounds. For this purpose, measurement of magnetic properties of simple and complex compounds of transition metals yielded useful information. A comprehensive study was made of complex compounds of biguanides and guanylureas with a number of metal ions. R C Ray (1890–1959) contributed to the chemistry of boron, by means of his elegant studies on the borohydrates. P B Sarkar (1893–1971) was perhaps the first to start work on the chemistry of rare earths.

The late N R Dhar, J C Ghosh (1893–1959), J N Mukherjee (1893–1983) and S S Bhatnagar (1884–1955) were the earliest to initiate researches in physical chemistry. They worked in the fields of colloids and emulsions, magnetochemistry, electrochemistry and photochemistry.

The contributions of Homi Bhabha and Vikarm Sarabhai, in science as well as in institution-building are widely known. □

In the beginning

Development from the food gathering stage to one of food production and settled life was a purposeful event in the Indian subcontinent as elsewhere. The period between 3000 and 1500 BC saw a spectrum of human settlements, both urban and rural, coexisting with or without communication among themselves. Around 2500 BC the subcontinent experienced its own struggles and endeavours culminating in what is now called the Indus Valley Civilization, the youngest but by far the largest of the three ancient civilisations. It flourished for nearly eight centuries.

Apart from Mohenjodaro and Harappa—the major cities of this civilization now in Pakistan—the excavations at Kalibangan in Rajasthan (c.2300 BC), Lothal in Gujarat (c.2000 BC) and other places, have brought to light the varied achievements of this period. Kalibangan was noted for its town planning, dwelling houses built with standardised burnt bricks, fire altars, inter-linked drainage system, tiled flooring, wheel-turned ceramics, terracota craft with animal motifs, bangles and intricate bead-making, solid-wheeled carts and, more importantly, the copper-bronze craftsmanship. The circle and the wheel had already become a part of their life.

Lothal was a planned township with civic amenities. It had a dockyard, regarded as the largest maritime structure ever built by any Bronze Age community. This dockyard with anchors at vantage points and a warehouse on a high platform, as well as a commercial street, speaks of flourishing maritime activities of the times, including ship-building. Lothal also had a bead-production unit and was noted for copper-bronze working and decorative pottery.

The fertile alluvial soil, monsoon rainfall and the water of the Indus were conducive to develop an agriculture-based economy and a settled life for arts and crafts. A flashback, especially on the dwelling structures, public bath system and granaries, suggests that the people of this civilisation had an egalitarian outlook and fostered wide-ranging technical skills for an enriched community living. In other words, the technological goals had, then as now, social overtones, and the technicians understandably could well have enjoyed a significant status in that society. Their scientific ideas, especially of geometry as evidenced by their town planning and standardisation techniques, were of a reasonably high order.

Astronomy

Said al-Andalusi, an Arab astronomer and historian of science of the 11th century AD, in his Kitab Tabakaāt al-Umam praised the philosophical wisdom and scientific inventions of the Hindus. By that time notable contributions had been made in this country in the fields of astronomy, mathematics, medicine, and metal-working and other techniques, through indigenous efforts as well as absorption from other cultures. The achievements of the Hindus were so deep in perception and varied in dimension that they attracted the attention of knowledge-seekers, specially of West Asia and, through them, of those of Latin medieval Europe.

Indian astronomical and mathematical achievements were well-known to the Arab compeers. In the 8th century AD there was perceptible contact of some Indian pandits or astronomers with the Abbasid Caliphate. Brahmagupta's works (the Brahmasphuta

'Like the crest of a peacock, like the gem on the head of a snake, so is mathematics at the head of all knowledge'
—Vedanga Jyotisha (c.500 BC)

Siddhanta and the Khandakhadyaka) were translated into Arabic by Mohammed ibn Abraham al-Fazar and Ya'qub ibn Tariq respectively with the help of Hindu scholars in the late 8th century AD. The great al-Khwarizmi prepared an abridged version of the former, besides writing an arithmetic, explaining the Hindu system of decimal place-value numeration. Al-Kindi, Habash al-Hasib, al-Nairizi, al-Hasan ibn Misbah and Ibn al-Adami were among the noted exponents of Indian mathematics and astronomy. Above all, the 11th century scholar al-Biruni was a remarkable transmitter and synthesiser of Indian astronomy and mathematics. Through the path of transmission of Arabic scientific knowledge, the Indian ideas passed into Latin Europe specially from the efforts of Adelard of Bath, John of Seville, Robert of Chester, Villedieu, Sacrobasco and Leonardo Pisano, in the 12th and 13th centuries AD.

Likewise, the Indian medical knowledge and surgical practices were known not only in the Arabic world but also in South-East Asia, Tibet and China. The Abbasid Caliphs encouraged the translation of the classics of Caraka, Susruta, Madhava and Vagbhata. Al-Razi, in the 9th/10th century AD, incorporated the Indian medical knowledge in his work known to medieval Europe as Liber Continens (Kitab-al-Hawi), translated into Latin by Moses Farachi (13th century AD), and which became the standard medical compendium of the middle ages.

Metallurgy

India was noted especially for iron metallurgy. The historic vestige, the unparalleled Iron Pillar at Delhi was an excellent metallurgical achievement of the 5th century AD. In many other techniques India displayed excellence sufficient to evoke interest of the outside world. Her geographical position enabled her to play a definitive role in the dynamics of scientific ideas and techniques. Her geological setting too provided the necessary stimuli for varied endeavours. The Himalayas on the one hand and the Deccan Plateau as well as the other more ancient geological formations on the other, shaped a subcontinent endowed with manifold natural wealth, majestic symphony of seas, rivers and variegated fauna and flora. That was indeed a great geological event. Greater still was the debut into the subcontinent of our ancestral human beings, possibly about a hundred thousand years ago, in their quest of

new congenial habitats. Soon the eastern sun witnessed them with their stone-tool making techniques, on the mountainous terrains, river-sides, valleys and plains. Who were they? What did they look like? We have no authentic evidence; perhaps we may never know about them at all. But the countless stone-tools—the hand-axes, choppers, points, burines and the like—of Old Stone Age or Paleolithic men, and the later microliths and other tools, testify to the technical skills of those who for thousands of years wandered and lived as food gatherers.

S&T up to 1800 AD

The story is, however, different from about 1500 BC when there entered a new wave of people (not a race), called the Vedic Aryans, heralding the dawn of new intellectual and technical endeavours. The Vedic and Post-Vedic literature provides a rare insight into some of their lofty conception and breadth of mathematical vision. For example, the Rigveda (c.1500 BC) describes the existence of a natural law (rta) as the governing principle of the universe and its events. The Vedic people had an intuitive conviction in the natural order to which even the Vedic gods had to conform, since they thought of the manifested world as an ordered whole and an integral part of Nature. Probably in no other contemporary speculation was there such a conception of natural law so vital to a coherent attitude towards Nature. In consonance with such an attitude, the highest monistic level was reached by the Vedic thinkers when they conceived a unitary world—ground (in the hymn of creation—nasadiya sukta) in terms of water as the first 'element' or the primordial stuff of the world.

The Vedic priests were also keen observers of the sky. They were aware of the Sun's path, the motion of the moon, eclipses, solstices, and developed luni-solar calendars with methods of intercalation. More

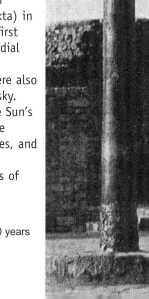

The Iron Pillar of Delhi that has remained rust free for nearly 1500 years

importantly, they formulated a stellar frame of reference in terms of 27 or 28 naksatras or star-groups which lie along or near the ecliptic, to follow the path of the sun, the moon and the planets.

The twelve-spoked wheel of the Rigveda was astronomy, metaphysics and perennial movement—all rolled into one cyclic concept. The circle became so fascinating that the ratio of its circumference to the diameter, i.e., pi—soon recognised as an immutable quantity—was sought to be determined by the later Indian mathematicians to a greater degree of precision. This cyclic concept was also woven into the religio-philosophical speculations encompassing the being and the non-being, the living and the non-living, in order to present a coherent and co-ordinated view of the world.

Five elements

Another development was an attempt to explain the maximum of 12 phenomena with the minimum of postulates. In consonance with the five senses, the gateways of human knowledge, a doctrine of five elements—earth (Prthvi), water (Ap), fire (Tejas), air (Vayu) and an ubiquitous one (Akasa)—was formulated. Though plural in its contents, the doctrine was holistic in nature and structure, in as much as it brought within its frame the human senses, the mind and the world of experience. The Indian doctrine was thus different from the Greek or the Chinese theory of elements. It was postulated that the five elements constituted the subtle and the gross, the living and the non-living. With such wide applications, the doctrine permeated the religio-philosophical systems as well as the scientific endeavours concerning the problems of matter and qualities, human physiology, disease and cure.

The Samkhya and the Nyaya-Vaisesika systems and the Sautrantrika school of

Buddhism elaborated upon this doctrine to throw light on the phenomenal world, specially the concept of substance itself. Be that as it may, the atomic nature of the elements was also speculated upon strictly logical grounds. From about the 5th century AD, the Indian atomism developed such epistemological frills that it sustained itself as a viable scientific attempt for over a thousand years, while the Greek atomism lay dormant in Europe. The Indian atomists were able to conceive of the qualities of a substance in terms of the structural arrangement of atoms. The nature and extent of space and time, and their absolute and relativistic characteristics were yet another field of inquiry of the Indian thinkers. There was even a view of the atomicity of time, specially conceived by the Jainas, in a space-time frame. The Classical Age of India and the succeeding centuries up to 12th century AD experienced an intellectual unfolding in the realms of mathematics, astronomy and medicine. There appeared a large number of scientific texts with accurate terminology; the mode of precise and stylish presentation of scientific ideas was standardised.

Mathematics

The most fundamental contribution of ancient Indian mathematics is undoubtedly the 'decimal system of enumeration' to represent all integers, using nine digits and a symbol for zero, dating back to the Vedic period. During the same period Pythagorean geometry was developed in the Sulba Sutras for the construction of sacrificial altars. The laws of indices and permutations and combinations were discovered by the Jainas. In the Bakhshali manuscript dated around 4th century AD, linear and quadratic equations were solved.

The more systematic development of Indian mathematics dates from Aryabhata I (15th century AD) who developed techniques for extracting square roots and cube roots of integers and also used trigonometrical ratios, sine and cosine, in his astronomical texts. Varahamihira (5th–6th century AD) was a great astronomer who prepared a corrected version of the Indian calendar. The most celebrated mathematicians after Varahamihira were Brahmagupta (7th century AD), Mahavira (8th century AD) and Bhaskara (12th century AD). This was probably the most productive period in the history of ancient Indian mathematics during which methods were developed to solve diophantine equations of degrees 1 and 2 and spherical trigonometry and many geometrical questions (cyclic quadrilaterals with rational numbers etc.) were studied.

The only mathematical activity in the post-Bhaskara period up to the 18th century seems to have been by the Kerala School of Astronomers who developed infinite series expansions for pi and trigonometric functions. Also in the court of Jai Singh of Jaipur lived Jagannatha Pandita (17th century AD) who translated Euclid's Elements from Arabic to Sanskrit.

Medicine

The science of life, body and mind was, and continues to be, as important as the science of heavens. With its origin in the healing art of the Vedic times, the Ayurveda emerged as the medical science par excellence by about the 6th century BC. For the harmonious existence of the individual within and outside, it derived its theoretical sustenance from the philosophical systems principally of the Samkhya and Yoga. Aiming not only at the cure of the disease but also at preserving health, the Ayurveda takes an integrated view of man and his body and mind, as also of the surroundings which include the plant, mineral and animal. The two great classics of the Ayurveda, the Susruta and the Caraka Samhitas, present a vivid and cogent account of the medical knowledge and surgical practices which were in vogue about 2500 years ago. The former under its six categories, sthanas and 184 chapters deals with fundamental postulates pathology, embryology and anatomy, therapeutic and surgical treatment, toxicology, medicinal herbs etc. The latter, under its eight categories and 150 chapters is an exhaustive work, among others, on the therapeutic medicine. The materia medica of the treatises is quite extensive and deals with over 600 drug-compositions of plant and even of animal and mineral origins.

The Ayurveda describes five fundamental treatments Pancakarma aiming at toning the bodily tissues for effective drug-action or surgical operation, as also at conditioning the body for medical care. Eliminative procedures and several applications including the oil and steam bath in a precise manner generate a potentiality in the body for combat-readiness against roots of the diseases. To the Ayurveda, the antidote is necessary but not sufficient. The vitiating roots of the disease should be eliminated totally.

It was in surgery, above all, that the ancient Hindus excelled. The Susruta Samhita which accords a pride of place to surgery, describes more than three hundred different operations and 121 (20 sharp and 101 accessories) surgical instruments—tongs, forceps, scalpels, catheters, trocar, syringes, speculums, needles, saws, lances, hooks, scissors and probes. The feats of the ancient Indian surgery were related to laparotomy, lithotomy and plastic operations with efficient pre-nand post-operative treatments. The Susruta Samhita is regarded as the earliest document which gives a detailed account of rhinoplasty.

Concept of Vayu

Indian medical knowledge and surgical practices influenced Greece and specially West Asia. The Hippocratic treatise On Breath discussed its concept of pneuma in more or less the same manner as the Indian concept of vayu. Plato in his Timaeos, strangely enough, dealt with pathology, almost in the same way as the doctrine of the tridosas. The Roman Celsius (1st century AD) gave in his medical works a graphic account of lithotomy which was practised in India much earlier. Galen of Pergamum (2nd century AD) makes no secret of his borrowing from the Indian sources the material relating to ointment for the eyes and the Indian plaster.

Our medical knowledge was not an one-sided affair. In the 12th century or so, the examination of urine and pulse was practised by the Indian medical men, perhaps learning the techniques from China and West Asia. About the same time, the earlier alchemical practices, possibly owing their ideas to Chinese alchemy, gave rise to a gamut of mineral medicines which, in the next two centuries, found their way into the Ayurvedic fold. But, the most important influence came from the Perso-Arabic culture area. The Unani medicine which in the 13th–14th centuries AD began to take roots in India under the Islamic rulers became popular with the advent of the Mughals. The Muslim rulers greatly encouraged both the Ayurveda and Unani Tibb and the Hakims and the Vaidyas worked together in hospitals and medical schools—a testimony to the Islamic patronage of scientific tradition. At the instance of Muhammad bin Tughlaq, Hakim Diya Muhammad compiled a treatise Majmuai-Diyaiyya, incorporating the Arabic, Persian and Ayurvedic medical knowledge. The Tibbi Aurangzebi seems to be based on Ayurvedic sources. The Muslajati-Darashikohi contains at the end almost the whole Ayurvedic materia medica.

Biology

In biological sciences, there is ample evidence to indicate that Indians had appreciable knowledge of histology, physiology, pathology, and reproduction of various plants, besides systematic classification. In respect of nomenclature, the system adopted by Indians had impressed William Jones, the President of the Asiatic Society, so much that he remarked that Linnaeus would have probably adopted the Hindu System had he known the Sanskrit language. The medieval period witnessed not a few developments in respect of the introduction of new plants, especially by the Portuguese and the Moghuls—tobacco, pineapple, chillies, coffee, cinchona, and the like which began to take roots in India from the 16th century AD onwards. The Moghuls gave encouragement to horticulture, and also fostered the grafting techniques specially in the evolution of mango varieties and gardening. Akbar who was passionately fond of animals from Central Asia and Kashmir was a great breeder of domestic animals including superior horses. Jahangir was undoubtedly the greatest naturalist among the Moghuls. He has left behind a fine record of his keen observations of a wide variety of birds and animals, their ecology and behaviour.

As to technological endeavours, the Vedic period and the succeeding centuries witnessed certain new trends in agriculture which revealed themselves through the effective use of plough, cultivation of rice and other new grains, and also supported an economy which had its own social implications. According to William Roxburgh, rotation of crops is India's contribution to world agriculture at an early period of history. A number of techniques and the associated professionalism in respect of metal-working, wood, leather, textiles, ceramics, construction and the like became specialised fields of craftsmanship. As students of Indian social history are well aware, certain professional activities resulted in a structuring of the society into four major castes and later into a number of subcastes.

There was the whole culture called the 'Megalithic Culture' which spanned several centuries (c.600 BC to c.200 AD) and to which iron had a special appeal. It would seem that, despite the extensive archaeological excavations concerning this culture, we have not yet clearly understood the magnitude of its impact on the contemporary society in fields as agriculture and irrigation, house building, temple construction, architecture and the like.

The techniques, albeit their traditional constraints, endeavoured, by and large, to attain new heights from the micro to macro levels from 5th century AD onwards. The huge copper statue of Buddha (discovered at Sultanganj in Bihar and now housed in the Birmingham Museum and Art Gallery) and the famous Iron Pillar at Delhi of the Classical Period testify to the extraordinary skills of the metalsmiths of the time. The former is about 2.1 metres high and weighs nearly one tonne. According to the Chinese pilgrim, Hieuen Tsang, a colossal copper image of the Buddha, and one brass temple of about 30 metres high were being built in an enchanting manner.

Iron Pillar

The Iron Pillar is about 7.5 metres in height with half metre below ground (its diameter diminishing from about 40 cm below to 30 cm above). The Pillar has been existing for the last 1500 years or so without any rust or signs of decay. The general view offered regarding its resistance to the ravages of climate is that there might be a thin protective oxide film formed on the surface as a result of special treatments. Also, the rather high phosphorus and the negligible sulphur and zero manganese contents may have given rise to a high corrosion resistancer. Of the technical skill which engineered this Pillar, there can be little doubt; but of its exact forging details, we have but scant information. A technique unparalleled elsewhere came to the fore as early as the 5th century AD. This technique was not shortlived either. The Iron Pillar at Dhar and that on Mount Abu, the beams of temples at Konark and Puri, to cite some examples of the 11th to 14th century AD, bear the stamp of this technique. Metalsmiths were also active in the production of agricultural implements, household articles and above all, the coveted jewellery.

Attractive ceramics and ivory and wood carvings, perfumery and toilet articles, fermented drinks and aphrodisiac preparations, intricate garments of linen, cotton, bark-silk, muslin and short silk, enriched living. In view of the importance of agriculture, it became necessary to have weather forecasts and to determine the quantities of rainfall. This resulted from the 5th century AD onwards, in the evolution of certain types of almanac computations and observations on the seasonal changes. Rain-gauges were thought of, and a sort of calendar for sowing, mid-treatment of crops, harvesting etc. was developed. The farmers had to depend upon the advice of the priestly class for agricultural operations. The time was ripe for the codification of agricultural technology. Many extant texts of this period contain references to agricultural practices, such as treatment of seeds, preparation of the soil, manuring, rotation of crops, irrigation, protection of crops from diseases and pests and farming implements.

Iconography

The technology of agricultural implements received a new fillip, with the village carpenters and blacksmiths assuming an important role. Iron emerged as the most important metal of the common man. The sharp iron implements were effectively used to clear the jungles with a view to acquiring land for cultivation and establishing new settlements. Alongside, the traditional jewellery craft had its own special techniques. The techniques of testing of gems was elevated to the status of one of 64 fine arts of the time. In tune with the varied religious practices, iconography became a specialised art with appropriate iconometry. The earlier rockcut temples (Mahabalipuram in the South, cave temples in Ajanta, Ellora, Elephanta and those in Orissa), and the later exquisitely built temples of brick and stone are representatives of harmony of geometry, knowledge of the building materials and construction techniques, marked by unique artistry in and outside. The ancient paintings

such as at Ajanta used elegant and stable pigments which withstood the ravages of time for nearly 1500 years. The arrival of paper in the 12th or 13th century AD, possibly from Central Asia, and also of the new linguistic influences, notably Arabic and Persian, resulted in a spate of manuscripts, artistic calligraphy and elegant presentation. This enabled meticulous preservation of knowledge, and marked a transition from an oral to a written tradition. The spinning wheel, which began to be used widely from the 14th century, provided a fillip to the textile industry, leading to an increase in cotton cultivation and an expansion of the weavers' community. Likewise, the Persian wheel for irrigation purposes expanded the agricultural community which became a source of revenue for the government. Allaudin Khilji and his successors (13th–14th century AD) introduced a new revenue system which was further strengthened in the Mughal period. Construction engineering and architecture assumed new dimensions, as evidenced by the impressive monuments—both Hindu and Indo-Islamic— using marble and stone with inlay work. Some of them are noted for their extraordinary acoustical features. The outstanding examples include the 'musical pillars' of the temple at Hampi, and the whispering gallery, multiple echo effect and the reverberations in Gol Gumbaz (round dome) in Bijapur. The Gol Gumbaz is unquestionably one of the finest structural triumphs of the Indian builders if only on account of its stupendous proportions; it is considerably larger in area than the Pantheon in Rome.

India's worldview

In the history of human progress, scientific and technological developments—innovations and their usefulness to the society at large—brought about changes in the socio-economic structures and the value-systems. The Indian cultural arena experienced such changes, albeit in a restricted manner, in the ancient and medieval periods. But, what was more pronounced was the spirit of open-mindedness which had its origin in the Rigveda which enjoined: 'Let noble thoughts come to us from all sides.' Such a spirit with attendant assimilative characteristics resulted in growth through the adaptation of new scientific ideas and techniques either from the Hellenistic or Islamic tradition. Even so, the ethos of the scientific endeavours in India centered on man as an integral part of the world around. It was not man versus nature but harmony between the two. □